COMPLEX ANALYSIS
AND ITS APPLICATIONS
Vol. **III**

INTERNATIONAL CENTRE FOR THEORETICAL PHYSICS, TRIESTE

COMPLEX ANALYSIS AND ITS APPLICATIONS

LECTURES PRESENTED AT
AN INTERNATIONAL SEMINAR COURSE
AT TRIESTE FROM 21 MAY TO 8 AUGUST 1975
ORGANIZED BY THE
INTERNATIONAL CENTRE FOR THEORETICAL PHYSICS, TRIESTE

In three volumes

VOL. III

INTERNATIONAL ATOMIC ENERGY AGENCY
VIENNA, 1976

THE INTERNATIONAL CENTRE FOR THEORETICAL PHYSICS (ICTP) in Trieste was established by the International Atomic Energy Agency (IAEA) in 1964 under an agreement with the Italian Government, and with the assistance of the City and University of Trieste.

The IAEA and the United Nations Educational, Scientific and Cultural Organization (UNESCO) subsequently agreed to operate the Centre jointly from 1 January 1970.

Member States of both organizations participate in the work of the Centre, the main purpose of which is to foster, through training and research, the advancement of theoretical physics, with special regard to the needs of developing countries.

COMPLEX ANALYSIS AND ITS APPLICATIONS
IAEA, VIENNA, 1976
STI/PUB/428
ISBN 92–0–130576–1

Printed by the IAEA in Austria
December 1976

FOREWORD

The International Centre for Theoretical Physics has maintained an interdisciplinary character in its research and training programmes in different branches of theoretical physics and related applied mathematics. In pursuance of this objective, the Centre has since 1964 organized extended research courses in various disciplines; most of the Proceedings of these courses have been published by the International Atomic Energy Agency.

In 1972 the ICTP held the first of a series of extended summer courses in mathematics and its applications. To date, the following courses have taken place: Global Analysis and its Applications (1972), Mathematical and Numerical Methods in Fluid Dynamics (1973), Control Theory and Topics in Functional Analysis (1974), and Complex Analysis and its Applications (1975). The present volumes consist of a collection of the long, basic courses (Volume I) and the individual lectures (Volumes II and III) given in Trieste at the 1975 Summer Course. The contributions are partly expository and partly research-oriented – in the spirit of the very wide range of interest of the participants. The programme of lectures was organized by Professors A. Andreotti (Pisa, Italy, and Oregon, United States of America), J. Eells (Warwick, United Kingdom) and F. Gherardelli (Florence, Italy).

Abdus Salam

EDITORIAL NOTE

The papers and discussions have been edited by the editorial staff of the International Atomic Energy Agency to the extent considered necessary for the reader's assistance. The views expressed and the general style adopted remain, however, the responsibility of the named authors or participants. In addition, the views are not necessarily those of the governments of the nominating Member States or of the nominating organizations.

Where papers have been incorporated into these Proceedings without resetting by the Agency, this has been done with the knowledge of the authors and their government authorities, and their cooperation is gratefully acknowledged. The Proceedings have been printed by composition typing and photo-offset lithography. Within the limitations imposed by this method, every effort has been made to maintain a high editorial standard, in particular to achieve, wherever practicable, consistency of units and symbols and conformity to the standards recommended by competent international bodies.

The use in these Proceedings of particular designations of countries or territories does not imply any judgement by the publisher, the IAEA, as to the legal status of such countries or territories, of their authorities and institutions or of the delimitation of their boundaries.

The mention of specific companies or of their products or brand names does not imply any endorsement or recommendation on the part of the IAEA.

Authors are themselves responsible for obtaining the necessary permission to reproduce copyright material from other sources.

CONTENTS OF VOLUME III

ELECTROMAGNETIC FIELD AND THE THEORY OF CONFORMAL AND BIHOLOMORPHIC INVARIANTS

J. ŁAWRYNOWICZ
Institute of Mathematics,
Polish Academy of Sciences,
Łodż Branch,
Łodż, Poland

Abstract

ELECTROMAGNETIC FIELD AND THE THEORY OF CONFORMAL AND BIHOLOMORPHIC INVARIANTS.

This paper contains sections on:
1. Conformal invariance and variational principles in electrodynamics. 2. The principles of Dirichlet and Thomson as a physical motivation for the methods of conformal capacities and extremal lengths. 3. Extension to pseudoriemannian manifolds. 4. Extension to hermitian manifolds. 5. An extension of Schwarz's lemma for hermitian manifolds and its physical significance. 6. Variation of "complex" capacities within the admissible class of plurisubharmonic functions. The author concentrates on motivations and interpretations connected with the electromagnetic field.

INTRODUCTION

The theory of conformal and biholomorphic invariants gives important information on holomorphic mappings. It has valuable mathematical applications e.g. to the problems of boundary behaviour of mappings, theory of removable singularities and, more generally, approximation theory. Here we only mention the fundamental monograph of Ahlfors [3] and Kobayashi [17], and three recent basic papers by Hedberg [14], Fefferman [12], and Chern and Moser [10].

In this paper, we concentrate on motivations and interpretations connected with the electromagnetic field. We begin with conformal invariance in electrodynamics and then obtain the principles of Dirichlet and Thomson which give a natural physical motivation for introducing conformal capacities and extremal lengths. Next we extend the methods to pseudoriemannian and hermitian manifolds, discussing in more detail an analogue of the Schwarz lemma. Finally we deal with the variation of "complex" capacities within the admissible class of plurisubharmonic functions.

For basic facts on quasiconformal mappings and manifolds (pseudoriemannian and hermitian) we refer to the papers by Gehring and Robertson, in these Proceedings, respectively.

1. CONFORMAL INVARIANCE AND VARIATIONAL PRINCIPLES IN ELECTRODYNAMICS

Let us recall first some basic theorems of the calculus of variations. Let $C^k(a \mapsto A; b \mapsto B)$ denote the class of all C^k smooth functions $\tilde{u}: [a; b] \to \mathbb{R}^m$ (in other words, $\tilde{u} \in \{C^k[a; b]\}^m$) such that $\tilde{u}(a) = A$, $\tilde{u}(b) = B$, and – analogously – let $C^k(s \mapsto f(s);\ s \in \partial D)$ denote the class of all C^k functions $\tilde{u}: D \to \mathbb{R}^m$ (in other words, $\tilde{u} \in [C^k(D)]^m$) such that D is a solid in $\mathbb{R}^n$ and $\tilde{u}(s) = f(s)$ for $s \in \partial D$, f being given. Then we have

Theorem 1.1. If the functional

$$I = \left(C^1(a \mapsto A;\, b \mapsto B) \ni \tilde{u} \mapsto \int_a^b F(x, \tilde{u}, \tilde{u}')\,dx\right)$$

where $F \in C^2([a;b] \times \mathbb{R}^{2m})$, attains an extremum for $\tilde{u} = u$, then

$$F_{u_j} - \frac{d}{dx} F_{u_j'} = 0, \qquad j = 1, \ldots, m \qquad \textbf{(Euler equations)}$$

The result remains valid if I is defined in $\{C^1[a;b]\}^m$.

Theorem 1.2. If the functional

$$I = \left(C^2(s \mapsto f(s);\, s \in \partial D) \ni \tilde{u} \mapsto \int \!\!\ldots\!\! \int_D F(x, \tilde{u}, \tilde{u}')\,dx_1 \ldots dx_n\right)$$

where $F \in C^2(D \times \mathbb{R}^{m(n+1)})$, $\tilde{u}' = [\tilde{u}_{j|k}]_{j \leqslant m, k \leqslant n}$, and $_{|k}$ denotes differentiation with respect to the kth co-ordinate, attains an extremum for $\tilde{u} = u$, then

$$F_{u_j} - \sum_{k=1}^{n} \frac{\partial}{\partial x_k} F_{u_{j|k}} = 0, \qquad j = 1, \ldots, m \qquad \textbf{(Euler-Brunacci equations)}$$

The result remains valid if I is defined in $[C^2(D)]^m$.

Now let τ_0 be an arbitrary positive number and $\tilde{D}$ an arbitrary closed domain in $\mathbb{R}^n$.

Theorem 1.3 (Emmy Noether). If for every $\tau \in [-\tau_0; \tau_0]$ and every $D \subset \tilde{D}$ the functional

$$I = \left([C^2(D)]^m \ni \tilde{u} \mapsto \int \!\!\ldots\!\! \int_D F(x, \tilde{u}, \tilde{u}')\,dx_1 \ldots dx_n \in \mathbb{R}\right)$$

where $F \in C^2(D \times \mathbb{R}^{m(n+1)})$, is invariant with respect to the transformation

$$\tilde{x}(\tau)(x) = x + \tau\varphi(x) + o(\tau), \quad \tilde{u}(\tau)(\tilde{x}(\tau)(x)) = u(x) + \tau\psi(x) + o(\tau), \qquad x \in D$$

where $\tilde{x}(\tau)$ is a diffeomorphism of D onto itself, then for any function $u \in [C^2(D)]^m$ we have

$$\sum_{k=1}^{n} \frac{\partial}{\partial x_k}\left(\sum_{j=1}^{m} F_{u_{j|k}} \tilde{\psi}_j + F\varphi_k\right) = -\sum_{j=1}^{m}\left(F_{u_j} - \sum_{k=1}^{n} \frac{\partial}{\partial x_k} F_{u_{j|k}}\right)\tilde{\psi}_j$$

where

$$\widetilde{\psi}_j = \psi_j - \sum_{k=1}^{n} u_{j|k}\varphi_k, \qquad j = 1, ..., m$$

Let us consider now a charged particle (treated as a material point) of mass m and charge e. For simplicity we ignore the relativistic effects. Denote by **v** the velocity of the particle, and by V and **A** the scalar and vector potential, respectively, of the field at the point where the particle actually appears. The potential energy U, kinetic energy T, and energy of interaction between the particle and the field S, are given by the formulae

$$U = eV, \quad T = \tfrac{1}{2}mv^2, \quad S = e\mathbf{A}\mathbf{v}, \quad \text{where} \quad v^2 = \mathbf{v}\cdot\mathbf{v}$$

Then, if we consider the field as given and make a variation of the particle trajectory, the variational principle has the form

$$\delta \int_{t_0}^{t_*} (\tfrac{1}{2}mv^2 + e\mathbf{A}\mathbf{v} - eV)dt = 0$$

where we assume that the hypotheses of Theorem 1.1 are fulfilled.

By this theorem the equations of motion have the form

$$\frac{d}{dt}\frac{\partial}{\partial v_j}(\tfrac{1}{2}mv^2 + e\mathbf{A}\mathbf{v} - eV) = \frac{\partial}{\partial x_j}(\tfrac{1}{2}mv^2 + e\mathbf{A}\mathbf{v} - eV), \qquad j = 1, 2, 3$$

or

$$(d/dt)\mathbf{p} = e\mathbf{E} + e\mathbf{v} \times \mathbf{B} \tag{1.1}$$

where

$$\mathbf{p} = m\mathbf{v} \qquad \textbf{(momentum)} \tag{1.2}$$

$$\mathbf{E} = -(\partial/\partial t)\mathbf{A} - \operatorname{grad} V \qquad \textbf{(intensity of the electric field)} \tag{1.3}$$

$$\mathbf{B} = \operatorname{rot} \mathbf{A} \qquad \textbf{(vector of the magnetic induction)} \tag{1.4}$$

Eliminating **A** and V from (1.3) and (1.4) we get

$$\operatorname{rot} \mathbf{E} = -(\partial/\partial t)\mathbf{B} \tag{1.5}$$

and

$$\operatorname{div} \mathbf{B} = 0 \tag{1.6}$$

The above considerations remain valid in the case of n charged particles of masses m_k and charges e_k, k = 1, ..., n. With the corresponding meaning of $\mathbf{v}_k$, V_k, and $\mathbf{A}_k$, the variational principle concerned with the action integral

$$\int_{t_0}^{t_*} \sum_{k=1}^{n} (\tfrac{1}{2} m_k v_k^2 + e_k \mathbf{A}_k \mathbf{v}_k - e_k V_k)\, dt \tag{1.7}$$

gives

$$(d/dt)\mathbf{p} = \sum_{k=1}^{n} e_k(\mathbf{E}_k + \mathbf{v}_k \times \mathbf{B}_k) \tag{1.8}$$

where

$$\mathbf{p} = \sum_{k=1}^{n} m_k \mathbf{v}_k, \quad \mathbf{E}_k = -\frac{\partial}{\partial t}\mathbf{A}_k - \operatorname{grad} V_k, \quad \mathbf{B}_k = \operatorname{rot} \mathbf{A}_k \tag{1.9}$$

Next we consider the motion of particles as given and make a variation of the field itself, i.e. of the potentials. We assume that the charge is distributed continuously, and, even more, that the mass density $\widetilde{\rho}$ as well as charge density ρ are in $C^2(D)$, where $D \times [t_0; t_*] \subset \mathbb{R}^4$ plays the role of those D appearing in Theorem 1.2. It is clear that the discrete case also could be reduced to this one by means of the theory of distributions. Under this hypothesis the action integral (1.7) has to be replaced by

$$\int_{t_0}^{t_*} \iiint_D (\tfrac{1}{2}\widetilde{\rho}\, v^2 + \rho\, \mathbf{A}\mathbf{v} - \rho V)\, dx_1\, dx_2\, dx_3\, dt \tag{1.10}$$

Since we shall now formulate the variational principle for variable potentials and consequently establish the equations governing the field itself, we have to add a term L depending only on the field in the absence of charges. Until now this term, being constant, had no meaning.

Assuming that the equations of the field should be linear, and applying the so-called (phenomenological) principle of superposition (which states that if one charge produces a certain field and another charge produces a second field, then the field produced by the two charges together is the result of a simple composition of the fields produced by each of the charges individually), we conclude that

$$L = \tfrac{1}{2}\epsilon_0 \breve{\epsilon}\, \mathbf{E}^2 - \tfrac{1}{2}\mu_0^{-1} \breve{\mu}^{-1} \mathbf{B}^2$$

$$\mathbf{E}^2 = [E_j E_k]_{j,k \leqslant 3}$$

$$\mathbf{B}^2 = [B_j B_k]_{j,k \leqslant 3}$$

where

$$\check{\epsilon} = [\epsilon_{j,k}]_{j,k \leqslant 3} \qquad \text{(tensor of dielectric permeability)}$$

$$\check{\mu} = [\mu_{j,k}]_{j,k \leqslant 3} \qquad \text{(tensor of magnetic permeability)}$$

$$\epsilon_{k,j} = \epsilon_{j,k}, \quad \mu_{k,j} = \mu_{j,k} \qquad \text{for } j, k = 1, 2, 3 \tag{1.11}$$

$$\det[\epsilon_{j,k}]_{j,k \leqslant 3} \neq 0, \quad \det[\mu_{j,k}]_{j,k \leqslant 3} \neq 0$$

while ϵ_0 and μ_0 denote the dielectric and magnetic permeability of the vacuum, respectively. Thus the variational principle has the form

$$\delta \int_{t_0}^{t_*} \iiint_D (\tfrac{1}{2}\tilde{\rho} v^2 + \rho \mathbf{A} \mathbf{v} - \rho V + \tfrac{1}{2}\epsilon_0 \check{\epsilon} \mathbf{E}^2 - \tfrac{1}{2}\mu_0^{-1}\check{\mu}^{-1}\mathbf{B}^2) dx_1\, dx_2\, dx_3\, dt = 0 \tag{1.12}$$

where we assume that the hypotheses of Theorem 1.2 are fulfilled.

By this theorem the equations governing the field have the form

$$\sum_{k=1}^{3} \frac{\partial}{\partial x_k}\left[\partial/\partial\left(\frac{\partial A_j}{\partial x_k}\right)\right] L^* + \frac{\partial}{\partial t}\left[\partial/\partial\left(\frac{\partial A_j}{\partial t}\right)\right] L^* = \frac{\partial L^*}{\partial A_j}, \qquad j = 1, 2, 3$$

$$\sum_{k=1}^{3} \frac{\partial}{\partial x_k}\left[\partial/\partial\left(\frac{\partial V}{\partial x_k}\right)\right] L^* + \frac{\partial}{\partial t}\left[\partial/\partial\left(\frac{\partial V}{\partial t}\right)\right] L^* = \frac{\partial L^*}{\partial V}$$

where L^* denotes the integrand in (1.12), or (by (1.3), (1.4), and (1.11))

$$\operatorname{rot} \mathbf{H} = (\partial/\partial t)\mathbf{D} + \mathbf{j} \tag{1.13}$$

and

$$\operatorname{div} \mathbf{D} = \rho \tag{1.14}$$

where

$$\mathbf{H} = \mu_0^{-1}\check{\mu}^{-1}\mathbf{B} \qquad \text{(intensity of the magnetic field)} \tag{1.15}$$

$$\mathbf{D} = \epsilon_0 \check{\epsilon} \mathbf{E} \qquad \text{(vector of the electric induction)} \tag{1.16}$$

$$\mathbf{j} = \rho \mathbf{v} \qquad \text{(vector of the electric current-density)} \tag{1.17}$$

Equations (1.5), (1.6), (1.13), (1.14), (1.16), and $\mathbf{B} = \mu_0 \check{\mu} \mathbf{H}$ are called the **Maxwell equations.**

The theorem of E. Noether now gives seven scalar invariants of the electromagnetic field – seven conservation laws. That is, suppose that $x = (x_1, x_2, x_3)$ ranges over a closed domain D,

$t \in [t_0; t_*]$, $\tau \in \mathbb{R}$, and $\varphi_1, \ldots, \varphi_7$ are real parameters. Then three scalar conditions follow from the invariance of the integral

$$\int_{t_0}^{t_*} \iiint_D L\, dx_1\, dx_2\, dx_3\, dt \tag{1.18}$$

under translations

$$\tilde{x}_j(\tau)(x, t) = x_j + \tau\varphi_j, \qquad j = 1, 2, 3; \quad \tilde{t}(\tau)(x, t) = t \tag{1.19}$$

within the set $D \times [t_0; t_*]$. One condition follows from the invariance of (1.18) under translations

$$\tilde{x}_j(\tau)(x, t) = x_j, \quad j = 1, 2, 3; \quad \tilde{t}(\tau)(x, t) = t + \tau\varphi_4 \tag{1.20}$$

and finally, three other conditions – from the invariance of (1.18) under rotations

$$\begin{aligned} \tilde{x}_1(\tau)(x, t) &= x_1 - \tau\varphi_5 x_2 - \tau\varphi_6 x_3 \\ \tilde{x}_2(\tau)(x, t) &= \tau\varphi_5 x_1 + x_2 - \tau\varphi_7 x_3 \\ \tilde{x}_3(\tau)(x, t) &= \tau\varphi_6 x_1 + \tau\varphi_7 x_2 + x_3 \\ \tilde{t}(\tau)(x, t) &= t \end{aligned} \tag{1.21}$$

In addition, the vectors **D** and **E**, and, consequently, the function L are invariant with respect to the transformation of the potentials

$$\tilde{\mathbf{A}}[f] = \mathbf{A} + \operatorname{grad} f, \qquad \tilde{V}[f] = V - (\partial/\partial t)f \tag{1.22}$$

where $f \in C^2(D \times [t_0; t_*])$. This is the so-called **gauge invariance** which allows the potentials **A** and V to be specified without any change of **D** and **E** via a suitable choice of an arbitrary function f.

Let us consider now in more detail the case of (1.20). Without any loss of generality we may set $\varphi_4 = 1$. Since transformation (1.20) does not change the trajectories of the particles, we make a variation of the potentials only. Thus the system (A_1, A_2, A_3, V) of the potentials in question represents an extremal in the variational problem (1.12). Consequently, by Theorems 1.2 and 1.3, we have

$$\sum_{k=1}^{3} \frac{\partial}{\partial x_k}\left\{\sum_{j=1}^{3}\left[\partial/\partial\left(\frac{\partial A_j}{\partial x_k}\right)\right] L\tilde{\psi}_j + \left[\partial/\partial\left(\frac{\partial V}{\partial x_k}\right)\right] L\tilde{\psi}_4 + L\cdot 0\right\}$$

$$+ \frac{\partial}{\partial t}\left\{\sum_{j=1}^{3}\left[\partial/\partial\left(\frac{\partial A_j}{\partial t}\right)\right] L\tilde{\psi}_j + \left[\partial/\partial\left(\frac{\partial V}{\partial t}\right)\right] L\tilde{\psi}_4 + L\cdot 1\right\}$$

$$= -\sum_{j=1}^{3}\left\{\frac{\partial \Delta L}{\partial A_j} - \sum_{k=1}^{3}\frac{\partial}{\partial x_k}\left[\partial/\partial\left(\frac{\partial A_j}{\partial x_k}\right)\right]\Delta L - \frac{\partial}{\partial t}\left[\partial/\partial\left(\frac{\partial A_j}{\partial t}\right)\right]\Delta L\right\}\widetilde{\psi}_j$$

$$-\left\{\frac{\partial \Delta L}{\partial V} - \sum_{k=1}^{3}\frac{\partial}{\partial x_k}\left[\partial/\partial\left(\frac{\partial V}{\partial x_k}\right)\right]\Delta L - \frac{\partial}{\partial t}\left[\partial/\partial\left(\frac{\partial V}{\partial t}\right)\right]\Delta L\right\}\widetilde{\psi}_4 \qquad (1.23)$$

where (see Fig. 1)

$$\widetilde{\psi}_j(x, t) = \widetilde{A}_j'(0)(x, t), \quad j = 1, 2, 3; \quad \widetilde{\psi}_4(x, t) = \widetilde{V}'(0)(x, t)$$

$$\widetilde{\mathbf{A}}(\tau)(x, t) = \mathbf{A}(x, t - \tau), \quad \widetilde{V}(\tau)(x, t) = V(x, t - \tau)$$

$$\Delta L = L - L^* = -\tfrac{1}{2}\widetilde{\rho}\, v^2 - \rho \mathbf{A}\mathbf{v} + \rho V$$

and the prime denotes differentiation with respect to τ. Hence

$$\widetilde{\psi}_j = -(\partial/\partial t)A_j, \quad j = 1, 2, 3; \quad \widetilde{\psi}_4 = -(\partial/\partial t)V$$

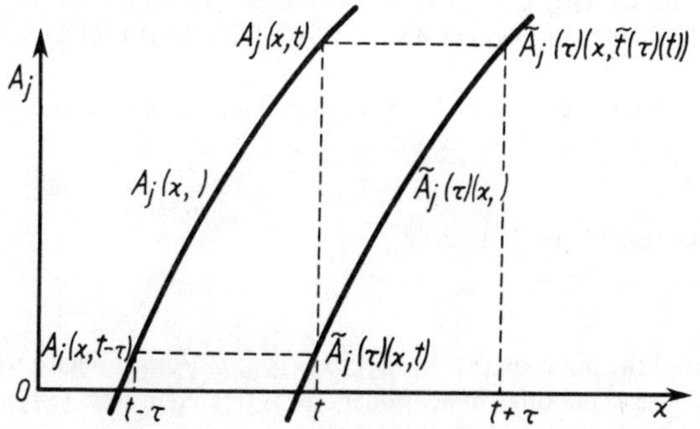

FIG. 1. Variation of the field vector potential.

By (1.11), (1.3), (1.4), and (1.13)–(1.17), relation (1.23) can be rearranged to the form $\frac{1}{2}(\partial/\partial t)(\mathbf{DE} + \mathbf{BH}) + \mathbf{jE} = -\operatorname{div}(\mathbf{E} \times \mathbf{H})$, i.e.

$$W(t) + \int_{t_0}^{t} \iiint_D \mathbf{jE}\, dx_1\, dx_2\, dx_3\, dt' = c_4 \qquad (1.24)$$

where

$$W = \tfrac{1}{2}\iiint_D (\mathbf{DE} + \mathbf{BH})\, dx_1\, dx_2\, dx_3 \qquad \textbf{(energy of the field)} \qquad (1.25)$$

whilst $-c_4$ is a constant equal to the integral of the **Poynting vector** $\mathbf{E}\times\mathbf{H}$ over the oriented surface ∂D.

Relation (1.24) has the following physical interpretation: if we suppose that all material bodies appearing in the field are at rest, the energy W of the field dissipates only as work done by the electric field of intensity **E** on the conducting currents of density **j**. Eliminating the vector **E** by virtue of the equation $\mathbf{j} = \lambda(\mathbf{E}+\mathbf{E}^*)$, where λ is a constant and $\mathbf{E}^*$ the external electromotive force, we obtain

$$\frac{\partial}{\partial t}W = P - Q \quad \text{where} \quad P = \iiint_D jE^* dx_1\, dx_2\, dx_3, \quad Q = \iiint_D \frac{1}{\lambda} j\cdot j\, dx_1\, dx_2\, dx_3$$

which is the following **energy conservation law**: if we suppose that all material bodies appearing in an electromagnetic field are at rest, then the entire energy increase $(\partial/\partial t)W$ of the field is equal to the excess of the work P done by the external electromotive forces with respect to the emitted Joule heat Q.

In the case where we do not ignore the relativistic effects, i.e. we consider the **relativistic Maxwell equations** in the Minkowski space-time, the analogue of the integral (1.18) is invariant under the **conformal group of transformations** and one obtains 15 scalar invariants which were effectively found by Bessel-Hagen [8].

2. THE PRINCIPLES OF DIRICHLET AND THOMSON AS A PHYSICAL MOTIVATION FOR THE METHODS OF CONFORMAL CAPACITIES AND EXTREMAL LENGTHS

According to (1.25), (1.16) and (1.3), the energy of a constant electric field is expressed by the formula

$$W = \tfrac{1}{2}\epsilon_0 \iiint_D (\check{\epsilon}\ \mathrm{grad}\ V)\, \mathrm{grad}\, V\, dx\, dy\, dz$$

where we have changed the notation (x_1, x_2, x_3) to (x, y, z). For simplicity we shall confine ourselves to the plane case (the three-dimensional case is treated in Refs [34] and [20]). Let us make the following substitution ([19], Part II, p.62):

$$V_x^* = \epsilon_*(V_x \cos\varphi - V_y \sin\varphi) \quad , \quad V_y^* = \frac{1}{\epsilon_*}(V_x \sin\varphi + V_y \cos\varphi)$$

where

$$\epsilon_* \cos^2\varphi + \frac{1}{\epsilon_*}\sin^2\varphi = \frac{1}{\epsilon^*}\epsilon_{1,1} \quad , \quad \epsilon_* \sin^2\varphi + \frac{1}{\epsilon_*}\cos^2\varphi = \frac{1}{\epsilon^*}\epsilon_{2,2}$$

$$\left(\epsilon_* - \frac{1}{\epsilon_*}\right)\cos\varphi\sin\varphi = \frac{1}{\epsilon^*}\epsilon_{1,2} \quad , \quad \epsilon^* = (\epsilon_{1,1}\epsilon_{2,2} - \epsilon_{1,2}^2)^{\frac{1}{2}}$$

(the physical sense implies $\epsilon_{1,1}\epsilon_{2,2} - \epsilon_{1,2}^2 > 0$ and $\epsilon_* > 0$). Hence

$$W = \tfrac{1}{2}\epsilon_0 \iint_D \epsilon^* (\mathrm{grad}\, V^*)^2\, dx\, dy \tag{2.1}$$

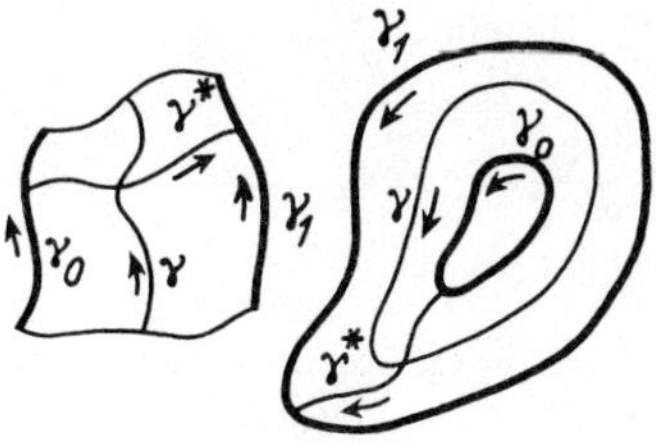

FIG.2. Plane condensers.

Thus we have reduced the problem to the **isotropic case**. To simplify notation, let us set $\epsilon^* = \epsilon$ and $V^* = V$. The fact that the energy of an isotropic constant electric field is expressed by the integral of the product of the dielectric permeability $\epsilon' = \epsilon_0 \epsilon$ and the squared gradient of the (scalar) potential V together with the energy conservation law (1.24), which in this case attains the form $W(t) = c_4$, $t_0 \leqslant t \leqslant t_*$, give a starting point for the variational potential theory of a constant electric field.

Now we shall point out another crucial fact. Suppose that D is a finite closed plane domain which is either Jordan with two distinguished boundary arcs γ_0 and γ_1, or whose boundary consists of two disjoint Jordan curves γ_0 and γ_1. In addition, let $V \in C^2(D)$, $V|\gamma_0 = V_0$, $V|\gamma_1 = V_1$, V_0 and V_1 being constants. Where D is Jordan we also suppose that $\partial D \setminus \gamma_0 \setminus \gamma_1$ consists of smooth curves along which the normal derivative of V vanishes. Then the triple $\mathbb{D} = (D, \gamma_0, \gamma_1)$ constitutes a **plane condenser** (Fig.2) whose **capacity** may be defined by one of two equivalent formulae:

$$\operatorname{cap}(\mathbb{D}, \epsilon') = \frac{\epsilon_0}{(V_1 - V_0)^2} \iint_D \epsilon (\operatorname{grad} V)^2 \, dx\, dy \tag{2.2}$$

or

$$\operatorname{cap}(\mathbb{D}, \epsilon') = \frac{\epsilon_0}{V_1 - V_0} \int_\gamma \epsilon(-V_y dx + V_x dy) \tag{2.3}$$

where for γ we may take an arbitrary smooth Jordan arc or smooth Jordan curve separating γ_0 and γ_1, and oriented according to the physical conventions. γ_0 and γ_1 are called the **plates** of $\mathbb{D}$. Without ambiguity we cannot distinguish between $\mathbb{D}$ and D. From (2.2) and (2.1), where $\epsilon^* = \epsilon$ and $V^* = V$, we infer that

$$W = \tfrac{1}{2} \operatorname{cap}(D, \epsilon')(V_1 - V_0)^2 \tag{2.4}$$

In turn we define the **electric charges** of the condenser plates γ_0 and γ_1 by the formulae

$$Q_j = (-1)^{j-1} \epsilon_0 \int_{\gamma_j} \epsilon(-V_y dx + V_x dy), \quad j = 0, 1 \tag{2.5}$$

respectively. Hence, by (2.3) we get at once

$$Q_1 = -Q_0 = (V_1 - V_0) \operatorname{cap}(D, \epsilon')$$

For simpler notation, set $Q_1 = Q$. Therefore

$$\frac{1}{\operatorname{cap}(D, \epsilon')} = \frac{V_1 - V_0}{Q} = \frac{1}{Q} \int_{\gamma^*} V_x dx + V_y dy \tag{2.6}$$

where γ^* is an arbitrary line of force for the potential V and joins the plate γ_0 to γ_1. Thus, from (2.2) and (2.1), where $\epsilon^* = \epsilon$ and $V^* = V$, we infer that

$$\frac{1}{\operatorname{cap}(D, \epsilon')} = \frac{\epsilon_0}{Q^2} \iint_D \epsilon (\operatorname{grad} V)^2 \, dx \, dy \tag{2.7}$$

and

$$W = \frac{\frac{1}{2} Q^2}{\operatorname{cap}(D, \epsilon')} \tag{2.8}$$

Finally we notice that, by Green's theorem, it is sufficient in (2.6) to assume that γ^* is an arbitrary smooth Jordan arc that joins ϵ_0 to ϵ_1, which gives the complete analogy with the formula (2.3).

Formulae (2.4) and (2.2) give a starting point for obtaining the **Dirichlet principle**: the energy of a constant electric field in the domain int D has the minimal value among the energies of all wireless fields $\widetilde{E} \in \mathscr{E}$, $\mathscr{E}$ being the class of all functions of the form $\widetilde{E} = -\operatorname{grad} \widetilde{V}$, $\widetilde{V} \in \mathscr{V}$, and $\mathscr{V}$ consisting of all $\widetilde{V} \in C^2(D)$, such that $\widetilde{V}|\gamma_0 = V_0$, $\widetilde{V}|\gamma_1 = V_1$, and the normal derivative of $\widetilde{V}$ along $\partial D \setminus \gamma_0 \setminus \gamma_1$ vanishes. In other words, we have

$$W = \tfrac{1}{2} \inf_{\widetilde{E} \in \mathscr{E}} \iint_D \epsilon_0 \epsilon \widetilde{E}^2 \, dx \, dy \quad \text{where} \quad \widetilde{E}^2 = \widetilde{E} \cdot \widetilde{E} \tag{2.9}$$

Further, formulae (2.8) and (2.6) give a starting point for obtaining the **Thomson principle**: the energy of a constant electric field in the domain int D has the minimal value among the energies of all sourceless fields $\widetilde{D} \in \mathscr{D}$, with the energy density $\frac{1}{2}\widetilde{E} \cdot \widetilde{D} = \frac{1}{2}(1/\epsilon_0 \epsilon)\widetilde{D} \cdot \widetilde{D}$, $\mathscr{D}$ being the class of all functions $\widetilde{D} \in [C^2(D)]^2$ whose integrals along the oriented curves γ_0 and γ_1 are equal to Q. In other words, we have

$$W = \tfrac{1}{2} \inf_{\widetilde{D} \in \mathscr{D}} \iint_D \frac{1}{\epsilon_0 \epsilon} \widetilde{D}^2 \, dx \, dy \quad \text{where} \quad \widetilde{D}^2 = \widetilde{D} \cdot \widetilde{D} \tag{2.10}$$

Thus the Dirichlet principle is connected with a variation of the intensity of an electric field, whereas the Thomson principle is connected with a variation of the vector of electric induction. The proofs of both principles may be left as an elementary exercise in the classical calculus of variations.

The principles of Dirichlet and Thomson may be reformulated in terms of capacity. From (2.4) and (2.8) we get $\operatorname{cap}(D, \epsilon') = 2W/(V_1 - V_0)^2$ and $\operatorname{cap}(D, \epsilon') = \frac{1}{2}Q^2/W$, respectively. Thus, in analogy to (2.2) and (2.7), we obtain

$$\operatorname{cap}(D, \epsilon') = \frac{\epsilon_0}{(V_1 - V_0)^2} \inf_{\widetilde{E} \in \mathscr{E}} \iint_D \epsilon \widetilde{E}^2 \, dx \, dy \qquad \textbf{(Dirichlet's principle)} \tag{2.11}$$

and

$$\mathrm{cap}(D,\epsilon') = \frac{Q^2}{\epsilon_0^{-1}} \sup_{\widetilde{D}\in\mathscr{D}} \left[1 \Big/ \iint_D \frac{1}{\epsilon} \widetilde{D}^2 \,dx\,dy \right] \qquad \textbf{(Thomson's principle)} \tag{2.12}$$

Let us further note that, in analogy with the Dirichlet principle (in the form (2.9) or (2.11)), where we confine ourselves to test intensities of the electric field of the form $\widetilde{E} = -\operatorname{grad}\widetilde{V}$ with $\widetilde{V}\in\mathscr{V}$; also in the Thomson principle (in the form (2.10) or (2.12)) we may confine ourselves to test vectors of the electric induction of the form $\widetilde{D} = -\epsilon_0\epsilon \operatorname{grad}\widetilde{V}$ with $\widetilde{V}\in\mathscr{V}$. This special form of the Thomson principle was (in the case ϵ = const) already known to Gauss and is called (also for $\epsilon \neq$ const) the **Gauss principle.**

Finally, we can get rid of the inconvenient boundary conditions by means of the formulae for the charge Q and the difference of potentials $V_1 - V_0$:

$$Q = \epsilon_0 \int_\gamma \epsilon(-V_y dx + V_x dy), \qquad V_1 - V_0 = \int_{\gamma^*} V_x dx + V_y dy$$

Denote by $\widetilde{\mathscr{V}}$ the class of all functions $\widetilde{V}\in C^2(D)$, admitting constant but distinct values on the plates (these constants depend on $\widetilde{V}$), satisfying the condition that their normal derivative along $\partial D \setminus \gamma_0 \setminus \gamma_1$ vanishes, and possessing disjoint lines of maximal growth (thus we may regard γ and γ^* as test equipotential lines and test lines of force, respectively, whereas $\widetilde{V}$ is a test potential). Then the principles of Dirichlet and Thomson attain the form

$$\mathrm{cap}(D,\epsilon') = \epsilon_0 \inf_{\widetilde{V}\in\mathscr{V}} \frac{\displaystyle\iint_D (\operatorname{grad}\widetilde{V})^2 \,dx\,dy}{\left(\displaystyle\inf_{\gamma^*\in C^{01}} \left| \int_{\gamma^*} \widetilde{V}_x dx + \widetilde{V}_y dy \right| \right)^2} \tag{2.13}$$

and

$$\mathrm{cap}(D,\epsilon') = \epsilon_0 \sup_{\widetilde{V}\in\mathscr{V}} \frac{\left(\displaystyle\inf_{\gamma\in C_{01}} \left| \int_\gamma -\epsilon\widetilde{V}_y dx + \epsilon\widetilde{V}_x dy \right| \right)^2}{\displaystyle\iint_D \frac{1}{\epsilon} (\operatorname{grad}\widetilde{V})^2 \,dx\,dy} \tag{2.14}$$

respectively, where C_{01} and C^{01} denote the families of all curves γ and γ^*, respectively, already described. The proof relies on the Schwarz inequality and is fairly easy. It becomes much more difficult if we allow critical points of the lines of force (cf. [3], pp.65–67).

Next we observe that, in the case of arc length parametrization $\widetilde{x}, \widetilde{y}$ of γ and $\widetilde{x}_*, \widetilde{y}_*$ of γ^*, we have $|-\widetilde{V}_y\widetilde{x}' + \widetilde{V}_x\widetilde{y}'| = |\operatorname{grad}\widetilde{V}|$ in (2.14) and $|\widetilde{V}_x\widetilde{x}_*' + \widetilde{V}_y\widetilde{y}_*'| = |\operatorname{grad}\widetilde{V}|$ in (2.13), respectively. If we set $|\operatorname{grad}\widetilde{V}| = \rho$ and $\operatorname{grad}\widetilde{\mathscr{V}} = \{\operatorname{grad}\widetilde{V} : \widetilde{V}\in\widetilde{\mathscr{V}}\}$, these formulae become

$$\operatorname{cap}(D, \epsilon') = \epsilon_0 \inf_{\rho \in \operatorname{grad} \mathscr{V}} \frac{\iint\limits_D \epsilon\rho^2\, dx\, dy}{\left(\inf\limits_{\gamma^* \in C^{01}} \int\limits_{\gamma^*} \rho\, ds \right)^2}$$

and

$$\operatorname{cap}(D, \epsilon') = \epsilon_0 \sup_{\rho \in \operatorname{grad} \mathscr{V}} \frac{\left(\inf\limits_{\gamma \in C_{01}} \int\limits_{\gamma} \rho\, ds \right)^2}{\iint\limits_D \frac{1}{\epsilon}\rho^2\, dx\, dy}$$

Now we are ready to introduce the general notion of extremal length, essentially due to Ahlfors and Beurling [4, 5], and then generalized by various authors [31]. To be more specific we shall confine ourselves to an arbitrary one-dimensional homology class Γ with real coefficients on a Riemann surface $\mathbb{N}$, or to a class of Jordan arcs or Jordan curves on $\mathbb{N}$. Consider further the family P of all non-negative Borel functions $\rho : \mathbb{N} \to \mathbb{R}$ which are not identically zero. We recall that $\rho : \mathbb{N} \to \mathbb{R}$ is called a **Borel function** (also for higher-dimensional topological spaces) if for every $a \in \mathbb{R}$ the set $\{z \in \mathbb{N} : \rho(z) > a\}$ is a Borel set. Finally, let $p \in [1; +\infty)$ and let $q : \mathbb{N} \to \mathbb{R}$, an **inhomogeneity function**, be a positive-valued continuous mapping. Then the (p, q)-**extremal length** of Γ is defined by the formula

$$\lambda_p(\Gamma, q) = \sup_{\rho \in P} \left[\left(\inf_{\gamma \in \Gamma} \int\limits_{\gamma} \rho\, ds \right)^2 \Big/ \iint\limits_{\mathbb{N}} \frac{1}{q} \rho^p\, d\sigma \right] \tag{2.15}$$

where ds and $d\sigma$ are the arc length and area elements on $\mathbb{N}$, respectively. Of course, without any loss of generality we may assume that the curvilinear integral in (2.15) is always not less than one.

Also, in the case of capacity let us forget about physics, change the notation from $\widetilde{V}$ to u, and suppose that $|\operatorname{grad} u|^p$ is Lebesgue integrable over any compact subset of $\mathbb{N}$, $u|\gamma_0 = 0$ and $u|\gamma_1 = 1$ (one may still weaken the assumptions; cf. the next section). Denote the class of all functions u by adm D (**admissible** for D), restricting (to be more specific) the class of condensers to doubly connected domains but allowing an arbitrary boundary (otherwise we have to assume extra conditions for u on $\partial D \setminus \gamma_0 \setminus \gamma_1$). It is also convenient to replace the conditions $u|\gamma_0 = 0$ and $u|\gamma_1 = 1$ by less restrictive conditions $u|C_0 = 0$ and $u|C_1 = 1$ where C_0 and C_1 are disjoint and constitute the complement of D to $\mathbb{N}$ so that finally, under a **condenser** D on $\mathbb{N}$ we mean a domain D on $\mathbb{N}$ whose complement consists of two disjoint closed sets C_0 and C_1 (the **condenser plates**). Then we have (cf. [6], pp. 225–227, [19], and [20]):

Theorem 2.1 (Dirichlet's principle). Suppose that D is a condenser whose closure is compact on a Riemann surface $\mathbb{N}$; C^{01} is the class of Jordan arcs joining in D the condenser plates C_0 and C_1; p is a real number, $p \in [1; +\infty)$; and q is an inhomogeneity function on $\mathbb{N}$. Then

$$\operatorname{cap}_p(D, q) \equiv \inf_{u \in \operatorname{adm} D} \iint\limits_D q|\operatorname{grad}_{\mathbb{N}} u| d\sigma = 1/\lambda_p(C^{01}, 1/q)$$

Theorem 2.2 (Thomson's principle). Suppose that D is a condenser whose closure is compact on a Riemann surface $\mathbb{N}$; C_{01} is the homology class of D with real coefficients, represented by a Jordan curve, separating in D the condenser plates C_0 and C_1; p is a real number, $p \in [1; +\infty)$; and q is an inhomogeneity function on $\mathbb{N}$. Then

$$\mathrm{cap}_p(D, q) = \lambda_p(C_{01}, q)$$

Moreover, it is not difficult to prove

Theorem 2.3. The (2, q)-capacities and (2, q)- extremal lengths on a Riemann surface are conformal invariants.

The (2, 1)-capacities as well as (2, 1)-extremal lengths may be used to define **quasiconformal** (in particular, conformal) **mappings** [2, 21], which physically describe the complex potential. Let us add that the above electrical interpretation for the (2, q)-capacities is not the only one: the others appear in terms of dielectric susceptibility, electric conductivity, magnetic permeability, magnetic susceptibility, filtration coefficients, diffusion coefficients, coefficients of heat conductivity, etc. [19, 24]. The use of Riemann surfaces is particularly convenient in the case of magnetic interpretations because the magnetic potential is multivalued in the plane but single-valued on a suitable Riemann surface.

In the case of riemannian manifolds, the theory of extremal lengths and conformal capacities is, in principle, analogous (cf. Refs [36] and [23]).

3. EXTENSION TO PSEUDORIEMANNIAN MANIFOLDS

On pseudoriemannian manifolds, conformal invariants are still very attractive for the theoretical physicist. This is not surprising because the light cone, apart from possible singularities, is invariant under the conformal group if the latter is considered as a space-time symmetry group. Important research in this direction was recently made by Flato, Simon and Sternheimer [13], and a new point of view has been obtained in the promising twistor formalism of Penrose (cf. e.g. Ref.[32]).

Let $\mathbb{N}$ be a pseudoriemannian manifold with metric g. Given a vector $v \neq$ of the tangent space $T_x\mathbb{N}$, $x \in \mathbb{N}$, and a differentiable function $u : \mathbb{N} \to \mathbb{R}$, we consider the equation $g(v, w) = v(u)$, where w is assumed to be a vector of $T_x\mathbb{N}$. It is easily verified that this equation has always a unique solution independent of v; we denote it by $(\mathrm{grad}_{\mathbb{N}} u)(x)$ (cf. e.g. Ref.[18], Vol.II, p.337). If $f : \mathbb{N} \to \mathbb{N}'$ (where $\mathbb{N}'$ is another pseudoriemannian manifold with metric g′) is a continuous function and $\check{u} : T\mathbb{N} \to T\mathbb{N}'$ ($T\mathbb{N}$ being the tangent bundle of $\mathbb{N}$) is a Borel function which maps each $T_x\mathbb{N}$ linearly into $T_{f(x)}\mathbb{N}'$, then the function $||\check{u}|| : \mathbb{N} \to \overline{\mathbb{R}}$, defined for every $x \in \mathbb{N}$ by

$$||\check{u}||(x) = \sup_{v \in V} |g'(\check{u}(x)(v), \check{u}(x)(v))|^{\frac{1}{2}}$$

(where V consists of $v \in T_x\mathbb{N}$ such that $|g(v, v)| \leqslant 1$), is well defined and Borel [28]. Hence $||\mathrm{grad}_{\mathbb{N}} u||$ is Borel.

Now let $\tau(\mathbb{N})$ denote the Lebesgue measure on $\mathbb{N}$ [28]. In the case of a riemannian manifold we say that $\mathrm{grad}_{\mathbb{N}} u$ is an **L^p-differential,** $p \in [1; +\infty)$, if $||\mathrm{grad}_{\mathbb{N}} u||^p$ is $\tau(\mathbb{N})$-integrable over any compact subset of $\mathbb{N}$ [36]. In the case of a pseudoriemannian manifold which is not riemannian we replace $||\check{u}||$ by a less restrictive Borel function $||\check{u}||^*$ which is necessary because although $||\check{u}|| : \mathbb{N} \to \mathbb{R}$ in the riemannian case [36], in the pseudoriemannian case we only know that $||\check{u}|| : \mathbb{N} \to \overline{\mathbb{R}}$, but we can prove that $||\check{u}||^* : \mathbb{N} \to \mathbb{R}$ [24].

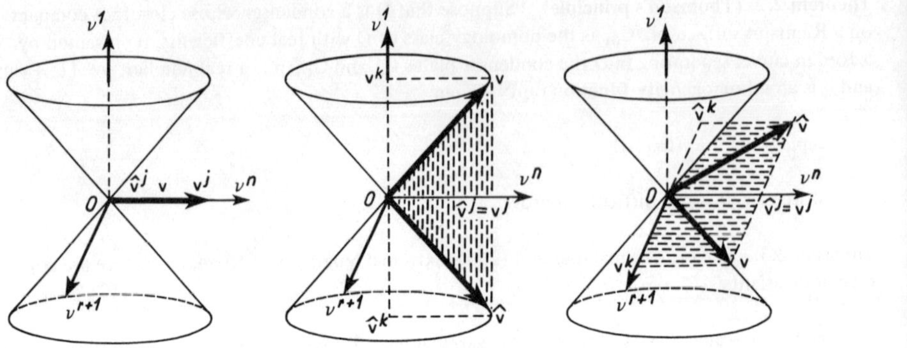

FIG.3. Different positions of vectors v *and* v̂ *with respect to the light (isotropic) cone.*

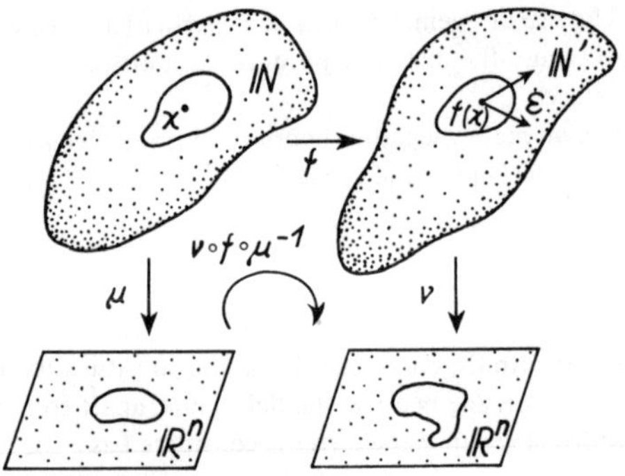

FIG.4. The co-ordinate mappings on the manifold ℕ *at* x *and on* ℕ′ *at* f(x).

Namely, let us consider the class V^* of vectors $v = (v^j)$ and the associated class $\hat{V}^*$ of vectors $\hat{v} = (\hat{v}^j)$ of the tangent space $T_x\mathbb{N}$ in an arbitrary orthonormal base $e = (e_j)$ such that $|\tilde{g}(v, v)| \leqslant 1$ and either

$$\hat{v}^j = 0, \quad v^s = \hat{v}^s = 0, \quad s \neq j, \quad j \text{ fixed}$$

or

$$v^j = \hat{v}^j, \quad v^k = -\hat{v}^k, \quad k \neq j, \quad j, k \text{ fixed}; \qquad v^s = \hat{v}^s = 0, \quad s \neq j, k$$

(see Fig.3) where

$$\tilde{g}(v, v) = g(v, v) - g(\hat{v}, \hat{v})$$

Further, for

$$w = Df(x)(v) = v^j(\nu^k \circ f \circ \mu^{-1})_{|j} \circ \mu(x)\epsilon_k \circ f(x)$$

in an arbitrary orthonormal base $\epsilon = (\epsilon_k)$ on $T_{f(x)}\mathbb{N}'$, where $\mu = (\mu^j)$ and $\nu = (\nu^k)$ are arbitrary co-ordinate C^∞ mappings on $\mathbb{N}$ at x and on $\mathbb{N}'$ at f(x), respectively (see Fig.4), and $_{|j}$ denotes differentiation with respect to μ^j, let

$$\tilde{g}'(w, w) = g'(w, w) - g'(\hat{w}, \hat{w}), \qquad \hat{w} = Df(x)(v)$$

Then the function

$$||\check{u}||^*(x) = \sup_{v \in \mathscr{V}^*} |\tilde{g}'\check{u}(x)(v), \check{u}(x)(v))|^{\frac{1}{2}}$$

is well defined and Borel [24]. Hence $||\mathrm{grad}_{\mathbb{N}} u||^*$ is Borel.

Under a **condenser** D on $\mathbb{N}$ we mean a domain D on $\mathbb{N}$ whose complement consists of two disjoint sets C_0 and C_1 (the **condenser plates**). Suppose next that $q: \mathbb{N} \to \mathbb{R}$, an **inhomogeneity function**, is a positive-valued continuous mapping and denote by adm D the class of all functions $u: \mathbb{N} \to \mathbb{R}$ that are continuous with $\mathrm{grad}_{\mathbb{N}} u$ being an L^p-differential, $u|C_0 = 0$ and $u|C_1 = 1$. We call the functions of adm D **admissible** for D. Then, for $p \in [1; +\infty)$, we define the (p, q)-**capacity** of D as follows:

$$\mathrm{cap}_p(D, q) = \inf_{u \in \mathrm{adm}\, D} \int_D q|g(\mathrm{grad}_{\mathbb{N}} u, \mathrm{grad}_{\mathbb{N}} u)|^{\frac{1}{2}p} d\tau(\mathbb{N}) \tag{3.1}$$

In the riemannian case it is convenient to include in adm D functions of the class ACL^p (for the definition we refer to Ref. [36]) and consequently we have to define $\mathrm{grad}_{\mathbb{N}} u$ for u continuous and differentiable almost everywhere. When studying quasiconformal mappings it is also convenient to restrict condensers to ring domains.

Extending now the notion of the inner product g(,) to each cotangent space $T_x\mathbb{N}$ (cf. e.g. Ref.[18], Vol.I, p.156, and Vol.II, p.338), we may rewrite (3.1) in an equivalent form:

$$\mathrm{cap}_p(D, q) = \inf_{u \in \mathrm{adm}\, D} \int_D q|g(du, du)|^{\frac{1}{2}p} d\tau(\mathbb{N}) \tag{3.2}$$

Suppose $\mathbb{N}$ and $\mathbb{N}'$ are of the same dimension n and of the same index. We have [24]

Theorem 3.1. If $f: \mathbb{N} \to \mathbb{N}'$ is a C^1-diffeomorphism and

$$0 < k \leqslant 1/||Df^{-1}(f(x))||^*, \qquad ||Df(x)||^* \leqslant K < +\infty \quad \text{for } x \in \mathbb{N}$$

then

$$(k^n/K^p)\mathrm{cap}_p(D, q) \leqslant \mathrm{cap}_p(f[D], q \circ f^{-1}) \leqslant (K^n/k^p)\mathrm{cap}_p(D, q) \tag{3.3}$$

for each condenser D and each inhomogeneity function q on $\mathbb{N}$. Both estimates in (3.3) are precise and we can replace k and K everywhere by arbitrary kh(x) and Kh(x), respectively.

In the case of space-time, the interpretation of the above capacities is analogous to that pointed out in the classical case. In particular, the capacities in question, being either conformal invariants (p = n) or quasi-invariants ($p \neq n$), seem to be important when the influence between electromagnetic and gravitational fields is studied. This influence has been described in detail for electromagnetic fields *in vacuo* and for an incoherent fluid composed of particles all charged with electricity of the same sign by Synge in Ref. [37], pp.354–371, and for more general situations in a series of papers by Pham Mau Quân. Here we confine ourselves to quoting [33] only, an adequate survey which, among other things, treats various aspects of Maxwell's equations very carefully, including their global form, which actually leads to the introduction of the capacities in question.

For the riemannian case we can also give the following quantum-mechanical interpretation [24], when a non-relativistic particle of mass m is considered. Let u be the argument of a complex wave function ψ in an element (D, C_0, C_1) of an n-dimensional configuration space $\mathbb{N}$, $q = (\hbar/m)$, $\hbar = h/2\pi$; h is the Planck constant, and $\rho(x)$ the probability density for the particle to occur at the point $x \in \mathbb{N}$. Thus $\psi = \rho^{\frac{1}{2}} \exp iu$ and $q \operatorname{grad}_{\mathbb{N}} u$ is the vector of the probability current density (an analogue of Ohm's law). Therefore $\operatorname{cap}_2(D, q)$ is the intensity of probability current in D, divided by $u_1 - u_0$.

4. EXTENSION TO HERMITIAN MANIFOLDS

Finally, let us move to the complex case. Let $\mathbb{M}$ be a complex manifold endowed with an hermitian metric h which is *not* supposed to be positive definite so that the manifold be compatible with its pseudoriemannian real submanifolds. With the usual meaning of ∂ and $\bar{\partial}$, let

$$d = \partial + \bar{\partial}, \quad d^c = i(\bar{\partial} - \partial)$$

Since in any local co-ordinate system $\mu = (\mu^j)$ on $\mathbb{N}$ we had

$$g(\operatorname{grad}_{\mathbb{N}} u, \operatorname{grad}_{\mathbb{N}} u) = g(du, du) = g^{jk} u_{:j} u_{:k}, \quad u_{:j} = (u \circ \mu^{-1})_{|j} \circ \mu$$

($g^{jk} = g^{j,k}$ etc.), it is natural to define in the complex case the corresponding **(p, q)-capacity** as follows:

$$\operatorname{cap}'_p(D, q) = \inf_{u \in \operatorname{adm}' D} \left| \int_D q[h(d^c u, d^c u)]^{\frac{1}{2}p} d\tau(\mathbb{M}) \right| \tag{4.1}$$

where

$$h(d^c u, d^c u) = h^{j\bar{k}} u_{:j} u_{:\bar{k}}$$

D is a **condenser** on $\mathbb{M}$, i.e. a domain whose complement consists of two distinguished disjoint closed sets C_0 and C_1 (the **condenser plates**), $q : \mathbb{M} \to \mathbb{C}$ is an **inhomogeneity function**, i.e. a complex-valued continuous mapping, $p \in [1; +\infty)$, and the branch of $h^{\frac{1}{2}p}$ is chosen so that $1^{\frac{1}{2}p} = 1$.

The Lebesgue measure $\tau(\mathbb{M})$ is well and uniquely defined (cf. Ref.[38], pp. 171–174) by means of Theorem 3.5 in [36] and Theorem 2 in [28]. It is a matter of taste whether to write $h^{j\bar{k}} u_{:j} u_{:\bar{k}}$ as $h(d^c u, d^c u)$ or $h(du, du)$ since d^c as well as d are differential operators, defined on C^1-smooth complex-valued differential forms which map a real form into a real form. It remains to decide which class of functions is the right choice for adm'D. To do this, we notice, following Chern, Levine and Nirenberg [9], that in the euclidean case

$$h(v, v) = v\bar{v}, \quad v \in T_z\mathbb{M}, \quad z \in \mathbb{M}$$

in every co-ordinate system at z, where $\mathbb{M}$ is assumed to admit such a metric h, the form $du \wedge d^c u \wedge (dd^c u)^{n-1}$ is a non-negative multiple of the volume element $d\tau$ provided that u is a strictly plurisubharmonic function of the class C^2 (the notion of a **plurisubharmonic function** is due to Lelong [22]). Here n denotes the complex dimension of $\mathbb{M}$. This result remains valid when we consider a complex manifold without any hermitian metric [9].

To extend this to the general hermitian case we observe that

$$dd^c u = 2iu_{:j\bar{k}}\, dz^j \wedge d\bar{z}^k = -d^c du$$

where hereafter $z = (z^j)$ is an arbitrary co-ordinate biholomorphic mapping from an open neighbourhood on $\mathbb{M}$ into $\mathbb{C}^n$. Thus it is natural to associate with $dd^c u$ the form

$$(dd^c u)_H = 2iH_j^\ell u_{:\ell\bar{k}}\, dz^j \wedge d\bar{z}^k$$

where H is an arbitrary C^1 tensor field of type (1, 1) on $\mathbb{M}$. In particular, we may let H depend on h or take as H an almost complex structure of the tangent bundle $T\mathbb{M}$, e.g. a complex structure which will lead to the case of [9]. Similarly we associate with

$$du \wedge d^c u = 2iu_{:j} u_{:\bar{k}}\, dz^j \wedge d\bar{z}^k$$

the form

$$(du \wedge d^c u)_H = 2iH_j^\ell u_{:\ell} u_{:\bar{k}}\, dz^j \wedge d\bar{z}^k$$

In fact we can extend the above result on plurisubharmonic functions to hermitian manifolds [27], so we have to take as adm′D the class of all plurisubharmonic C^2-functions u on $c\ell D$, satisfying the conditions $0 < u(z) < 1$ for $z \in D$, $u|\partial C_0 = 0$ and $u|\partial C_1 = 1$. In addition, one obtains [27]

Theorem 4.1. Suppose that $\mathbb{M}$ is an hermitian manifold of complex dimension n and metric h, endowed with a C^1 tensor field H of type (1, 1). Then the capacity

$$\mathrm{cap}_p''(D, q) = \inf_{u \in \mathrm{adm}'D} \left| \int_D q[h(d^c u, d^c u)]^{\frac{1}{2}p-1} (du \wedge d^c u)_H \wedge (dd^c u)_H^{n-1} \right| \qquad (4.2)$$

is equivalent to (4.1) for any $p \in [1; +\infty)$, each condenser D, and each inhomogeneity function q on $\mathbb{M}$, in the sense that there is a positive constant A, independent of D and depending only on $\mathbb{M}$ (including H), p and q, such that

$$(1/A)\,\mathrm{cap}_p'(D, q) \leqslant \mathrm{cap}_p''(D, q) \leqslant A\, \mathrm{cap}_p'(D, q)$$

Lemma 4.1. Under the hypotheses of Theorem 4.1 we have

$$(du \wedge d^c u)_H \wedge (dd^c u)_H^{n-1} = \det H\, du \wedge d^c u \wedge (dd^c u)^{n-1}$$

Theorem 4.2. If $\mathbb{M}$ is as in Theorem 4.1, then

$$\mathrm{cap}_p''(D, q) = \inf_{u \in \mathrm{adm}'D} \left| \int_D q[h(d^c u, d^c u)]^{\frac{1}{2}p-1} \det H \, du \wedge d^c u \wedge (dd^c u)^{n-1} \right|$$

for any $p \in [1; +\infty)$, each condenser D, and each inhomogeneity function q on $\mathbb{M}$.

Let us consider now the system of differential equations

$$d^c(Fu) = q[h(d^c u, d^c u)]^{\frac{1}{2}p-1} \det H \, d^c u \tag{4.3}$$

where the unknown function $F: c\ell D \to \mathbb{C}$ is assumed to be of the class C^1, which have non-trivial solutions at least for some H different from the complex structure of $T\mathbb{M}$. Thus it seems reasonable to prove the following

Theorem 4.3. Suppose that D has a piecewise C^1-smooth boundary and compact closure and let Γ denote the $(2n-1)$-dimensional homology class of the level hypersurfaces $\{z \in c\ell D : u(z) = \mathrm{const}\}$, where u is a given function admissible for D. Then, if u satisfies the equation

$$dd^c(Fu) \wedge (dd^c u)^{n-1} = 0 \tag{4.4}$$

where $F: c\ell D \to \mathbb{C}$ is a fixed C^2-function, we have

$$\int_D du \wedge d^c(Fu) \wedge (dd^c u)^{n-1} = \int_T d^c(Fu) \wedge (dd^c u)^{n-1}, \quad T \in \Gamma \tag{4.5}$$

Formula (4.5) with F satisfying equation (4.4) inspires a further generalization of the idea of capacity so that in the case where H is the complex structure of $T\mathbb{M}$, $p = 2$, and $q = \mathrm{const}$, it corresponds to an intrinsic seminorm of Chern, Levine and Nirenberg [9], which is itself a generalization of the pseudo-distances due to Carathéodory and Kobayashi (cf. [16] and [17]).

Let us recall the definition of an r-current on $\mathbb{M}$ in the sense of de Rham (cf. e.g. [11], Vol.III, pp. 241–255). Let $\mathscr{E}_r(\mathbb{M})$ denote the space of all complex-valued C^1-differentiable r-forms on $\mathbb{M}$, $\mathscr{D}_r(\mathbb{M}, E)$ the subspace of $\mathscr{E}_r(\mathbb{M})$ consisting of r-forms with supports contained in the compact set $E \subset \mathbb{M}$, and $\mathscr{D}_r(\mathbb{M})$ the union of the $\mathscr{D}_r(\mathbb{M}, E)$ for all compact subsets E of $\mathbb{M}$. Then an **r-current** on $\mathbb{M}$ is a linear functional T of $\mathscr{D}_r(\mathbb{M})$ such that for every sequence of $\varphi_k \in \mathscr{D}_r(\mathbb{M}, E)$ which converges to 0 in $\mathscr{E}_r(\mathbb{M})$, the corresponding sequence of $T[\varphi_k]$ converges to 0 in $\mathbb{C}$.

Suppose now again that D is a condenser on $\mathbb{M}$. Let Γ be a homology class of D with real coefficients and $\dim \Gamma = r$. Consider all currents of Γ (more precisely, corresponding to the elements of Γ) in the sense of de Rham. Next, let adm*D, the class of functions **admissible** for D, be the class of all plurisubharmonic C^2-functions u of D satisfying the condition $0 < u(z) < 1$ for $z \in D$. With p and q as at the beginning of this section, extending the concept of [9], we define the **(p, q, Γ)-capacity** of D as follows:

$$\mathrm{cap}_p(D, q, \Gamma) = \sup_{u \in \mathrm{adm}^* D} \inf_{T \in \Gamma} |T[q[h(d^c u, d^c u)]^{\frac{1}{2}p-1} \det H \, D^r u]| \tag{4.6}$$

where

$$D^r u = \begin{cases} d^c u \wedge (dd^c u)^{\frac{1}{2}r - \frac{1}{2}} & \text{for } r \text{ odd} \\ du \wedge d^c u \wedge (dd^c u)^{\frac{1}{2}r-1} & \text{for } r \text{ even} \end{cases}$$

and the branch of $h^{\frac{1}{2}p}$ is chosen so that $1^{\frac{1}{2}p} = 1$. If adm*D = ∅, we put $\text{cap}_p(D, q, \Gamma) = 0$. It is a matter of taste whether to call (4.6) an intrinsic seminorm (cf. [9]) or a capacity – this depends on whether one thinks about its interpretation in the functional analysis or in physics.

Unfortunately, if $\mathbb{M}$ is a compact manifold, the family adm*$\mathbb{M}$ will consist only of constant functions and every corresponding (p, q, Γ)-capacity will be equal to zero. To avoid this, let us consider a locally finite open covering $\mathscr{U} = \{U_j : j \in I\}$ of $\mathbb{M}$ and denote by adm(D,$\mathscr{U}$) the family of all plurisubharmonic C^2-functions u_j of $U_j \cap D$, defined in each member of the covering which satisfy the following conditions:

(i) the oscillation of u_j in $U_j \cap D$ is less than one;
(ii) $du_j = du_k$ in $U_j \cap U_k \cap D \neq \emptyset$.

Condition (ii) describes a closed real one-form in D. Similarly d^cu_j and dd^cu_j are also well defined in D. Without ambiguity, we can denote them omitting the indices. In analogy with (4.6), we define the **(p, q, Γ,$\mathscr{U}$)-capacity** of D as follows:

$$\text{cap}_p(D, q, \Gamma, \mathscr{U}) = \sup_{u \in \text{adm}(D,\mathscr{U})} \inf_{T \in \Gamma} |T[q[h(d^cu, d^cu)]^{\frac{1}{2}p-1} \det H\, D^r u]| \tag{4.7}$$

where the branch of $h^{\frac{1}{2}p}$ is chosen so that $1^{\frac{1}{2}p} = 1$. If adm(D,$\mathscr{U}$) = ∅, we put $\text{cap}_p(D, q, \Gamma, \mathscr{U}) = 0$. We have (cf. [9] and [2])

Theorem 4.4. If q is of the class C^1 and for any u ∈ adm*D there exists a C^1-solution of (4.3):

$$0 \leqslant \text{cap}_p(D, q, \Gamma) \leqslant \text{cap}_p(D, q, \Gamma, \mathscr{U}) < +\infty$$

5. AN EXTENSION OF SCHWARZ'S LEMMA TO HERMITIAN MANIFOLDS AND ITS PHYSICAL SIGNIFICANCE

The classical Schwarz lemma in its invariant form formulated by G. Pick in 1915 states that every holomorphic mapping of the unit disc into itself is distance-decreasing with respect to the Poincaré-Bergman metric [7]. The essence of further generalizations, originated by Ahlfors [1], is that, given complex manifolds $\mathbb{M}$ and $\mathbb{M}'$ endowed with either metrics or volume elements, every holomorphic mapping $f: \mathbb{M} \to \mathbb{M}'$ is distance- or volume-decreasing under the conditions that $\mathbb{M}$ is a ball or a symmetric domain in $\mathbb{C}^n$, and that $\mathbb{M}'$ has negative curvature in one sense or another.

Further generalizations in this direction have been given by several authors, in particular by Siciak [35], Kobayashi [16], Chern, Levine and Nirenberg [9], and Chern and Moser [10]. Each of these results leads to theorems assuring some control over the family of holomorphic mappings $f: \mathbb{M} \to \mathbb{M}'$. For an orientation within the recent development on complex manifolds we also refer to Kobayashi's book [17]. In our context we begin with the following [25]

Theorem 5.1. Let $f: \mathbb{M} \to \mathbb{M}'$ be a holomorphic mapping and f_* the induced homomorphism on the homology classes, where $\mathbb{M}'$ is an hermitian manifold of metric h′, endowed with the C^1 tensor field H′ of type (1,1) such that:

(i) The hermitian metric h′ is given, in local co-ordinates, by the relations

$$h'^{\ell\bar{m}} \circ f = h^{j\bar{k}} f^{\ell}_{:j} \bar{f}^{\bar{m}}_{:\bar{k}}$$

(ii) The tensor field H′ is given accordingly, in local co-ordinates, by the relations

$$(H'^{\ell}_{m} \circ f) f^{m}_{:k} = H^{j}_{k} f^{\ell}_{:j}$$

Then, if q is an inhomogeneity function on $\mathbb{M}'$ and f[D] is a condenser on $\mathbb{M}'$, we have

$$\mathrm{cap}_p(f[D], q, f_*\Gamma) \leqslant \mathrm{cap}_p(D, q \circ f, \Gamma)$$

$$\mathrm{cap}_p(f[D], q, f_*\Gamma, f[\mathscr{U}]) \leqslant \mathrm{cap}_p(D, q \circ f, \Gamma, \mathscr{U})$$

We turn our attention now to the case where f is biholomorphic. Now Theorem 5.1 is also valid for the inverse mapping, so we obtain the following

Theorem 5.2. Let $f: \mathbb{M} \to \mathbb{M}'$ be a biholomorphic mapping and f_* the induced homomorphism on the homology classes, where $\mathbb{M}'$ is an hermitian manifold of metric h′, endowed with the C^1 tensor field H′ of type (1.1) such that

(i) The hermitian metric h′ is given, in local co-ordinates, by the relations

$$h'^{\ell\overline{m}} = (h^{j\overline{k}} \circ f^{-1})(f^{\ell}_{:j} \circ f^{-1})(\overline{f}^{\overline{m}}_{:\overline{k}} \circ f^{-1})$$

or, equivalently, by

$$h'_{\ell\overline{m}} = (h_{j\overline{k}} \circ f^{-1}) f^{-1j}_{:\ell} \, \overline{f}^{-1k}_{:\overline{m}}$$

(ii) the tensor field H′ is given accordingly, in local co-ordinates, by the relations

$$H'^{\ell}_{m} = (H^{j}_{k} \circ f^{-1})(f^{\ell}_{:j} \circ f^{-1}) f^{-1k}_{:m}$$

Then, if q is an inhomogeneity function on $\mathbb{M}$, we have

$$\mathrm{cap}_p(f[D], q \circ f^{-1}, f_*\Gamma) = \mathrm{cap}_p(D, q, \Gamma)$$

$$\mathrm{cap}_p(f[D], q \circ f^{-1}, f_*\Gamma, f[\mathscr{U}]) = \mathrm{cap}_p(D, q, \Gamma, \mathscr{U})$$

The relation between the metrics h and h′ is very natural — it is a straightforward generalization of the relation between the Bergman metrics of two bounded domains D and f[D] in $\mathbb{C}^n$, where f is assumed biholomorphic (cf. e.g. [18], Vol. II, p. 163). The relation between the tensor fields H and H′ is constructed similarly. It is also clear that Theorems 5.1 and 5.2 remain valid if we generalize the capacities in question so that the term $[h(d^c u, d^c u)]^{\frac{1}{2}p-1} \det H$ in (4.6) and (4.7) be replaced by an arbitrary continuous complex-valued function of two variables $h(d^c u, d^c u)$ and det H, provided that the capacities remain finite.

Theorems 5.1 and 5.2 can be used for studying holomorphic and biholomorphic continuation of quasiconformal mappings on product complex manifolds [26] which may have a non-trivial electromagnetic interpretation. In fact, the author and L. Wojtczak [30] proposed a description of the properties of elementary particles by a suitable choice of three fibre bundles. One of these bundles has as its fibre space a pseudoriemannian manifold $\mathbb{M}$ – the space of observations (a curved Minkowski space-time). Two other bundles have as their fibre space general riemannian manifolds $\mathbb{N}_e$ and $\mathbb{N}_n$ – the spaces of the particle, connected with the external electromagnetic and nuclear fields, respectively.

Now it is natural to establish relations between the curvature from Ω^2 of some principal fibre bundle $\mathbb{L}$ derived from $\mathbb{N}_e$ and $\mathbb{N}_n$ and the curved space-time $\mathbb{M}$ via some induced C^1-smooth quasiconformal mappings $v_e: \mathbb{N}_e \to \mathbb{M}$ and $v_n: \mathbb{N}_n \to \mathbb{M}$ [29]. The form Ω^2 stands for the meson field M and the baryon field B simultaneously, i.e. $\Omega^2 = M + iB$, where

$$M = \begin{bmatrix} 2^{-\frac{1}{2}}\pi^0 + 6^{-\frac{1}{2}}\eta & \pi^+ & K^+ \\ \pi^- & -2^{-\frac{1}{2}}\pi^0 + 6^{-\frac{1}{2}}\eta & K^0 \\ K^- & \bar{K}^0 & -2\cdot 6^{-\frac{1}{2}}\eta \end{bmatrix}$$

$$B = \begin{bmatrix} 6^{-\frac{1}{2}}\Lambda + 2^{-\frac{1}{2}}\Sigma^0 & \Sigma^+ & p \\ \Sigma^- & 6^{-\frac{1}{2}}\Lambda - 2^{-\frac{1}{2}}\Sigma^0 & n \\ \Xi^- & \Xi^0 & -2\cdot 6^{-\frac{1}{2}}\Lambda \end{bmatrix}$$

The elements of matrices M and B are C^1-differentiable 2-forms corresponding to the SU(3) classification table, where the Lie algebra of SU(3) is generated, as usual, by the elements $(I_1, ..., Y)$. The form Ω^2 accounts for symmetry classification schemes within the frame of principal fibre bundles, while the mappings v_e and v_n characterize nuclear reactions of the type $N + \pi \rightleftharpoons N$, where N is some nucleon and π the virtual π-meson of this reaction. The topological and metrical properties of the curved space-time $\mathbb{M}$ manifest themselves as electric charge, magnetic dipole, nuclear charge, nuclear dipole, and mass. Thus the relations in question are the key relations for a classification scheme of elementary particles.

It is worth while to add that in the case of Riemann surfaces the capacity $\mathrm{cap}_p(D, q, \Gamma, \mathscr{U})$, defined by (4.7), is, under some regularity conditions, equivalent (in the sense explained in the formulation of Theorem 4.1) to an extremal length of Γ provided that $1 \leqslant p \leqslant 3$ [26, 9].

6. VARIATION OF "COMPLEX" CAPACITIES WITHIN THE ADMISSIBLE CLASS OF PLURISUBHARMONIC FUNCTIONS

Let us consider now the capacity (4.2) in the case where D is a bounded domain in $\mathbb{M} = \mathbb{C}^n$, $p = 2$, $q = \mathrm{const}$ (we put $q = 1$ identically), and H is the complex structure of $\mathbb{C}^n$. Hence

$$\mathrm{Cap}\, D \equiv \mathrm{cap}_2''(D, 1) = \inf_{u \in \mathrm{adm}' D} \left| \int_D du \wedge d^c u \wedge (dd^c u)^{n-1} \right|$$

Suppose that $\mathrm{adm}' D \neq \emptyset$. J. Kalina, a student of mine, considered in Ref. [15] the functional

$$J = (\mathrm{adm}' D \ni \tilde{u} \mapsto \int_D d\tilde{u} \wedge d^c \tilde{u} \wedge (dd^c \tilde{u})^{n-1}$$

He found the explicit formulae for the first and second variation of J within the class adm′D and proved that the second variation is non-negative.

He also proved that the functional J attains the maximum for $\tilde{u} = u$ if and only if

$$(dd^c u) = 0 \qquad (6.1)$$

Equation (6.1) is a special case of (4.4) with F = 1 everywhere and, on the other hand, is the complex analogue of the **Monge-Ampère equation**:

$$\det[u_{:j,k}]_{j,k\leqslant n} = 0 \qquad (6.2)$$

discussed, e.g. in [9]. Kalina also demonstrated the existence of an extremal function u for condensers biholomorphically equivalent to an annulus, whence in particular it follows that two annuli with different ratio of radii are not biholomorphically equivalent.

Finally, Kalina was concerned with a conjecture of Chern, Levine and Nirenberg [9], according to which (cf. Theorem 4.3) $\mathrm{Cap}\,D = \mathrm{cap}_2(D, 1, \Gamma)$, where Γ is as in Theorem 4.3. He proved it in the case where D is biholomorphically equivalent to an annulus.

Added in proof: The solvability of the generalized complex Monge-Ampère equation (4.4) and the related equation (4.3) is specially treated in the papers:

ANDREOTTI, A., ŁAWRYNOWICZ, J., On the generalized complex Monge-Ampère equation on complex manifolds and related questions (to appear in Bull. Acad. Polon. Sci., Sér. Sci. Math. Astron. Phys.).

ANDREOTTI, A., ŁAWRYNOWICZ, J., The generalized complex Monge-Ampère equation and a variational capacity problem (to appear in the same journal).

REFERENCES

[1] AHLFORS, L.V., An extension of Schwarz's lemma, Trans. Am. Math. Soc. **43** (1938) 359.

[2] AHLFORS, L.V., Lectures on Quasiconformal Mappings, Van Nostrand, Princeton (1966).

[3] AHLFORS, L.V., Conformal Invariants: Topics in Geometric Function Theory, McGraw-Hill, New York (1973).

[4] AHLFORS, L.V., BEURLING, A., Invariants conformes et problèmes extrémaux, C.R. Dixième Congrès des Mathématiciens Scandinaves, Copenhagen (1946) 341.

[5] AHLFORS, L.V., BEURLING, A., Conformal invariants and function-theoretic null-sets, Acta Math. **83** (1950) 101.

[6] AHLFORS, L.V., SARIO, L., Riemann Surfaces, Princeton Univ. Press (1960).

[7] BERGMAN, S., Über die Kernfunktion eines Bereiches und ihr Verhalten am Rande, J. Reine Angew. Math. **169** (1933) 1, 172.

[8] BESSEL-HAGEN, E., Über die Erhaltungssätze der Elektrodynamik, Math. Annalen **84** (1921) 258.

[9] CHERN, S.S., LEVINE, H.I., NIRENBERG, L., "Intrinsic norms on a complex manifold", Global Analysis, papers in honor of K. Kodaira (SPENCER, D.C., IYNAGA, S., Eds), Univ. Tokyo Press and Princeton Univ. Press, Tokyo (1969) 141.

[10] CHERN, S.S., MOSER, J.K., Real hypersurfaces in complex manifolds, Acta Math. **133** (1974) 219.

[11] DIEUDONNE, J., Treatise on Analysis III (transl. from French), Academic Press, New York–London (1972).

[12] FEFFERMAN, C., The Bergman kernel and biholomorphic mappings of pseudoconvex domains, Invent. Math. **26** (1974) 1.

[13] FLATO, M., SIMON, J., STERNHEIMER, D., Conformal covariance of field equations, Ann. Phys. **61** (1970) 78

[14] HEDBERG, L.I., Removable singularities and condenser capacities, Ark. Mat. **12** (1974) 181.

[15] KALINA, J., A variational characterization of condenser capacities in $\mathbb{C}^n$ within a class of plurisubharmonic functions (to appear in Ann. Pol. Math.).

[16] KOBAYASHI, S., Invariant distances on complex manifolds and holomorphic mappings, J. Math. Soc. Jap. **19** (1967) 460.

[17] KOBAYASHI, S., Hyperbolic Manifolds and Holomorphic Mappings, Marcel Dekker, New York (1970).

[18] KOBAYASHI, S., NOMIZU, K., Foundations of Differential Geometry I–II, Interscience, New York–London–Sydney (1963–1969).

[19] KÜHNAU, R., Quasikonforme Abbildungen und Extremalprobleme bei Feldern in inhomogenen Medien, J. Reine Angew. Math. **231** (1968) 101; **243** (1970) 184.

[20] KÜHNAU, R., Der Modul von Kurven- und Flächenscharen und räumliche Felder in inhomogenen Medien, J. Reine Angew. Math. **243** (1970) 184.
[21] LEHTO, O., VIRTANEN, K.I., Quasiconformal Mappings in the Plane (transl. from German), 2nd ed., Springer, Berlin–Heidelberg–New York (1973).
[22] LELONG, P., Définition des fonctions plurisousharmoniques, C.R. Acad. Sci. Paris **215** (1942) 398.
[23] LELONG-FERRAND, J., Etude d'une classe d'applications liées à des homomorphismes d'algèbres de fonctions, et généralisant les quasi conformes, Duke Math. J. **40** (1973) 163.
[24] ŁAWRYNOWICZ, J., Capacities as conformal quasi-invariants on pseudo-riemannian manifolds, Rep. Math. Phys. **5** (1974) 203.
[25] ŁAWRYNOWICZ, J., Condenser capacities and an extension of Schwarz's lemma for hermitian manifolds, Bull. Acad. Pol. Sci., Sér. Sci. Math. Astron. Phys. **23** (1975) 839.
[26] ŁAWRYNOWICZ, J., On quasiconformality of projections of biholomorphic mappings, ibid. **23** (1975) 845.
[27] ŁAWRYNOWICZ, J., On a class of capacities on complex manifolds endowed with an hermitian structure and their relation to elliptic and hyperbolic quasiconformal mappings (to appear in Dissertationes Math.).
[28] ŁAWRYNOWICZ, J., WALISZEWSKI, W., Conformality and pseudo-riemannian manifolds, Math. Scand. **28** (1971) 45.
[29] ŁAWRYNOWICZ, J., von WESTENHOLZ, C., WOJTCZAK, L., On an almost complex manifold approach to elementary particles (in preparation).
[30] ŁAWRYNOWICZ, J., WOJTCZAK, L., A concept of explaining the properties of elementary particles in terms of manifolds, Z. Naturforsch. A **29** (1974) 1407.
[31] OHTSUKA, M., Dirichlet's Principle, Extremal Length and Prime Ends, Van Nostrand, New York (1970).
[32] PENROSE, R., MacCALLUM, M.A.H., Twistor theory: An approach to the quantisation of fields and space-time, Phys. Rep. **66** (1973) 241.
[33] PHAM MAU QUÂN, Etude électromagnétique et thermodynamique d'un fluide relativiste chargé, J. Rational Mech. Anal. **5** (1956) 473.
[34] PÓLYA, G., SZEGÖ, G., Isoperimetric Inequalities in Mathematical Physics, Princeton Univ. Press (1951).
[35] SICIAK, J., A generalization of Schwarz's lemma and of Hadamard's three circles theorem, Colloq. Math. **11** (1964) 203.
[36] SUOMINEN, K., Quasiconformal maps in manifolds, Ann. Acad. Sci. Fenn., Ser. A I **393** (1966) 1.
[37] SYNGE, J.L., Relativity: The General Theory, North-Holland, Amsterdam (1960).
[38] WELLS, R.O., Jr., Differential Analysis on Complex Manifolds, Prentice Hall, Englewood Cliffs (1973).

RATIONAL APPROXIMATION BY APPROXIMANTS IN $\mathbb{C}^n$

C.H. LUTTERODT
Department of Mathematics,
University of Cape Coast,
Cape Coast, Ghana

Abstract

RATIONAL APPROXIMATION BY APPROXIMANTS IN $\mathbb{C}^n$.

A reformulation of rational approximants to holomorphic function in $\mathbb{C}^n$ is given. A convergence theorem providing the multidegree of convergence for $(\mu, 1)$-approximants under certain restrictions is discussed.

1. INTRODUCTION

In recent papers [1, 2], the author formulated an n-dimensional generalization of the Padé approximant theory. In [1] the author proved certain algebraic properties partly restricted to the multidiagonal approximants. In [2], notions of "boundary" and normality for rational approximants in several variables were discussed as well as a simple method of constructing "boundaries" for these approximants.

The present paper, which outdates [1] and [2] in the formulation of some of the basic ideas, introduces new notions: the **Padé family** of coefficients of a given power series in n dimensions, and the **trivial** and **non-trivial** segments of the boundary of each member of the Padé family. By restricting the class of rational approximants to those with coefficients in the Padé family we are able to prove a simple convergence theorem for the $(\mu, 1)$-type approximants as $\mu = (\mu_1, \ldots, \mu_n) \to (\infty, \ldots, \infty)$. The theorem enables an important inequality to be deduced in terms of sup-norms, which implicitly provides the multidegree of convergence for the types of rational approximants considered. Walsh [3, 4] has discussed extensively a one-dimensional generalization of the above inequality involving meromorphic functions.

The paper is divided into three sections. In § 2 the reformulation of basic definitions and notation is discussed; in § 3 a convergence for the $(\mu, 1)$-type approximants is proved on suitably chosen compact sets under certain stipulations; and in § 4 an example is provided which fulfils the conditions of the theorem.

2. NOTATION AND DEFINITIONS

Let $D^n = \{\zeta \in \mathbb{C}^n : |z_j| < r, \quad j = 1, \ldots, n\}$ be a polydisc neighbourhood of the origin, where $\zeta = (z_1, \ldots, z_n)$. Let $f(\zeta)$ be holomorphic in D^n, i.e.

$$f(\zeta) = \sum_{\lambda \in \mathbb{N}^n} c_\lambda \zeta^\lambda \tag{1}$$

is convergent in D^n; where $\mathbb{N} = \{\text{set of non-negative integers}\}$ and $\mathbb{N}^n = \mathbb{N} \times \ldots \times \mathbb{N}$ n-times; $c_\lambda \equiv c_{\lambda_1 \ldots \lambda_n}$ and $\zeta^\lambda = z_1^{\lambda_1} \ldots z_n^{\lambda_n}$. We shall assume that $c_{0 \ldots 0} \neq 0$. This assumption is not too restrictive, for, if a holomorphic function has a zero of multiple order at the origin, we can factorize out the prime factors $h(\zeta)$ to give $f(\zeta) = h(\zeta)g(\zeta)$, where $g(\zeta)$ is a unit of the form (1). The definition of a rational approximant to be given later will then apply to $g(\zeta)$.

By a rational function $R_{\mu\nu}(\zeta)$ we mean $R_{\mu\nu}(\zeta) = P_\mu(\zeta)/Q_\nu(\zeta)$, where

$$P_\mu(\zeta) = \sum_{\alpha_1=0}^{\mu_1} \cdots \sum_{\alpha_n=0}^{\mu_n} a_\alpha \zeta^\alpha \quad \text{and} \quad Q_\nu(\zeta) = \sum_{\beta_1=0}^{\nu_1} \cdots \sum_{\beta_n=0}^{\nu_n} b_\beta \zeta^\beta$$

are polynomials such that $(P_\mu(\zeta), Q_\nu(\zeta)) = 1$ in D^n. The indeterminate points of $R_{\mu\nu}(\zeta)$ which belong to the analytic variety $P_\mu^{-1}(0) \cap Q_\nu^{-1}(0)$ will be ignored in our formulation. The notation a_α and b_β respectively stand for $a_{\alpha_1 \ldots \alpha_n}$ and $b_{\beta_i \ldots \beta_n}$. We shall further assume that $b_{0\ldots0} \neq 0$.

In one variable, the degree of a rational function R_{mn} is the max(m,n). We want to retain this flavour as much as possible in several variables and this leads to the following definition.

Definition 1. *By the multidegree of* $R_{\mu\nu}(\zeta)$ *we mean the n-tuple* $(\mu_1^*, \ldots, \mu_n^*)$ *where* $\mu_j^* = \max(\mu_j, \nu_j)$, $j = 1, \ldots, n$.

We shall write

$$\frac{1}{\lambda!}\frac{\partial^{|\lambda|}}{\partial \zeta^\lambda} \equiv \frac{1}{\lambda_1! \ldots \lambda_n!} \frac{\partial^{\lambda_1 + \ldots + \lambda_n}}{\partial z_1^{\lambda_1} \ldots \partial z_n^{\lambda_n}}$$

Let $\mathbb{C}_{\mathbb{N}^n}$ be the set of all the coefficients of $f(\zeta)$ in (1). We want to endow $\mathbb{C}_{\mathbb{N}^n}$ with a lattice structure identical to $\mathbb{N}^n$ and this is done by introducing the following bijective mapping:

$$\Psi : \lambda \rightarrow \frac{1}{\lambda!}\frac{\partial^{|\lambda|}}{\partial \zeta^\lambda}$$

It should be borne in mind that we are only interested in identifying the two lattice frames without worrying about the evaluation of the coefficients from the

$$\frac{1}{\lambda!}\frac{\partial^{|\lambda|}}{\partial \zeta^\lambda}$$

operators. Thus when we speak of lattice isomorphism between $\mathbb{N}^n$ and $\mathbb{C}_{\mathbb{N}^n}$ we mean isomorphism in the sense just explained.

The total number of coefficients of $R_{\mu\nu}(\zeta)$ is at most

$$N_{\mu\nu} = \prod_{j=1}^{n} (\mu_j + 1) + \prod_{j=1}^{n} (\nu_j + 1)$$

We normalize $b_{0\ldots0} = 1$, which effectively means we need at most $N_{\mu\nu} - 1$ equations to determine the remaining coefficients of $R_{\mu\nu}$. Before we can set up the equation to determine these coefficients we need further definitions.

Definition 2. *A subset* A *of* $\mathbb{C}_{\mathbb{N}^n}$ *which is finite and contains* $c_{0\ldots0}$ *is said to have the* **inclusion property** *if whenever* $c_\lambda \in A$, *then* $c_\gamma \in A$ *for all* $0 \prec \gamma \prec \lambda$ *(i.e.* $0 \leqslant \gamma_j \leqslant \lambda_j$, $j = 1, \ldots, n$).

Of particular interest amongst the finite subsets $A \subset \mathbb{C}_{\mathbb{N}^n}$ are those that possess the inclusion property and contain $N_{\mu\nu} - 1$ elements. Such subsets of $\mathbb{C}_{\mathbb{N}^n}$ can be chosen in several ways but we restrict ourselves to those which embed Padé coefficients in each variable and have $N_{\mu\nu} - 1$ elements. By Padé coefficients we simply mean the coefficients needed in each variable for constructing Padé approximants.

Definition 3. *We call the family of finite subsets of* $\mathbb{C}_{\mathbb{N}^n}$ *with the inclusion property and* $N_{\mu\nu} - 1$ *elements, which embed Padé coefficients in each variable, the* **Padé family**. *It is denoted by* $\mathscr{P}_{\mu\nu} = \{A^{\mu\nu}\}, \ \forall \mu\nu$.

The difference between the members of the Padé family $\mathscr{P}_{\mu\nu}$ for all $\mu\nu$ are in their boundary structure. The part of their boundary embedding the Padé coefficients in each variable is called the **trivial segment** of the boundary $\partial A^{\mu\nu}$ for each $A^{\mu\nu} \in \mathscr{P}_{\mu\nu}$. The remaining "segment" of $\partial A^{\mu\nu}$ is referred to as the **non-trivial segment** and is denoted by $L_{\mu\nu}$. In Ref. [2] this was identified with the "boundary" of a rational approximant.

We now discuss the construction of rational approximants with respect to any fixed $A^{\mu\nu} \in \mathscr{P}_{\mu\nu}$. The image of this member $A^{\mu\nu}$ of $\mathscr{P}_{\mu\nu}$ under the lattice isomorphism Ψ^{-1} in $\mathbb{N}^n$ is denoted by $E^{\mu\nu} = \Psi^{-1}(A^{\mu\nu})$. Thus $E^{\mu\nu}$ and $A^{\mu\nu}$ have the same boundary structure, i.e. $\partial A^{\mu\nu} = \partial E^{\mu\nu}$.

Definition 4. *The rational function* $R_{\mu\nu}(\zeta)$ *is a rational approximant to* $f(\zeta)$ *provided*

$$\frac{\partial^{|\lambda|}}{\partial \zeta^{\lambda}} (Q_\nu(0) f(0) - P_\mu(0)) = 0 \ , \ \lambda \in E^{\mu\nu}, \qquad \mu_j, \nu_j = 0, 1, \ldots ; \qquad j = 1, \ldots, n. \tag{2}$$

An alternative definition to the one above[1] is to define the rational approximant in terms of "order" of contact or the coefficients shared with the function $f(\zeta)$, so that instead of (2) we may have

$$\frac{\partial^{|\lambda|}}{\partial \zeta^{\lambda}} \left(f(0) - \frac{P_\mu(0)}{Q_\nu(0)} \right) = 0 \quad , \quad \lambda \in E^{\mu\nu} \tag{2'}$$

The two forms are, in fact, equivalent (see [1]). The linearity of (2) makes it more useful than (2′) as it readily provides the following systems of equations for the a and b coefficients:

$$\sum_{\lambda=0}^{\min(s,\nu)} b_\lambda c_{s-\lambda} = a_s, \quad s \in E^1 = \{\lambda \in E^{\mu\nu} : 0 \prec \lambda \prec \mu\} \tag{3}$$

$$\sum_{\lambda=0}^{\min(s,\nu)} b_\lambda c_{s-\lambda} = 0, \quad s \in E^{\mu\nu} \backslash E^1 \tag{4}$$

Here,

$$\sum_{\lambda=0}^{\min(s,\nu)} \equiv \sum_{\lambda_1=0}^{\min(s_1,\nu_1)} \cdots \sum_{\lambda_n=0}^{\min(s_n,\nu_n)} \quad , \qquad c_{s-\lambda} \equiv c_{s_1-\lambda_1,\ldots,s_n-\lambda_n}$$

and $\min(s_j, \nu_j)$ stands for minimum of s_j, ν_j, $\quad j = 1, \ldots, n$.

[1] Pointed out by Professor A.A. Gonchar.

By recalling that we normalized $b_{0\ldots0} = 1$ and substituting for this in (4), we convert (4) into an inhomogeneous system of equations. From that we can solve for the b coefficients of the denominator polynomial $Q_\nu(\zeta)$, provided $\det(c_{s-\lambda}) \neq 0$, where $0 \prec \lambda \prec \min(s,\nu)$ and $s \in E^{\mu\nu}\backslash E^1$. The a coefficients of the numerator can then be readily obtained from (3) and hence determined uniquely a family of rational approximants for $\mu_j,\nu_j = 0,1, \ldots,\quad j = 1, \ldots, n,$ with respect to the fixed $A^{\mu\nu}$.

The family of rational approximants thus generated are wholly analogous to the one-dimensional family known as the Padé table. We call it the generalized Padé table or the "tensor table" as referred to in earlier work.

If $\det(c_{s-\lambda}) \neq 0$ for $0 \prec \lambda \prec \min(s,\nu)$ and $s \in E^{\mu\nu}\backslash E^1$ for $\mu_j,\nu_j = 0,1, \ldots,\quad j = 1, \ldots, n,$ the generalized Padé table is said to be **normal** (see [2]).

Remark. There appears to be a one-to-one correspondence between the generalized Padé tables and the non-trivial segment of the boundary, $L_{\mu\nu}$, which distinguishes members of $\mathscr{P}_{\mu\nu}$, $\forall \mu\nu$. This suggests that there are as many generalized Padé tables as there are members in $\mathscr{P}_{\mu\nu}$. In the one-dimensional theory there is a unique Padé table which may be seen as a direct consequence of the fact that the boundary $\partial A^{\mu\nu}$ is a single point. Thus $\partial A^{\mu\nu} = L_{\mu\nu}$, and for $n > 1$ we clearly have $\partial A^{\mu\nu} \supset L_{\mu\nu}$.

3. CONVERGENCE

In this section we shall consider rational approximants of the type $(\mu, 1)$ with respect to any fixed member $A^{\mu 1} \in \mathscr{P}_{\mu 1}$. We shall study the convergence of these approximants with some restriction on the behaviour of their denominator coefficients for sufficiently large values of μ_j, $j = 1, \ldots, n$. The results obtained are uniform with respect to members of $\mathscr{P}_{\mu 1}$.

Let $\hat{\zeta} = (z_1, \ldots, z_{n-1})$ and $\hat{s} = (s_1, \ldots, s_{n-1})$ and let $b^{(\mu)}_{i_1\ldots i_n}$ denote the b coefficients obtained from solving Eq. (4). The zero set of the denominator polynomial $Q_1(\zeta) = Q_{1\ldots1}(\zeta)$ is defined as follows.

Definition 5. *The zero set of the denominator polynomial* $Q_1(\zeta)$, *which is written* $Q_1^{-1}(0) = \{\zeta \in \mathbb{C}^n;\ Q_1(\zeta) = 0\}$, *is defined by*

$$S_\mu = \{(\hat{\zeta}, z_n^{(\mu)}) \in \mathbb{C}^n : z_n^{(\mu)} = g_\mu(\hat{\zeta}),\quad \hat{\zeta} \in \mathbb{C}^{n-1}\}$$

where

$$g_\mu(\hat{\zeta}) = \frac{\sum_{\hat{s}=0}^{1} b^{(\mu)}_{\hat{s},0}\,\hat{\zeta}^{\hat{s}}}{\sum_{\hat{s}=0}^{1} b^{(\mu)}_{\hat{s},1}\,\hat{\zeta}^{\hat{s}}} \qquad \textit{and} \qquad b_{0\ldots0} = 1$$

so that its μ*-dependence becomes explicit. Of course,*

$$\sum_{\hat{s}=0}^{1} b^{(\mu)}_{\hat{s},1}\,\hat{\zeta}^{\hat{s}} \neq 0$$

except at the exceptional or the singular points on the zero surface where

$$\frac{\partial Q_1(\zeta)}{\partial z_n^{(\mu)}} = 0$$

the notation $b^{(\mu)}$ *and* $z_n^{(\mu)}$ *is used to emphasize the* μ*-dependence and*

$$\sum_{\hat{s}=0}^{1} \equiv \sum_{s_1=0}^{1} \cdots \sum_{s_{n-1}=0}^{1}$$

Proposition

(i) *Suppose* $\hat{\zeta} \in D^{n-1}$ *and* $\hat{\zeta} \neq 0$.

(ii) *Suppose* $|b^{(\mu)}_{i_1 \ldots i_n}| \to 0$ *as* $\mu_j \to \infty$, $j = 1, \ldots, n$, *where* $i_k = \{^0_1$, $k = 1, \ldots, n$, *excluding* $i_1 = i_2 = \ldots = i_n = 0$. *Then for sufficiently large* μ_j, $j = 1, \ldots, n$, *we have*

$$\bar{D}^n \cap S_\mu = \emptyset$$

where $\bar{D}^n$ *is the closure of* D^n.

Proof. If $\hat{\zeta} = 0$, then $z_n^{(\mu)} = \infty$, $\forall_\mu$. The result is trivial, hence the assumption $\hat{\zeta} \neq 0$. To prove the proposition we suppose $\bar{D}^n \cap S_\mu \neq \emptyset$, $\forall \mu$. Then for $\zeta \in \bar{D}^n \cap S_\mu$ we must have $\zeta \in S_\mu$ and $\zeta \in \bar{D}^n$. Now $\zeta \in \bar{D}^n \Rightarrow |z_j| \leqslant r$, $j = 1, \ldots, n-1$, and $|z_n^{(\mu)}| \leqslant r$, $\forall_\mu$. But from the definition of S_μ, we get by (ii) that

$$|z_n^{(\mu)}| = |g_\mu(\hat{\zeta})| \geqslant \frac{\left|\sum\limits_{\hat{s}=0}^{1} b^{(\mu)}_{\hat{s},0}\, \zeta^{\hat{s}}\right|}{\sum\limits_{\hat{s}=0}^{1} |b^{(\mu)}_{\hat{s},1}|\, r^{|\hat{s}|}} \to \infty \text{ as } \mu_j \to \infty, \qquad j = 1, \ldots, n$$

Thus, taking $k > r$, we can find N such that $\mu_j > N$, $j = 1, \ldots, n \Rightarrow |z_n^{(\mu)}| > k$, which establishes a contradiction. Hence $\bar{D}^n \cap S_\mu = \emptyset$ for sufficiently large μ_j, $j = 1, \ldots, n$.

Corollary 1. *If the conditions of the proposition are satisfied, then for sufficiently large values of* μ_j, $j = 1, \ldots, n$, *we have*

$$D^n \cap S_\mu = \emptyset$$

Corollary 2. *Suppose the conditions of the proposition are satisfied. Let* K *be a compact subset of* D^n. *Then* $K \cap S_\mu = \emptyset$ *for sufficiently large values* μ_j, $j = 1, \ldots, n$.

Theorem

(i) *Let* $f(\zeta) = \sum\limits_{\lambda \in \mathbb{N}^n} c_\lambda \zeta^\lambda$, $\quad \zeta \in D^n$.

(ii) *Let* $\pi_\mu(\zeta)$ *be a multiple partial sum of multidegree* $\mu = (\mu_1, \ldots, \mu_n)$, *and let* $R_{\mu 1}(\zeta)$ *be a normal* $(\mu, 1)$ *rational approximant of* $f(\zeta)$ *in* D^n, *also of multidegree* μ, *with respect to any fixed* $A^{\mu 1} \in \mathscr{P}_{\mu 1}$.

(iii) *Suppose the coefficients of the denominator polynomial* $Q_1(\zeta)$ *satisfy conditions (ii) of the proposition.*

(iv) *If* K *is any compact subset of* D^n *and we let*

$$\|\pi_\mu(\zeta) - R_{\mu 1}(\zeta)\|_K = \sup_{\zeta \in K} |\pi_\mu(\zeta) - R_{\mu 1}(\zeta)|$$

then, given $\epsilon > 0$, $\exists N$ *such that* $\mu_j > N$, $j = 1, \ldots, n \Rightarrow$

$$\|\pi_\mu(\zeta) - R_{\mu 1}(\zeta)\| < \epsilon$$

The proof of this theorem depends on the following lemmas.

Lemma 1. *If conditions (i) and (ii) of the theorem are satisfied*

$$Q_1(\zeta)\pi_\mu(\zeta) - P_\mu(\zeta) = -\sum_{s \in E^{\mu 1}\backslash E^1} \left(\sum_{\lambda \in E^{\mu 1}\backslash E^1} b^{(\mu)}_{s-\lambda} c_\lambda \right) \zeta^s \tag{5}$$

Proof. $\pi_\mu(\zeta)$ is the multiple partial sum to $f(\zeta)$ of multidegree μ. Thus, using the system of equations (3) and simplifying, we get

$$Q_1(\zeta)\pi_\mu(\zeta) - P_\mu(\zeta) = \sum_{s \in E^{\mu 1}\backslash E^1} \left(\sum_{\lambda \in F} b^{(\mu)}_{\lambda} c_{s-\lambda} \right) \zeta^s \tag{6}$$

F is some subset of $E^{\mu 1}$ which overlaps E^1 but does not contain $\lambda = (0, \ldots, 0)$. Now note that by (4),

$$\sum_{\lambda \in F} b^{(\mu)}_{\lambda} c_{s-\lambda} = - \sum_{\lambda \in E^{\mu 1}\backslash E^1} b^{(\mu)}_{s-\lambda} c_\lambda \tag{7}$$

where $\max(s - \lambda) \prec 1$ and the desired result follows.

Remark. The advantage of changing from (6) to (5) is to have the $b^{(\mu)}_\lambda$ suffixes nicely ordered, starting with $\lambda = (0, \ldots, 0)$. This facilitates counting the terms in the sum.

Lemma 2. *Suppose the first three conditions of the theorem are satisfied, then* $\sigma(>0)$ *and* $M(>0)$ *such that*

$$\left| \sum_{\lambda, s \in E^{\mu 1}\backslash E^1} b^{(\mu)}_{s-\lambda} c_\lambda \right| \leqslant \begin{cases} \dfrac{M\sigma}{r^{|s|}} & \text{if } 0 < r \leqslant 1 \\[2ex] \dfrac{M\sigma}{r^{|s-1|}} & \text{if } r > 1 \end{cases} \tag{8}$$

where $\max(s - \lambda) \prec 1$ *and* $|s| = s_1 + \ldots + s_n$.

Proof

$$\sum_{\lambda, s \in E^{\mu 1} \setminus E^1} |b^{(\mu)}_{s-\lambda}|$$

consists of a finite number of $b^{(\mu)}$'s and for sufficiently large μ_j, $j = 1, \ldots, n$, can be made small except for $b_{0\ldots 0} = 1$. Thus we can find a number $\sigma(>0)$ such that

$$\sum_{\lambda, s \in E^{\mu 1} \setminus E^1} |b^{(\mu)}_{s-\lambda}| \leqslant \sigma, \qquad \max(s-\lambda) \prec 1 \tag{9}$$

Cauchy inequality for the coefficients of f provides

$$|c_\lambda| \leqslant \frac{M}{r^{|\lambda|}}, \quad \lambda \in \mathbb{N}^n, \qquad M = \sup_{\zeta \in \partial D^n} |f(\zeta)| \tag{10}$$

now

$$\left| \sum_{\lambda, s \in E^{\mu 1} \setminus E^1} b^{(\mu)}_{s-\lambda} c_\lambda \right| \leqslant M \sum_{\lambda, s \in E^{\mu 1} \setminus E^1} \frac{|b^{(\mu)}_{s-\lambda}|}{r^{|\lambda|}} \leqslant \begin{cases} \dfrac{M\sigma}{r^{|s|}} & \text{if } 0 < r \leqslant 1 \\[2ex] \dfrac{M\sigma}{r^{|s-1|}} & \text{if } r > 1 \end{cases}$$

by (9) as required.

Proof of the theorem

By the condition (iii) and Corollary 1, we have that $D^n \cap S_\mu = \emptyset$ for μ_j sufficiently large, $j = 1, \ldots, n$, and therefore $Q_1(\zeta) \neq 0$ on D^n. Thus $\exists \delta > 0$ such that $|Q_1(\zeta)| \geqslant \delta > 0$ for μ_j sufficiently large, $j = 1, \ldots, n$. Hence for such values of μ_j, $j = 1, \ldots, n$:

$$|\pi_\mu(\zeta) - R_{\mu 1}(\zeta)| \leqslant |Q_1(\zeta)\pi_\mu(\zeta) - P_\mu(\zeta)|\delta^{-1}$$

$$\leqslant \begin{cases} \dfrac{M\sigma}{\delta} \displaystyle\sum_{s \in E^{\mu 1} \setminus E^1} \left(\frac{|z_j|}{r}\right)^{s_j}, & 0 < r \leqslant 1 \\[3ex] \dfrac{r^n M\sigma}{\delta} \displaystyle\sum_{s \in E^{\mu 1} \setminus E^1} \left(\frac{|z_j|}{r}\right)^{s_j}, & r > 1 \text{ (by Lemmas 1 and 2)} \end{cases}$$

$$\leqslant \begin{cases} \dfrac{M\sigma}{\delta} \displaystyle\prod_{j=1}^{n} \left[\left(\frac{|z_j|}{r}\right)^{\mu_j + 1} \Big/ \left(1 - \frac{|z_j|}{r}\right)\right], & 0 < r \leqslant 1 \\[3ex] \dfrac{r^n M\sigma}{\delta} \displaystyle\prod_{j=1}^{n} \left[\left(\frac{|z_j|}{r}\right)^{\mu_j + 1} \Big/ \left(1 - \frac{|z_j|}{r}\right)\right], & r > 1 \end{cases} \tag{11}$$

since $0 \leqslant |z_j|/r < 1$, $j = 1, \ldots, n$, given $\epsilon > 0$, $\exists N_j$ such that $\forall \mu_j > N_j$, $j = 1, \ldots, n$, we have

$$0 \leqslant \left(\frac{|z_j|}{r}\right)^{\mu_j + 1} < \begin{cases} \left(\dfrac{\epsilon\delta}{M\sigma}\right)^{1/n}\left(1 - \dfrac{|z_j|}{r}\right), & 0 < r \leqslant 1 \\ \left(\dfrac{\epsilon\delta}{M\sigma}\right)^{1/n}\dfrac{1}{r}\left(1 - \dfrac{|z_j|}{r}\right), & r > 1 \end{cases} \tag{12}$$

Take

$$N = \max_{1 \leqslant j \leqslant n} (N_j)$$

then for $\mu_j > N$, $j = 1, \ldots, n$, (11) and (12) would imply that

$$|\pi_\mu(\zeta) - R_{\mu 1}(\zeta)| < \epsilon, \qquad \zeta \in D^n$$

Then on any compact subset K of D^n we must have

$$\sup_{\zeta \in K} |\pi_\mu(\zeta) - R_{\mu 1}(\zeta)| < \epsilon, \qquad \mu_j > N, \quad j = 1, \ldots, n$$

establishing the uniform convergence on K.

Corollary 3. *Suppose the conditions of the theorem are satisfied and* K *is any compact subset of* D^n; *for sufficiently large* μ_j, $j = 1, \ldots, n$, *we have*

$$||f(\zeta) - R_{\mu 1}(\zeta)||_K \leqslant ||f(\zeta) - \pi_\mu(\zeta)||_K \tag{13}$$

Proof. $\forall \mu$, we have

$$||f(\zeta) - R_{\mu 1}(\zeta)||_K \leqslant ||f(\zeta) - \pi_\mu(\zeta)||_K + ||\pi_\mu(\zeta) - R_{\mu 1}(\zeta)||_K \tag{14}$$

From the theorem above, given $\epsilon > 0$, $\exists N$ such that

$$||\pi_\mu(\zeta) - R_{\mu 1}(\zeta)||_K < \epsilon, \qquad \forall \mu_j > N, \qquad j = 1, \ldots, n \tag{15}$$

Thus by (14) and (15) we get $\forall \mu_j > N$, $j = 1, \ldots, n$

$$||f(\zeta) - R_{\mu 1}(\zeta)||_K < ||f(\zeta) - \pi_\mu(\zeta)||_K + \epsilon$$

Since $\epsilon > 0$ is arbitrary, the desired result follows.

These results were obtained using any fixed member $A^{\mu 1} \in \mathscr{P}_{\mu 1}$. Since $A^{\mu 1}$ is arbitrary in $\mathscr{P}_{\mu 1}$, the results therefore hold for all members in $\mathscr{P}_{\mu 1}$ (i.e. uniform with respect to $\mathscr{P}_{\mu 1}$).

4. AN EXAMPLE IN 2-DIM$\mathbb{C}$

Consider the entire holomorphic function in $\mathbb{C}^2$:

$$f(z_1,z_2) = \frac{z_1 e^{z_1} - z_2 e^{z_2}}{z_1 - z_2} = \sum_{\lambda_1,\lambda_2=0}^{\infty} \frac{1}{(\lambda_1+\lambda_2)!} z_1^{\lambda_1} z_2^{\lambda_2} \tag{16}$$

We want to compute the denominator polynomial of $R_{\mu 1}(\zeta)$ with respect to a fixed $A^{\mu 1}$ and examine the "asymptotic" behaviour of its zero set. Here $\mu = (m,n)$.

We determine the set $E^{\mu 1}\backslash E^1$ by using the following expansion for the product

$$\prod_{j=1}^{2} (\nu_j + 1) - 1$$

as explained in Ref. [2]:

$$\prod_{j=1}^{2} (\nu_j + 1) - 1 = \nu_1(\nu_2 + 1) + \nu_2 \tag{17}$$

In the example we are considering, $\nu_1 = \nu_2 = 1$, which determines the set $E^{\mu 1}\backslash E^1$ as:

$$\begin{aligned} &\nu_1(\nu_2+1): \lambda_1 = m+1, && 0 \leqslant \lambda_2 \leqslant 1 \\ &\nu_2: \lambda_1 = 0, && \lambda_2 = n+1 \end{aligned} \tag{18}$$

Using (18), the equations involving the denominator coefficients from (4) are

$$0 = b_{00}c_{m+1,0} + b_{10}c_{m,0}$$

$$0 = b_{00}c_{m+1,1} + b_{10}c_{m,1} + b_{11}c_{m,0}$$

$$0 = b_{00}c_{0,n+1} + b_{01}c_{0n}$$

where $b_{00} = 1$ and $c_{mn} = 1/(m+n)!$. Thus the denominator polynomial is given by

$$Q_{11}^{(m,n)}(\zeta) = 1 - \frac{1}{m+1} z_1 - \frac{1}{n+1} z_2 + \frac{1}{(m+1)^2(m+2)} z_1 z_2$$

The set of the zeros of this polynomial is

$$S_{mn} = \left\{ (z_1, g_{mn}(z_1)) \in \mathbb{C}^2 : g_{mn}(z_1) = \frac{1 - \frac{1}{m+1} z_1}{\frac{1}{n+1} - \frac{1}{(m+1)^2(m+2)} z_1} \right\}$$

with exceptional or singular points at

$$z_1 = \frac{(m+1)^2(m+2)}{(n+1)}, \qquad m,n = 0,1 \ldots$$

Clearly $z_2^{(m,n)} =: g_{mn}(z_1) \to \infty$ as $m,n \to \infty$. Thus if

$$D^2 = \{(z_1, z_2) \in \mathbb{C}^2 : |z_j| < r, \qquad i = 1,2\}$$

then for sufficiently large m, n, $\quad D^2 \cap S_{mn} = \emptyset$.

Using the form of the set $E^{\mu 1} \backslash E^1$ in (4.3), it can be determined by elementary computation that

$$R_{11,11}(z_1, z_2) = \frac{1 + \frac{1}{2} z_1 + \frac{1}{2} z_2 - \frac{5}{12} z_1 z_2}{1 - \frac{1}{2} z_1 - \frac{1}{2} z_2 + \frac{1}{12} z_1 z_2}$$

$$R_{21,11}(z_1, z_2) = \frac{1 + \frac{2}{3} z_1 + \frac{1}{2} z_2 - \frac{11}{36} z_1 z_2 + \frac{1}{6} z_1^2 - \frac{2}{9} z_1^2 z_2}{1 - \frac{1}{3} z_1 - \frac{1}{2} z_2 + \frac{1}{36} z_1 z_2}$$

POSTSCRIPT

Professor Gonchar has just shown me his somewhat different formulation of the rational approximant theory [5] in several variables. He uses homogeneous polynomials in projective space to construct the rational approximants and has proved numerous results on convergence in measure and in capacity.

ACKNOWLEDGEMENTS

The author would like to thank the University of Cape Coast for financial support which made it possible for him to attend the Summer Course on Complex Analysis during which this work was conceived and worked out. He would like to thank Professors A.A. Gonchar, P. Gauthier and C. Pommerenke for fruitful discussions.

REFERENCES

[1] LUTTERODT, C.H., J. Math. Anal. Appl. **53** (1976) 89–98.
[2] LUTTERODT, C.H., On boundary of rational approximants, Ghana J. Sc. (to appear 1976).
[3] WALSH, J.L., Interpolation and approximation, AMS Colloq. **20** (1935) 378.
[4] WALSH, J.L., J. Approx. Theory **2** (1969) 160–166.
[5] GONCHAR, A.A., Mat. Sb. **93** (1974) 296–313 (in Russian).

IAEA-SMR-18/106

RIEMANN MATRICES WITH MANY POLARIZATIONS

H.H. MARTENS
Institutt for Matematikk,
Norges Tekniske Høgskole,
Trondheim, Norway

Abstract

RIEMANN MATRICES WITH MANY POLARIZATIONS.

Riemann matrices occur naturally as period matrices of closed Riemann surfaces and of multiply periodic meromorphic functions. In this expository paper some of the basic properties of such matrices are reviewed in order to point out an area of open problems and draw attention to the beautiful and profound work of Hayashida and Nishi.

1. DEFINITION AND A BASIC PROPERTY

1.1. Let Π be a matrix of complex numbers with n rows and 2n columns. Π is called a Riemann matrix if there is a $2n\times 2n$ skew-symmetric matrix P of rational numbers such that

1.1.1. $\Pi P\,{}^t\Pi = 0$ and

1.1.2. $i\Pi P\,{}^t\overline{\Pi} > 0$ (positive definite)

If so, we shall call P a <u>polarizing matrix</u> for Π. (This is not standard; in the literature the overworked adjective "principal" is common. Note that we use the presuperscript "t" to denote matrix transposition).

1.2. Let Π be a Riemann matrix. The set of polarizing matrices for Π is clearly closed under addition and scalar multiplication by a positive rational number, and hence forms a cone in the space of skew-symmetric matrices of rational numbers of the appropriate dimension. By a <u>polarization</u> of Π, we shall mean a ray in the cone of its polarizing matrices. Any polarization contains an integral polarizing matrix; if it contains a unimodular matrix, then it is said to be a <u>principal polarization</u> (this <u>is</u> standard). A pair consisting of a Riemann matrix Π and a (principal) polarization of Π will be called a (<u>principally</u>) <u>polarized Riemann matrix</u>.

Not all Riemann matrices admit a principal polarization.

1.3. Let Π be a Riemann matrix, and let P be a polarizing matrix for Π. Then

1.3.1. P _is non-singular_,

1.3.2. _the columns of_ Π _are linearly independent over the real numbers_, _and_

1.3.3. _there is an_ $n\times 2n$ _matrix_ Λ _of complex numbers such that_ $P^{-1} = {}^t\Pi\Lambda - {}^t\Lambda\Pi$.

Proof: Consider the product of $2n\times 2n$ matrices

$$\begin{pmatrix}\Pi\\ \overline{\Pi}\end{pmatrix} P^t \begin{pmatrix}\Pi\\ \overline{\Pi}\end{pmatrix} = \begin{pmatrix}\Pi P^t\Pi & \Pi P^t\overline{\Pi}\\ \overline{\Pi}P^t\Pi & \overline{\Pi}P^t\overline{\Pi}\end{pmatrix}$$

It follows from 1.1.1 and 1.1.2 that the matrix on the right has the form

$$\frac{1}{i}\begin{pmatrix}0 & H\\ -{}^tH & 0\end{pmatrix}$$

where H is positive definite. Hence the matrix is non-singular and it follows that P is non-singular and that the columns of Π are linearly independent over the reals. Finally we get

$$P^{-1} = {}^t\begin{pmatrix}\Pi\\ \overline{\Pi}\end{pmatrix}\begin{pmatrix}0 & -i\,{}^tH^{-1}\\ iH^{-1} & 0\end{pmatrix}\begin{pmatrix}\Pi\\ \overline{\Pi}\end{pmatrix}$$

$$= -i\,{}^t\Pi\,{}^tH^{-1}\overline{\Pi} + i\,{}^t\overline{\Pi}H^{-1}\Pi$$

which proves 1.3.3 with $\Lambda = -i\,{}^tH^{-1}\overline{\Pi}$.

2. EXAMPLES

2.1. Let X be a closed Riemann surface of genus $g \geq 2$. Let $\gamma_1,\ldots,\gamma_{2g}$ be a canonical homology basis on X, and let $\omega^1,\ldots,\omega^g$ be a normalized basis for the holomorphic differentials on X. Let

$$\langle\omega^i,\gamma_j\rangle = \int_{\gamma_j}\omega^i$$

Interpreting ω as a column of g entries and γ as a row of 2g entries, a well-known result of Riemann expresses that the period matrix $\langle\omega,\gamma\rangle$ has the form

$$\langle\omega,\gamma\rangle = (E\ Z)$$

where E is the g×g unit matrix and Z is a symmetric g×g matrix whose imaginary part (the matrix of the imaginary parts of the entries) is positive definite. It is easily verified that (E Z) is a Riemann matrix with principal polarizing matrix

$$J = \begin{pmatrix} 0 & E \\ -E & 0 \end{pmatrix}$$

If ω and γ are arbitrary bases for holomorphic differentials and homology, respectively, the resulting period matrix will be a Riemann matrix with polarizing matrix given by the transposed inverse of the intersection matrix of the basis γ (see e.g. Gunning [1]).

If $\tilde{X}$ is a closed Riemann surface with bases $\tilde{\omega}$ and $\tilde{\gamma}$, and if $f:\tilde{X}\to\tilde{X}$ is a holomorphic map of $\tilde{X}$ onto X, then we have

$$\omega^i \circ f = \Sigma h_{ij}\tilde{\omega}^j$$

and $$f(\tilde{\gamma}_j) = \Sigma m_{ji}\tilde{\gamma}_i$$

with h_{ij} complex and m_{ji} integers. We then have

$$H\langle\tilde{\omega},\tilde{\gamma}\rangle = \langle\omega,\gamma\rangle M$$

with obvious notation. In particular, a change of bases for a given Riemann surface results in a change of period matrix given by the above formula with non-singular H and unimodular M. If the homology bases are canonical, the intersection matrix J is preserved and ${}^tMJM = J$.

2.2. Riemann matrices also occur naturally as period matrices of multiply periodic meromorphic functions of n complex variables. If Π is an n×2n matrix of complex numbers whose column vectors are linearly independent over the reals, then a necessary and sufficient condition for the existence of non-degenerate meromorphic functions with these columns as periods is that Π be a Riemann matrix. In this connection it is natural to consider the complex torus $T = \mathbb{C}^n/\Pi$ obtained by identifying points of $\mathbb{C}^n$ under the action of the group of translations generated by the column vectors of Π.

If we have a second complex torus $\tilde{T} = \mathbb{C}^m/\tilde{\Pi}$, it is not hard to show that any holomorphic map $f:\tilde{T}\to\tilde{T}$ which preserves the "origin" must be induced by a linear map $h:\mathbb{C}^m\to\mathbb{C}^n$ which takes periods into periods. Thus we must have a relation

$$H\tilde{\Pi} = \Pi M$$

where H is an m×n matrix of complex numbers and M is a 2m×2n matrix of integers. In particular, a change of coordinates in $\mathbb{C}^n$ and a change of basis for the group of translations gives rise to a new matrix related to the old by an equation of the above form with invertible matrices (unimodular M).

When the Riemann matrix is the period matrix of a closed Riemann surface, the associated torus is called the Jacobian variety of the surface. Maps between Riemann surfaces induce maps between their Jacobian varieties.

2.3. The connection with Riemann surfaces provides one of the major sources of problems in the theory of Riemann matrices. It is still an outstanding open problem to characterize those Riemann matrices in dimension $n \geq 4$ which are period matrices of closed Riemann surfaces of genus g=n. For g=4 famous necessary conditions were discovered by Schottky [2], whose work was greatly clarified by the recent efforts of Farkas and Rauch [3]. For more information on the material of this section we refer to Siegel's work [4] and to the elegant monograph [5] of Swinnerton-Dyer.

3. EQUIVALENCE RELATIONS

3.1. In view of the applications to Riemann surfaces and to complex tori, it is natural to introduce certain equivalence relations between Riemann matrices. We consider first a more general relation.

Let Π and Π_1 be n×2n and m×2m matrices, respectively, of compl numbers whose column vectors are linearly independent over the real numbers. By a <u>Hurwitz relation between</u> Π and Π_1 we shall mean an equation

3.1.1. $$H\Pi = \Pi_1 M$$

where H is an m×n matrix of complex numbers and M is a 2m×2n matrix of rational numbers. By a <u>simultaneous matrix for</u> Π <u>and</u> Π_1 we shall mean a 2m×2n matrix Q of rational numbers such that

3.1.2. $$\Pi_1 Q {}^t\Pi = 0$$

Note that if Q is a simultaneous matrix for Π and Π_1, then ${}^tQ$ is a simultaneous matrix for Π_1 and Π.

3.2. Let Π and Π_1 be as above and assume in addition that Π is a Riemann matrix with polarizing matrix P. Then

3.2.1. *Π and Π_1 satisfy a Hurwitz relation with a given matrix M if and only if the matrix Q=MP is a simultaneous matrix for Π and Π_1.*

<u>Proof:</u> If $H\Pi = \Pi_1 M$, then

$$\Pi_1 MP {}^t\Pi = H\Pi P {}^t\Pi = 0$$

by the definition of Riemann matrices. If $\Pi_1 Q {}^t\Pi = 0$, then

$$\Pi_1 QP^{-1} = \Pi_1 Q {}^t\Pi\Lambda - \Pi_1 Q {}^t\Lambda\Pi = \Pi_1 Q {}^t\Lambda\Pi$$

which is a Hurwitz relation with $M = QP^{-1}$ and $H = -\Pi_1 Q {}^t\Lambda$.

3.2.2. (Corollary) *Given a Hurwitz relation (3.1.1) between two Riemann matrices Π and Π_1 with polarizing matrices P and P_1 there is a "transposed" Hurwitz relation $H_1\Pi_1 = \Pi M_1$ with $M_1 = P {}^tM P_1^{-1}$ and $H_1 = -\Pi P {}^tM {}^t\Lambda_1$.*

<u>Proof</u>: By assumption MP is a simultaneous matrix for Π and Π_1, hence $P {}^tM = -{}^t(MP)$ is a simultaneous matrix for Π_1 and Π and the result follows by (3.2.1).

Going back to the situation where only Π is assumed to be a Riemann matrix, we have

3.2.3. <u>If</u> $m \leq n$ <u>and if</u> Π <u>and</u> Π_1 <u>satisfy a Hurwitz relation</u> (3.1.1) <u>with</u> M <u>of maximal rank, then</u> Π_1 <u>is a Riemann matrix and</u> $P_1 = MP^tM$ <u>is a polarizing matrix for</u> Π_1.

<u>Proof</u>: From the defining relations for Π, we have

$$\Pi_1 MP^tM^t\Pi_1 = H\Pi P^t\Pi^tH = 0$$

and

$$i\Pi_1 MP^tM^t\overline{\Pi}_1 = iH\Pi P^t\overline{\Pi}^t\overline{H}$$

where $i\Pi P^t\overline{\Pi} > 0$. Since M is of maximal rank, so is H and the positive definiteness of $i\Pi_1 MP^tM^t\overline{\Pi}_1$ follows easily.

<u>Remark</u>: A complex torus defined by a Riemann matrix is called an Abelian variety. The content of (3.2.3) in that context is that the homomorphic image of an abelian variety is an abelian variety.

The "transposition" of (3.2.2) was introduced by Rosati in the context of a study of correspondence of algebraic curves.

3.3. Let Π and Π_1 be Riemann matrices. They are said to be <u>isogenous</u> if they satisfy a Hurwitz relation with non-singular M. This is clearly an equivalence relation, and it is also clear that isogenous matrices satisfy a Hurwitz relation with non-singular, <u>integral</u> M. The corresponding homomorphism of complex tori is characterized by being surjective with finite kernel, and such a homomorphism is called an <u>isogeny</u>.

It appears that this was the first equivalence relation to be studied systematically. A key result was the <u>complete reducibility theorem</u> of Poincaré according to which a Riemann matrix of the form

$$\begin{pmatrix} \Pi_1 & 0 \\ \Pi_3 & \Pi_2 \end{pmatrix} \quad \text{is isogenous to} \quad \begin{pmatrix} \Pi_1 & 0 \\ 0 & \Pi_2 \end{pmatrix}$$

and Π_1 and Π_2 are Riemann matrices. This was proved in general by Scorza who also proved a "unique factorization theorem" according to which a Riemann matrix is isogenous to a direct sum of simple (isogenously irreducible) Riemann matrices whose isogeny types are uniquely determined up to order of appearance (see Swinnerton-Dyer [5], p. 56).

Scorza [6] [7] pioneered the study of the algebra of complex multiplications (Hurwitz relations of Π with itself), which is an invariant of the isogeny class of the Riemann matrix. A salient feature of these algebras, which are division algebras when the matrix is simple, is the presence of the Rosati involution

$$M \to P^{t}MP^{-1}$$

Scorza's work was extended by Lefschetz [8], who introduced Albert to the field. Albert in turn succeeded in completely classifying all possible multiplication algebras. Later contributions are due to Weyl and Siegel, see [9] and the literature there listed.

3.4. Two polarized Riemann matrices (Π,P) and (Π_1,P_1) are said to be <u>symplectically equivalent</u> if they satisfy a Hurwitz relation with unimodular M such that $MP^{t}M = P_1$. This is again clearly an equivalence relation.

Siegels symplectic geometry [10] with its beautiful generalization of the group of Möbius transformations of the upper half-plane, is based on the relation of symplectic equivalence, which also corresponds to biholomorphic equivalence of closed Riemann surfaces.

Suppose that Π is principally polarized. Then, by a unimodular M, P may be normalized to

$$J = MP^{t}M = \begin{pmatrix} 0 & E \\ -E & 0 \end{pmatrix}$$

Hence (Π,P) is symplectically equivalent to (Π_1,J) where Π_1 is given by

$$\Pi_1 = H\Pi M^{-1}$$

where H may be chosen arbitrary as a non-singular $n\times n$ matrix of complex numbers. It is not difficult to see that H may be chosen so that Π_1 gets the form

$$\Pi_1 = (E\ \ Z)$$

where Z is symmetric with positive definite imaginary part. Such matrices form Siegel's generalized upper half-plane, and the above considerations show that the unimodular 2n×2n matrices M which satisfy $J = MJ^{t}M$ form a group which acts on this upper half-plane in a natural fashion.

The symplectic equivalence relation also yields a "unique factorization". In this case the polarization determines a "theta-divisor" whose components correspond to the factors, (see e.g. Clemens and Griffiths [11]). It is clear that a symplectically reducible matrix is also isogenously reducible, but the converse need not hold. It is known, for instance, that the canonically polarized period matrix of a closed Riemann surface is symplectically irreducible (see e.g. [12]), but Poincaré's theorem of complete reducibility shows that such a matrix is isogenously reducible whenever the Riemann surface is a covering of a surface of smaller, positive genus.

3.5. We shall say that the Riemann matrices Π and Π_1 are <u>isomorphic</u> if they satisfy a Hurwitz relation with unimodular M. While this equivalence relation would be the most natural one from the point of view of complex tori, it is in many ways quite unwieldy, and appears to be the least studied. In the case of Riemann matrices which admit only one polarization, isomorphism coincides with symplectic equivalence and nothing new appears. Its special characteristics are therefore only visible in connection with Riemann matrices with many polarizations. We shall try to illustrate some of the phenomena and problems with some simple examples in the next section.

4. RIEMANN MATRICES WITH MANY POLARIZATIONS

4.1. Let Π be a Riemann matrix and let P be a polarizing matrix for Π. By a theorem of Frobenius, P may be normalized to the form

$$MP^{t}M = \begin{pmatrix} 0 & D \\ -D & 0 \end{pmatrix}$$

by a unimodular M, where D is a diagonal matrix. By a procedure like that of (3.4), it can be shown that Π is symplectically equivalent to a matrix of the form $(D^{-1}\ Z)$ where Z is symmetric with positive definite imaginary part. Conversely, any matrix of this form is a Riemann matrix with MP^tM as polarizing matrix. If such a Riemann matrix admits a second polarization, then the entries of Z must satisfy certain non-trivial polynomial equations with integral coefficients. Since the number of possible polarizing matrices is countable, it follows that the set of matrices admitting a second polarization form a subset of measure zero in the set of Riemann matrices polarized by P (and considered as an open subset of an appropriate Euclidean space). It can be shown, on the other hand, that the subset is dense (see e.g. Conforto[13]).

4.2. We consider now the case where Π is the direct product of two sub-matrices:

$$\Pi = \begin{pmatrix} \Pi_1 & 0 \\ 0 & \Pi_2 \end{pmatrix}$$

The polarizing matrix P may then be written as

$$P = \begin{pmatrix} P_1 & Q \\ -^tQ & P_2 \end{pmatrix}$$

and from the equation

$$\Pi P^t\Pi = \begin{matrix} \Pi_1 P_1^t\Pi_1 & \Pi_1 Q^t\Pi_2 \\ -\Pi_2^t Q^t\Pi_1 & \Pi_1 P_2^t\Pi_2 \end{matrix}$$

and the analogous expression for $\Pi P^t\overline{\Pi}$, we conclude that P_i is a polarizing matrix for Π_i (thus the Π_i are Riemann matrices) and Q is a simultaneous matrix for Π_1 and Π_2.

Let $\tilde{\Pi}$ be a Riemann matrix and let $\tilde{P}$ be a polarizing matrix for $\tilde{\Pi}$. The polarization determined by P will be called a <u>product polarization</u> for $\tilde{\Pi}$ if $(\tilde{\Pi},\tilde{P})$ is symplectically equivalent to (Π,P) where Π and P are as above with Q=0.

4.2.1. <u>Let a Riemann matrix Π be the direct product of two sub-matrices Π_1 and Π_2. Then Π_1 and Π_2 are Riemann matrices and Π admits a non-product polarization only if Π_1 and Π_2 satisfy a non-trivial Hurwitz relation.</u>

<u>Proof</u>: It only remains to remark that the last assertion follows from (3.2.1) and the observation that we must have $Q \neq 0$.

Remark: We have not shown that the condition for non-product polarizations is sufficient (it isn't). The problem of deciding whether a given polarization is a product polarization appears to be quite difficult. Non-product polarizations can most easily be produced by taking the matrix as the canonically polarized period matrix of a closed Riemann surface.

4.3. A case of special interest arises if we restrict our attention to principally polarized matrices. Consider the matrix

$$\Pi = \begin{pmatrix} E & Z & 0 & 0 \\ 0 & 0 & E & Z \end{pmatrix}$$

with polarizing matrix

$$P = \begin{pmatrix} J & 0 \\ 0 & J \end{pmatrix}$$

(a product of two equal principally polarized factors). Assuming that (E Z) does not admit any other polarizations, the only possible candidates for principal polarizing matrices are those of the form

$$R = \begin{pmatrix} rJ & sJ \\ sJ & tJ \end{pmatrix}$$

with $rt-s^2=1$, and $r > 0$. Taking into account that the matrix

$$\begin{pmatrix} r & s \\ s & t \end{pmatrix}$$

can be diagonalized by a unimodular matrix, it is clear that R can be transformed to the form

$$MR\,{}^tM = \begin{pmatrix} J & 0 \\ 0 & J \end{pmatrix}$$

by a unimodular matrix M of the form

$$M = \begin{pmatrix} aE & bE \\ cE & dE \end{pmatrix}$$

But then

$$\Pi M = \begin{pmatrix} aE & aZ & bE & bZ \\ cE & cZ & dE & dZ \end{pmatrix} = H\Pi$$

where H is like M, but with unit matrices of one-half the size.

Hence R determines a product polarization, and we have

4.3.1. The direct product of a principally polarized Riemann matrix with itself admits infinitely many principal polarizations. These are all product polarizations unless the matrix admits a complex multiplication not a multiple of the identity.

Proof: All that has to be verified is that if the matrix only satisfies Hurwitz relations with itself that are multiples of the identity, then it admits no simultaneous matrix with itself other than a multiple of the principal polarizing matrix, and hence no other polarization. But that follows from (3.2.1).

Remark: Again the condition for a non-product principal polarization is only necessary and not sufficient.

4.4 It is natural to define an automorphism of a Riemann matrix as a complex multiplication with unimodular M. This corresponds to an automorphism of the associated torus.

The previous examples show that there are Riemann matrices with infinitely many principal polarizations. It follows that they must have infinite automorphism groups, since if P and P_1 are principal polarizing matrices, PP_1^{-1} will define an automorphism, by (3.2.1). (These automorphisms generate a normal subgroup of the group of all automorphisms).

This should be contrasted with the case of symplectic automorphisms (definition obvious) which always form a finite group.

It is also easy to show that the automorphisms above are of infinite order and hence cannot preserve *any* polarization by the preceding remark.

The presence of an infinite automorphism group is always the case with a product of two Riemann matrices admitting a non-trivial simultaneous matrix. For if P_1 and P_2 are polarizing matrices for Π_1 and Π_2, and if Q is a simultaneous matrix, then

$$\begin{pmatrix} P_1 & rQ \\ 0 & P_2 \end{pmatrix}$$

is a simultaneous matrix for the product (with itself) and

$$\begin{pmatrix} E_1 & rQP_2^{-1} \\ 0 & E_2 \end{pmatrix}$$

defines an automorphism, r being chosen to make the matrix integral. This automorphism clearly has infinite order. It again cannot preserve any polarizing matrix, and hence any given polarization is transformed into infinitely many distinct ones.

These observations are closely related to classical results, originating with Poincaré, according to which (e.g) if a Riemann surface has more than g (=genus) elliptic "involutions", then it has infinitely many (see Severi [14], p. 293). The significance of the "unique factorization" of Riemann matrices for the existence of maps of Riemann surfaces does not seem to have been explored.

One may reasonably ask whether the presence of an infinite automorphism group is characteristic of products, whose factors admit non-trivial simultaneous matrices.

4.5 Hayashida and Nishi [15] have shown that there are Riemann surfaces of genus 2 whose period matrices are isomorphic to principally polarized products. Weil has an unpublished example of a Riemann surface of genus 4 whose period matrix is isomorphic to a product. It is not known whether such examples exist in all genera.

It would be of interest to have examples of this kind not involving elliptic factors. Elliptic curves occupy a special position in the theory, partly because they always admit a unique principal polarization, and partly because a non-trivial Hurwitz relation between the period matrix of a Riemann surface with that of an elliptic curve is always associated with a map of the surface onto the curve. (In general, maps between Jacobian varieties need not come from maps between the Riemann surfaces).

Combining the examples of Hayashida and Nishi with the preceding results, we see that there are Riemann matrices which carry infinitely many distinct polarizations as canonically polarized period matrix of the same Riemann surface. It is natural to ask whether a matrix could be the period matrix of conformally distinct Riemann surfaces. By Torelli's theorem (see [12]) these must correspond to distinct polarizations, and the corresponding polarized matrices must be symplectically non-equivalent.

This suggests introducing an equivalence relation on the set of polarizations of a Riemann matrix. Two polarizations P and P_1 of a Riemann matrix Π, will be called isomorphic if there is an automorphism of Π given by a matrix M such that $MP{}^tM = P_1$.

So far as I know, it is an open question whether a Riemann matrix can carry an infinite number of isomorphism classes of principal polarizations. It is natural to conjecture that it cannot. The only systematic treatment of such questions is the pioneering work of Hayashida and Nishi ([15], [16], [17], [18]), which deals with the case of products of two elliptic curves. They have investigated the case where the two curves are identical and the endomorphism ring is isomorphic to the principal order of an imaginary quadratic number field $Q(\sqrt{-m})$, and the case where the curves are without complex multiplication but related by an isogeny whose kernel is cyclic of order m. They find that the number of isomorphism classes of principal polarizations is finite in both cases, but tends to infinity with m. In the first case, the product carries a non-product polarization if and only if m is different from 0,1,3,7 and 15.

REFERENCES

[1] GUNNING, R.C., Lectures on Riemann Surfaces, Princeton Univ. Press (1965).
[2] SCHOTTKY, F., Zur Theorie der Abelschen Funktionen von vier Variabeln, J. Reine Angew. Math. **102** (1888) 304–352.
[3] FARKAS, H.M., RAUCH, H.E., Period relations of Schottky type on Riemann surfaces, Ann. Math. **92** (1970) 434–461.
[4] SIEGEL, C.L., Topics in Complex Function Theory (3 Vols), Wiley-Interscience, New York (1969, 1971, 1973).
[5] SWINNERTON-DYER, H.P.F., Analytic Theory of Abelian Varieties, Cambridge Univ. Press (1974).
[6] SCORZA, G., Intorno alla teoria generale delle matrici di Riemann e ad alcune sere applicazioni, Rend. Circ. Mat. Palermo **41** (1916) 263–380.

[7] SCORZA, G., Le algebre di ordine qualunque e le matrici di Riemann, Rend. Circ. Mat. Palermo **45** (1921) 1–204.
[8] LEFSCHETZ, S., On certain numerical invariants of algebraic varieties with application to abelian varieties, Trans. Am. Math. Soc. **22** (1921) 327–482.
[9] SIEGEL, C.L., Symplectic Geometry, Academic Press, New York (1964).
[10] SIEGEL, C.L., Lectures on Riemann Matrices, Tata Inst. Fundamental Research, Bombay (1963).
[11] CLEMENS, C.H., GRIFFITHS, P.A., The intermediate Jacobian of the cubic threefold, Ann. Math. **95** (1972) 281–356.
[12] MARTENS, H.H., Torelli's theorem and a generalization for hyper-elliptic surfaces, Commun. Pure Appl. Math. **16** (1963) 97–110.
[13] CONFORTO, F., Abelsche Funktionen und algebraische Geometrie, Springer, Berlin (1956).
[14] SEVERI, F., Vorlesungen über algebraische Geometrie, Teubner, Leipzig (1921).
[15] HAYASHIDA, T., NISHI, M., Existence of curves of genus two on a product of two elliptic curves, J. Math. Soc. Jap. **17** (1965) 1–16.
[16] HAYASHIDA, T., NISHI, M., On certain type of Jacobian varieties of dimension 2, Nat. Sci. Rep. Ochanomizu Univ. **16** (1965) 49–57.
[17] HAYASHIDA, T., A class number associated with the product of an elliptic curve with itself, J. Math. Soc. Jap. **20** (1968) 26–43.
[18] HAYASHIDA, T., A class number associated with a product of two elliptic curves, Nat. Sci. Rep. Ochanomizu Univ. **16** (1965) 9–19.

STABILITY OF ISOMETRIES AMONG HARMONIC MAPPINGS

J.C. MITTEAU
Ecole nationale supérieure
de l'aéronautique et de l'espace,
Toulouse, France

Abstract

STABILITY OF ISOMETRIES AMONG HARMONIC MAPPINGS.

A generalization is presented of some results on stability for harmonic mappings of riemannian manifolds so far obtained in the case of non-positive sectional curvature or in the case of holomorphic or antiholomorphic mappings of Kähler manifolds. A condition is obtained for a harmonic mapping (in a homotopy class) to be an isometry. This condition is related to the existence of solutions for a second-order elliptic differential operator on vector fields. In some cases this condition can be expressed in terms of the eigenvalues of the Laplace operator for functions. Some examples are given.

INTRODUCTION

The aim of this paper is to find some conditions for a harmonic mapping to be an isometry. This problem drives us to a real analogue of the following theorem of A. Lichnerowicz [4]:

Let (M,g,F) *and* (M′,g′,F′) *be almost Kähler manifolds. Assume* M *to be compact. Let* $f: M \times [0,1] \to M'$ *be a* C^2*-family of harmonic mappings. Then* f_0 *is holomorphic (antiholomorphic) if and only if* f_1 *is holomorphic (antiholomorphic).*

Throughout the text M and M′ are riemannian manifolds without boundaries, with metric g and g′ respectively. We use i's as indices in M and α's in M′; n is the dimension of M; M is compact.

Recall that a C^2-mapping $f: M \to M'$ is called harmonic if the tension field $\tau(f)$ of f satisfies the equation:

$$\tau(f) = 0$$

where the differential operator τ is given in local co-ordinate charts by

$$[\tau(f)]^\alpha = g^{ij}\left[\frac{\partial^2 f}{\partial x_i\, \partial x_j} + (\Gamma^\alpha_{\beta\gamma} \circ f)\frac{\partial f^\beta}{\partial x_i}\frac{\partial f^\gamma}{\partial x_j} - \Gamma^k_{ij}\frac{\partial f^\alpha}{\partial x_k}\right]$$

For $k \geqslant 2$ a C^k-family of harmonic mappings is a C^k-mapping $f: M \times [0,1] \to M'$ such that f_t, defined by $f_t(x) = f(x,t)$ for all x, is harmonic for all t on [0, 1]. f can also be considered as a C^k-mapping of unit interval in the Banach manifold $C^k(M,M')$.

1. THE GENERAL STABILITY THEOREM

Let $f: [0,1] \to C^k(M,M')$ be a C^k-family of harmonic mappings. We introduce the vector field $X \in C^2(E)$ defined by

$$X(x, t) = \frac{\partial f}{\partial t}(x, t), \quad x \in M, \quad t \in [0, 1] \tag{1}$$

where $E = f^*TM'$ is the induced bundle:

$$\begin{array}{ccc} E & \longrightarrow & TM' \\ \downarrow & & \downarrow \\ M & \xrightarrow{f} & M' \end{array}$$

We can consider on the vector bundle E the canonical pull-back $\overline{\nabla}$ of connection ∇ on TM′ (Levi-Cività's connection). This gives rise to a connection also named $\overline{\nabla}$ in every tensor product

$$(TM)^p \otimes (T^*M)^q \otimes E$$

(on M we also use the connection induced by the metric g). Using the connection $\overline{\nabla}$, we can compute the partial differential equation which is satisfied by X.

Lemma 1. f *as above. Then we have*

$$\overline{\nabla}_t (Tf) = \overline{\nabla} X$$

Recall that we can consider Tf as a section of $T^*M \otimes E$. The proof of this lemma is very simple in a local co-ordinate chart.

As we have by hypothesis

$$\tau(f_t)(x) = 0 \tag{2}$$

for all t and x, we can derive Eq. (2). We get

$$\overline{\nabla}_t [\tau(f_t)] = \overline{\nabla}_t [\mathrm{Tr}_g \overline{\nabla}(T(f_t))] = 0$$

from an expression of $\tau(f)$ which can be found in Ref. [5]. Since $\overline{\nabla}$ is a metric connection with respect to metric g on M and f^*g' on E, we have

$$\overline{\nabla}_t [\tau(f_t)] = \mathrm{Tr}_g [\overline{\nabla}_t \overline{\nabla}(T(f_t))]$$

and we can use Ricci's formula and lemma to get

Proposition 1. *Let* f *be a* C^2*-family of harmonic mappings. Then the vector field* X *defined by Eq. (1) satisfies the equation*

$$\Delta_f X = 0$$

where the operator Δ_f *is the second-order symmetric partial differential operator given by*

$$\Delta_f X = -[\mathrm{Tr}_g \overline{\nabla}^{(2)} X + \underline{R}_f X]$$

with $\underline{R}_f$ *the "Ricci curvature" of E:*

$$[\underline{R}_f X]^\alpha = R'^\alpha_{\beta\gamma\delta}(Tf)^\beta_i X^\gamma (Tf)^\delta_j g^{ij}$$

R′ *is the curvature tensor of* (M′, g′).

Remark. This operator is the first variation of tension field. It can be considered as the second variation of energy functional (see [6]). It plays an important role: it is the generalization of the operator of the Jacobi equation for geodesics to a greater dimension of base space.

We call Δ_f the Laplacian for vector fields along f and section X of E satisfying $\Delta_f X = 0$ f-harmonic vector fields.

Example. Consider M = M′ and $f = 1_M$ the identity mapping. Then the vector bundle E → M is the bundle TM → M and $\Delta = \Delta_{1_M}$ is a second-order PDO on TM which is often called the Laplacian for vector fields. This operator is not the one obtained by duality from de Rham's $\hat{\Delta}$ defined by $\hat{\Delta} = d\delta + \delta d$. The relationship between the two operators is given by

Proposition 2. *For all* $X \in C^2(TM)$ *we have*

$$\Delta X = \#\hat{\Delta}\, b\, X - 2\underline{R}X$$

where $\# : T^*M \to TM$ *is the duality operator given by the riemannian metric* g *on* M, $b = (\#)^{-1}$ *and* $\underline{R}$ *is the usual Ricci operator.*

Proof. We have for 1-form θ:

$$\hat{\Delta}\theta = -\mathrm{Tr}_g \nabla^{(2)}\theta + \underline{R}\theta \tag{3}$$

As $f = 1_M$, we just have $\overline{\nabla} = \nabla$. From the definition of ΔX given in Proposition 1, we have

$$\Delta X = -\mathrm{Tr}_g \nabla^{(2)} X - \underline{R}X \tag{4}$$

As duality goes over trace, ∇ and $\underline{R}$, we get the result by subtracting (3) and (4). q.e.d.

Let us now go back to our problem.

Proposition 3. *Suppose* f : M → M *is a harmonic diffeomorphism and X is a* C^2*-section of* E = f*TM. *Define* $\widetilde{X}$ *by*

$$\widetilde{X} = X \circ f^{-1} \tag{5}$$

$\widetilde{X}$ *is a section of bundle* TM → M. *Assume* $\widetilde{X}$ *is a Killing vector field on* (M, g). *Then* $\Delta_f X = 0$.

Recall that a Killing vector field or infinitesimal isometry is a section of bundle TM → M satisfying the Killing equation

$$\mathscr{L}_{\widetilde{X}}\, g = 0$$

i.e. in a local co-ordinate chart,

$$\nabla_i \widetilde{X}_j + \nabla_j \widetilde{X}_i = 0$$

Let us denote by K(M) the set of all Killing vector fields on M. By linearity of the Killing equation, we obtain that K(M) is a vector subspace of $C^1(TM)$. It is well known that K(M) is a Lie subalgebra.

Lemma 2. *Let* $f : M \to M$ *be a harmonic diffeomorphism. Then the mapping defined by Eq.(5) is a bundle isomorphism of* $E = f^*TM$ on TM *and we have in local co-ordinate charts*

$$(\widetilde{\Delta_f X})^k = -\tilde{g}^{ij}[\nabla_i \nabla_j \tilde{X}^k + R^k_{imj}\tilde{X}^m]$$

where $\tilde{g}$ *is defined by* $\tilde{g}^{ij} = (Tf)^i_{\bar{i}}(Tf)^j_{\bar{j}} g^{\bar{i}\bar{j}} \circ f^{-1}$

We denote by $\bar{i}$'s the indices in M as source manifold and i's in M as target manifold.

Proof. From Proposition 1 we have

$$-\Delta_f X^k = g^{\bar{i}\bar{j}}[\bar{\nabla}_{\bar{i}}\bar{\nabla}_{\bar{j}} X^k + R^k_{imj}(Tf)^i_{\bar{i}} X^m (Tf)^j_{\bar{j}}]$$

From the definition of connection $\bar{\nabla}$ we have

$$\bar{\nabla}_{\bar{j}} X^k = (\nabla_j \tilde{X}^k \circ f)(Tf)^j_{\bar{j}}$$

and for second order

$$\bar{\nabla}_{\bar{i}}\bar{\nabla}_{\bar{j}} X^k = (\nabla_i \nabla_j \tilde{X}^k \circ f)(Tf)^i_{\bar{i}}(Tf)^j_{\bar{j}} + (\nabla_j \tilde{X}^k \circ f)\,\bar{\nabla}_{\bar{i}}(Tf)^j_{\bar{j}}$$

Now take the trace of this expression with respect to metric g and compose with f^{-1}

$$-(\widetilde{\Delta_f X})^k = [\nabla_i \nabla_j \tilde{X}^k + R^k_{imj}\tilde{X}^m]\tilde{g}^{ij} + \nabla_i \tilde{X}^k[\tau(f) \circ f^{-1}]^i$$

By assumption the last term is 0. q.e.d.

Proof of Proposition 3. By Lemma 1 we have

$$-g_{ij}\widetilde{\Delta_f X^j} = [\nabla_j \nabla_k \tilde{X}_i + R_{ijmk}\tilde{X}^m]\tilde{g}^{jk}$$

By Bianchi's identity we obtain

$$-g_{ij}\widetilde{\Delta_f X^j} = [\nabla_j \nabla_k \tilde{X}_i + R^m_{jik}\tilde{X}_m]\tilde{g}^{jk}$$

and by Ricci's

$$-g_{ij}\widetilde{\Delta_f X^j} = [\nabla_j(\nabla_k \tilde{X}_i + \nabla_i \tilde{X}_k) - \tfrac{1}{2}\nabla_i(\nabla_j \tilde{X}_k + \nabla_k \tilde{X}_j)]\tilde{g}^{jk}$$

This expression shows that $\Delta_f X = 0$ if $\tilde{X}$ is assumed to be Killing. q.e.d.

Remarks. In the case where $f = 1_M$ more can be proved (see Theorem 2). Proposition 3 can also be generalized to the case where f is a covering map (use local diffeomorphisms).

Theorem 1. *Let* $f : M \times [0, 1] \to M$ *be a* C^3*-family of harmonic mappings. Assume:*

(i) M *is compact*
(ii) f_0 *is a diffeomorphism*
(iii) $\widetilde{\text{Ker}\,\Delta_{f_0}} = K(M)$

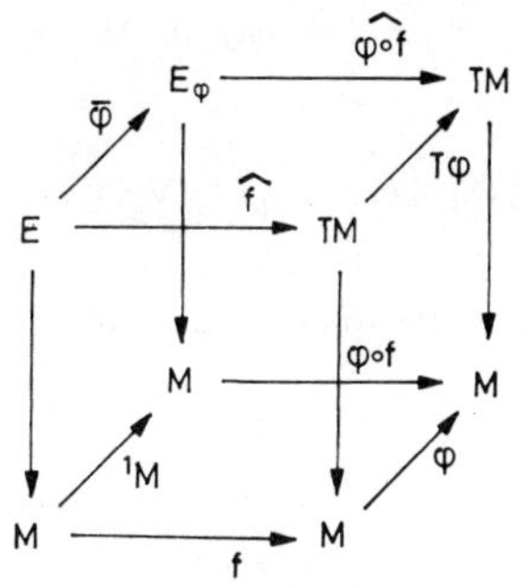

FIG.1. Commutative diagram for proof of Theorem 1.

Then f_1 *is a diffeomorphism and there exists an isometry* φ *of* (M,g) *such that*

$$f_1 = \varphi \circ f_0$$

For the proof let us first consider the commutative diagram (Fig. 1) where $\hat{f}$ and $\widehat{\varphi \circ f}$ are the canonical morphisms of induced bundles. $E = f^*TM$ and $E_\varphi = (\varphi \circ f)^*TM$. We introduce into bundles E and E_φ, which have canonical metrics and connections the norms

$$\|X\|^2_{L^2} = \int_M |X|^2$$

$$\|X\|_{H^2} = \|X\|_{L^2} + \|\overline{\nabla} X\|_{L^2} + \|\overline{\nabla}\,\overline{\nabla} X\|_{L^2}$$

using canonical measure in the manifold (M, g). We denote by $L^2(E) = H^0(E)$ and $H^2(E)$ the Hilbert spaces of sections of bundle E associated with the above norms.

Lemma 3. *Suppose mapping* φ *is a diffeomorphism. Then mapping* $\overline{\varphi}$ *uniquely defined by Fig.1 is an isomorphism of bundles. In canonical trivializations for bundles* E *and* E_φ, $\overline{\varphi}$ *in every fibre is the mapping* $T\varphi$ *restricted to the fibre.*

Proof. In every canonical trivialization for bundles E and E_φ, mappings $\hat{f}$ and $\widehat{\varphi \circ f}$ are given by the identity on every fibre. q.e.d.

Lemma 4. *Assume* f *to be a harmonic diffeomorphism and* φ *an isometry. Then we have*

$$[\overline{\varphi}^{-1} \cdot \Delta_{\varphi \circ f} \cdot \overline{\varphi}](X) = \Delta_f(X), \qquad \forall X \in C^2(E)$$

In fact, Lemma 4 is a particular case of

Lemma 5. *Assume* f *to be a harmonic diffeomorphism. Let* φ *be a diffeomorphism of* M *such that there exists an isometry* j *of* (M, g) *satisfying*

$$\|\varphi - j\|_{C^3} \leqslant \alpha \leqslant \tfrac{1}{2}\|Tj\|_{C^0}$$

Assume $\varphi \circ f$ *to be harmonic.*

Then there exists a constant C *depending only on* (M, g) *and* f *such that we have the estimate:*

$$\|[\bar\varphi^{-1}\cdot\Delta_{\varphi\circ f}\cdot\bar\varphi](X)-\Delta_f(X)\|_{L^2}\leqslant C\alpha(\|X\|_{L^2}+\|\bar\nabla X\|_{L^2})$$

Proof. We use indices i, $\bar{i}$ and A as in the following diagram:

$$\begin{array}{ccccc} M & \xrightarrow{\ f\ } & M & \xrightarrow{\ \varphi\ } & M \\ (A) & & (i) & & (\bar{i}) \end{array}$$

Since f and $\varphi\circ f$ are harmonic diffeomorphisms, we may use Lemmas 2 and 3 to obtain

$$[\bar\varphi^{-1}\cdot\Delta_{\varphi\circ f}\cdot\bar\varphi](X)^k = T\varphi^k_{\bar k}g^{AB}T\varphi^{\bar i}_i T\varphi^{\bar j}_j Tf^i_A Tf^j_B[\nabla_{\bar i}\nabla_{\bar j}(T\varphi^{\bar k}_m X^m) + R^{\bar k}_{\bar i\bar m\bar j}T\varphi^{\bar m}_m X^m] \tag{6}$$

We have to compare this quantity with

$$\Delta_f X^k = g^{AB}Tf^i_A Tf^j_B[\nabla_i\nabla_j X^k + R^k_{imj}X^m] \tag{7}$$

For this purpose we compute the quantities

$$T\varphi^k_{\bar k}T\varphi^{\bar i}_i T\varphi^{\bar j}_j\nabla_{\bar i}\nabla_{\bar j}(T\varphi^{\bar k}_m X^m) - \nabla_i\nabla_j X^k \tag{8}$$

and

$$T\varphi^{\bar i}_i T\varphi^{\bar j}_j T\varphi^k_{\bar k}T\varphi^{\bar m}_m R^{\bar k}_{\bar i\bar m\bar j} - R^k_{imj} \tag{9}$$

(8) is equal to

$$(\nabla_i\nabla_j T\varphi^{\bar k}_m X^m + \nabla_j T\varphi^{\bar k}_m\nabla_i X^m + \nabla_i T\varphi^{\bar k}_m\nabla_j X^m - \nabla_i T\varphi^{\bar j}_j T\varphi^n_{\bar j}\nabla_n T\varphi^{\bar k}_m X^m)T\varphi^k_{\bar k}$$

$$-\nabla_i T\varphi^{\bar j}_j T\varphi^m_{\bar j}\nabla_m X^k \tag{10}$$

Introducing isometry j, we get

$$\|\bar\nabla\bar\nabla T\varphi\|_{C^0}\leqslant\alpha,\qquad \|\bar\nabla T\varphi\|_{C^0}\leqslant\alpha,\qquad \|T\varphi-Tj\|_{C^0}\leqslant\alpha$$

for, since j is an isometry, we have $\bar\nabla Tj = 0$ and $\bar\nabla\bar\nabla Tj = 0$. When $\alpha = 0$, (9) and (10) are equal to 0 so we obtain Lemma 4.

In the general case, there exist constants C_1 and C_2 such that

$$|T\varphi^{-1}-Tj^{-1}|\leqslant C_1\alpha,\qquad |T\varphi^{-1}|\leqslant C_2$$

for $\alpha\leqslant\frac{1}{2}\|Tj\|_{C^0}$ (we denote by simple | . | the norm in a fixed point x of M).

Thus, because the metric $g^{AB}Tf^i_A Tf^j_B$ is again positive definite and gives norms equivalent to g^{ij}'s, and as the curvature of (M, g) is bounded (M is compact), there exists a constant C such that (9) has in every point of M a norm bounded by $C\alpha$ and (8) = (10) less than $C\alpha(|X| + |\overline{\nabla}X|)$.

Then for the difference (6) minus (7) we have the right estimate in every point of M and we can integrate this estimate all over M. q.e.d.

Lemma 6 (Green's formula). M *compact. Consider* Δ_f *defined in Proposition 1. Then* $\Delta_f : L^2(E) \to L^2(E)$ *with domain* $C^2(E)$ *is symmetric.*

Proof. In a chart of M trivializing $E = f^*TM$ we have

$$-(\Delta_f X)^{\bar{k}} = \overline{\nabla}_i \overline{\nabla}^i X^{\bar{k}} + \underline{R}^{\bar{k}}_{f\bar{m}} X^{\bar{m}}$$

Then

$$\int_M (\Delta_f X, Y) = \sum_U \int_U -g'_{\bar{i}\bar{j}}(\overline{\nabla}_k \overline{\nabla}^k X^{\bar{i}} + \underline{R}^{\bar{i}}_{f\bar{k}} X^{\bar{k}}) Y^{\bar{j}}$$

Using now the divergence formula (in the orientable riemannian covering of M), $\overline{\nabla}g' = \overline{\nabla}g = 0$ and symmetry of $\underline{R}_f$, we obtain

$$\int_M (\Delta_f X, Y) = \int_M (X, \Delta_f Y) \qquad \text{q.e.d.}$$

Lemma 7. *Let* $f :]\alpha,\beta[\to C^3(M,M')$ *be a* C^3*-family of harmonic diffeomorphisms. Assume M compact and for some* $t \in]\alpha,\beta[$ $\operatorname{Ker}\Delta_{f_t} = K(M)$.

Then there exists $\epsilon > 0$ *such that for all* $u \in]t-\epsilon, t+\epsilon[$ *we have*

$$\operatorname{Ker}\Delta_{f_u} = K(M)$$

Proof. Consider the weak operator $\overline{\Delta}_{f_u}$ defined in $H^2(E)$ by

$$\langle \overline{\Delta}_{f_u} X, Y\rangle = \langle X, \Delta_{f_u} Y\rangle$$

for all Y in $C^\infty(E)$, the bracket $\langle \ldots \rangle$ being the duality between $\mathscr{D}'(M)$ and $\mathscr{D}(M)$. From Lemma 6, $\overline{\Delta}_{f_u}$ is an extension of Δ_{f_u}.

$\overline{\Delta}_{f_u}$ is self-adjoint: in fact let $X \in H^2(E)$. For $Y \in C^\infty(E)$ we have

$$\int_M (\overline{\Delta}_{f_u} X, Y) = \langle \overline{\Delta}_{f_u} X, Y\rangle = \langle X, \Delta_{f_u} Y\rangle$$

So, since X is in L^2, we have

$$\int_M (\overline{\Delta}_{f_u} X, Y) = \int_M (X, \Delta_{f_u} Y)$$

and taking the limit for Y in $H^2(E)$ we obtain

$$\int_M (\overline{\Delta}_{f_u} X, Y) = \int_M (X, \overline{\Delta}_{f_u} Y)$$

for all X and Y in $H^2(E)$.

$\overline{\Delta}_{f_u}$, being self-adjoint and densely defined in $H^0(E)$, is closed, and

$$\text{Coker}\ \overline{\Delta}_{f_u} = \text{Ker}\ \overline{\Delta}^*_{f_u} = \text{Ker}\ \overline{\Delta}_{f_u}$$

so $\overline{\Delta}_{f_u}$ is Fredholm for u = t (by the regularity theorem, see below).

Consider now Lemma 5. We shall prove that the perturbation

$$A = \overline{\varphi}_u^{-1} \cdot \overline{\Delta}_{f_u} \cdot \overline{\varphi} - \overline{\Delta}_{f_t}$$

where $\varphi_u = f_u \circ f_t^{-1}$ is $\overline{\Delta}_{f_t}$-bounded with bound close enough to 0.

f_u and φ_u are diffeomorphisms, f_u and f_t are harmonic, and since f is a C^3-family there exists $\eta(\alpha) > 0$ such that $\|\varphi_u - 1_M\|_{C^3} \leqslant \alpha$, for all $u \in]t - \eta(\alpha), t + \eta(\alpha)[$. So we may use Lemma 5 and obtain

$$\|AX\|_{L^2} \leqslant C\alpha \|X\|_{H^1} \tag{11}$$

But now we have

$$\|\overline{\nabla} X\|^2_{L^2} = \langle \overline{\nabla} X, \overline{\nabla} X \rangle = -\langle X, \overline{\nabla}_i \overline{\nabla}^i X \rangle$$

by the divergence formula so we have

$$\|\overline{\nabla} X\|^2_{L^2} = \langle X, \overline{\Delta}_f X \rangle + \langle X, \underline{R}_f(X) \rangle$$

(remember f is harmonic) and

$$\|\overline{\nabla} X\|_{L^2} \leqslant C_1(\|X\|_{L^2} + \|\overline{\Delta}_{f_t} X\|_{L^2}) \tag{12}$$

(11) and (12) give

$$\|AX\|_{L^2} \leqslant C'\alpha (\|X\|_{L^2} + \|\overline{\Delta}_{f_t} X\|_{L^2})$$

This last inequality shows that A is $\overline{\Delta}_{f_t}$-bounded with bound $C'\alpha$.

Now use the perturbation theorem (Ref. [3], Theorem 5.22). Since $\overline{\Delta}_{f_t}$ is Fredholm and A is $\overline{\Delta}_{f_t}$-bounded with bound small enough, we can find α_0 such that

$$\dim \text{Ker}\ \overline{\Delta}_{f_u} \leqslant \dim \text{Ker}\ \overline{\Delta}_{f_t} \tag{13}$$

for all $u \in]t - \eta(\alpha_0), t + \eta(\alpha_0)[$. Put $\epsilon = \eta(\alpha_0)$.

From the regularity theorem for elliptic operators with C^∞ coefficients we have that $\operatorname{Ker} \overline{\Delta}_{f_t} \subset H^2(E)$ is in fact a subspace of $C^\infty(E)$. Thus $\operatorname{Ker} \overline{\Delta}_{f_t} = K(M)$ from assumption (iii) of the theorem. But (13) implies $\dim \operatorname{Ker} \overline{\Delta}_{f_u} \leqslant \dim K(M)$ and so

$$\operatorname{Ker} \Delta_{f_u} = K(M) \qquad \text{q.e.d.}$$

Proof of the theorem. Let us define $\varphi_t = f_t \circ f_0^{-1}$ (different from φ_u used in the proof of the preceding lemma). Introduce the set Θ of $t \in [0, 1]$ such that "φ_t is an isometry". For all $t \in \Theta$, f_t is a diffeomorphism for $f_t = \varphi_t \circ f_0$.

By assumption $0 \in \Theta$. This set is non-empty. We shall prove that Θ is open and closed in $[0, 1]$. So $\Theta = [0, 1]$ and in particular $1 \in \Theta$. This is the conclusion of the theorem.

(a) Θ *is open in* $[0, 1]$

Fix $t \in \Theta$. φ_t is an isometry and f_t is a diffeomorphism which is harmonic. By Lemma 4 and assumption (iii) we get that $\operatorname{Ker} \Delta_{f_t}$ is the image of K(M) under $\overline{\varphi}_t$. So we have

$$\widetilde{\operatorname{Ker} \Delta_{f_t}} = K(M)$$

Now we can always find $\eta > 0$ with the property that for all $u \in]t-\eta, t+\eta[$, f_u is a diffeomorphism. This is just stability of diffeomorphisms in the C^1-topology.

Consider now mapping $\varphi_u = f_u \circ f_0^{-1}$. For $u = t$, φ_u is an isometry and for all u in $]t-\eta, t+\eta[$, f_u is a harmonic diffeomorphism and we can use Lemma 7 in the interval $]t-\eta, t+\eta[$: there exists $\epsilon > 0$ such that for all u in $]t-\epsilon, t+\epsilon[$, we have

$$\widetilde{\operatorname{Ker} \Delta_{f_u}} = K(M) \tag{14}$$

But since f_u is harmonic for all u, we have that $(d/du)\, f_u$ is f_u-harmonic and so, by Eq. (14), is Killing. Thus we have

$$f_u^* g = f_t^* g, \quad \forall\, u \in]t-\epsilon, t+\epsilon[$$

and this implies

$$\varphi_u^* g = (f_0^{-1})^* f_u^* g = (f_0^{-1})^* f_t^* g = g \tag{15}$$

since φ_t is an isometry. By (15) φ_u is an isometry.

(b) Θ *is closed in* $[0, 1]$

This point is just that the set of isometries is closed in C^1-topology. q.e.d.

Corollary 1. *Assume riemannian manifold* (M, g) *compact and let* $f_t : M \to M$, $t \in [0, 1]$ *be a* C^3*-family of harmonic mappings. Assume:*

(i) f_0 *is a diffeomorphism;*

(ii) $\widetilde{\operatorname{Ker} \Delta_{f_0}} = K(M)$.

Then f_1 *is a diffeomorphism.*

Corollary 2. *Assume riemannian manifold* (M, g) *compact and let* $f_t: M \to M$, $t \in [0, 1]$, *be a* C^3-*family of harmonic mappings. Assume:*

(i) f_0 *is an isometry;*

(ii) Ker Δ = K(M) *where* Δ *is the Laplace operator on vector fields (see Proposition 2).*

Then f_1 *is an isometry.*

Proof. The first corollary is immediate. For the second, since f_0 is an isometry we have $\Delta_{f_0} = \Delta_{1_M} = \Delta$ by Lemma 4. Then we can use the theorem. f_1 is an isometry by composition of isometries.

Remarks

This is the case, for instance, if we take f_0 to be the identity mapping. Actually all the results given here directly depend on the hypothesis that the kernel of the operator Δ_f is the subspace of Killing vector fields. This is not always the case, as can be seen in the following example.

Let f be the identity on sphere (S^2, g_0), g_0 being the usual metric. Then it can be proved that the kernel of Δ is the algebra of conformal infinitesimal transformations (see Ref. [4]). This is quite natural since in dimension 2, conformal transformations do not affect the energy of mappings. So in that case we have dim Ker Δ = 6 although dim K(M) = 3. Thus Ker $\Delta \neq$ K(M) and the theorem cannot be used.

In the case where the assumptions of the theorem are satisfied, we get a procedure to "isolate" the harmonic diffeomorphisms.

There is an extension of Theorem 1 in the non-compact case.

2. THE CASE OF IDENTITY ON EINSTEIN MANIFOLDS

In this section we show that the manifolds to be considered and their identities satisfy the assumptions of Corollary 2 of the preceding theorem. So we have a geometrical study of some harmonic maps in the case where the target manifold has strictly positive sectional curvature.

Remember that a riemannian manifold is called Einstein if there exists a C^∞ function k on it satisfying

$$\underline{R}_x = k(x) g_x$$

for all x in M, $\underline{R}$ being the Ricci curvature of (M, g). It can be shown, using Bianchi identity, that if dimension M $\geqslant 3$, then the function k is necessarily a constant. In the following we shall study the case of Einstein manifolds of positive Ricci curvature which are compact. We then have

$$\underline{R} = kg \tag{16}$$

with k positive constant. The case $k \leqslant 0$ is treated by Hartman's theorem. For n = 2 the theory looks different.

From (16) and Proposition 2 we obtain the following relationship with de Rham's operator:

$$\Delta_f X = \Delta X = \#[\hat{\Delta} - 2k]\, \flat X$$

so that $\flat X$ appears to be an eigenform for eigenvalue 2k of de Rham's $\hat{\Delta}$, when X is a harmonic vector field.

Recall that any $X \in C^\infty(TM)$ can uniquely be decomposed as

$$X = Y + \# df$$

with divergence $Y = 0$. As the operators d, δ and # commute with operator Δ (in the case of Einstein manifolds) we are led to

Theorem 2. *Let* M *be a compact Einstein manifold,* $\dim M \geqslant 3$. *Let* $X \in C^\infty(TM)$ *be a harmonic vector field. Then* X *can be uniquely decomposed as*

$$X = Y + \# df$$

where Y *is a Killing vector field and* $f \in C^\infty(M)$ *is an eigenfunction of the Laplace operator for eigenvalue* 2k:

$$\Delta f = 2kf$$

Remark. This result is trivial in the case of non-positive curvature, for X harmonic implies in that case X parallel: $\nabla X = 0$ (see Ref. [6]).

Proof. Associate with X 1-form $\varphi = bX$. By de Rham's decomposition, φ can be written as $\varphi = \psi + df$, with $\delta\psi = 0$, in a unique way. But we now have $\hat{\Delta}\varphi - 2k\varphi = 0$ so

$$(\hat{\Delta}\psi - 2k\psi) + d(\Delta f - 2kf) = 0$$

By commutativity and orthogonality relations we obtain

$$\hat{\Delta}\psi - 2k\psi = 0 \qquad\qquad d(\Delta f - 2kf) = 0$$

(a) The second equation gives

$$\Delta f - 2kf = C^{te}$$

which has a general solution $f_0 + C^{te}$ where f_0 is a solution of

$$\Delta f_0 - 2kf_0 = 0$$

Then note that we can modify the constant without altering the result, since we have $df = df_0$.

(b) The other equation is treated by

Lemma (Lichnerowicz [4]). *Let* (M, g) *be any compact riemannian manifold. Suppose 1-form* ψ *verifies*

$$\begin{cases} \Delta\psi - 2\underline{R}\psi = 0 \\ \delta\psi = 0 \end{cases}$$

Then $Y = \#\psi$ *is a Killing vector field on* M.

Proof. It is equivalent to solve the system

$$\begin{cases} \Delta Y = 0 \\ \operatorname{div} Y = 0 \end{cases}$$

Everything is done by the following formula:

$$\Delta Y = \delta_s[\mathscr{L}_Y g] - d[\operatorname{div} Y]$$

where the symmetric divergence δ_s is the formal adjoint for the operator $Y \mapsto \mathscr{L}_Y g$, the Lie derivative of the tensor g. Thus we have

$$0 = \langle \Delta Y, Y \rangle = \langle \delta_s[\mathscr{L}_Y g], Y \rangle = \langle \mathscr{L}_Y g, \mathscr{L}_Y g \rangle$$

which implies $\mathscr{L}_Y g = 0$, i.e. Y is a Killing vector field. q.e.d.

Remark. This decomposition is not valid for the general operator Δ_f.

Corollary. *Let* M *be a compact Einstein manifold of positive sectional curvature and dimension* $n \geqslant 3$. *If* 2k ($\underline{R}$ = kg) *is not an eigenvalue for the Laplace operator on functions, then*

$$\operatorname{Ker} \Delta = K(M)$$

Examples. This is the case for spheres S^n, $n \geqslant 3$, with the usual metric, since we have in that case $k = n - 1$ and

$$\lambda_1 = n < \lambda_2 = 2(n+1) < \lambda_3 \ldots$$

as eigenvalues for the Laplace operator (see Ref. [1]). So we obtain the stability of isometries among harmonic mappings in spite of the existence of a pure conformal transformation which gives an absolutely decreasing family of mappings whose energy tends to 0. In fact, spheres are a bad case since this is quite the only case where the conformal group is not compact.

This remark tends to prove that there is no proof of Theorem 1 from an energetic point of view (using, for instance, convexity).

It will be interesting to study this method in the case of Einstein manifolds which are homogeneous spaces.

3. THE COMPLEX CASE

It seems to be of no interest to consider the above method from the complex point of view. The reason for this could be the following.

It you try to prove Lichnerowicz's theorem (in compact Kähler manifolds) by the method used in this paper, you will discover that if f_0 is holomorphic (everything can be transposed to antiholomorphic) then $\Delta_{f_0} X = 0$ if and only if X is a holomorphic vector field without any further considerations. For instance, when f_0 = identity, then Δ is just the operator obtained by duality from that of de Rham; there is no Ricci curvature to appear in the formulas. So in this case the situation is rather trivial, as in the non-positive sectional curvature case.

In conclusion, our method does not give new information in the complex case.

REFERENCES

[1] BERGER, M., GAUDUCHON, P., MAZET, E., Le spectre du laplacien, Springer Lecture Notes No. 194 (1971).
[2] EELLS, J., SAMPSON, J.H., Harmonic mappings of riemannian manifolds, Am. J. Math. **86** (1964) 109-160.
[3] KATO, T., Perturbation Theory for Linear Operators, Springer, Berlin (1966).
[4] LICHNEROWICZ, A., Géométrie des groupes de transformations, Dunod, Paris (1958).
[5] LICHNEROWICZ, A., Applications harmoniques et variétés kählériennes, Istituto Nazionale di Alta Matematica, Bologna (1970).
[6] MAZET, E., La variation seconde de l'énergie, J. Diff. Geom. **8** (1973) 279-296.

VECTOR BUNDLES ON COMPACT RIEMANN SURFACES

M.S. NARASIMHAN
School of Mathematics,
Tata Institute of Fundamental Research,
Bombay, India

Abstract

VECTOR BUNDLES ON COMPACT RIEMANN SURFACES.

1. Cohomology of vector bundles and the duality theorem. 2. Divisors, line bundles and the Riemann-Roch theorem. 3. Projective embedding of a compact Riemann surface. 4. Genus and first Betti number. 5. Chern class and degree. 6. The Jacobian. 7. Line bundles and characters. 8. Poincaré bundle. 9. The Picard manifold of a compact Kähler manifold. 10. Vector bundles on a compact Riemann surface. 11. The Riemann-Roch theorem for vector bundles. 12. Indecomposable bundles and the Krull-Remak-Schmidt theorem. 13. Weil's theorem; unitary bundles. Appendix: Factors of automorphy.

1. COHOMOLOGY OF VECTOR BUNDLES AND THE DUALITY THEOREM

Let X be a compact Riemann surface, i.e. a compact connected complex manifold of complex dimension one. Let V be a (holomorphic) vector bundle of rank n on X. We shall denote by **V** the sheaf of holomorphic sections of V. If $\mathcal{O}$ denotes the sheaf of holomorphic functions on X, then **V** is a sheaf of $\mathcal{O}$-modules locally isomorphic to $\mathcal{O}^n = \mathcal{O} \oplus \dots \oplus \mathcal{O}$ (n factors). Conversely, given such a locally free sheaf of $\mathcal{O}$-modules of rank n, it defines in a canonical way a vector bundle of rank n (Ref. [11], §4).

Let $H^i(X,V)$ denote the ith cohomology space of X with coefficients in the sheaf **V**. We then have the following facts (see Refs [4, 11] and the paper by M.J. Field in these Proceedings).

(a) For all i, $H^i(X,V)$ are finite-dimensional vector spaces over $\mathbb{C}$ and $H^i(X,V) = 0$ for $i \geqslant 2$.

(b) **Duality theorem.** Let K denote the holomorphic cotangent bundle of X and V* the dual bundle of V. We then have

$$\dim_{\mathbb{C}} H^1(X,V) = \dim_{\mathbb{C}} H^0(X,K \otimes V^*)$$

(in fact, the spaces are canonically dual to each other).

Remarks

(i) The space $H^0(X,V)$ is the space of holomorphic sections of V over X. It is easy to prove its finite dimensionality, for instance by using Montel's theorem.

(ii) A vector bundle of rank 1 will be called a line bundle. The bundle K is called the **canonical bundle** of X.

2. DIVISORS, LINE BUNDLES AND THE RIEMANN-ROCH THEOREM

2.1. Divisors

An element of the free abelian group over the set X will be called a **divisor** on X. A divisor D is of the form

$$D = \sum_{P \in X} m_P P$$

where $m_P \in \mathbb{Z}$ and $m_P = 0$ for all but a finite number of points P of X. The integer

$$\sum_{P \in X} m_P$$

is defined to be the **degree** of the divisor D and is denoted by d(D).

Let U be an open subset of X and f a meromorphic function on U which is not identically zero on any connected component of U. For $P \in U$, define:

$$\nu_P(f) = \begin{cases} \text{order of the zero of f at P, if f is holomorphic at P} \\ -(\text{order of the pole of f at P}), \text{ if f has a pole at P} \end{cases}$$

Now if $f \not\equiv 0$ is a meromorphic function on X, then f defines a divisor

$$(f) = \sum_{P \in X} \nu_P(f) P$$

which is of degree 0 (see Ref. [7], Ch. III, §13, p. 43).

2.2. The line bundle associated to a divisor

Let $D = \sum m_P P$ be a divisor on X. For every point P of X, choose a meromorphic function $g_P \not\equiv 0$ in a connected neighbourhood U_P of P such that for $Q \in U_P$ we have

$$\nu_Q(g_P) = \begin{cases} m_P \text{ if } Q = P \\ 0 \text{ if } Q \neq P \end{cases}$$

Let $\mathbf{L}_D$ denote the sheaf which associates to an open set U of X the space of meromorphic function f on U such that fg_P is holomorphic at P for all $P \in U$. It is easy to check that $\mathbf{L}_D$ is a locally free sheaf of rank 1 and that $\mathbf{L}_D$ depends only on D and not on the choice of $\{g_P\}$. We denote by L_D th line bundle determined by $\mathbf{L}_D$ and call it the line bundle associated to the divisor D.

Remarks

(i) A set of transition functions for the line bundle L_D is given by the non-vanishing holomorphic functions

$$g_{ij} = \frac{g_{P_i}}{g_{P_j}} \text{ on } U_{P_i} \cap U_{P_j},\ P_i, P_j \in X$$

(ii) If D_1 and D_2 are divisors on X, $L_{D_1 + D_2} \simeq L_{D_1} \otimes L_{D_2}$; moreover, L_{D_1} and L_{D_2} are isomorphic as line bundles if and only if $D_1 - D_2$ is the divisor associated to a meromorphic function.

2.3. Euler characteristics of sheaves

Let $\mathscr{F}$ be a sheaf of $\mathbb{C}$-vector spaces over X such that $H^i(X,\mathscr{F})$ are finite dimensional for $i \geqslant 0$ and vanish for all large i. We define the Euler characteristic, $\chi(\mathscr{F})$, of $\mathscr{F}$ by:

$$\chi(\mathscr{F}) = \sum_{i=0}^{\infty} (-1)^i \dim_{\mathbb{C}} H^i(X,\mathscr{F})$$

Proposition 2.3.1. *Let*

$$0 \to \mathscr{F}_1 \to \mathscr{F}_2 \to \mathscr{F}_3 \to 0$$

be an exact sequence of sheaves on X *where* $\mathscr{F}_i$ *satisfy the above condition. We then have*

$$\chi(\mathscr{F}_2) = \chi(\mathscr{F}_1) + \chi(\mathscr{F}_3)$$

We first prove

Lemma 2.3.2. *Let*

$$0 \to W_1 \to \ldots \to W_i \to \ldots \to W_k \to 0$$

be an exact sequence where W_i *are finite-dimensional vector spaces over* $\mathbb{C}$, *the maps being* $\mathbb{C}$*-linear. Then we have*

$$\sum_{i=1}^{k} (-1)^i \dim W_i = 0$$

Proof. The proof is by induction on k, the lemma being evident for $k \leqslant 3$. If W'_{k-1} is the kernel of $W_{k-1} \to W_k$, we have two exact sequences:

$$0 \to W_1 \to \ldots \to W'_{k-1} \to 0$$

$$0 \to W'_{k-1} \to W_{k-1} \to W_k \to 0$$

By induction hypothesis we have

$$\sum_{i=1}^{k-2} (-1)^i \dim W_i + (-1)^{k-1} \dim W'_{k-1} = 0$$

and $\dim W'_{k-1} - \dim W_{k-1} + \dim W_k = 0$ which yield the lemma.

Proof of Proposition 2.3.1. The proposition follows from Lemma 2.3.2 applied to the exact cohomology sequence:

$$0 \to H^0(X,\mathscr{F}_1) \to \ldots \to H^i(X,\mathscr{F}_1) \to H^i(X,\mathscr{F}_2) \to H^i(X,\mathscr{F}_3) \to H^{i+1}(X,\mathscr{F}_1) \to \ldots$$

arising from the exact sequence of sheaves:

$$0 \to \mathscr{F}_1 \to \mathscr{F}_2 \to \mathscr{F}_3 \to 0$$

2.4. Line bundles and divisors

Theorem 2.4.1. *Let* L *be a line bundle on* X. *Then there exists a divisor* D *on* X *such that* L *is isomorphic to the line bundle* L_D *associated to* D.

We first prove

Lemma 2.4.2. *Let* $P \in X$. *Then the line bundle* $L \otimes L_{kP}$ *admits a non-zero (holomorphic) section, for some* $k \in \mathbb{Z}$.

Proof. Let $\mathscr{I}_P = L_{-P}$ be the sheaf of holomorphic functions vanishing at P. Since $L \otimes L_{kP}$ is a locally free sheaf, tensoring the exact sequence

$$0 \to \mathscr{I}_P \to \mathscr{O} \to \mathscr{O}/\mathscr{I}_P \to 0$$

by $L \otimes L_{kP}$ gives rise to the exact sequence:

$$0 \to L \otimes L_{(k-1)P} \to L \otimes L_{kP} \to Q \to 0$$

where $Q = L \otimes L_{kP} \otimes_{\mathscr{O}} \mathscr{O}/\mathscr{I}_P$. Now the support of the sheaf Q is P and the stalk at P is a one-dimensional vector space over $\mathbb{C}$ (in fact the stalk is canonically isomorphic to the fibre at P of the line bundle $L \otimes L_{kP}$). Hence

$$\dim H^i(X,Q) = \begin{cases} 0 \text{ for } i \geqslant 1 \\ 1 \text{ for } i = 0 \end{cases}$$

so that $\chi(Q) = 1$. By Proposition 2.3.1,

$$\chi(L \otimes L_{kP}) = \chi(L \otimes L_{(k-1)P}) + 1$$

which implies that

$$\chi(L \otimes L_{kP}) = \chi(L) + k$$

Now

$$\dim H^0(X, L \otimes L_{kP}) = \dim H^1(X, L \otimes L_{kP}) + \chi(L) + k \geqslant \chi(L) + k$$

If we choose k such that $\chi(L) + k \geqslant 1$, we obtain $\dim H^0(X, L \otimes L_{kP}) \geqslant 1$, which proves the lemma.

Proof of Theorem 2.4.1. By Lemma 2.4.2 there exists a non-zero section s of $L \otimes L_{kP}$ for some k. Let D_1 be the divisor defined by the zeros of s, counted with multiplicity. Then $L \otimes L_{kP}$ is isomorphic to L_{D_1} and hence

$$L \simeq L_{D_1} \otimes L_{-kP} \simeq L_{(D_1 - kP)}$$

2.4.3. Degree of a line bundle

Let L be a line bundle on X. Choose a divisor D with $L \simeq L_D$. We define the degree, d(L), of L to be the degree of the divisor D. This is well defined, for if $L \simeq L_{D'}$, then $D - D'$ is the divisor of a meromorphic function so that $d(D - D') = 0$. (See Remark (ii) in §2.2)

2.5. Riemann-Roch Theorem

The **genus** *of* X *is defined to be* $\dim_{\mathbb{C}} H^1(X, \mathcal{O})$ *and will be denoted by* g.

Theorem 2.5.1 **(Riemann-Roch).** *Let* L *be a line bundle on* X. *Let* L* *denote the dual bundle of* L, *and* K *the canonical line bundle on* X. *We then have:*

(i) $\dim H^0(X, L) - \dim H^1(X, L) = d(L) - g + 1$

(ii) $\dim H^0(X, L) - \dim H^0(X, K \otimes L^*) = d(L) - g + 1$

when g *is the genus of* X *and* d(L) *is the degree of* L.

Proof. We shall prove (i). The duality theorem and (i) would then give (ii). By Theorem 2.4.1 we can assume that $L \simeq L_{D_0}$ for some divisor D_0. Note that for the divisor $D = 0$, $\chi(L_D) = \chi(\mathcal{O}) = 1 - g$, since $H^0(X, \mathcal{O}) \simeq \mathbb{C}$. The theorem follows from

Lemma 2.5.2. $\chi(L_D) - d(D)$ *is independent of the divisor* D.

Proof. It is enough to show that, for $P \in X$,

$$\chi(L_D) - d(D) = \chi(L_{D+P}) - d(D+P)$$

As in the proof of Lemma 2.4.2, we have an exact sequence

$$0 \to L_D \to L_{D+P} \to L_{D+P} \underset{\mathcal{O}}{\otimes} \mathcal{O}/\mathcal{I}_P \to 0$$

yielding

$$\chi(L_{D+P}) = \chi(L_D) + 1$$

Since $d(D+P) = d(D) + 1$, we have

$$\chi(L_{D+P}) - d(D+P) = \chi(L_D) - d(D)$$

2.6. Some consequences of the Riemann-Roch theorem

(1) There exist non-constant meromorphic functions on X. In fact, let D be any divisor with $d(D) \geqslant (g+1)$. Applying the Riemann-Roch theorem, we have $\dim H^0(X,L_D) \geqslant 2$. Since $H^0(X,L_D)$ can be identified with a space of meromorphic functions (see §2.2), it follows that there exist non-constant meromorphic functions on X.

(2) The degree of the canonical line bundle K is (2g-2). Applying the Riemann-Roch theorem for K,we get

$$\dim H^0(X,K) - \dim H^0(X,\mathcal{O}) = d(K) - g + 1$$

while $\dim H^0(X,K) = \dim H^1(X,\mathcal{O}) = g$, by duality. Hence $d(K) = (2g-2)$.

2.7. Vanishing theorem

Proposition. *Let* L *be a line bundle with* $d(L) \geqslant (2g-1)$. *Then* $H^1(X,L) = 0$.

Proof. By duality, $\dim H^1(X,L) = \dim H^0(X,K \otimes L^*)$; but $d(K \otimes L^*) = d(K) + d(L^*) = (2g-2) - d(L)$ < 0. This implies that $H^0(X,K \otimes L^*) = 0$. For, if M is a line bundle with a non-zero section s, then $d(M) \geqslant 0$ as $M \simeq L_D$, where D is the divisor defined by the zeros of s.

3. PROJECTIVE EMBEDDING OF A COMPACT RIEMANN SURFACE

If W is a finite-dimensional vector space over $\mathbb{C}$, we denote by $\mathbb{P}(W)$ the projective space of one dimensional subspaces of W. The space $\mathbb{P}(W)$ has a natural structure of a compact complex manifold (see Ref. [10], Lecture 16).

Definition 3.1. *Let* L *be a line bundle on* X. *We say that* L *is generated by its sections if the evaluation map* $H^0(X,L) \to L(P)$ *is surjective for all* $P \in X$, *where* L(P) *is the fibre of* L *at* P. (This is equivalent to requiring that, given $P \in X$, there exists a holomorphic section s of L with $s(P) \neq 0$.)

Proposition 3.2. *Let* L *be a line bundle on* X *generated by its sections. Then there exists a canonical holomorphic map*

$$\varphi_L : X \to \mathbb{P}(H^0(X,L)^*) = \mathbb{P}_L$$

where $H^0(X,L)^*$ *denotes the dual space of* $H^0(X,L)$.

Proof. Let $P \in X$. By hypothesis, the evaluation map at $P, H^0(X,L) \to L(P)$, is surjective; hence the dual map $L(P)^* \to H^0(X,L)^*$ is injective and we define $\varphi(P) \in \mathbb{P}_L$ to be the image. (The space of sections vanishing at P is of codimension one in $H^0(X,L)$ and $\varphi(P)$ is the subspace of $H^0(X,L)^*$ orthogonal to this space.)

Let $s_0, \ldots, s_N$ be a basis of $H^0(X,L)$ and let s_i be given, with respect to a trivialization of L in a neighbourhood of P, by the function f_i. Then it is easily checked that φ is given locally by

$$z \mapsto (f_0(z), \ldots, f_N(z))$$

in terms of homogeneous co-ordinates with respect to the dual basis $s_0^*, \ldots, s_N^*$. This proves that φ_L is holomorphic.

Definition 3.3. *A line bundle* L *on* X *is said to be* **very ample** *if it is generated by its sections and the map* $\varphi_L : X \to \mathbb{P}_L$ *is an embedding.* (The second condition means that φ_L is injective and that the differential of φ_L is injective at every point of X.)

Theorem 3.4. *Let* L *be a line bundle on* X *with* $d(L) \geqslant 2g + 1$. *Then* L *is very ample.*

Corollary. *Any compact Riemann surface can be embedded in a complex projective space.*

We first prove

Lemma 3.5. *A line bundle* L *with* $d(L) \geqslant 2g$ *is generated by its sections.*

Proof. Let $P \in X$. Tensoring the exact sequence

$$0 \to \mathscr{I}_P \to \mathscr{O} \to \mathscr{O}/\mathscr{I}_P \to 0$$

with **L** gives

$$0 \to \mathbf{L} \otimes_{\mathscr{O}} \mathscr{I}_P \to \mathbf{L} \to \mathbf{L} \otimes_{\mathscr{O}} \mathscr{O}/\mathscr{I}_P \to 0$$

The associated exact cohomology sequence yields the exact sequence

$$H^0(X,L) \xrightarrow{\eta} H^0(X, \mathbf{L} \otimes_{\mathscr{O}} \mathscr{O}/\mathscr{I}_P) \to H^1(X, L \otimes L_{-P})$$

By the vanishing theorem 2.7, we have $H^1(X, L \otimes L_{-P}) = 0$, since $d(L \otimes L_{-P}) = d(L) - 1 \geqslant 2g-1$, so that $H^0(X,L) \xrightarrow{\eta} H^0(X, \mathbf{L} \otimes \mathscr{O}/\mathscr{I}_P)$ is surjective. But $H^0(X, L \otimes \mathscr{O}/\mathscr{I}_P)$ is canonically isomorphic to the fibre L(P) of L at P and the map η is then the evaluation map.

Lemma 3.6. *Let* L *be a line bundle with* $d(L) \geqslant 2g + 1$. *Given* $P, Q \in X$ *with* $P \neq Q$, *there exists a section* s *of* L *with* $s(P) = 0$ *and* $s(Q) \neq 0$.

Proof. Let $\mathscr{I}_{P,Q} = \mathbf{L}_{-P-Q}$ denote the sheaf of holomorphic functions vanishing at P and Q. We then have the exact sequence of sheaves

$$0 \to \mathbf{L} \otimes \mathbf{L}_{-P-Q} \to \mathbf{L} \to \mathbf{L} \otimes_{\mathscr{O}} \mathscr{O}/\mathscr{I}_{P,Q} \to 0$$

Since $d(L \otimes L_{-P-Q}) = d(L) - 2 \geqslant 2g - 1$, we have $H^1(X, L \otimes L_{-P-Q}) = 0$ by 2.7. This shows that

$$H^0(X,L) \to H^0(X, \mathbf{L} \otimes_{\mathscr{O}} \mathscr{O}/\mathscr{I}_{P,Q}) \simeq L(P) \oplus L(Q)$$

is surjective. The lemma follows by interpreting the map $H^0(X,L) \to L(P) \oplus L(Q)$ as the sum of evaluation maps at P and Q.

Proof of Theorem 3.4. Let L be a line bundle with $d(L) \geqslant 2g + 1$. By Lemma 3.5, the map φ_L is defined. By Lemma 3.6, given P,Q with $P \neq Q$, the space of sections vanishing at P is different from the space of sections vanishing at Q. It follows that φ_L is injective.

We shall now show that φ_L is of rank 1 at any $P \in X$. Let $\mathscr{I}_P^2 = \mathbf{L}_{-2P}$ be the sheaf of functions vanishing to the second order at P. From the exact sequence

$$0 \to \mathbf{L} \otimes \mathscr{I}_P^2 \to \mathbf{L} \otimes \mathscr{I}_P \to \mathbf{L} \otimes \mathscr{I}_P/\mathscr{I}_P^2 \to 0$$

we obtain the exact sequence

$$0 \to H^0(X, L \otimes \mathscr{I}_P^2) \to H^0(X, L \otimes \mathscr{I}_P) \to H^0(X, L \otimes \mathscr{I}_P/\mathscr{I}_P^2) \to 0$$

since $H^1(X, L \otimes \mathscr{I}_P^2) = H^1(X, L \otimes L_{-2P}) = 0$. But dim $H^0(X, L \otimes \mathscr{I}_P/\mathscr{I}_P^2) = 1$ while $H^0(X, L \otimes \mathscr{I}_P)$ and $H^0(X, L \otimes \mathscr{I}_P^2)$ are, respectively, the space of sections vanishing at P and of sections vanishing to the second order at P. Hence there exists a basis $s_0, \ldots, s_N$ for $H^0(X,L)$ such that $s_0(P) \neq 0$, $s_i(P) = 0$ for $1 \leqslant i \leqslant N$, and s_1 does not vanish to the second order at P. If f_i is the local expression of s_i, the mapping φ_L is given in a neighbourhood of P by

$$z \mapsto \left(\frac{f_1(z)}{f_0(z)}, \ldots, \frac{f_N(z)}{f_0(z)} \right)$$

Further,

$$\frac{d(f_1/f_0)}{dz}(P) = \frac{d f_1}{dz}(P) / f_0(P) \neq 0$$

Thus the differential of φ_L at P is of rank 1.

Remark. It can be shown that X is a projective variety, i.e. X is the set of zeros in the projective space $\mathbb{P}_L$ of a family of homogeneous polynomials. This is a special case of Chow's theorem (see Ref. [1]).

4. GENUS AND FIRST BETTI NUMBER

Proposition 4.1. *Let* $\mathbb{C}$ *denote the constant sheaf on* X *with stalk* $\mathbb{C}$. *We then have*

$$\dim_{\mathbb{C}} H^1(X, \mathbb{C}) = 2g$$

where g *is the genus of* X.

Proof. Consider the exact sequence of sheaves (of $\mathbb{C}$-modules)

$$0 \to \mathbb{C} \to \mathscr{O} \xrightarrow{d} K \to 0 \qquad (4.2)$$

where d is given by the exterior derivation, $f \mapsto df$. The sequence is exact at **K**, as any holomorphic differential is locally the derivative of a holomorphic function (Cauchy's theorem). Since $H^0(X, \mathbb{C}) \xrightarrow{\sim} H^0(X, \mathscr{O})$ and $H^2(X, \mathscr{O}) = 0$, we then have an exact sequence:

$$0 \to H^0(X,K) \to H^1(X,\mathbb{C}) \to H^1(X,\mathscr{O}) \to H^1(X,K) \to H^2(X,\mathbb{C}) \to 0$$

But $H^2(X,\mathbb{C}) \simeq \mathbb{C}$ by Poincaré duality (see also §5.3) and dim $H^1(X,K) = \dim H^0(X,\mathscr{O}) = 1$; we obtain the exact sequence;

$$0 \to H^0(X,K) \to H^1(X,\mathbb{C}) \to H^1(X,\mathscr{O}) \to 0$$

However, dim $H^0(X,K) = \dim H^1(X,\mathscr{O}) = g$. This proves the proposition.

Remark. The proposition shows that the genus depends only on the topology of X.

5. CHERN CLASS AND DEGREE

5.1. Chern classes

Let $\mathcal{O}^*$ denote the sheaf of non-vanishing holomorphic functions on X. The group $H^1(X,\mathcal{O}^*)$ is canonically isomorphic to the group (under tensor product) of isomorphism classes of holomorphic line bundles on X. If $\ell \in H^1(X,\mathcal{O}^*)$ is represented, with respect to an open covering $\{U_i\}$, by the non-vanishing holomorphic functions g_{ij} in $U_i \cap U_j$, then under this isomorphism ℓ is mapped into the isomorphism class of the line bundle with transition functions g_{ij}.

Consider the exact sequence of sheaves

$$0 \to \mathbb{Z} \to \mathcal{O} \to \mathcal{O}^* \to 0 \tag{5.1.1}$$

where the map $\mathcal{O} \to \mathcal{O}^*$ is given by $f \mapsto e^{2\pi i f}$ $(i = \sqrt{-1})$. We then have the connecting homomorphism

$$b : H^1(X,\mathcal{O}^*) \to H^2(X,\mathbb{Z}) \tag{5.1.2}$$

Definition 5.1.3. *Let* L *be a line bundle on* X. *We define the (first) Chern class* $C_1(L)$ *of* L *by*

$$C_1(L) = -b(\widetilde{L}) \in H^2(X,\mathbb{Z})$$

where $\widetilde{L}$ *denotes the isomorphism class of* L.

5.2. Topological line bundles

The Chern class is defined for any topological line bundle on X. In fact, let $\mathcal{C}$ and $\mathcal{C}^*$ denote, respectively, the sheaf of continuous complex-valued functions and non-vanishing continuous functions. Then the group of isomorphism classes of topological line bundles on X is canonically identified with the group $H^1(X,\mathcal{C}^*)$ and the Chern class is defined by means of the connecting homomorphism

$$H^1(X,\mathcal{C}^*) \to H^2(X,\mathbb{Z})$$

arising from the exact sequence

$$0 \to \mathbb{Z} \to \mathcal{C} \xrightarrow{e^{2\pi i(\ )}} \mathcal{C}^* \to 0 \tag{5.2.1}$$

Comparing the exact cohomology sequences arising from (5.1.1) and (5.2.1), it is clear that the Chern class of a holomorphic line bundle depends only on the underlying structure of topological line bundle.

Proposition 5.2.2

(1) *The homomorphism* $H^1(X,\mathcal{C}^*) \to H^2(X,\mathbb{Z})$ *is an isomorphism. In particular, a line bundle is characterized topologically by its Chern class.*

(2) *Every topological line bundle on a compact Riemann surface can be endowed with the structure of a holomorphic line bundle.*

Proof

(1) Since $\mathcal{C}$ is a fine sheaf, we have $H^1(X,\mathcal{C}) = H^2(X,\mathcal{C}) = 0$. From the cohomology sequence associated to (5.2.1) we see that $H^1(X,\mathcal{C}^*) \to H^2(X,\mathbb{Z})$ is an isomorphism.

(2) From the exact sequence of sheaves (5.1.1) we get an exact sequence:

$$H^1(X, \mathcal{O}^*) \to H^2(X, \mathbb{Z}) \to H^2(X, \mathcal{O})$$

But $H^2(X, \mathcal{O}) = 0$; hence $H^1(X, \mathcal{O}^*) \to H^2(X, \mathbb{Z})$ is surjective. Comparing the exact cohomology sequences arising from (5.1.1) and (5.2.1), we get a commutative diagram:

$$\begin{array}{ccc} H^1(X, \mathcal{O}^*) & \to & H^2(X, \mathbb{Z}) \to 0 \\ \downarrow & & \downarrow \mathrm{id} \\ H^1(X, \mathcal{C}^*) & \to & H^2(X, \mathbb{Z}) \end{array}$$

It now follows from (1) that $H^1(X, \mathcal{O}^*) \to H^1(X, \mathcal{C}^*)$ is surjective.

From now on we shall mean, as before, by a line bundle a holomorphic line bundle.

5.3. Chern class and degree

We now define a canonical homomorphism:

$$I' : H^2(X, \mathbb{C}) \to \mathbb{C}$$

Let $v \in H^2(X, \mathbb{C})$ and let v be represented by a (closed) 2-form ω under the de Rham isomorphism. Define

$$I'(v) = \int_X \omega$$

the integration being with respect to the canonical orientation on X given by the complex structure on X. ($I'(v)$ does not depend on the choice of ω, by Stokes' theorem.) The linear map $I' : H^2(X, \mathbb{C}) \to \mathbb{C}$ is an isomorphism.

The canonical map $H^2(X, \mathbb{Z}) \to H^2(X, \mathbb{C})$ is injective. We denote by I:

$$I : H^2(X, \mathbb{Z}) \to \mathbb{C}$$

the composite of this map and I'. (It follows from the next proposition that I maps $H^2(X, \mathbb{Z})$ onto

Proposition 5.3.1. *Let* D *be a divisor on* X *and* L_D *the associated line bundle on* X. *We then have*

$$I(C_1(L_D)) = d(D)$$

where d(D) *is the degree of* D *and* $C_1(L_D)$ *is the Chern class of* L_D.

Corollary 5.3.2. *A line bundle* L *on* X *is of degree zero if and only if* $C_1(L) = 0$.

We first prove a lemma which gives an alternative description of the Chern class.

Lemma 5.3.3. *Consider the homomorphism* $\mathcal{O}^* \to K$ *given by* $f \mapsto \frac{1}{2\pi i} \cdot \frac{df}{f}$ *and let* $b' : H^1(X, \mathcal{O}^*) \to H^1(X, K)$ *be the induced homomorphism. If* $\ell \in H^1(X, \mathcal{O}^*)$, *we have*

$$b(\ell) = (\eta \circ b')(\ell)$$

where $\eta : H^1(X, K) \to H^2(X, \mathbb{C})$ *is the isomorphism given by (4.2)* (for the definition of b see (5.1.2

Proof. Consider the commutative diagram of exact sequences:

$$\begin{array}{ccccccccc} 0 & \to & \mathbb{Z} & \to & \mathcal{O} & \xrightarrow{e^{2\pi i(\ )}} & \mathcal{O}^* & \to & 0 \\ & & \downarrow & & \downarrow & & \downarrow & & \\ 0 & \to & \mathbb{C} & \to & \mathcal{O} & \xrightarrow{d} & K & \to & 0 \end{array}$$

where $\mathcal{O}^* \to K$ is given by $f \mapsto \frac{1}{2\pi i} \cdot \frac{df}{f}$. This gives rise to the commutative diagram:

$$\begin{array}{ccc} H^1(X, \mathcal{O}^*) & \xrightarrow{b} & H^2(X, \mathbb{Z}) \\ \downarrow{\scriptstyle b'} & & \downarrow \\ H^1(X,K) & \xrightarrow{\eta} & H^2(X, \mathbb{C}) \end{array}$$

which proves the lemma.

Remark 5.3.4. If $\xi \in H^1(X,K)$ is represented (under the Dolbeault isomorphism) by a form ψ of type (1,1) then $\eta(\xi)$ is represented in $H^2(X,\mathbb{C})$ by the same form ψ (under the de Rham isomorphism).

Proof of Proposition 5.3.1. It is sufficient to prove the proposition in the case D = (P) where P is a point of X. Choose a local co-ordinate system z at P in a disc U. Let $U_1 = U$ and $U_2 = X\text{-}P$. Then $\{U_1,U_2\}$ form an open covering of X, and L_P is given by the transition function $f_{12} = z$, $f_{21} = z^{-1}$ in $U_{12} = U_1 \cap U_2$. We wish to find a (1,1) form representing $b'(L_P)$ and then integrate it over X. Let

$$\omega_{12} = \frac{1}{2\pi i} \cdot \frac{df_{12}}{f_{12}} \text{ and } \omega_{21} = -\omega_{12}$$

in U_{12}. We shall find explicitly C^∞ (1,0) forms ω_1 in U_1 and ω_2 in U_2 such that $\omega_2 - \omega_1 = \omega_{12}$ in $U_1 \cap U_2$; then a form ψ (defined over X) representing $\{\omega_{12}\}$ would be given by

$$\psi = \bar\partial \omega_i \text{ in } U_i$$

Note that $\psi = \bar\partial \omega_i = d\omega_i$, as every (2,0) form on X is zero.

To find ω_i, let W and V be discs round P with $\overline{W} \subset V$ and $\overline{V} \subset U$. Let φ be a C^∞ function in U whose support is contained in V and such that $\varphi(Q) = 1$ for all $Q \in W$. Consider φ as a C^∞ function on X by extending it by zero outside U. Set:

$$\omega_1 = -(1-\varphi)\,\omega_{12} \text{ in } U_1 \text{ (defined to be 0 at P)}$$

$$\omega_2 = \varphi\,\omega_{12} \text{ in } U_2 \text{ (defined to be 0 outside V)}$$

Then $\omega_2 - \omega_1 = \omega_{12}$ in $U_1 \cap U_2$. If $\psi = d\omega_1 = d\omega_2$, then

$$\int_X \psi = \int_V \psi \text{ (as } \psi \text{ is 0 outside V)} = \int_V d\omega_1 = \int_{\partial V} \omega_1 = -\int_{\partial V} \omega_{12} = -\frac{1}{2\pi i}\int_{\partial V} \frac{dz}{z} = -1$$

(∂V denotes the boundary of V). Now the proposition follows from Lemma 5.3.3 and Remark 5.3.4 recalling that $C_1(\ell) = -b(\ell)$ for $\ell \in H^1(X,\mathcal{O}^*)$.

6. THE JACOBIAN

Theorem 6.1. *The group of isomorphism classes of (holomorphic) line bundles on* X *of degree zero has a natural structure of a complex torus of complex dimension* g.

This complex torus is called the **Jacobian** of X. We first prove

Lemma 6.2. *The map* $H^1(X,\mathbb{R}) \to H^1(X,\mathcal{O})$, *induced by the natural inclusion of the constant sheaf* $\mathbb{R}$ *in* $\mathcal{O}$, *is an isomorphism of real vector spaces.*

Proof. By Proposition 4.1,

$$\dim_{\mathbb{R}} H^1(X,\mathbb{R}) = \dim_{\mathbb{R}} H^1(X,\mathcal{O})$$

So Lemma 6.2 follows from

Lemma 6.3. *The map* $H^1(X,\mathbb{R}) \to H^1(X,\mathcal{O})$ *is injective.*

Proof. Let $\omega \in H^1(X,\mathbb{R})$ be in the kernel. We can then find an open covering $\{U_i\}$ of X in which ω is represented by a cocycle $r_{ij} \in H^0(U_i \cap U_j, \mathbb{R})$ and holomorphic functions f_i in U_i such that $f_j - f_i = r_{ij}$ in $U_i \cap U_j$. Let $h_j = \operatorname{Im} f_j$, where Im denotes the imaginary part. Since r_{ij} are real-valued, $h_i = h_j$ in $U_i \cap U_j$ and hence define a global harmonic function h on X. By the maximum principle h is constant. It follows that $\operatorname{Rl} f_i$ is constant on each connected component of U_i, so that it defines a section of the sheaf $\mathbb{R}$ over U_i. We have

$$\operatorname{Rl} f_j - \operatorname{Rl} f_i = r_{ij} \text{ in } U_i \cap U_j$$

which shows that r_{ij} is a coboundary, i.e. $\omega = 0$ in $H^1(X, \mathbb{R})$.

Remark. Lemma 6.3. and its proof are valid in any compact complex manifold.

Proof of Theorem 6.1. Starting from the exact sequence

$$0 \to \mathbb{Z} \to \mathcal{O} \to \mathcal{O}^* \to 0$$

we obtain the exact sequence

$$0 \to H^1(X,\mathbb{Z}) \to H^1(X,\mathcal{O}) \to H^1(X,\mathcal{O}^*) \xrightarrow{b} H^2(X,\mathbb{Z})$$

If J denotes the group of isomorphism classes of line bundles of degree 0, we see by Corollary 5.3.2 that $J = \ker b$ so that we have an exact sequence

$$0 \to H^1(X,\mathbb{Z}) \to H^1(X,\mathcal{O}) \to J \to 0$$

Now $H^1(X,\mathbb{Z})$ is a lattice in $H^1(X,\mathbb{R})$ and, by Lemma 6.2, $H^1(X,\mathbb{R}) \to H^1(X,\mathcal{O})$ is an isomorphism of real vector spaces. Thus $H^1(X,\mathbb{Z})$ is a lattice in $H^1(X,\mathcal{O})$ and since $H^1(X,\mathcal{O})$ is a complex vector space, J acquires a natural structure of a complex torus.

Remark. If D_1 and D_2 are divisors on X, we say that D_1 and D_2 are **linearly equivalent** if the divisor $D_1 - D_2$ is the divisor of a meromorphic function $f \not\equiv 0$ on X. In view of Remark (ii) in §2.2, we can rephrase Theorem 6.1 as follows: the group of linear equivalence classes of divisors of degree 0 on X has a natural structure of a complex torus of dimension g.

7. LINE BUNDLES AND CHARACTERS

By $H_1(X,\mathbb{Z})$ and π we denote, respectively, the first homology group of X with integer coefficients and the fundamental group of X. Let $\rho : \pi \to \mathbb{C}^*$ be a homomorphism; since the quotient of π by the commutator subgroup of π is $H_1(X,\mathbb{Z})$, ρ is the same as a homomorphism of $H_1(X,\mathbb{Z})$ into $\mathbb{C}^*$. We denote by L_ρ the line bundle on X associated to ρ. We recall that L_ρ is defined as follows. Let $\widetilde{X} \to X$ be the universal covering of X, considered as a holomorphic principal fibre space with structure group π. The group π acts on $\widetilde{X} \times \mathbb{C}$, the action $\pi \times X \times \mathbb{C} \to \widetilde{X} \times \mathbb{C}$ being given by $(\gamma,x,v) \mapsto (x\gamma,\rho(\gamma)^{-1} v)$ for $\gamma \in \pi$, $x \in X$ and $v \in \mathbb{C}$. The orbit space for this action is then a (holomorphic) line bundle L_ρ over X. If $\{\gamma_{ij}\}$, $\gamma_{ij} \in \pi$, are the transition functions for the principal bundle $\widetilde{X} \to X$ with respect to a suitable open covering U_i of X, then $\rho(\gamma_{ij})$ give a set of transition functions for L_ρ.

Remark 7.1. More generally if $\rho : \pi \to GL(n,\mathbb{C})$ is a homomorphism, we can construct similarly a holomorphic vector bundle E_ρ of rank n on X. We say that E_ρ is associated to the representation ρ of the fundamental group of X.

Remark 7.2. In particular, if $\chi : H_1(X,\mathbb{Z}) \to \mathbb{C}_1^*$ denotes a character of $H_1(X,\mathbb{Z})$, where $\mathbb{C}_1^*$ denotes the group of complex numbers of modulus 1, we have a line bundle L_χ associated to the character χ. If $\mathbb{C}_1^*$ also denotes the constant sheaf with stalk $\mathbb{C}_1^*$, the group $H^1(X,\mathbb{C}_1^*)$ is canonically identified with Hom $(H_1(X,\mathbb{Z}), \mathbb{C}_1^*)$. (This follows, e.g., from the universal coefficient theorem or from A.10 of the Appendix.) The map $H^1(X,\mathbb{C}_1^*) \to H^1(X,\mathcal{O}^*)$ induced by the natural inclusion $\mathbb{C}_1^* \to \mathcal{O}^*$ of sheaves associates then to a character χ, the isomorphism class of the line bundle L_χ.

Theorem 7.3. *A line bundle associated to a character of* $H_1(X,\mathbb{Z})$ *is of degree* 0 *and any line bundle of degree* 0 *is associated to a character. Moreover, two characters of* $H_1(X,\mathbb{Z})$ *are the same if and only if the associated line bundles are isomorphic.*

Remark. The content of the theorem is that the underlying topological torus of the Jacobian J is the character group of $H_1(X,\mathbb{Z})$.

Proof. Consider the commutative diagram of exact sequences of sheaves:

$$\begin{array}{ccccccccc} 0 & \to & \mathbb{Z} & \to & \mathbb{R} & \xrightarrow{e^{2\pi i(\ )}} & \mathbb{C}_1^* & \to & 0 \\ & & \| & & \downarrow & & \downarrow & & \\ 0 & \to & \mathbb{Z} & \to & \mathcal{O} & \longrightarrow & \mathcal{O}^* & \to & 0 \end{array}$$

Since $H^2(X,\mathbb{Z})$ has no torsion, the map $H^2(X,\mathbb{Z}) \to H^2(X,\mathbb{R})$ is injective and we get a commutative diagram of exact sequences:

$$\begin{array}{ccccccccc} 0 & \to & H^1(X,\mathbb{Z}) & \to & H^1(X,\mathbb{R}) & \to & H^1(X,\mathbb{C}_1^*) & \to & 0 \\ & & \| & & \downarrow & & \downarrow & & \\ 0 & \to & H^1(X,\mathbb{Z}) & \to & H^1(X,\mathcal{O}) & \longrightarrow & J & \longrightarrow & 0 \end{array}$$

But $H^1(X,\mathbb{R}) \to H^1(X,\mathcal{O})$ is an isomorphism of real vector spaces (Lemma 6.2). It follows that $H^1(X,\mathbb{C}_1^*) \to J$ is an isomorphism. This proves the theorem in view of Remark 7.2.

8. POINCARE BUNDLE

Theorem 8.1. *Let* J *be the Jacobian of* X. *There exists a (holomorphic) line bundle* $\mathcal{P}$ *on* $J \times X$, *such that for each* $j \in J$ *the restriction of* $\mathcal{P}$ *to* $j \times X$, *considered as a line bundle on* X, *is in the isomorphism class* j.

Such a bundle $\mathcal{P}$ will be called a **Poincaré bundle.**

Remarks: factors of automorphy. Let $B \to M$ be a holomorphic principal bundle with structure group a complex Lie group G, acting on the right. A holomorphic function $f : B \times G \to \mathbb{C}^*$ is called a **factor of automorphy** on $B \times G$ with values in $\mathbb{C}^*$, if for $x \in B$, $g_1, g_2 \in G$, we have

$$f(x,g_1 g_2) = f(x,g_1)\, f(xg_1,g_2) \tag{8.2}$$

Writing $f_g(x) = f(x,g)$, the above condition can be written as

$$f_{g_1 g_2}(x) = f_{g_1}(x)\, f_{g_2}(xg_1)$$

Given a factor of automorphy f, we can construct a line bundle L_f on M as follows. The map

$$B \times \mathbb{C} \times G \to B \times \mathbb{C}$$

given by

$$(x,v,g) \mapsto (xg,\, f(x,g)^{-1} v),\ x \in B,\ g \in G,\ v \in \mathbb{C}$$

is an action of G on $B \times \mathbb{C}$ in view of the condition (8.2) and the quotient space L_f is a line bundle on M.

For more details on the factors of automorphy, see the Appendix.

Proof of Theorem 8.1. We first show that $H^1(X,\mathbb{C}^*)$ can be considered as a holomorphic principal bundle over J with structure group $H^0(X,K)$. The commutative diagram of exact sequences of sheav

$$\begin{array}{ccccccccc}
 & & 0 & & 0 & & & & \\
 & & \uparrow & & \uparrow & & & & \\
0 & \to & \mathbb{C}^* & \longrightarrow & \mathcal{O}^* & \xrightarrow{df/2\pi i f} & K & \to & 0 \\
 & & \uparrow{\scriptstyle e^{2\pi i(\ )}} & & \uparrow{\scriptstyle e^{2\pi i(\ )}} & & \| & & \\
0 & \to & \mathbb{C} & \longrightarrow & \mathcal{O} & \xrightarrow{d} & K & \to & 0 \\
 & & \uparrow & & \uparrow & & & & \\
 & & \mathbb{Z} & \xrightarrow{\sim} & \mathbb{Z} & & & & \\
 & & \uparrow & & \uparrow & & & & \\
 & & 0 & & 0 & & & &
\end{array}$$

gives rise to the following commutative diagram of exact sequences:

$$\begin{array}{ccccccccc}
 & & & & 0 & & 0 & & \\
 & & & & \uparrow & & \uparrow & & \\
0 & \to & H^0(X,K) & \to & H^1(X,\mathbb{C}^*) & \to & J & \to & 0 \\
 & & \| & & \uparrow & & \uparrow & & \\
0 & \to & H^0(X,K) & \to & H^1(X,\mathbb{C}) & \to & H^1(X,\mathcal{O}) & \to & 0 \\
 & & & & \uparrow & & \uparrow & & \\
 & & & & H^1(X,\mathbb{Z}) & \xrightarrow{\sim} & H^1(X,\mathbb{Z}) & & \\
 & & & & \uparrow & & \uparrow & & \\
 & & & & 0 & & 0 & &
\end{array}$$

Introduce on $H^1(X,\mathbb{C}^*)$ the complex structure induced by the natural complex structure on the quotient $H^1(X,\mathbb{C})/H^1(X,\mathbb{Z})$. Since $H^1(X,\mathbb{C}) \to H^1(X,\mathbb{C}^*)$ and $H^1(X,\mathcal{O}) \to J$ are local isomorphisms, we see that $H^1(X,\mathbb{C}^*) \to J$ is a principal bundle with structure group $H^0(X,K)$.

Let $\widetilde{X}$ be the universal covering of X. Put $R = H^1(X,\mathbb{C}^*)$. Then $R \times \widetilde{X} \to J \times X$ is a principal fibre bundle with structure group $G = G_0 \times \pi$, where $G_0 = H^0(X,K)$ and π is the fundamental group of X. We shall construct a Poincaré bundle on $J \times X$ by means of a factor of automorphy on $(G_0 \times \pi) \times (R \times X)$ with values in $\mathbb{C}^*$.

We identify $H^1(X,\mathbb{C}^*)$ with $\mathrm{Hom}(\pi,\mathbb{C}^*)$. If $\omega \in H^0(X,K)$, denote by χ_ω the corresponding element in $\mathrm{Hom}(\pi,\mathbb{C}^*)$ given by the map $H^0(X,K) \to H^1(X,\mathbb{C}^*)$. Let $\widetilde{\omega}$ denote the pullback of ω to $\widetilde{X}$. Since $\widetilde{X}$ is simply connected, we can find a holomorphic function $\varphi_\omega : \widetilde{X} \to \mathbb{C}^*$ such that $\varphi_\omega^{-1}\, d\varphi_\omega = -2\pi i\, \widetilde{\omega}$ and $\varphi_\omega(x_0) = 1$, where x_0 is a (fixed) point of $\widetilde{X}$. Note that φ_ω is uniquely determined by these conditions and, in fact,

$$\varphi_\omega(x) = \exp \int_{x_0}^{x} (-2\pi i\widetilde{\omega}),\ x \in \widetilde{X} \tag{8.3}$$

This shows that $\varphi_\omega(x) = \varphi(\omega,x)$ is holomorphic in (ω,x) and that

$$\varphi_\omega(x\gamma) = \chi_\omega(\gamma)\,\varphi_\omega(x) \text{ for } \gamma \in \pi \tag{8.4}$$

We now define the factor of automorphy. Set

$$f_{\omega,\gamma}(\rho,x) = \chi_\omega(\gamma)\,\rho(\gamma)\,\varphi_\omega(x)$$

for $\rho \in R$, $x \in X$, $\omega \in G_0$ and $\gamma \in \pi$. We have

$$\begin{aligned}
f_{\omega_1+\omega_2,\gamma_1,\gamma_2}(\rho,x) &= \chi_{\omega_1+\omega_2}(\gamma_1\gamma_2)\,\rho(\gamma_1\gamma_2)\,\varphi_{\omega_1+\omega_2}(x)\\
&= \chi_{\omega_1}(\gamma_1\gamma_2)\,\chi_{\omega_2}(\gamma_1\gamma_2)\,\rho(\gamma_1\gamma_2)\,\varphi_{\omega_1}(x)\,\varphi_{\omega_2}(x)\\
&= \chi_{\omega_1}(\gamma_1)\,\chi_{\omega_1}(\gamma_2)\,\chi_{\omega_2}(\gamma_1)\,\chi_{\omega_2}(\gamma_2)\,\rho(\gamma_1)\,\rho(\gamma_2)\,\varphi_{\omega_1}(x)\,\varphi_{\omega_2}(x)
\end{aligned}$$

On the other hand, we have

$$f_{\omega_1,\gamma_1}(\rho,x) = \chi_{\omega_1}(\gamma_1)\,\rho(\gamma_1)\,\varphi_{\omega_1}(x)$$

and

$$f_{\omega_2,\gamma_2}((\rho,x)(\omega_1,\gamma_1)) = f_{\omega_2,\gamma_2}(\chi_{\omega_1}\rho, x\gamma_1)$$

$$= \chi_{\omega_2}(\gamma_2)\,(\chi_{\omega_1}\rho)(\gamma_2)\,\varphi_{\omega_2}(x\gamma_1)$$

$$= \chi_{\omega_2}(\gamma_2)\,\chi_{\omega_1}(\gamma_2)\,\rho(\gamma_2)\,\chi_{\omega_2}(\gamma_1)\,\varphi_{\omega_2}(x)$$

using (8.4). Hence

$$f_{\omega_1+\omega_2,\gamma_1\gamma_2}(\rho,x) = f_{\omega_1,\gamma_1}(\rho,x)\, f_{\omega_2,\gamma_2}((\rho,x)(\omega_1,\gamma_1))$$

which shows that f is a factor of automorphy.

The factor of automorphy f defines a line bundle $\mathscr{P}$ on $R \times \tilde{X}/G_0 \times \pi = J \times X$. We claim that $\mathscr{P}$ satisfies the requirement in Theorem 8.1. If $j \in J$ and ρ in $H^1(X,\mathbb{C}^*)$ is mapped into j we shall show that the restriction of $\mathscr{P}$ to $j \times X$ is isomorphic to the line bundle associated to the homomorphism $\rho : \pi \to \mathbb{C}^*$. We have the commutative diagram:

$$\begin{array}{ccc} \tilde{X} & \xrightarrow{e_\rho} & R \times \tilde{X} \\ \downarrow & & \downarrow \\ X & \xrightarrow{e_j} & J \times X \end{array}$$

where $e_\rho(x) = (\rho,x)$ for $x \in X$ and $e_j(y) = (j,y)$, $y \in X$. The map e_ρ clearly satisfies the condition

$$e_\rho(x\gamma) = e_\rho(x)\,(0,\gamma),\ (0,\gamma) \in G_0 \times \pi$$

It follows that the inverse image $e_j^*(\mathscr{P})$ of $\mathscr{P}$ by the map e_j is given by the factor of automorphy $f_{0,\gamma}(\rho,x) = \rho(\gamma)$ on $\pi \times \tilde{X}$, i.e. $e_j^*(\mathscr{P}) \approx L_\rho$ (see also A.9 of the Appendix). This proves the theorem.

Remark. The idea of the proof of Theorem 8.1 is the following. Let $R = H^1(X,\mathbb{C}^*) = \mathrm{Hom}\,(\pi,\mathbb{C}^*)$. It is easy to construct a line bundle $\mathscr{L}$ on $R \times X$ such that $\mathscr{L}|\rho \times X \approx L_\rho$ for $\rho \in R$, where L_ρ is the line bundle associated to ρ. In fact $\mathscr{L}$ is the quotient space for the action of π on $R \times \tilde{X} \times \mathbb{C}$ given by

$$(\rho,x,v,\gamma) \mapsto (\rho, x\gamma, \rho(\gamma)^{-1} v)$$

$\rho \in R$, $x \in \tilde{X}$, $v \in \mathbb{C}$ and $\gamma \in \pi$. Note that if $\rho_1, \rho_2 \in \mathrm{Hom}\,(\pi,\mathbb{C}^*)$, the bundles L_{ρ_1} and L_{ρ_2} are isomorphic if there exists a holomorphic function $\varphi : \tilde{X} \to \mathbb{C}^*$ satisfying

$$\varphi(x\gamma) = \rho_1(\gamma)\,\varphi(x)\,\rho_2(\gamma)^{-1},\ x \in \tilde{X},\ \gamma \in \pi$$

If ρ_1 and ρ_2 differ by an element $\omega \in H^0(X,K)$, the exponential of the abelian integral, φ_ω in (8.3), associated to ω gives an isomorphism between L_{ρ_1} and L_{ρ_2} (see (8.4)). Moreover, the abelian integral depend holomorphically on ω if suitably normalized. These isomorphisms can then be used to "descend" the line bundle $\mathscr{L}$ into a line bundle $\mathscr{P}$ on $J \times X$.

9. THE PICARD MANIFOLD OF A COMPACT KÄHLER MANIFOLD

The results of §7 and §8 carry over with little change to the case of a compact connected Kähler manifold M [13].

(1) The set of isomorphism classes of holomorphic line bundles on M with zero Chern class has a natural structure of a complex torus, $Pic_0(M)$, called the Picard manifold of M. We have $\dim_{\mathbb{C}} Pic_0(M) = \dim_{\mathbb{C}} H^1(M,\mathcal{O})$. The proof of Theorem 6.1 carries over once one knows that $H^1(M,\mathbb{R}) \to H^1(M,\mathcal{O})$ is an isomorphism over $\mathbb{R}$; this isomorphism results from Hodge theory of Kähler manifolds [11,13].

(2) The underlying topological torus of $Pic_0(M)$ is the character group of the free abelian group $\{H_1(M,\mathbb{Z})/\text{Torsion subgroup of } H_1(M,\mathbb{Z})\}$. By slightly modifying the proof of Theorem 8.1 we can construct a Poincaré bundle on $Pic_0(M) \times M$ (e.g. one has to work with the sheaf Ω^1_c of closed holomorphic 1-forms on M instead of **K**).

10. VECTOR BUNDLES ON A COMPACT RIEMANN SURFACE

Let V be a vector bundle of rank n on X. The line bundle $\overset{n}{\wedge} V$, the nth exterior power of V, will be denoted by det V. If g_{ij} is a set of transition functions for V, det g_{ij} form a set of transition functions for det V, where det $g_{ij}(x)$ denotes the determinant of the matrix $g_{ij}(x)$.

We define the degree of V, d(V), by

$$d(V) = d(\det V)$$

Remark 10.1

(a) Let V_1 and V_2 be vector bundles on X and $f: V_1 \to V_2$ be a (holomorphic) homomorphism. Let $f(P): V_1(P) \to V_2(P)$ denote the induced map on the fibres of V_1 and V_2 at $P \in X$. Then if $P_0 \in X$, there exists a neighbourhood U of P_0 such that

$$\dim \ker f(P) \leqslant \dim \ker f(P_0), \text{ for } P \in U$$

(b) If dim ker f(P) is independent of P in X, we say that f is of constant rank. If f is of constant rank, then ker f (kernel of f) and Im f (Image of f) form subbundles of V_1 and V_2 respectively (for proofs see Ref. [5], Ch.III).

Lemma 10.2. *Let V_1 be a subbundle of V and let V_2 be the quotient bundle. We have*

$$d(V) = d(V_1) + d(V_2)$$

Proof. We can assume that the transition functions $\{g_{ij}\}$ of V are of the form

$$g_{ij} = \begin{pmatrix} h_{ij} & * \\ 0 & k_{ij} \end{pmatrix}$$

where h_{ij} and k_{ij} are transition functions for V_1 and V_2. Hence $\det V \cong \det V_1 \otimes \det V_2$, which gives $d(V) = d(V_1) + d(V_2)$.

Lemma 10.3. *Let $P \in X$. Then the vector bundle $V \otimes L_{kP}$ admits a non-zero section for some $k \in \mathbb{Z}$.*

Proof. The proof is similar to that of Lemma 2.4.2. We have an exact sequence

$$0 \to V \otimes L_{(k-1)P} \to V \otimes L_{kP} \to Q \to 0$$

where Q is a sheaf with support at P and whose stalk at P is an n-dimensional vector space (canonically isomorphic to the fibre of $V \otimes L_{kP}$ at P). Hence

$$\chi(V \otimes L_{kP}) = \chi(V \otimes L_{(k-1)P}) + n$$

which implies that

$$\chi(V \otimes L_{kP}) = \chi(L) + kn$$

Choosing k large, we obtain

$$\dim H^0(X, V \otimes L_{kP}) \geqslant 1$$

10.4. The projective bundle associated to a vector bundle

Let V be a vector bundle on X. The group $\mathbb{C}^*$ acts on $V - \sigma_0(X)$ by multiplication, where σ_0 is the zero section of V, and the quotient is a locally trivial holomorphic fibre bundle, $\mathbb{P}(V)$, over X of fibre type $\mathbb{P}(\mathbb{C}^n)$. The fibre of $\mathbb{P}(V)$ at $P \in X$ is identified canonically with the projective space of one-dimensional subspaces of the fibre of V at P. A line subbundle of V defines clearly a (holomorphic) section of $\mathbb{P}(V)$ over X, and conversely a section of $\mathbb{P}(V)$ over X defines a line subbundle of V.

Theorem 10.5. *A vector bundle (of rank $\geqslant 1$) on a compact Riemann surface admits a filtration by subbundles such that the successive quotients are line bundles. That is, if* V *is a vector bundle of rank* $n \geqslant 1$, *there exist subbundles* $V_1, \ldots, V_{n-1}$ *of* V *with rank* $V_i = i$ *and* $V_1 \subset V_2 \subset \cdots \subset V_{n-1} \subset$

Proof. It is sufficient to show that V has a line subbundle L, for then we can prove the theorem by induction on the dimension of V and using the induction hypothesis for V/L. In turn, it suffices to show that for some line bundle L' on X, $V \otimes L'$ has a line subbundle; for if L'' is a subbundle of $V \otimes L'$, the bundle $(L')^* \otimes L''$ would be a subbundle of V. Thus we may assume, in view of Lemma 10.3, that V has a non-zero section s and prove that V has a line subbundle.

If $s(P) \neq 0$ for all $P \in X$, s clearly defines a section of the projective bundle $\mathbb{P}(V)$ and hence V has a line subbundle (see §10.4). Otherwise let S denote the finite set of points P with $s(P) = 0$. Then s defines a section, $\tilde{s}$, of $\mathbb{P}(V)$ in the complement of S. We shall show that $\tilde{s}$ extends to a section of $\mathbb{P}(V)$ over X, which will complete the proof of the theorem.

Let $P \in S$. We may suppose that in a connected co-ordinate neighbourhood U of P, the section s is given by

$$s = (f_1, \ldots, f_m, 0, \ldots, 0)$$

where f_i are holomorphic functions in U, $f_i \not\equiv 0$ and $f_i(P) = 0$ for $1 \leqslant i \leqslant m$. If z is a local co-ordinate system in U with $z(P) = 0$, write $f_i = z^{k_1} g_i$, $1 \leqslant i \leqslant m$, where g_i are holomorphic and non-vanishing in a neighbourhood U' of P with $U' \subset U$. Let

$$k = \min_{1 \leqslant i \leqslant m} k_i$$

be the minimum of k_i. We may assume that $k = k_1$. Consider

$$s' = (f_1/z^k, \ldots, f_m/z^k, 0, \ldots, 0)$$

Noting that $(f_1/z^k)(Q) = (f_1/z^{k_1})(Q) = g_1(Q) \neq 0$, for $Q \in U_1$, we see that s′ defines a section $\widetilde{s}'$ of $\mathbb{P}(V)$ in U′. Since the function $1/z^k$ does not vanish in U′– P, we have $\widetilde{s}' = \widetilde{s}$ in U′ – P. It follows that $\widetilde{s}$ extends to a section of $\mathbb{P}(V)$ over X.

Proposition 10.6. *Let* V *be a vector bundle on* X. *There exists a real number* C_0, *depending on* V, *such that for all subbundles* W *of* V *we have* $d(W) \leqslant C_0$.

Proof. Note that if W is a subbundle of rank $k \geqslant 2$ of V, $\overset{k}{\wedge} W$ is a line subbundle of $\overset{k}{\wedge} V$ and $d(\overset{k}{\wedge} W) = d(W)$. Hence it is sufficient to prove that for a vector bundle V the degree of line subbundles of V is bounded above.

Let L be a line subbundle of V. Let $0 \subset V_1 \subset \ldots \subset V_{n-1} \subset V_n = V$ be a filtration on V, where V_i are subbundles of V and $V_i/V_{i-1} = L_i$ are line bundles for $1 \leqslant i \leqslant n$ (Theorem 10.5). Now it is clear that the natural map $L \to L_i$ is non-zero for some i. This shows that $d(L) \leqslant d(L_i)$; for $L^* \otimes L_i$ has a non-zero section so that $d(L^* \otimes L_i) \geqslant 0$. Thus

$$d(L) \leqslant \sup_i d(L_i)$$

11. THE RIEMANN-ROCH THEOREM FOR VECTOR BUNDLES

Theorem 11.1. *Let* V *be a vector bundle of rank* n *on* X. *Then*

(1) $\dim H^0(X,V) - \dim H^1(X,V) = d(V) + n(1-g)$

(2) $\dim H^0(X,V) - \dim H^0(X,K \otimes V^*) = d(V) + n(1-g)$

where V^* *is the dual bundle of* V, d(V) *is the degree of* V *and* g *is the genus of* X.

Proof. It is sufficient to prove (1), in view of the duality theorem. The theorem has been proved already for n = 1 (Theorem 2.5.1). Assume that the theorem has already been proved for vector bundles of rank n–1. Let L be a line subbundle of V, which exists by Theorem 10.5. From the exact sequence

$$0 \to L \to V \to V/L \to 0$$

we have, by Proposition 2.3.1,

$$\begin{aligned}\chi(V) &= \chi(L) + \chi(V/L)\\ &= d(L) + (1-g) + d(V/L) + (n-1)(1-g)\\ &\qquad \text{(by induction hypothesis)}\\ &= d(V) + n(1-g)\\ &\qquad \text{(by Lemma 10.2).}\end{aligned}$$

12. INDECOMPOSABLE BUNDLES AND THE KRULL-REMAK-SCHMIDT THEOREM

Definition 12.1. *A vector bundle* V *on* X *is said to be indecomposable if it cannot be written as a direct sum of proper subbundles of* V.

Lemma 12.2. *Let* W *be a vector bundle on* X *and* p_1, p_2 *be endomorphisms of* W *such that* $p_i^2 = p_i (i = 1,2)$ *and* $p_1 + p_2 = Id_W$ *(identity map of* W*). Then* Im p_1 *(image of* p_1*) and* Im p_2 *are subbundles of* W *and* W = Im p_1 + Im p_2.

Proof. If $P \in X$ and for $i = 1,2$, $p_i(P) : V(P) \to V(P)$ is the induced map on the fibre at P, we have $V(P) = \text{Im } p_1(P) \oplus \text{Im } p_2(P)$. By Remark 10.1(a) it follows that p_1 and p_2 are of constant rank. By Remark 10.1(b), Im p_i are subbundles and $W = \text{Im } p_1 + \text{Im } p_2$.

Theorem 12.3. *Let* V *be a vector bundle on* X. *Then*
(1) V *can be written as a finite direct sum of indecomposable subbundles of* V;
(2) *If*

$$V = \bigoplus_{i=1}^{k} W_i = \bigoplus_{j=1}^{m} W'_j$$

where W_i *and* W'_j *are indecomposable subbundles* ($\neq 0$) *of* V, *we have* $k = m$ *and there exists a permutation* σ *of* $[1, ..., k]$ *and an automorphism* T *of* V *such that* $TW_i = W'_{\sigma(i)}$, *for* $1 \leqslant i \leqslant k$.

For the proof we need

Theorem 12.4 (**Krull-Remak-Schmidt**). *Let* A *be a ring and* M *a module over* A *of finite length (i.e.* M *satisfies ascending and descending chain conditions for submodules). Then* M *is a finite direct sum of indecomposable submodules. Moreover, if*

$$M = \bigoplus_{i=1}^{k} M_i = \bigoplus_{j=1}^{m} M'_j$$

are two decompositions of M *into indecomposable submodules* $\neq 0$, *then* $k = m$ *and there exists a permutation* σ *of* $[1, ..., k]$ *and an automorphism* T_0 *of* M *such that* $T_0 M_i = M'_{\sigma(i)}$, *for* $1 \leqslant i \leqslant k$.

For a proof see Ref. [3], Ch.8, §2.2, p.23.

Remark 12.5. We shall prove Theorem 12.3 by applying Theorem 12.4 in the following situation. Let A denote the ring of endomorphisms of the vector bundle V. We take M = A, considered as a right module over A. Since $A = H^0(X, V \otimes V^*)$, we see that A is a finite-dimensional algebra over $\mathbb{C}$ and is hence of finite length over A.

Lemma 12.6. *Suppose that* $V = W \oplus W'$ *where* W ($\neq 0$) *is indecomposable. Let* $p : V \to W$ *be the corresponding projection. Then the right ideal generated by* p *in* A *is indecomposable, as a right submodule of* A (A = *the ring of endomorphisms of* V).

Proof. Let (p) be the right ideal generated by p. Suppose that (p) is decomposable and $(p) = C_1 \oplus C_2$, $C_i \neq 0$ being right ideals. Write $p = r_1 + r_2$ with $r_i \in C_i$. We claim that

$$r_1 r_2 = r_2 r_1 = 0 \text{ and } r_i^2 = r_i \qquad (12.7)$$

To prove this, note that $r_1 r_2 \in C_1$. But $r_1 r_2$ also belongs to C_2; for if $r_2 = p\,a$, for some $a \in A$, we have

$$r_1 r_2 = pr_2 - r_2^2 = p^2 a - r_2^2 = pa - r_2^2 = r_2 - r_2^2 \in C_2$$

Thus $r_1 r_2 \in C_1 \cap C_2$ and hence $r_1 r_2 = 0$. Similarly $r_2 r_1 = 0$. Since $(r_1 + r_2)^2 = r_1 + r_2$, it follows that $r_i^2 = r_i$.

We have, from Eq. (12.7), that $pr_i = r_i$. Hence r_i (i = 1,2) maps W into W and $\text{Id}_W = r_1|W + r_2|W$. By Lemma 12.2, W must then be decomposable.

Proof of Theorem 12.3. Note that the first part of the theorem is clear by induction on the rank of V. For, a line bundle is indecomposable and if a bundle is decomposable it is the direct sum of subbundles of strictly lower rank.

We use the notation of Remark 12.5. Let p_i and p_j' denote, respectively, the projection onto W_i and W_j'; (p_i) and (p_j') denote, respectively, the right ideal generated by p_i and p_j' in A. By Lemma 12.6

$$A = \bigoplus_{i=1}^{k} (p_i) = \bigoplus_{j=1}^{m} (p_j')$$

give two decompositions of A into indecomposable submodules. By Theorem 12.4, we have k = m and there exists a permutation σ of [1, ..., n] and an automorphism T_0 of A (considered as a right module over itself) with $T_0((p_i)) = (p'_{\sigma(i)})$. But T_0 is given by multiplication on the left by an element T (= $T_0(Id_V)$) which is invertible in A. Thus T is an automorphism of V mapping W_i onto $W'_{\sigma(i)}$ as $Tp_i = p'_{\sigma(i)}a$ for some $a \in A$. This proves (2).

Proposition 12.8. *Let* V *be a vector bundle on* X. *Then* V *is indecomposable if and only if every endomorphism of* V *is of the form* $\lambda\, Id_V + N$, *where* $\lambda \in \mathbb{C}$ *and* N *is nilpotent.* (Id_V *is the identity endomorphism* of V.)

Proof. Suppose $V = V_1 \oplus V_2$, $V_i \neq 0$. Let $\lambda \in \mathbb{C}$, $\lambda \neq 0$, and T be the endomorphism of V such that $T|V_1 = \lambda\, Id_V$ and $TV_2 = 0$. Suppose that T is of the form $\nu\, Id_V + N$ with $\nu \in \mathbb{C}$ and N nilpotent. Then we would have $N = -\nu\, Id_{V_2}$ on V_2, and as N is nilpotent, $\nu = 0$. But then $T|V_1 = N|V_1 = \lambda\, Id_{V_1}$, which implies that $\lambda = 0$, a contradiction.

Let V be a vector bundle of rank n and T an endomorphism of V. For $x \in X$ let T_x be the endomorphism of the fibre V_x induced by T and

$$P_x(t) = \sum_{0 \leqslant i \leqslant n} a_i(x)\, t^i$$

be the characteristic polynomial of T_x. Since $a_i(x)$ are holomorphic functions on X, $a_i(x)$ are constant equal to, say, a_i. Let

$$P(t) = \sum_{0 \leqslant i \leqslant n} a_i\, t^i = \prod_{j=1}^{k} (t - \lambda_j)^{n_j}$$

with $\lambda_j \in \mathbb{C}$ distinct. Let $V_{j,x}$ be the kernel of $(T_x - \lambda_j)^{n_j}$, i.e. the generalized eigenspace of T_x corresponding to λ_j. Then, as is well known, dim $V_{j,x} = n_j$, a constant. Hence by Remark 10.1(b), $V_{j,x}$ build a subbundle V_j of V and $V = \oplus V_j$. So if V is indecomposable $P(t) = (t - \lambda)^n$, which means that $(T - \lambda\, Id_V)$ is nilpotent.

Remark. Theorem 12.3 and Proposition 12.8 (and their proofs) are valid for holomorphic vector bundles on any compact connected complex manifold.

13. WEIL'S THEOREM; UNITARY BUNDLES

In this section we state without proofs two theorems on vector bundles on compact Riemann surfaces.

Theorem (A. Weil). *A vector bundle on a compact Riemann surface X is associated to a representation of the fundamental group of X (see §7.1) if and only if each of its indecomposable components is of degree zero.*

For a proof see Ref. [2], §7, and Ref. [13].

We next state a generalization of Theorem 7.3 for vector bundles of higher rank.

Definition. *A vector bundle V of degree zero is said to be* **stable** *if for every proper subbundle W of V we have* $d(W) < 0$.

Let ρ be an n-dimensional unitary representation of $\pi_1(X)$, i.e. ρ is a homomorphism of $\pi_1(X)$ into $U(n)$, the group of $n \times n$ unitary matrices. We then have a holomorphic vector bundle E_ρ of rank n associated to ρ (§7.1). The bundle E_ρ is said to be associated to the unitary representation ρ and is called a unitary bundle.

Let us recall that two n-dimensional unitary representations ρ_1 and ρ_2 are said to be equivalent if there exists $T \in U(n)$ such that $\rho_1(\gamma) = T \rho_2(\gamma) T^{-1}, \forall \gamma \in \pi_1(X)$.

We then have

Theorem. *Let $g \geqslant 2$. A vector bundle on X is associated to a* **unitary** *representation of the fundamental group of X if and only if each of its indecomposable components is* **stable** *and of degree 0. Moreover, two vector bundles associated to unitary representations are isomorphic (as holomorphic bundles) if and only if the representations are equivalent.*

For a proof see Refs [8, 9].

APPENDIX

FACTORS OF AUTOMORPHY

A.1. Let G and G' be (complex Lie) groups and M a (complex) manifold. Let $p : P \rightarrow M$ and $p' : P' \rightarrow M$, respectively, be principal bundles with structure group G and G', the groups acting as usual on the right. Suppose that the pullback $p^*(P')$ is trivial on P. Let then $\sigma : P \rightarrow p^*(P')$ be a section and set $i_\sigma = \sigma \circ \tilde{p}$, where $\tilde{p} : p^*(P') \rightarrow P'$ is the natural projection:

$$
\begin{array}{ccc}
p^*(P') & \xrightarrow{\tilde{p}} & P' \\
\sigma \Big\uparrow\Big\downarrow \quad {\large\nearrow}^{i_\sigma} & & \Big\downarrow p' \\
P & \xrightarrow[p]{} & M
\end{array}
$$

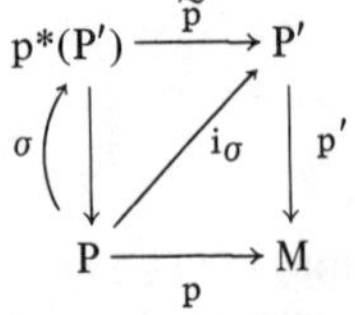

For $g \in G$ and $x \in P$ the points $i_\sigma(xg)$ and $i_\sigma(x)$ lie on the same fibre of the map $p' : P' \rightarrow M$ and hence there exists a unique element $f(x,g) \in G'$ such that

$$i_\sigma(xg) = i_\sigma(x) f(x,g)$$

We have for $x \in P$ and $g_1, g_2 \in G$,

$$i_\sigma(x)\, f(x,g_1 g_2) = i_\sigma(xg_1 g_2) = i_\sigma(xg_1)\, f(xg_1,g_2)$$

$$= i_\sigma(x)\, f(x,g_1)\, f(xg_1, g_2)$$

so that

$$f(x, g_1 g_2) = f(x, g_1)\, f(xg_1, g_2)$$

If σ' is another section of $p^*(P')$ over P we have $\sigma'(x) = \sigma(x)\, h(x)$, $x \in P$ and $h(x) \in G'$. Let $i_{\sigma'}(xg) = i_{\sigma'}(x)\, f'(x,g)$. We then have $i_{\sigma'}(xg) = i_{\sigma'}(x)\, f'(x,g) = i_\sigma(x)\, h(x)\, f'(x,g)$ and

$$i_{\sigma'}(xg) = i_\sigma(xg)\, h(xg) = i_\sigma(x)\, f(x,g)\, h(xg)$$

Hence

$$h(x)\, f'(x,g) = f(x,g)\, h(xg)$$

which may be written as

$$f'(x,g) = h(x)^{-1}\, f(x,g)\, h(xg)$$

This motivates

Definition A.2. *Let* G *and* G′ *be (complex Lie) groups and* $P \to M$ *be a principal* G-*bundle. A* **factor of automorphy** *on* $P \times G$ *with values in* G′ *is a (holomorphic) function* $f : P \times G \to G'$ *satisfying*

$$f(x,g_1 g_2) = f(x,g_1)\, f(xg_1,g_2) \qquad (\mathscr{A})$$

for $x \in P$ *and* $g_1, g_2 \in G$. *Two factors of automorphy* $f, f' : P \times G \to G'$ *are said to be* **equivalent** *if there exists a (holomorphic) function* $h : P \to G'$ *satisfying*

$$f'(x,g) = h(x)^{-1}\, f(x,g)\, h(xg)$$

for $x \in P$, $g \in G$.

Remark A.3. If we write $f_g(x) = f(g,x)$ the condition $(\mathscr{A})$ becomes

$$f_{g_1 g_2}(x) = f_{g_1}(x)\, f_{g_2}(xg_1)$$

Thus f may be viewed as a 1-cocycle of G with values in the group of (holomorphic) functions on P with values in G′. Equivalence of two factors of automorphy means that the corresponding cocycles are cohomologous.

Remark A.4. If $\rho : G \to G'$ is a homomorphism, the function $f(x,g) = \rho(g)$ defines a factor of automorphy.

Remark A.5. Suppose that G′ is **discrete** and P is connected. Then all the factors of automorphy are of the form $f(x,g) = \rho(g)$ where $\rho : G \to G'$ is a (holomorphic) homomorphism; moreover, two factors of automorphy ρ and ρ' are equivalent if and only if there exists $T \in G'$ with $\rho'(g) = T^{-1} \rho(g)T$ for all $g \in G$. These results follow if we remark that, for $g \in G$, the functions $x \mapsto f(x,g)$ and $x \mapsto h(x)$ are constant.

A.6. Bundle associated to a factor of automorphy

Let $p : P \to M$ be a principal G-bundle and G′ a group. Suppose we are given a factor of automorphy $f : P \times G \to G'$. We can then construct a (holomorphic) principal G′-bundle E_f on M whose pullback on P has a canonical trivialization such that the factor of automorphy associated to this trivialization as in (A.1) is the given f.

In fact consider the map

$$(P \times G') \times G \to P \times G'$$

$$(x, g', g) \mapsto (xg, f(x,g)^{-1} g')$$

for $x \in P$, $g \in G$, $g' \in G'$. The condition ($\mathscr{A}$) precisely means that this gives a right action of G on $P \times G'$. The orbit space E_f exists as a complex manifold. Moreover the action

$$(P \times G') \times G' \to P \times G'$$

$$(x, g', g'') \mapsto (x, g' g'')$$

of G′ on $P \times G'$ induces an action of G′ on E_f and makes of it a principal G′-bundle with base M [6]. If $\eta : P \times G' \to E_f$ is the canonical projection then the map $i_\sigma : x \mapsto \eta(x,e)$, $x \in P$, e the identity element of G′, gives rise to a trivialization of $p^*(E_f)$. We have

$$i_\sigma(xg) = \eta(xg,e) = \eta((x,f(x,g))g)$$

$$= \eta(x,f(x,g)) = i_\sigma(x)\, f(x,g) \text{ for } x \in P,\ g \in G$$

Let $f, f' : P \times G \to G'$ be two factors of automorphy. Then the G′-bundles E_f and $E_{f'}$ are isomorphic if and only if f and f′ are equivalent. In fact if

$$f'(x,g) = h(x)^{-1} f(xg)\, h(xg)$$

the map $P \times G' \to P \times G'$, $(x,g') \mapsto (x,h(x)^{-1} g')$, induces an isomorphism between E_f and $E_{f'}$. Conversely let $\varphi : E_f \to E_{f'}$ be an isomorphism of G′-bundles. Let $i_\sigma : P \to E_f$ and $i_{\sigma'} : P \to E_{f'}$ be the canonical maps defined above. We then have

$$i_{\sigma'}(x) = (\varphi \circ i_\sigma)(x)\, h(x) \text{ for } h(x) \in G'$$

It is easy to check, using φ as a G′-morphism, that

$$f'(x,g) = h(x)^{-1} f(xg)\, h(xg)$$

Moreover, if f is a factor of automorphy defined by a section σ of $p^*(P')$, with the notation of §A.1, we have an isomorphism between E_f and P′ induced by the map

$$P \times G' \to P', \quad (x,g') \mapsto i_\sigma(x) g'$$

Remark A.7. The bundle E_ρ associated to the factor of automorphy corresponding to a homomorphism $\rho : G \to G'$ (A.4) is known as the bundle obtained from P by extending the structure group by ρ to G′.

The above discussion may be summarized in

Proposition A.8. *Let* $P \to M$ *be a principal* G*-bundle and* G′ *a group. Then the set of isomorphism classes of principal* G′*-bundles on* M *whose pullbacks on* P *are trivial is in canonical bijective correspondence with the set of equivalence classes of factors of automorphy on* $P \times G$ *with values in* G′.

Remark A.9. Let $P_1 \to M_1$ and $P_2 \to M_2$ be, respectively, principal bundles with G_1 and G_2 as structure group and let $\rho : G_1 \to G_2$ be a homomorphism. A map $\Phi : P_1 \to P_2$ is said to be a ρ-morphism if $\Phi(xg) = \Phi(x)\,\rho(g)$ for $x \in P_1, g \in G_1$. We see that Φ induces a map $\widetilde{\Phi} : M_1 \to M_2$. Let $f : P_2 \times G_2 \to G_3$ be a factor of automorphy with values in a group G_3. Let P′ be the G_3-bundle on M_2 associated to f (A.6). Then $\widetilde{\Phi}^*(P')$ is isomorphic (on M_1) to the bundle associated to the factor of automorphy $f' : P_1 \times G_1 \to G_3$ given by

$$f'(x,g) = f(\Phi(x), \rho(g)), \; x \in P_1, g \in G_1$$

A.10. Representations of the fundamental group and bundles with discrete structure group

Let M be a connected manifold and $P : \widetilde{M} \to M$ its universal covering considered as a principal $\pi_1(M)$-bundle. If $\rho : \pi_1(M) \to G'$ is a homomorphism we denote by E_ρ the bundle obtained from $\widetilde{X}$ by extending the structure group by ρ to G′ (A.7). Recall that two homomorphisms ρ_1, ρ_2 from $\pi_1(M)$ to a group G′ are said to be equivalent if there exists $T \in G'$ such that $\rho_1(\gamma) = T^{-1}\rho_2(\gamma)\,T$, for $\gamma \in \pi_1(M)$.

Proposition. *Let* G′ *be a discrete group and* M *a connected manifold. There is a canonical bijective correspondence between the set of equivalence classes of homomorphisms of* $\pi_1(M)$ *into* G′ *and the set of isomorphism classes of principal* G′*-bundles over* M. *(The map is induced by* $\rho \mapsto$ *isomorphism class of* E_ρ*)*

Proof. In view of Remark A.5 and Proposition A.8, it is enough to show that if P′ is a principal G′-bundle on M, the pullback of P′ to $\widetilde{M}$ is trivial. But if M′ is a connected component of $p^*(P')$ it is easily checked that the restriction of the map $p^*(P') \to \widetilde{M}$ to M′ is a covering space of $\widetilde{M}$ and hence is an isomorphism, as $\widetilde{M}$ is simply connected. This means that $p^*(P')$ admits a section over $\widetilde{M}$.

REFERENCES

[1] ANONYMOUS, Correspondence, Am. J. Math. 78 (1956) 898.

[2] ATIYAH, M.F., Complex analytic connections on fibre bundles, Trans. Am. Math. Soc. **85** (1957) 181-207.

[3] BOURBAKI, N., Algèbre, Ch.8: Modules et anneaux semi-simples, Hermann, Paris (1958).

[4] HIRZEBRUCH, F., Topological Methods in Algebraic Geometry, Springer, Berlin (1966).

[5] HUSEMOLLER, D., Fibre Bundles, McGraw-Hill (1966).

[6] KOSZUL, J.L., Lectures on fibre bundles and differential geometry, Tata Inst. of Fundamental Research, Bombay (1960).

[7] NARASIMHAN, M.S., SIMHA, R.R., NARASIMHAN, R., SESHADRI, C.S., Riemann Surfaces, Math. Pamphlet No. 1, Tata Inst. of Fundamental Research, Bombay (1963).

[8] NARASIMHAN, M.S., SESHADRI, C.S., Holomorphic vector bundles on a compact Riemann surface, Math. Ann. **155** (1964) 69-80.
[9] NARASIMHAN, M.S., SESHADRI, C.S., Stable and unitary vector bundles on a compact Riemann surface, Ann. Math. **82** (1965) 540-567.
[10] SCHWARTZ, L., Lectures on complex analytic manifolds, Tata Inst. of Fundamental Research, Bombay (195
[11] SERRE, J.P., Un théorème de dualité, Commun. Math. Helv. **29** (1955) 9-26.
[12] WEIL, A., Généralisation des fonctions abéliennes, J. Math. Pures Appl. **17** (1938) 47-87.
[13] WEIL, A., Introduction à l'étude des variétés kähleriennes, Hermann, Paris (1958).

LOCAL PROPERTIES OF ANALYTIC FUNCTIONS AND NON-STANDARD ANALYSIS

N.R. O'BRIAN*
Institute for Advanced Study,
Princeton, New Jersey,
United States of America

Abstract

LOCAL PROPERTIES OF ANALYTIC FUNCTIONS AND NON-STANDARD ANALYSIS.
This is an expository account which shows how the methods of non-standard analysis can be applied to prove the *Nullstellensatz* for germs of analytic functions. This method of proof was discovered originally by Abraham Robinson. The necessary concepts from model theory are described in some detail and the *Nullstellensatz* is proved by investigating the relation between the set of infinitesimal elements in the complex n-plane and the spectrum of the ring of germs of analytic functions.

1. INTRODUCTION

Let $\mathbb{C}[z_1,\ldots,z_n]$ be the ring of polynomials in n variables with coefficients in the complex numbers $\mathbb{C}$, regarded as functions on the complex n-plane $\mathbb{C}^n$. The famous nullstellensatz, or zero-point theorem, of D. Hilbert says the following:

Theorem. Let $f_1,\ldots,f_m, g \in \mathbb{C}[z_1,\ldots,z_m]$ and suppose that at every point of $\mathbb{C}^n$ where all the f_i are zero, g is also zero. Then there exists an integer N such that g^N is in the ideal of $\mathbb{C}[z_1,\ldots,z_n]$ generated by $f_1,\ldots,f_m$.

A proof of Hilbert's theorem, valid over any algebraically closed field, can be found in most introductory texts on algebraic geometry or commutative algebra, for example [14]. A very unusual proof for the complex numbers is given in [10].

* Supported in part by National Science Foundation grant MPS 72-05055 A02.

An analogue of Hilbert's theorem for analytic functions of several variables exists. The proof was given by Rückert in [12]; more recent versions can be found in [2] and [13]. In all cases the proof is more difficult and technical than for the algebraic nullstellensatz. The main aim of this paper is to give a proof of Rückert's theorem which is totally different from any of these accounts, and will hopefully be found conceptually much simpler.

The proof follows the ideas of Abraham Robinson, contained in his paper [7b], and is based on the methods of nonstandard analysis.

Nonstandard analysis was invented by Robinson in 1960 and uses tools from mathematical logic to provide, to quote the inventor, a 'framework for the development of the differential and integral calculus using infinitely small and infinitely large numbers'. It has since become apparent that the applicability of Robinson's ideas extends considerably beyond this aim, and it is hoped that this paper will give some indication of the power of the theory.

The next section introduces the terminology of function germs, which is needed for the statement of the Rückert nullstellensatz.

2. RÜCKERT'S NULLSTELLENSATZ

Recall the definition of the ring A_n of germs of analytic functions at the origin in $\mathbb{C}^n$. The ring A_n may simply be taken to be the ring of all power series in n variables with complex coefficients which converge in some nhbd of the origin. Alternatively A_n can be defined at the set of equivalence classes of pairs (U,f) where U is an open nhbd of the origin in $\mathbb{C}^n$ and f is an analytic function on U, with the equivalence relation given by $(U,f) \sim (V,g)$ if there exists a nhbd W of the origin with $W \subset U \cap V$ and $f|W = g|W$. The set of equivalence classes is given the ring structure induced by pointwise addition and multiplication of the corresponding functions. When no confusion can arise, analytic functions defined in a nhbd of the origin will be identified with their germs.

We can now state the analytic version of the nullstellensatz.

Theorem. Let $f_1, \ldots, f_m$, g be analytic functions defined on the nhbd U of the origin in $\mathbb{C}^n$. Suppose that at every point of U where all the f_i are zero, g is also zero. Then there exists an integer N such that the germ of g^N is in the ideal of A_n generated by the germs of $f_1, \ldots, f_m$.

Note that there is no harm in replacing U by a smaller open set if this will help achieve the hypothesis of the theorem.

The proof will be given in the subsequent sections. In order to describe the nonstandard techniques which are used, a short excursion into the realm of mathematical logic is necessary. Fortunately all the required concepts are fairly simple. Also these same techniques have very wide-ranging applications outside the present context, which justify the effort involved in establishing them.

The basic idea of the proof will be to regard the elements of A_n as functions on the set of 'infinitely small' elements of $\mathbb{C}^n$. Each such 'infinitesimal point' gives rise to a prime ideal of A_n, namely the set of functions which vanish on that point. It will be seen that the structure of this set of 'infinitesimals' is sufficiently rich for every prime ideal to arise in this way. If no power of g lies in the ideal generated by the f_i then a prime ideal can be found which contains the f_i but not g. The theorem then follows by contradiction: take an infinitesimal point which defines this prime ideal, then all the f_i vanish there but g does not, contrary to hypothesis! This is a typical nonstandard argument — the infinitesimals appear as aids to reasoning, and disappear in the final result.

3. STRUCTURES, FORMULAE AND STATEMENTS

First, some very general definitions.

Definition. A structure M consists of a non-empty set (which will also be called M) on which, for each positive integer n certain n-ary relations, e.g. R(, ,...), are given. That is, if $a_1,...,a_n$ is an ordered n-tuple of elements of M then one can determine, at least in principle, whether or not $R(a_1,...,a_n)$ holds, or is true in M. (In fact n-ary relations can be identified with subsets of the n-fold cartesian product M^n.)

Examples. (i) A group is a set on which a binary relation E(,) is given, together with a tertiary relation P(, ,). Here E(x,y) holds if $x = y$ and P(x,y,z) holds if $z = xy$. Of course the properties of these relations must be such that the group axioms are satisfied.

(ii) If X is a set and P(X) its power set, let $X' = X \cup P(X)$. Then X' has binary relations corresponding to '$x = y$' and '$x \in y$.'

(iii) In the preceding example, a topology on X can be considered as a subset of P(X), and this defines a 1-ary relation on X'.

It should not be difficult to accept that all the commonly used 'structures' of mathematics can be considered as structures in this strict sense. The notion of a mathematical structure having been formalized, a corresponding formalization can be made in the 'language' used to talk about such a structure.

Thus by filling the empty places in an n-ary relation of M with either elements of M ('constants') or with 'variable symbols,' we obtain a so-called atomic formula of M.

The formulae of M are then obtained inductively. An atomic formula is a formula, and a formula of M is obtained by combining together other formulae by the use of logical connectives ($\neg$ (not),

$\vee$ (or), $\wedge$ (and), $\Longrightarrow$ (implies), $\Longleftrightarrow$ (equivalence)) or by quantification ($\exists$ (there exists), $\forall$ (for all)) over the variables of an existing formula. All this must be done according to well-known grammatical rules. Brackets can be used to avoid ambiguities.

A variable in a formula is said to be free if it is not quantified in the formula, and a statement of M is a formula without free variables.

Thus one can, at least in principle, say whether a particular statement holds, or is true, on M.

In the next section it is shown how, given a structure M another, larger, structure can be constructed which, in a very precise sense, has the same properties as M.

Remark. In order to avoid an unnecessarily abstract approach we will not confine ourselves to this formal language when actually making statements about a structure. It should be clear in each case, however, that such a formalization is possible.

4. ULTRAFILTERS AND ULTRAPRODUCTS

Now let I be any set. A filter on I is a collection $\mathcal{F}$ of subsets of I satisfying conditions 1F - 4F below. The filter $\mathcal{F}$ is said to be an ultrafilter if it also satisfies condition UF.

1F: $\emptyset \notin \mathcal{F}$

2F: $I \in \mathcal{F}$

3F: If $E \in \mathcal{F}$ and $E \subset F$, then $F \in \mathcal{F}$

4F: If $E_1, E_2 \in \mathcal{F}$, then $E_1 \cap E_2 \in \mathcal{F}$

UF: For all $E \subset I$, either $E \in \mathcal{F}$ or $I \setminus E \in \mathcal{F}$

An alternative definition of an ultrafilter is that it is a filter which is not properly contained in any other filter (i.e. a maximal filter). Thus by Zorn's lemma, every filter is contained in an ultrafilter. Also if any set $\mathcal{G}$ of subsets of I has the finite intersection property, i.e. every finite intersection of elements of $\mathcal{G}$ is non-empty, then $\mathcal{G}$ is contained in some filter $\mathcal{F}$. Simply take $\mathcal{F}$ to be the set of subsets of I which contain some finite intersection of elements of $\mathcal{G}$.

Given a structure M and a set I equipped with an ultrafilter $\mathcal{U}$, define another structure $^*M$ as follows:

The elements of $^*M$ are the functions from I to M. Thus if I is regarded as an index set the elements of $^*M$ can be written e.g. $\xi = (\xi^i)$ where the index runs over I and each $\xi^i \in M$.

The relations of $^*M$ are the same as those of M, and if R(, ,....) is an n-ary relation on M we say that $R(\xi_1,\ldots,\xi_n)$ holds in $^*M$ just in case the set of $i \in I$ for which $R(\xi_1^i,\ldots,\xi_n^i)$ holds in M is in the ultrafilter $\mathcal{U}$. The structure $^*M$ is called an ultraproduct of M.

Note that there is a natural map $M \longrightarrow {}^*M$ given by $a \longmapsto (\xi^i)$, where $\xi^i = a$ for all $i \in I$. The image of a under this map will also be denoted by a. Suppose $a, b \in M$ and ' = ' is the usual binary relation of equality on M. Then if 'a = b' holds in $^*M$, we have by 1F that a = b holds in M. Thus, in this sense, the map is injective.

Now given any formula Φ of M, a corresponding formula, which will also be called Φ, exists for $^*M$. Simply replace all elements of M appearing in Φ by their images in $^*M$, regard the relations as relations on $^*M$, and quantify over the elements of $^*M$ rather than M. The resulting formula is called the extension of Φ to $^*M$.

Given a formula Φ of M, number the variables occurring in Φ as x_1, x_2, x_3, etc. Let $\underline{a}$ denote a sequence $a_1, a_2, a_3, \ldots$ of elements of M. If Φ contains the free variables $x_{i_1},\ldots,x_{i_m}$ then the statement obtained by replacing each x_{i_k} by a_{i_k} will be denoted by $\Phi(\underline{a})$. Similarly a sequence $\underline{\alpha}$ of elements of $^*M$ gives rise to a statement $\Phi(\underline{\alpha})$ of ${}^*M$. The following is the fundamental result in the theory of ultraproducts.

Theorem. Let Φ be a formula of M, $\underline{\alpha}$ a sequence of elements of ${}^*M$. Then $\Phi(\underline{\alpha})$ holds in ${}^*M$ if and only if $\{i \mid \Phi(\underline{\alpha}^i) \text{ holds in } M\} \in \mathcal{U}$.

Proof. The proof is by induction on the length of the formula. The theorem holds for atomic formulae by definition, so assume it holds for the formulae Φ_1 and Φ_2. To make the induction step it is only necessary to prove the theorem for $\Phi_1 \wedge \Phi_2$, $\neg\Phi_1$ and $(\exists x_j)\Phi_1$ since all other methods for making new formulae can be built up using these three. If the statement Ψ holds in M and ${}^*M$ we write (respectively) $\Psi \models M$ and $\Psi \models {}^*M$. Also for Φ, $\underline{\alpha}$ as above let $\langle \Phi, \underline{\alpha} \rangle \subset I$ be the set $\{i \mid \Phi(\underline{\alpha}^i) \models M\}$. Now

$$(\Phi_1 \wedge \Phi_2)(\underline{\alpha}) \models {}^*M$$

$$\Longleftrightarrow \Phi_1(\underline{\alpha}) \models {}^*M \text{ and } \Phi_2(\underline{\alpha}) \models {}^*M$$

$$\Longleftrightarrow \langle \Phi_1, \underline{\alpha} \rangle \in \mathcal{U} \text{ and } \langle \Phi_2, \underline{\alpha} \rangle \in \mathcal{U}$$

$$\Longleftrightarrow \langle \Phi_1, \underline{\alpha} \rangle \cap \langle \Phi_2, \underline{\alpha} \rangle \in \mathcal{U} \quad \text{(by 3F and 4F)}$$

But $\langle \Phi_1, \underline{\alpha} \rangle \cap \langle \Phi_2, \underline{\alpha} \rangle = \langle \Phi_1 \wedge \Phi_2, \underline{\alpha} \rangle$.

The proof for $\neg\Phi_1$ is similar; use property UF.

Suppose $((\exists x_j)\Phi_1)(\underline{\alpha}) \models {}^*M$. This means that we can choose $\underline{\beta}$ with $\beta_k = \alpha_k$ for all $k \neq j$ such that $\Phi_1(\underline{\beta}) \models {}^*M$. By induction $\langle \Phi_1, \underline{\beta} \rangle \in \mathcal{U}$. But $\langle \Phi_1, \underline{\beta} \rangle \subset \langle (\exists x_j)\Phi_1, \underline{\beta} \rangle$ and $\langle (\exists x_j)\Phi_1, \underline{\beta} \rangle = \langle (\exists x_j)\Phi_1, \underline{\alpha} \rangle$ since x_j is not free. Thus $\langle (\exists x_j)\Phi_1, \underline{\alpha} \rangle \in \mathcal{U}$ by 3F.

Conversely, suppose $\langle (\exists x_j)\Phi_1, \underline{\alpha} \rangle \in \mathcal{U}$. Define $\underline{\beta}$ by $\beta_k = \alpha_k$ if $k \neq j$, and if $i \in \langle (\exists x_j)\Phi_1, \underline{\alpha} \rangle$ choose β_j^i such that $\Phi_1(\underline{\beta}^i)$ holds in M. For all other i choose β_j^i arbitrarily. By induction $\Phi_1(\underline{\beta}) \models {}^*M$ and so $((\exists x_j)\Phi_1)(\underline{\alpha}) \models {}^*M$ since $x_j = \beta_j$ works.

Corollary (TRANSFER PRINCIPLE)

Let Φ be a statement in M. Then Φ holds in M if and only if Φ holds in $^*M$.

In the terminology of mathematical logic this corollary says that $^*M$ is a model of M, in fact a so-called nonstandard model. This result is absolutely basic, and will be used continually in the following discussion, both explicitly and implicitly.

For example, if M is a group or a field, the transfer principle allows us to conclude immediately that $^*M$ is a group, or a field, etc. Note also that since ' = ' is an equivalence relation on M its extension to $^*M$ is also, by transfer. In fact $^*M$ can be replaced by the set of equivalence classes. This approach is often used, and has the advantage that ' = ' then has its usual meaning on $^*M$.

5. IDEAL ELEMENTS

The structure $^*M$ has little interest in its own right because, by the transfer principle it is indistinguishable from M as far as its properties are concerned. The power of the construction lies in the relationship between the two structures. As we have seen, M can be considered as a subset of $^*M$ via the natural map $M \to {}^*M$. The image of this map is called the set of standard elements of $^*M$.

Example. Let $M = \mathbb{R}$, the real numbers. Let $I = \mathbb{Z}^+$, the positive integers, and let $\mathcal{G}$ be the set of all subsets of I which have finite complement. It is easily checked that $\mathcal{G}$ is a filter. Let $\mathcal{U}$ be any ultrafilter containing $\mathcal{G}$, and let $^*\mathbb{R}$ be the corresponding ultrapower. Define $\xi \in {}^*\mathbb{R}$ by $\xi_i = i$. Clearly, if x is any standard real number the relation $\xi_i > x$ is true for all $i \in I$ except a finite number, and hence for all i in an element of the ultrafilter U.

Thus $\xi > x$ holds in ${}^*\mathbb{R}$ for all standard x, and ξ can be considered as an infinite number.

Similarly if $\eta \in {}^*\mathbb{R}$ is defined by $\eta_i = 1/i$ then $\eta \neq 0$ and $\eta < x$ for all standard positive x. Thus η is an infinitesimal. In fact $\eta = 1/\xi$.

More generally it will be shown that if ${}^*M$ is "sufficiently large" in a sense to be made precise, then ${}^*M$ will contain so-called ideal elements, which are a natural generalization of the concepts of infinite and infinitesimal numbers.

In order to define what is meant by 'sufficiently large' consider the map from the elements of ${}^*M$ to the set of ultrafilters on M obtained as follows.

A subset U of M can be considered as a 1-ary relation on M. Say $U(x)$ holds in M if and only if $x \in U$. Now suppose $\xi \in {}^*M$.
Define a set $\mathcal{U}_\xi$ of subsets of M by

$$U \in \mathcal{U}_\xi \Longleftrightarrow U(\xi) \text{ holds in } {}^*M$$

It is easy to check that $\mathcal{U}_\xi$ is an ultrafilter on M.

Definition. ${}^*M$ is an adequate ultrapower of M if the above map $\xi \mapsto \mathcal{U}_\xi$ from ${}^*M$ to the set of ultrafilters on M is surjective.

We briefly indicate one way in which such an ultrapower can be constructed. Take for the index set I the set $P_{fin}P(M)$ of finite sets of subsets of M. Let F_A be the set of elements of I which contain some fixed subset A of M. The set $\{F_A | A \subset M\}$ has the finite intersection property and so is contained in an ultrafilter $\mathcal{U}$. Let $^*M$ be the ultraproduct of M constructed using I and $\mathcal{U}$, and let $\mathcal{V}$ be an ultrafilter on M. Then for $i = \{A_1, \ldots, A_M\} \in I$ choose ξ^i to lie in the necessarily non-empty intersection of those A_i which are also in $\mathcal{V}$. (The intersection of an empty set of subsets is M itself.) It is now an easy exercise to show that $\mathcal{V} \subset \mathcal{U}_\xi$, but this means that $\mathcal{V} = \mathcal{U}_\xi$ since $\mathcal{V}$ is an ultrafilter and so maximal.

From now on it will be assumed that $^*M$ is an adequate ultrapower of M.

<u>Definition</u>. Let $R(\ ,\ )$ be a binary relation on M. The <u>left domain</u> $L_M(R)$ of R in M is the set of elements a of M such that there exists an element b in M such that $R(a,b)$ holds in M.

<u>Definition</u>. A binary relation $R(\ ,\ )$ is said to be <u>concurrent</u> if for every finite set $a_1, \ldots, a_n$ of elements of $L_M(R)$ there exists $b \in M$ such that $R(a_i, b)$ holds in M for $1 \leq i \leq n$.

<u>Examples</u>. (i) For any M the relation '$\neq$' is concurrent if and only if M is infinite.

(ii) If $M = \mathbb{R}$, the real numbers, the relations $>, <$ are concurrent.

The following is the fundamental result on adequate ultrapowers.

<u>Theorem</u>. Suppose, as always, that $^*M$ is an adequate ultrapower of M. Let $R(\ ,\ )$ be a concurrent binary relation on M. Then there exists an element ξ of $^*M$ such that $R(a, \xi)$ holds in $^*M$ for <u>all</u> $a \in L_M(R)$.

Such a ξ is called an <u>ideal element</u> for the relation R.

Proof. For $a \in L_M(R)$ let $R_a = \{b | R(a,b) \text{ holds in } M\}$. The set of subsets $\{R_a | a \in L_M(R)\}$ has the finite intersection property and so is contained in an ultrafilter of M which, since ${}^*M$ is an adequate ultrapower, is of the form $\mathcal{U}_\xi$ for some $\xi \in {}^*M$. But then, in our previous notation, $R_a(\xi)$ holds in ${}^*M$ for all $a \in L_M(R)$. Thus ξ is the required ideal element.

Example. Take $M = \mathbb{R}$ and let $R(a,b)$ stand for '$0 < b < a$.' Clearly R is concurrent and so there exists an ideal element ξ in ${}^*\mathbb{R}$. Moreover, ξ is infinitesimal since $0 < \xi < a$ holds for all positive $a \in \mathbb{R}$. Similarly, for the relation '$b > a$', an ideal element is larger than any standard real number, i.e. it is an 'infinite number.'

If we define an infinitesimal in ${}^*\mathbb{R}$ to be an element ξ such that $|\xi| < a$ for all standard positive real numbers a, then we can reformulate the definition of continuity as follows. If $f : \mathbb{R} \longrightarrow \mathbb{R}$ then f can be regarded as a binary relation on $\mathbb{R}$. The fact that a binary relation represents a function can be expressed as a statement about the structure $\mathbb{R}$. Thus by the transfer principle the relation f defines a function $f : {}^*\mathbb{R} \longrightarrow {}^*\mathbb{R}$.

Proposition. The function f is continuous at $x \in \mathbb{R}$ if and only if, for all $y \in {}^*\mathbb{R}$ such that $x - y$ is infinitesimal, $f(x) - f(y)$ is infinitesimal.

Proof. Without loss of generality assume $x = f(x) = 0$. Suppose f is continuous in the usual ε, δ sense. If y is infinitesimal then it is smaller than all possible δ, so $f(y)$ is smaller than any ε which can be chosen. Thus $f(y)$ is also infinitesimal. Conversely let $\varepsilon \in \mathbb{R}$ be positive, then

$$(\exists\delta)[[\delta > 0] \wedge (\forall x)[[|x| < \delta] \Longrightarrow [|f(x)| < \varepsilon]]$$

holds in ${}^*\mathbb{R}$; take δ to be any positive infinitesimal. By transfer the statement holds in $\mathbb{R}$, but this means precisely that f is continuous at 0.

In fact all the concepts and proofs used in elementary calculus can be reformulated along similar lines; see [11]. The concept of infinitesimals admits a generalization to arbitrary topological spaces. To describe this it is convenient to introduce the following notation.

As has already been noted, a subset U of a structure M can be regarded as a 1-ary relation U( ) on M, and hence on ${}^*M$. We define a subset ${}^*U$ of ${}^*M$ by

$$ {}^*U = \{\xi \mid U(\xi) \text{ holds in } {}^*M\} $$

By transfer the images of all elements of U in ${}^*M$ are in ${}^*U$.

If the structure already has the relation '$\in$' defined on it, as was the case with example (ii) of §3, a careful distinction should be made between the ordinary set-theoretical inclusion on ${}^*M$ and the extension of the relation '$\in$' of M to ${}^*M$. Thus if $M = X \cup \mathbf{P}(X)$ and $U \subset X$ then

$$ {}^*U = \{\xi \mid {}'\xi \in U' \text{ holds in } {}^*M\} $$

but ${}^*U$ is not in general equal to the image of the element U of M in ${}^*M$.

Now let X be a topological space and p a point of X. The set of nhbd's of p will be denoted by $\mathcal{N}_p$.

<u>Definition</u>. The <u>monad</u> $\mu(p)$ of p in X is defined to be the subset of ${}^*X$ given by

$$ \mu(p) = \bigcap_{U \in \mathcal{N}_p} {}^*U $$

It is easy to see that the monad of the origin on the real line is precisely the set of infinitesimals already referred to. In the case of the topological space $\mathbb{C}^n$ the monad of the origin provides precisely the concept which is needed to prove the nullstellensatz.

It is not difficult to extend the nonstandard definition of continuity to general topological spaces. Choice of a suitable structure gives, for topological spaces X, Y and $f : X \longrightarrow Y$, that f is continuous at $p \in X$ if and only if $f(\mu(p)) \subset \mu(f(p))$.

6. MONADS AND GERMS

Let $M = \mathbb{C}^{n+1} \cup P(\mathbb{C}^{n+1})$. This choice is somewhat arbitrary and is simply intended to be adequate for the present discussion. The structure can be considered to contain $\mathbb{C}$, $\mathbb{C}^n$ and, by identifying a function with its graph, all complex-valued functions on $\mathbb{C}^n$.

If f is a complex-valued function on $U \subset \mathbb{C}^n$, then this fact can be expressed by a statement of M. Thus, by the transfer principle, f is a function from ${}^*U$ to ${}^*\mathbb{C}$ in ${}^*M$. Given an element $f \in A_n$, any representative function for f can be restricted to a ${}^*\mathbb{C}$-valued function on the monad $\mu(0)$ of the origin in ${}^*\mathbb{C}^n$. The resulting function, which will also be called f, is clearly independent of the representative chosen. The plan outlined in the Introduction can now be carried out. Let Spec A_n denote the spectrum of the ring A_n, i.e. the set of prime ideals of A_n, and let $\nu : \mu(0) \longrightarrow \text{Spec } A_n$ be the map defined by

$$\nu(\xi) = \{f \in A_n | f(\xi) = 0\}$$

Theorem (Robinson). The map ν is surjective.

Before proving the theorem, we show how it leads immediately to the nullstellensatz. The theorem can be interpreted as saying that every prime ideal of A_n has a generic point in $\mu(0)$. In other words, a point such that a function germ is in the ideal if and only if it vanishes at that point.

So, with the notation of §2, suppose that no power of g lies in the ideal J of A_n generated by $f_1,\dots,f_m$. Thus the image of g in the quotient A_n/J is not nilpotent. It is well-known (e.g. [14], vol. I, p. 151) that the intersection of all prime ideals in a commutative ring is precisely the set of nilpotent elements, and so there exists a prime ideal $\underline{q}$ in A_n/J which does not contain the image of g. Let $\underline{p} \in \operatorname{Spec} A_n$ be the inverse image of $\underline{q}$. Thus $f_1,\dots,f_m \in \underline{p}$ but $g \notin \underline{p}$. Let $\xi \in \mu(0)$ be a generic point for $\underline{p}$. By hypothesis the statement

$$(\forall x)[[[x \in U] \wedge [f_1(x) = 0] \wedge \dots \wedge [f_m(x) = 0]] \Longrightarrow [g(x) = 0]]$$

holds in M. By transfer it holds in $^*M$. But this is a contradiction — the statement is false for $x = \xi$. Hence $g^N \in J$ for some N.

It only remains to show the existence of generic points. For the zero ideal $(0) \subset A_n$ the existence of such a point follows by considering the relation $R(f,a)$ given by 'f is a holomorphic function on an open nhbd U of the origin, $a \in U$ and $f(a) \neq 0$'.

This is clearly concurrent. Let ξ be an ideal element. Then $\xi \in \mu(0)$ since '$\xi \in U$' holds in $^*M$ for all open nhbd's of the origin. Also if $f = 0 \in A_n$ then by transfer $f(\xi) = 0$. Conversely, if $f(\xi) = 0$ then f cannot be in the left domain of R and so must be identically zero. Thus $\nu(\xi) = (0)$.

The general case is proved by induction on n. We first need two (standard) definitions. Let $A_{n-1} \subset A_n$ be identified with the germs of functions which depend only on the first $n-1$ coordinates $(z_1,\dots,z_{n-1})$ of $\mathbb{C}^n$. An element $h \in A_n$ is said to be a Weierstrass polynomial of degree p if it is of the form

$$h = z_n^p + u_{p-1}z_n^{p-1} + \dots + u_1 z_n + u_0$$

with each $u_i \in A_{n-1}$ and $u_i(0) = 0$.

An element $f \in A_n$ is said to be <u>regular of order</u> p if $f(0,\ldots,0,z_n)$ can be written as $z_n^p\, g(z_n)$ with $g(0) \neq 0$. By a suitable linear change of coordinates every $f \neq 0 \in A_n$ can be made regular of order p for some $p > 0$.

As is usual in dealing with A_n, the induction step is accomplished by the use of the following two (standard) theorems, the proof of which can be found, for example, in [2], Chapter II or [4], Chapter VI.

Theorem (Weierstrass preparation theorem)

Suppose $f \in A_n$ is regular of order p. Then f can be written as $f = uh$ where h is a Weierstrass polynomial of degree p and u is a unit in A_n (i.e. $u(0) \neq 0$).

Theorem (Weierstrass division theorem)

Let f be any element of A_n, and h a Weierstrass polynomial of degree p. Then f can be written as $f = qh + r$ for some $q, r \in A_n$, and r of the form $r_{p-1} z_n^{p-1} + \ldots + r_1 z_n + r_0$, where all $r_i \in A_{n-1}$.

The induction starts with the case $n = 0$, which is trivial. Let $\mathfrak{p}$ be a non-zero prime ideal of A_n and suppose for the induction that $\mathfrak{p}' = \mathfrak{p} \cap A_{n-1}$ has a generic point $\zeta \in \mu(0) \cap {}^*\mathbb{C}^{n-1}$.

Let S denote the set of non-zero elements of $A_{n-1}/\mathfrak{p}'$. Let $\underline{k}$ be the field of fractions of this ring, i.e. the set of 'fractions' a/s with $a \in A_{n-1}/\mathfrak{p}'$ and $s \in S$, modulo the usual equivalence relation. The ring $A_{n-1}/\mathfrak{p}'$ is a subring of $A_n/\mathfrak{p}$ and we can also form the ring of fractions b/s with $b \in A_n/\mathfrak{p}$ and $s \in S$, again taken modulo the usual equivalence relation. This ring will be denoted by B_n. Then there is a commutative diagram

$$\begin{array}{ccc} A_{n-1}/\mathfrak{p}' & \longrightarrow & \underline{k} \\ \downarrow & & \downarrow \\ A_n/\mathfrak{p} & \longrightarrow & B_n \end{array}$$

where the horizontal maps are the natural injections $a \longmapsto a/1$.

The map $\underline{k} \longrightarrow B_n$ extends to a map of the polynomial ring $\underline{k}[X] \longrightarrow B_n$ by the assignment $X \longmapsto z_n$. This extension is <u>surjective</u>. For, by the preparation theorem, $\underline{p}$ contains a non-zero Weierstrass polynomial h and so by the division theorem every element of A_n is equivalent mod $\underline{p}$ to $r(z_n)$ for some $r(X) \in A_{n-1}[X]$.

Since $\underline{k}[X]$ is a principal ideal domain and B_n is an integral domain the kernel is of the form $(f(X))$ for some irreducible polynomial $f(X)$.

By the induction hypothesis there is an injective map $e_\zeta : A_{n-1}/\underline{p}' \longrightarrow {}^*\mathbb{C}$ given by evaluating a germ at the generic point ζ. Since $\mathbb{C}$ is an algebraically closed field, so is ${}^*\mathbb{C}$, by the transfer principle. Thus e_ζ extends to maps $\underline{k} \longrightarrow {}^*\mathbb{C}$ and $\underline{k}[X] \longrightarrow {}^*\mathbb{C}[X]$, which will also be denoted by e_ζ. The image of a polynomial $q(X)$ in ${}^*\mathbb{C}[X]$ will then be denoted by $\overline{q}(X)$. Let $\eta \in {}^*\mathbb{C}$ be a root of $\overline{f}(X)$. The following argument shows that η is infinitesimal.

Let $h(X) \in \underline{k}[X]$ be the polynomial such that $h(z_n) = h$. Then $f(X)$ divides $h(X)$ and so $\overline{h}(\eta) = 0$. Suppose η is not infinitesimal. Then $\eta = - u_{p-1}(\zeta) - \ldots - u_1(\zeta)\eta^{-p+2} - u_0(\zeta)\eta^{-p+1}$. But each u_k is continuous and $u_k(0) = 0$ so because ζ is infinitesimal $u_k(\zeta)$ is also. Since η^{-1} is finite, each term on the right must be infinitesimal, and a sum of infinitesimals is infinitesimal. But this is a contradiction. It is now claimed that $\xi = (\zeta, \eta)$ is a generic point for $\underline{p}$. To see this, note that we have a commutative diagram

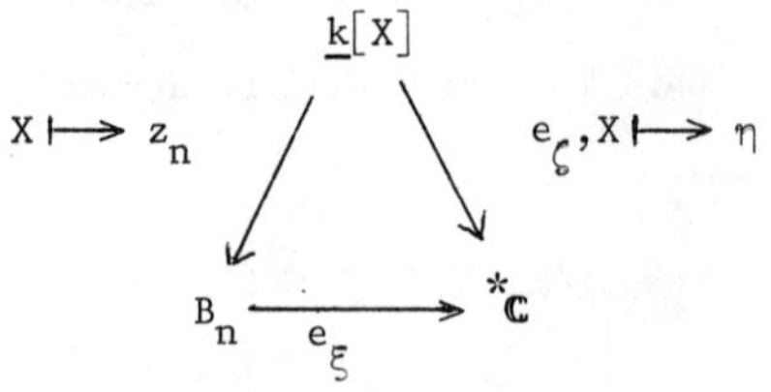

The kernel of both the maps from $\underline{k}[X]$ is $(f(X))$ and the left-hand map is surjective. Thus e_ξ is injective, and therefore so is the

composition $A_n/\underline{p} \longrightarrow B_n \longrightarrow {}^*\mathbb{C}$. That is, the map $A_n \longrightarrow {}^*\mathbb{C}$ given by evaluation at ξ has kernel $\underline{p}$, as required.

7. REMARKS

It should be emphasized that any proof of a 'standard' result using nonstandard methods can be translated into a standard proof, although in most cases it is likely that this would lead to a considerable increase in complexity.

Nonstandard analysis is an application of the part of mathematical logic known as model theory. There are many ways to lay down the foundations for nonstandard analysis, the one described here being chosen purely for its simplicity. Several more elegant approaches can be found in the literature, e.g. [1], [7c], [11]. The best general reference, especially for applications, is [11], which gives nonstandard treatments of such diverse topics as measure theory, complex function theory, topological groups, general topology and Hilbert space theory. A very good introduction to the subject is contained in the papers by Vaught and Luxemburg in [1], and an account of the theory of ultraproducts can be found in [6], which also describes the slightly more versatile concept of an ultralimit.

The literature on applications of nonstandard analysis is still relatively small; the collections [5], [7], [8] contain many interesting articles on both foundations and applications.

Other introductory accounts can be found in [3], [9] and [7a]. A further collection of papers on non-standard analysis will be published in a special issue of the Israel Journal of Mathematics.

REFERENCES

[1] AMERICAN MATHEMATICAL MONTHLY, **80** (6) Part II (suppl.), Papers in the Foundations of Mathematics, 13 of the Herbert Ellsworth Slaught Memorial Papers (1973).

[2] GUNNING, R.C., ROSSI, H., Analytic Functions of Several Complex Variables, Prentice-Hall, Englewood Cliffs (1965).

[3] HIRSCHFELDER, J.J., "Nonstandard analysis in a nutshell", Value Distribution Theory, Part A (Proc. Conf. Tulane Univ. 1973), Marcel Dekker (1974) 13–28.

[4] HÖRMANDER, L., An Introduction to Complex Analysis in Several Variables, 2nd edn, North-Holland, Amsterdam (1973).

[5] (HURD, A.E., LOEB, P., Eds), Proc. Symp. Nonstandard Analysis, Victoria, B.C., Springer Lecture Notes in Math. **369** , Springer, Berlin (1974).

[6] KOCHEN, S., Ultraproducts in the theory of models, Ann. Math. **74** (2) (1961) 221–261.

[7] (LUXEMBURG, W.A.J., Ed.), Applications of Model Theory to Algebra, Analysis, and Probability (Proc. Int. Symp. Pasadena, 1967), Holt, Rinehart and Winston, New York (1969). Includes:
(a) LUXEMBURG, W.A.J., A general theory of monads, 18–86.
(b) ROBINSON, A., Germs, 138–149.
(c) ROBINSON, A., ZAKON, E., A set-theoretical characterization of enlargements, 109–122.

[8] LUXEMBURG, W.A.J., ROBINSON, A., (Eds), Contributions to Nonstandard Analysis (Studies in Logic and the Foundations of Mathematics **69**), North-Holland, Amsterdam (1972).

[9] MACHOVER, M., HIRSCHFELD, J., Lectures on Nonstandard Analysis, Springer Lecture Notes in Math. **94** (1969).

[10] QUILLEN, D., On the representation of hermitian forms as sums of squares, Inventiones Math. **5** (1968) 237–242.

[11] ROBINSON, A., Non-standard Analysis (Studies in Logic and the Foundations of Mathematics) 2nd edn, North-Holland, Amsterdam (1968).

[12] RÜCKERT, W., Zum Eliminationsproblem der Potenzreihenideale, Math. Ann. **107** (1932).

[13] TOUGERON, J.C., Idéaux de fonctions différentiables, Ergebnisse **71**, Springer-Verlag, New York (1972).

[14] ZARISKI, O., SAMUEL, P., Commutative Algebra, Van Nostrand, New York (1958).

HOLOMORPHIC FUNCTIONS WITH BOUNDS

B.E. PETERSEN*
Department of Mathematics,
Oregon State University,
Corvallis, Oregon,
United States of America

Abstract

HOLOMORPHIC FUNCTIONS WITH BOUNDS.

Let P be a p X q matrix of polynomials in n complex variables. If Ω is a domain of holomorphy in complex n-space and if f is a p-tuple of holomorphic functions in Ω and if the system of linear equations Pu = f has a solution u which is a holomorphic q-tuple in Ω, then it has a solution which satisfies an estimate in terms of f. The paper discusses in outline the proof of such a result published by the author. The discussion is motivated by a simple illustration in the case p = q = 1. In addition the proof is given of a theorem on trivial cohomology with bounds announced without proof in the author's paper mentioned above. As an application of his main result, the author generalizes to systems a theorem of Komeč concerning the possibility of solving constant coefficient partial differential equations where the solution is required to be a temperate distribution with support in a cone.

1. INTRODUCTION

Let $P \neq 0$ be a polynomial in $\mathbb{C}[z_1, ..., z_n]$ of degree m. On the average P is "large". For example, there exists a constant C and a finite set Θ in the open unit ball in $\mathbb{C}^n$ such that

$$1 \leqslant C r^{-m} \max_{\theta \in \Theta} \inf_{|\tau| = 1} |P(z + r\tau\theta)|, \quad (\tau \in \mathbb{C}) \tag{1}$$

for any $r > 0$, $z \in \mathbb{C}^n$. The set Θ may be chosen to depend only on m and n, and the constant C to depend only on m, n and the top-order coefficients of P. This inequality is Lemma 7.6.6 in Ref. [1] together with the remark at the top of p. 190 in Ref. [1]. Suppose now Ω is an open set in $\mathbb{C}^n$ and $u, f \in A(\Omega)$, where $A(\Omega)$ is the space of holomorphic functions in Ω. Suppose moreover that Pu = f and

$$|f(z)| \leqslant C_0 \, d(z)^{-k} (1 + |z|)^N, \quad z \in \Omega \tag{2}$$

where $d(z) = \min(1, \operatorname{dist}(z, \partial\Omega))$, and k and N are non-negative integers. From (1) and (2) we easily obtain an estimate for u. Indeed, fix any point z in Ω and choose $r = d(z)$. For some θ_0 in Θ we have $1 \leqslant Cr^{-m}|P(z + r\tau\theta_0)|$ for complex numbers τ with $|\tau| = 1$. Then by the maximum principle

$$|u(z)| \leqslant \sup_{|\tau| = 1} |u(z + r\tau\theta_0)| \leqslant C r^{-m} \sup_{|\tau| = 1} |f(z + r\tau\theta_0)|$$

Now $1 + |z + r\tau\theta_0| \leqslant 2(1 + |z|)$ and $d(z + r\tau\theta_0) \geqslant r(1-t)$, where t is the maximum of $|\theta|$ for θ in Θ.

* Supported in part by National Science Foundation Grant MPS 74-06803 A01.

Thus we obtain

$$|u(z)| \leqslant C_0\, C_1\, d(z)^{-m-k} (1+|z|)^N \tag{3}$$

where $C_1 = 2^N(1-t)^{-k} C$ depends only on k, N, m, n and the top-order coefficients of P.

We may use these remarks to prove a generalization of a theorem of Komeč [2]. Let P(D) be the partial differential operator with constant coefficients obtained by replacing z_j in P(z) by $\partial/\partial x_j$. Let Γ be a closed convex salient cone in $\mathbb{R}^n$ and let

$$\Gamma^+ = \{\xi \in \mathbb{R}^n | \langle \xi, x\rangle \geqslant 0,\ x \in \Gamma\}$$

be the dual cone. That Γ is salient means Γ contains no non-trivial subspace. This condition is equivalent to Γ^+ having non-empty interior Γ_0^+. Let f be a temperate distribution with support in Γ. The Laplace transform F of f, defined *formally* by $F(z) = \int \exp(-\langle z,x\rangle)\, f(x)\, dx$, is then a holomorphic function in $\Omega = \Gamma_0^+ + i\mathbb{R}^n$ and $|F(z)| \leqslant C_0\, d(z)^{-k} (1+|z|)^N$ (see Ref. [3]).

Theorem 1. *The equation* P(D)g = f *has a solution* g, *where* g *is a temperate distribution with support in* Γ, *if and only if there exists a holomorphic function* G *in* Ω *such that* P(z)G(z) = F(z) *for each* z *in* Ω.

The necessity is trivial. For the sufficiency, if G exists, by the above remarks $|G(z)| \leqslant C_1\, C_0\, d(z)^{-k-m} (1+|z|)^N$ and hence by Ref. [3] G is the Laplace transform of a temperate distribution g with support in Γ. Komeč proves Theorem 1 only under the assumption that P satisfies an ellipticity condition.

We wish to extend results of the type described above to systems. Let Ω be a domain of holomorphy in $\mathbb{C}^n$, let P be a p × q matrix of polynomials in $\mathbb{C}[z_1, \ldots, z_n]$ and let $f \in A(\Omega)^p$. Our main theorem (Theorem 2) states that if f satisfies certain growth conditions and if the system of linear equations P(z)u(z) = f(z) has a solution u in $A(\Omega)^q$ then it has a solution v in $A(\Omega)^q$ which satisfies an estimate in terms of f. Results of this type may be found in Refs [1, 4–7]. As an application of the main theorem we obtain a generalization of Theorem 1 to systems.

2. STATEMENT OF MAIN THEOREM

Let Ω be a domain of holomorphy in $\mathbb{C}^n$ and let P be a p × q matrix of polynomials in $\mathbb{C}[z_1, \ldots, z_n]$. Let d(z) be defined as before and let

$$\psi(z) = -\log d(z), \qquad \theta(z) = \log(1+|z|^2)$$

Let ϕ be a plurisubharmonic function in Ω such that there exists a constant ζ such that

$$|\phi(z) - \phi(w)| \leqslant \zeta \text{ if } z \in \Omega \text{ and } |z-w| \leqslant \tfrac{1}{2} d(z) \tag{4}$$

Note that if m and N are non-negative integers, then $\phi + m\psi + N\theta$ is a plurisubharmonic function in Ω which satisfies (4), with a different constant. If $u \in A(\Omega)^q$ we set $|u|^2 = |u_1|^2 + \ldots + |u_q|^2$. Our main result is the following theorem.

Theorem 2. *If* $u \in A(\Omega)^q$ *there exists* $v \in A(\Omega)^q$ *such that* Pv = Pu *in* Ω *and*

$$\int_\Omega |v|^2\, e^{-\phi - m\psi - N\theta}\, dV \leqslant C \int_\Omega |Pu|^2\, e^{-\phi} dV \tag{5}$$

Here m *and* N *are non-negative integers which depend only on* P; C *is a constant which depends only on* ζ *and on* P, *and* dV *is Lebesgue measure in* $\mathbb{C}^n$.

For emphasis we note that, as in the scalar case, m, N and C do not depend on Ω. This theorem is proved by Hörmander [1] for the case $\Omega = \mathbb{C}^n$ ($\psi = 0$), and for arbitrary Ω by Petersen [7]. The method of proof in [7] is a modification of the proof in [1], and makes use of the refined L^2 existence and estimate theorems for the Cauchy-Riemann operator of Hörmander [8]. Here we shall only sketch the idea of the proof, except for Theorem 6, where the complete proof is given since it was omitted from [7]. At the end we give the generalization of Theorem 1 to systems and mention a related conjecture of K.T. Smith [9].

3. IDEA OF PROOF

The proof of Theorem 2 is carried out in essentially three steps.

(A) We construct local solutions with estimates by means of the Weierstrass division theorem and an inductive argument of Oka.

(B) By means of a Hilbert resolution we establish a theorem on trivial cohomology with bounds for the sheaf of relations of the columns of P, i.e. a Cartan theorem B with bounds.

(C) The local solutions are now corrected by means of the result of step (B) to fit together to give a global solution with an estimate.

The proof of step (B) requires first a result on trivial cohomology with bounds for the sheaf $\mathscr{A}$ of germs of holomorphic functions. Such results are established by means of existence theorems with estimates for the Cauchy-Riemann equations.

4. COHOMOLOGY WITH BOUNDS FOR SHEAF $\mathscr{A}$

We use the notation of [1, 7, 8]. If Ω is an open set in $\mathbb{C}^n$, ϕ is a real-valued measurable function, locally bounded from above in Ω, we denote by $L^2_{(p,q)}(\Omega,\phi)$ the forms of type (p,q) in Ω in L^2 with respect to the density $e^{-\phi}\,dV$. The corresponding L^2 norm is denoted by $\|\cdot\|_\phi$. The existence and L^2 estimate theorem for the Cauchy-Riemann equations which we need is the following.

Theorem 3. *Let* Ω *be a domain of holomorphy in* $\mathbb{C}^n$, *let* ϕ *be a strictly plurisubharmonic function in* Ω, *and let* e^κ *be a lower bound for the plurisubharmonicity of* ϕ.

If $q > 0$, $f \in L^2_{(p,q)}(\Omega,\phi)$, $\bar\partial f = 0$ *and if* $\|f\|_{\phi+\kappa} < \infty$, *then there exists* $u \in L^2_{(p,q-1)}(\Omega,\phi)$ *such that*

$$\bar\partial u = f \text{ and } \|u\|^2_\phi \leqslant \frac{1}{q}\,\|f\|^2_{\phi+\kappa}$$

Corollary 4. *Let* Ω *be a bounded domain of holomorphy in* $\mathbb{C}^n$ *with diameter* D *and let* ϕ *be a plurisubharmonic function in* Ω.

If $q > 0$, $f \in L^2_{(p,q)}(\Omega,\phi)$ *and* $\bar\partial f = 0$ *then there exists* $u \in L^2_{(p,q-1)}(\Omega,\phi)$ *such that*

$$\bar\partial u = f \text{ and } \|u\|^2_\phi \leqslant \frac{eD^2}{q}\,\|f\|^2_\phi$$

These two results are due to Hörmander [8].

Let Ω be an open subset of $\mathbb{C}^n$, and let $(\Omega_\nu)_{\nu\geqslant 1}$ be an open covering of Ω such that there is an integer M such that for any M + 1 distinct positive integers ν_j we have

$$\Omega_{\nu_0} \cap \Omega_{\nu_1} \cap \ldots \cap \Omega_{\nu_M} = \emptyset$$

If $s \geqslant 0$ is an integer we denote by

$$C^s((\Omega_\nu), Z_{(p,q)}, \phi)$$

the set of all alternating cochains $c = \{c_\alpha\}$ where $\alpha = (\alpha_0, \ldots, \alpha_s)$ is an (s + 1)-tuple of positive integers and

$$c_\alpha \in L^2_{(p,q)}(\Omega_\alpha, \phi), \ \bar\partial c_\alpha = 0$$

where

$$\Omega_\alpha = \Omega_{\alpha_0} \cap \ldots \cap \Omega_{\alpha_s}$$

and

$$\|c\|_\phi^2 = \sum_{|\alpha| = s+1}' \int_{\Omega_\alpha} |c_\alpha|^2 e^{-\phi} dV < +\infty$$

where $\sum'$ means we sum only over α's that are increasing. For a cochain c we define the coboundary δc in the usual way. An application of the Cauchy-Schwarz inequality shows that

$$\|\delta c\|_\phi \leqslant M \|c\|_\phi$$

We shall need an open covering of Ω with a number of properties.

Lemma 5. *Let Ω be a proper non-empty open subset of $\mathbb{C}^n$. There exists an open covering $(\Omega_\nu)_{\nu\geqslant 1}$ of Ω and positive constants A, B and an integer $M > 1$, where A, B and M depend only on n, with the following properties:*

(a) *If $z \in \Omega_\nu$ then B^{-1} diam $(\Omega_\nu) \leqslant d(z) \leqslant A$ diam (Ω_ν). In particular B is an upper bound for the diameters of the open sets Ω_ν.*

(b) *If $\alpha = (\alpha_0, \ldots, \alpha_s)$, $s \geqslant M$, $\alpha_0 < \alpha_1 < \ldots < \alpha_s$, then $\Omega_\alpha = \emptyset$.*

(c) *There exists a partition of unity $(\chi_\nu)_{\nu\geqslant 1}$ with $\chi_\nu \in C_c^\infty(\Omega_\nu)$ and*

$$\sum_{\nu\geqslant 1} |\bar\partial \chi_\nu(z)| \leqslant A\, d(z)^{-1}, z \in \Omega$$

(d) *Each Ω_ν is a domain of holomorphy.*

Indeed, the Ω_ν may be chosen to be cubes and the proof of the lemma is a small modification of an argument due to H. Whitney (see Ref. [7] and pp. 167–170 of Ref. [10]).

We can now obtain a theorem B with bounds for the sheaf $\mathscr{A}$. I give the complete details since they were omitted from Ref. [7]. The proof (even the notation!) is essentially the same as Theorem 2.4.1 in Hörmander [8], except for differences arising from the fact that we have different estimates, because Hörmander works only with $\Omega = \mathbb{C}^n$.

Theorem 6. *Let* Ω *be a domain of holomorphy in* $\mathbb{C}^n$ *and let* $(\Omega_\nu)_{\nu \geq 1}$ *be an open covering of* Ω *with the properties listed in Lemma 5. Let* ϕ *be a strictly plurisubharmonic function in* Ω (in the sense of Ref. [8]) *and suppose* e^κ *is a lower bound for the plurisubharmonicity of* ϕ *where* $\kappa \in C(\Omega)$ *is chosen so that* $\kappa \leq a$ *for some real number* a.

If $s \geq 1$ *then for each* $c \in C^s((\Omega_\nu), Z_{(p,q)}, \phi + \kappa)$ *with* $\delta c = 0$ *there exists*

$$c' \in C^{s-1}((\Omega_\nu), Z_{(p,q)}, \phi + 2\psi)$$

such that $\delta c' = c$ *and*

$$\|c'\|_{\phi + 2\psi} \leq K \|c\|_{\phi + \kappa}$$

Here $\psi(z) = -\log d(z)$ *and* K *is a constant which depends only on* A, a, B *and* M.

By a simple trick we can remove the condition that ϕ be *strictly* plurisubharmonic.

Corollary 7. *Let* Ω *and* Ω_ν *be as in Theorem 6. Let* ϕ *be any plurisubharmonic function in* Ω. *If* $s \geq 1$ *then for each* $c \in C^s((\Omega_\nu), Z_{(p,q)}, \phi)$ *with* $\delta c = 0$ *there exists*

$$c' \in C^{s-1}((\Omega_\nu), Z_{(p,q)}, \phi + 2\psi + 2\theta)$$

such that $\delta c' = c$ *and*

$$\|c'\|_{\phi + 2\psi + 2\theta} \leq K' \|c\|_\phi$$

Here $\theta(z) = \log(1 + |z|^2)$ *and* K' *is a constant which depends only on* A, B *and* M.

Proof (Corollary 7): Let $\phi' = \phi + 2\theta - \log 2$. Then ϕ' is strictly plurisubharmonic (in the sense of [8]) and $e^\kappa = 2(1 + |z|^2)^{-2}$ is a lower bound for the plurisubharmonicity of ϕ'. Moreover, $\phi' + \kappa = \phi$ and $\kappa = -2\theta + \log 2 \leq \log 2$. Now use Theorem 6 with ϕ replaced by ϕ' and with $a = \log 2$ (this trick I learned from Hörmander [1], p. 93).

Remark. Corollary 7 is the main result of this section. We are really only interested in the case $p = q = 0$, but general q is needed in the proof of Theorem 6 (see below). Note in case $s = 1$ and $p = q = 0$ the corollary says:

Given $h_{ij} \in A(\Omega_i \cap \Omega_j)$ such that $h_{ij} + h_{ji} = 0$, $h_{jk} + h_{ki} + h_{ij} = 0$ and

$$\|h\|_\phi^2 = \sum_{i<j} \int_{\Omega_i \cap \Omega_j} |h_{ij}|^2 e^{-\phi} \, dV < \infty$$

there exist $g_i \in A(\Omega_i)$ such that $h_{ij} = g_j - g_i$ in $\Omega_i \cap \Omega_j$ and

$$\sum_i \int_{\Omega_i} |g_i(z)|^2\ d(z)^2\ (1+|z|^2)^{-2}\, e^{-\phi(z)}\ dV(z) \leqslant K^2\ \|h\|_\phi^2$$

i.e. we can solve Cousin I with bounds.

We now give the proof of Theorem 6.

Proof (Theorem 6): Define

$$b_\alpha = \sum_\nu \chi_\nu c_{\nu,\alpha}\ ,\ |\alpha| = s$$

where $\chi_\nu c_{\nu,\alpha}$ is defined to be 0 outside the support of χ_ν. Then b is an (s−1)-chain and an easy computation shows that $\delta c = 0$ implies

$$\delta b = c \tag{6}$$

Now $b_\alpha = \sum (\chi_\nu)^{1/2}\ (\chi_\nu^{1/2}\, c_{\nu,\alpha})$ and hence by the Cauchy-Schwarz inequality $|b_\alpha|^2 \leqslant \sum \chi_\nu |c_{\nu,\alpha}|^2$, since $\sum \chi_\nu = 1$. If we integrate over Ω_α and sum over increasing α, $|\alpha| = s$, we obtain

$$\|b\|_{\phi+\kappa} \leqslant M^{1/2}\ \|c\|_{\phi+\kappa} \tag{7}$$

Now $\bar\partial b_\alpha = \sum \bar\partial\chi_\nu \wedge c_{\nu,\alpha}$ and therefore by the Cauchy-Schwarz inequality as above, and because $\sum |\bar\partial\chi_\nu| \leqslant A\ d^{-1}$, we have

$$|\bar\partial b_\alpha|^2 \leqslant A\ d^{-1} \sum |\bar\partial\chi_\nu|\ |c_{\nu,\alpha}|^2$$

Since $|\bar\partial\chi_\nu|$ vanishes in the complement of $\Omega_{\nu,\alpha}$ in Ω_α and is bounded by $A\ d^{-1}$ in Ω_α, we obtain

$$\int_{\Omega_\alpha} d^2\ |\bar\partial b_\alpha|^2\ e^{-\phi-\kappa}\ dV \leqslant A^2 \sum_\nu \int_{\Omega_{\nu,\alpha}} |c_{\nu,\alpha}|^2\ e^{-\phi-\kappa}\ dV$$

Since $d = e^{-\psi}$ we obtain easily

$$\|\bar\partial b\|_{\phi+\kappa+2\psi} \leqslant A\ M^{1/2}\ \|c\|_{\phi+\kappa} \tag{8}$$

Of course, $\bar\partial\,\bar\partial b = 0$ and hence we have

$$\bar\partial b \in C^{s-1}\ ((\Omega_\nu),\ Z_{(p,q+1)},\ \phi+\kappa+2\psi)$$

Assume now that s = 1. Then $\delta\bar\partial b = \bar\partial\delta b = 0$ implies that $\bar\partial b$ defines a global form of type (p,q+1). For this form, which we denote by f, we have the estimate

$$\|f\|_{\phi+\kappa+2\psi} \leqslant \|\bar\partial b\|_{\phi+\kappa+2\psi} \tag{9}$$

Since $e^\kappa \leqslant e^a$ we have

$$\|f\|_{\phi+2\psi} \leqslant e^a\ \|f\|_{\phi+\kappa+2\psi}$$

Thus f is in $L^2_{(p,q+1)}(\Omega,\phi+2\psi)$ and clearly $\bar\partial f = 0$. By Theorem 3, there exists u in $L^2_{(p,q)}(\Omega,\phi+2\psi)$ such that

$$\bar\partial u = f \tag{10}$$

$$\|u\|^2_{\phi+2\psi} \leqslant \|f\|^2_{\phi+\kappa+2\psi} \tag{11}$$

Now

$$\sum_\nu \int_{\Omega_\nu} |u|^2 e^{-\phi-2\psi}\, dV \leqslant M \|u\|^2_{\phi+2\psi} \tag{12}$$

and hence if we define

$$c'_\nu = b_\nu - u \text{ in } \Omega_\nu$$

then

$$\delta c' = \delta b = c, \quad \bar\partial c' = \bar\partial b - \bar\partial u = f - f = 0$$

and

$$\|c'\|_{\phi+2\psi} \leqslant \|b\|_{\phi+2\psi} + M^{1/2} \|u\|_{\phi+2\psi}$$

by (12). Since $e^{-\psi} = d \leqslant 1$ and $e^\kappa \leqslant e^a$ we have

$$\|b\|_{\phi+2\psi} \leqslant \|b\|_\phi \leqslant e^a \|b\|_{\phi+\kappa}$$

and therefore by (11), (9), (8) and (7) we obtain

$$\|c'\|_{\phi+2\psi} \leqslant M^{1/2} (e^a + AM) \|c\|_{\phi+\kappa} \tag{13}$$

Assume now that s > 1. We make the inductive hypothesis that the theorem has already been proved for smaller values of s, for all p and q, with a certain constant K_s. Since $\delta\bar\partial b = \bar\partial\delta b = \bar\partial c = 0$, the inductive hypothesis applied to $\bar\partial b$ implies there exists

$$b' \in C^{s-2}((\Omega_\nu), Z_{(p,q+1)}, \phi + 4\psi)$$

such that $\delta b' = \bar\partial b$ and

$$\|b'\|_{\phi+4\psi} \leqslant K_{s-1} \|\bar\partial b\|_{\phi+\kappa+2\psi} \tag{14}$$

Since $\bar\partial b'_\alpha = 0$ and Ω_α is a bounded domain of holomorphy, Corollary 4 implies we can choose $b''_\alpha \in L^2_{(p,q)}(\Omega_\alpha, \phi+4\psi)$ such that $b'_\alpha = \bar\partial b''_\alpha$ and

$$\int_{\Omega_\alpha} |b''_\alpha|^2 e^{-\phi-4\psi}\, dV \leqslant 4(\operatorname{diam}(\Omega_\alpha))^2 \int_{\Omega_\alpha} |b'_\alpha|^2 e^{-\phi-4\psi}\, dV$$

Now the 4ψ in the left-hand side here is a nuisance, since we are in the middle of an induction, and the number of ψ's will grow with each inductive step. Hence we wish to erase two of the ψ's, so to speak. We note that $\operatorname{diam}(\Omega_\alpha) \leqslant \min \operatorname{diam}(\Omega_{\alpha_j}) \leqslant B\, d(z)$ if $z \in \Omega_\alpha$, i.e.

$$e^{-2\psi} \geqslant B^{-2} (\operatorname{diam}(\Omega_\alpha))^2 \text{ in } \Omega_\alpha$$

Thus

$$\int_{\Omega_\alpha} |b''_\alpha|^2 e^{-\phi-2\psi}\, dV \leqslant 4B^2 \int_{\Omega_\alpha} |b'_\alpha|^2 e^{-\phi-4\psi}\, dV$$

which implies

$$\|b''\|_{\phi+2\psi} \leqslant 2B\, \|b'_\alpha\|_{\phi+4\psi} \tag{15}$$

We now define $c' = b - \delta b''$. Then

$$\delta c' = \delta b = c$$

$$\bar\partial c' = \bar\partial b - \delta\bar\partial b'' = \bar\partial b - \delta b' = 0$$

and

$$\|c'\|_{\phi+2\psi} \leqslant \|b\|_{\phi+2\psi} + \|\delta b''\|_{\phi+2\psi} \leqslant e^a\, \|b\|_{\phi+\kappa} + M\|b''\|_{\phi+2\psi}$$

If we apply (7), (15), (14) and (8) we obtain

$$\|c'\|_{\phi+2\psi} \leqslant M^{1/2} (e^a + 2ABMK_{s-1})\, \|c\|_{\phi+\kappa}$$

By parts (a) and (b) of Lemma 5 we have $AB \geqslant 1$ and $c = 0$ if $s + 1 > M$. Thus we see easily that we may take $K = (2ABM^{3/2})^M (A + e^a)$. The proof is complete.

5. STEP A: OKA THEOREM WITH BOUNDS

Let U be the open unit ball centred at the origin in $\mathbb{C}^n$.

Theorem 8. *Let* P *be a* $p \times q$ *matrix over* $\mathbb{C}[z_1, \ldots, z_n]$. *Let* $B > 0$. *There exist non-negative integers* m *and* N *and a constant* t, $0 < t < 1$, *depending on* P, *and a constant* $C > 0$ *depending on* P *and* B, *such that if* $z \in \mathbb{C}^n$, $0 < r \leqslant B$, *and* $u \in A(z+rU)^q$ *then there exists* $v \in A(z+trU)^q$ *such that* $Pv = Pu$ *in* $z + trU$ *and if* ϕ *is any measurable real-valued function on* $z + rU$ *such that* $|\phi(z') - \phi(z'')|$ *is bounded on* $(z+rU) \times (z+rU)$ *by a constant* ζ *then*

$$r^m \int_{z+trU} |v|^2 e^{-\phi-N\theta}\, dV \leqslant C\, e^{\zeta} \int_{z+rU} |Pu|^2 e^{-\phi}\, dV$$

where $\theta(z) = \log(1 + |z|^2)$.

If $0 < t < 1$ satisfies the conclusion of Theorem 8 we shall say that t is *good* for P. The proof of Theorem 8 is given in Ref. [7]. The proof there is a modification of the corresponding result in Ch. 7 of Ref. [1], which in turn is an adaptation of the inductive argument of Oka that $\mathscr{A}^p$ is coherent. One first shows that if the theorem is true for a fixed $n \geqslant 1$ and for $p = 1$, then it is true for the given n, for all $p \geqslant 1$. This part of the proof, induction on p, is essentially linear algebra. One then shows that if the theorem is true in dimension $n-1$ for all p, then it is true in dimension n for $p = 1$. Roughly speaking, one uses the Weierstrass division theorem to reduce the problem to the case where Pu is a polynomial in z_n and then looks for v a polynomial in z_n. By equating coefficients of z_n in $Pv = Pu$ we obtain a system of equations for holomorphic functions in $z_1, \ldots, z_{n-1}$. Keeping track of the estimates does make the proof rather long and technical.

6. STEP B: THEOREM B WITH BOUNDS FOR THE SHEAF OF RELATIONS

Let P be a $p \times q$ matrix over $\mathbb{C}[z_1, \ldots, z_n]$. Then we can construct a Hilbert resolution for the sheaf of relations $\mathscr{R}(P)$ of the columns of P. $\mathscr{R}(P)$ is just the kernel of the homomorphism $P : \mathscr{A}^q \to \mathscr{A}^p$ (see [7]). We obtain an exact sequence

$$0 \longrightarrow \mathscr{A}^{s_n} \xrightarrow{Q^n} \mathscr{A}^{s_{n-1}} \xrightarrow{Q^{n-1}} \cdots \xrightarrow{Q^0} \mathscr{A}^q \xrightarrow{P} \mathscr{A}^p$$

where Q^k is an $s_{k-1} \times s_k$ matrix of polynomials (where $s_{-1} = q$). Then by Theorem 7.2.9 in Ref. [1] or by Cartan's theorem B, if ω is any domain of holomorphy in $\mathbb{C}^n$ we have an exact sequence

$$0 \longrightarrow A(\omega)^{s_n} \xrightarrow{Q^n} A(\omega)^{s_{n-1}} \xrightarrow{Q^{n-1}} \cdots \xrightarrow{Q^0} A(\omega)^q \xrightarrow{P} A(\omega)^p \tag{16}$$

Now let Ω be an open subset of $\mathbb{C}^n$ and let $(\Omega_\nu)_{\nu \geqslant 1}$ be an open covering of Ω with intersection number M as before. If $s \geqslant 0$ is an integer we denote by

$$C^s((\Omega_\nu), \mathscr{R}(P), \phi)$$

the set of all alternating cochains $c = \{c_\alpha\}$ where $\alpha = (\alpha_0, \ldots, \alpha_s)$ is an $(s+1)$-tuple of positive integers and

$$c_\alpha \in A(\Omega_\alpha)^q, \quad Pc_\alpha = 0 \text{ in } \Omega_\alpha$$

and

$$\|c\|_\phi^2 = \sum_{|\alpha| = s+1}' \int_{\Omega_\alpha} |c_\alpha|^2 e^{-\phi} \, dV < \infty$$

where $\sum'$ means we sum only over increasing α. As before, ϕ is a real-valued measurable function in Ω, locally bounded from above.

We need a refinement of Lemma 5. As before, the proof is an idea of H. Whitney and may be found in Ref. [7].

Lemma 9. *Let $0 < t < 1$ be given. There exist open coverings $(\Omega_\nu^k)_{\nu \geqslant 1}$, $k = -1, 0, 1, \ldots, n, n+1$ of Ω, a positive constant A, and an integer $M > 0$ with the following properties:*

(a) *If $z \in \Omega_\nu^k$ then* $2 \operatorname{diam}(\Omega_\nu^k) \leqslant d(z) \leqslant A \operatorname{diam}(\Omega_\nu^k)$.

(b) *For each k, $(\Omega_\nu^k)_{\nu \geqslant 1}$ has intersection number* M.

(c) *There exists a partition of unity* $(\chi_\nu)_{\nu \geq 1}$ *with* $\chi_\nu \in C_c^\infty(\Omega_\nu^{n+1})$ *such that*

$$\sum_{\nu \geq 1} |\bar{\partial}\chi_\nu(z)| \leq A\, d(z)^{-1},\ z \in \Omega$$

(d) *Each* Ω_ν^k *is a domain of holomorphy.*

(e) *For each* ν, $\Omega_\nu^{k+1} \subset \Omega_\nu^k$, $k = -1, 0, \ldots, n$ *and*

$$\operatorname{dist}(\Omega_\nu^{k+1}, \partial\Omega_\nu^k) \geq t^{-1} \operatorname{diam}(\Omega_\nu^{k+1})$$

The constants A *and* M *depend on* n *and* t.

If $k < \ell$ and c is a cochain relative to the covering $(\Omega_\nu^k)_{\nu \geq 1}$ we denote by ρc the restriction of c to $(\Omega_\nu^\ell)_{\nu \geq 1}$ defined by $(\rho c)_\alpha = c_{\alpha|\Omega_\alpha{}^\ell}$.

Theorem 10. *Let* $\Omega \neq \mathbb{C}^n$ *be a domain of holomorphy in* $\mathbb{C}^n$ *and let* P *be a* $p \times q$ *matrix over* $\mathbb{C}[z_1, \ldots, z_n]$. *Let* ϕ *be a plurisubharmonic function in* Ω *such that*

$$|\phi(z) - \phi(w)| \leq \zeta \text{ if } z \in \Omega,\ |z - w| \leq \tfrac{1}{2} d(z) \tag{17}$$

Let $(Q^k)_{0 \leq k \leq n}$ *be a Hilbert resolution for* P *and assume* $0 < t < 1$ *where* t *is good for* $Q^0, \ldots, Q^n$. *Let* (Ω_ν^k) *be open coverings of* Ω *with the properties listed in Lemma* 9.

If $s \geq 1$ *and* $c \in C^s((\Omega_\nu^0), \mathscr{R}(P), \phi)$ *and* $\delta c = 0$ *then there exists* $c' \in C^{s-1}((\Omega_\nu^{n+1}), \mathscr{R}(P), \phi + m\psi + N\theta)$ *such that* $\delta c' = \rho c$ *and*

$$\|c'\|_{\phi + m\psi + N\theta} \leq K\, \|c\|_\phi$$

Here m, N *are non-negative integers which depend on* P, *and* $K > 0$ *is a constant which depends on* ζ *and* P.

If we denote P by Q^{-1}, then the idea of the proof is to prove by induction the following statement:

If $s > 0$ *and* $c \in C^s((\Omega_\nu^{k+1}), \mathscr{R}(Q^k), \phi)$ *and* $\delta c = 0$ *then there exists* $c' \in C^{s-1}((\Omega_\nu^{n+1}), \mathscr{R}(Q^k), \phi + m\psi + N\theta)$ *such that* $\delta c' = \rho c$ *and* $\|c'\|_{\phi + m\psi + N\theta} \leq K\, \|c\|_\phi$. (18)

When $k = -1$ then (18) is the statement of the theorem. When $k = n$ then $\mathscr{R}(Q^n) = 0$ and so (18) is trivially true. Now assume that $n > k \geq 1$ and that we have proved (18) for all larger values of k and for all plurisubharmonic functions ϕ which satisfy (17). We sketch the remainder of the proof.

Let $\alpha = (\alpha_0, \ldots, \alpha_s)$ where $\alpha_0 < \alpha_1 < \ldots < \alpha_s$ and $\Omega_\alpha^{k+2} \neq \emptyset$. Property (e) in Lemma 9 implies that we have $r > 0$ such that if $z \in \Omega_\alpha^{k+2}$ then $(At)^{-1} d(z) \leq r$ and there exist concentric open balls U and U′ of radius r and radius tr, respectively, such that

$$\Omega_\alpha^{k+2} \subset U' \subset U \subset \Omega_\alpha^{k+1} \tag{19}$$

By the exactness of (16) with $\omega = \Omega_\alpha^{k+1}$ we have $c_\alpha = Q^{k+1} g'_\alpha$ where

$$g'_\alpha \in A(\Omega_\alpha^{k+1})^{s_{k+1}}$$

In view of (19) we may use Theorem 8 with $B = (2t)^{-1}$ to produce

$$g_\alpha \in A(\Omega_\alpha^{k+2})^{s_{k+1}}$$

such that $Q^{k+1} g_\alpha = c_\alpha$ in Ω_α^{k+2} and

$$r^{m'} \int_{\Omega_\alpha^{k+2}} |g_\alpha|^2 e^{-\phi - N'\theta} \, dV \leqslant C e^{\zeta} \int_{\Omega_\alpha^{k+1}} |c_\alpha|^2 e^{-\phi} \, dV \tag{20}$$

Here we have used (17) and the fact that if $z, w \in \Omega_\alpha^{k+1}$ then $|z-w| < \operatorname{diam}(\Omega_\alpha^{k+1}) \leqslant \frac{1}{2} d(z)$. Now since $(At)^{-1} d \leqslant r$ in Ω_α^{k+2}, we have constructed

$$g \in C^s((\Omega_\nu^{k+2}), \mathscr{A}^{s_{k+1}}, \phi + m'\psi + N'\theta)$$

such that $Q^{k+1} g = \rho c$ and

$$\|g\|^2_{\phi + m'\psi + N'\theta} \leqslant C e^{\zeta} (At)^{m'} \|c\|^2_\phi$$

For the rest of the proof I will omit mentioning the open covers and I will omit the estimates. We note $Q^{k+1} \delta g = \rho \delta c = 0$ implies that $\delta g \in C^{s+1}(\mathscr{R}(Q^{k+1}))$. By the inductive hypothesis there is f in $C^s(\mathscr{R}(Q^{k+1}))$ such that $\delta f = \rho \delta g$. Then

$$\rho g - f \in C^s(\mathscr{A}^{s_{k+1}})$$

and $\delta(\rho g - f) = 0$. Thus by Corollary 7 (with $p = q = 0$) there exists h in

$$C^{s-1}(\mathscr{A}^{s_{k+1}})$$

such that $\delta h = \rho g - f$. Now let $c' = Q^{k+1} h$. Then $\delta c' = Q^{k+1} \delta h = Q^{k+1}(\rho g - f) = \rho Q^{k+1} g = \rho c$ and of course $Q^k c' = 0$. The estimates may easily be filled in, or may be found in Ref. [7]. The proof is complete.

Remark. Theorem 7.6.10 in Ref. [1] is similar to Theorem 10 here, except that Hörmander works with $\Omega = \mathbb{C}^n$ and downward induction on s. Hörmander's argument works because when $\Omega = \mathbb{C}^n$ we can choose a sequence of open coverings which refine each other nicely and which all have the same intersection number M. In the present case the intersection number M tends to grow with the number of refinements required (if we require all the properties in Lemma 9) and as a result downward induction on s does not seem to work. Fortunately the Hilbert resolution provides us with a different approach. We note that in the next section we use Theorem 10 only in the case $s = 1$. The inductive proof of (18) above, however, requires all s, since s increases by 1 in the inductive step. Now Theorem 6 (through Corollary 7) is used in the proof of Theorem 10 only in the case $p = q = 0$, but for all s by the above remarks. The proof of Theorem 6 is simple for $s = 1$ and could be written out just for $p = q = 0$ should that be desirable. For $s > 1$, however, we require the statement of Theorem 6 for general q, to make the induction work. Thus, for the present method of proof of Theorem 2, all the cohomology ingredients presented are necessary in the degree of generality stated.

7. STEP C: CORRECTION OF LOCAL SOLUTIONS

We recall Ω is a domain of holomorphy in $\mathbb{C}^n$, ϕ is a plurisubharmonic function in Ω such that $|\phi(z)-\phi(w)| \leqslant \zeta$ if $z \in \Omega$ and $|z-w| \leqslant \frac{1}{2}d(z)$, and P is a p × q matrix over $\mathbb{C}[z_1, ..., z_n]$. We are given $u \in A(\Omega)^q$ and we wish to produce $v \in A(\Omega)^q$ such that $Pv = Pu$ in Ω and

$$\int_\Omega |v(z)|^2 \, d(z)^m \, (1+|z|^2)^{-N} \, e^{-\phi(z)} \, dV(z) \leqslant C \int_\Omega |Pu|^2 \, e^{-\phi} \, dV \tag{21}$$

We choose a Hilbert resolution $(Q^k)_{0 \leqslant k \leqslant n}$ for $\mathscr{R}(P)$ as before and choose $0 < t < 1$ good for Q^k, $0 \leqslant k \leqslant n$, and also good for P, and choose open coverings of Ω as in Lemma 9. For each $\nu \geqslant 1$ let

$$h_\nu = Pu \Big|_{\Omega_{\nu-1}}$$

Then $h \in C^0((\Omega_\nu^{-1}), \mathscr{A}^p, \phi)$ and

$$\|h\|_\phi^2 \leqslant M \int_\Omega |Pu|^2 \, e^{-\phi} \, dV$$

Since t is good for P, by brute force, i.e. Oka with bounds, as in the proof of Theorem 10, we produce $g \in C^0((\Omega_\nu^0), \mathscr{A}^q, \phi + m'\psi + N'\theta)$ such that $Pg = \rho h$ and $\|g\|_{\phi + m'\psi + N'\theta} \leqslant K\|h\|_\phi$. For the rest of the proof I will omit mentioning the open covers and I will omit the estimates. These details may easily be filled in (see Ref. [7]). Since $P\delta g = \delta P g = \rho \delta h = 0$ we have $\delta g \in C^1(\mathscr{R}(P))$. By Theorem 10 there exists $f \in C^0(\mathscr{R}(P))$ such that $\delta f = \rho \delta g$. Then $\delta(\rho g - f) = 0$ implies there exists $v \in A(\Omega)^q$ such that $v = g_\nu - f_\nu$ in Ω_ν^{n+1}. Clearly $Pv = Pu$ and we have the required estimate for v.

8. APPLICATION

We give a generalization of Theorem 1. Let Γ be a closed convex salient cone in $\mathbb{R}^n$ and let $\Omega = \Gamma_0^+ + i\mathbb{R}^n$.

Theorem 11. *Let* P *be a* p × q *matrix over* $\mathbb{C}[z_1, ..., z_n]$. *Let* f *be a p-tuple of temperate distributions with supports in* Γ. *Let* $F \in A(\Omega)^p$ *be the Laplace transform of* f.

The equation

$$P(D)g = f$$

has a solution g, *where* g *is a q-tuple of temperate distributions with supports in* Γ, *if and only if there exists* $G \in A(\Omega)^q$ *such that*

$$P(z)G(z) = F(z), \quad z \in \Omega$$

The necessity is trivial. For the sufficiency, suppose G exists. By Ref. [3], F satisfies an estimate of the form

$$|F(z)|^2 \leqslant C_0 \, d(z)^{-k} \, (1+|z|^2)^L$$

for z in Ω, and hence

$$C_1 = \int_\Omega |F|^2 e^{-\phi} dV < \infty$$

where $\phi = k\psi + (L + n + 1)\theta$. Since G exists, by Theorem 2 we may choose G so that G satisfies an estimate:

$$\int_\Omega |G|^2 e^{-\phi - m\psi - N\theta} dV \leqslant C C_1$$

Then

$$\int_\Omega |G_k(z)|^2 d(z)^{m+k} (1 + |z|^2)^{-N-L-n-1} dV(z) \leqslant C C_1$$

Now if $z \in \Omega$ and D is the polydisc with centre z and radii all equal to $\delta = \frac{1}{2} n^{-1/2} d(z)$ then, since G_k is plurisubharmonic,

$$|G_k(z)| \leqslant \pi^{-n} \delta^{-2n} \int_D |G_k| dV$$

Thus if s, $t \geqslant 0$, then we have

$$|G_k(z)| \leqslant \pi^{-n} \delta^{-2n} \int_D |G_k| d^t (1 + |w|^2)^{-s} dV \cdot \sup_D d^{-t} (1 + |w|^2)^s$$

and hence by Cauchy-Schwarz

$$|G_k(z)|^2 \leqslant \pi^{-n} \delta^{-2n} \int_D |G_k|^2 (1 + |w|^2)^{-2s} d^{2t} dV \cdot \sup_D d^{-2t} (1 + |w|^2)^{2s}$$

If we set $2s = N + L + n + 1$ and $2t = m + k$ we obtain

$$|G_k(z)|^2 \leqslant \pi^{-n} \delta^{-2n} C C_1 \sup_D (1 + |w|^2)^{2s} d(w)^{-2t}$$

Now $w \in D$ implies $|z - w| \leqslant n^{1/2} \delta = \frac{1}{2} d(z)$ and so $d(w) \geqslant \frac{1}{2} d(z)$. Also $(1 + |w|^2) \leqslant (1 + 2|z - w|^2 + 2|z|^2)$ and $|z - w| \leqslant \frac{1}{2} d(z) \leqslant \frac{1}{2}$ implies $(1 + |w|^2) \leqslant 2(1 + |z|^2)$. Thus

$$|G_k(z)|^2 \leqslant C_2 d(z)^{-m-k-2n} (1 + |z|^2)^{N+L+n+1} \tag{22}$$

where $C_2 = \pi^{-n} n^n 2^{m+k+3n+N+L+1} C C_1$. But (22) implies G_k is the Laplace transform of a temperate distribution g_k with support in Γ (see Ref.[3]). The proof is complete.

Since Ω is a domain of holomorphy, by Cartan's Theorem B, or by Theorem 7.2.9 in [1], it suffices in Theorem 11 to assume that G exists locally in Ω. We therefore immediately obtain the following corollary.

Corollary 12. *Let* $P_1, ..., P_q \in \mathbb{C}[z_1, ..., z_n]$. *Then* $P_1, ..., P_q$ *have no common zero in* Ω *if and only if there exist temperate distributions* $g_1, ..., g_q$ *with supports in* Γ *such that*

$$\sum_k P_k(D)g_k = \delta$$

where δ *is the Dirac measure.*

Corollary 12 is related to a conjecture of K.T. Smith [9].

Conjecture. *Suppose* $P_1, ..., P_q$ *are homogeneous polynomials of degrees* $m_1, ..., m_q$ *respectively, and* Γ *is a closed convex salient cone. Then* $P_1, ..., P_q$ *have no common non-trivial zero in* $\Gamma^+ + i\mathbb{R}^n$ *if and only if there exist functions* $K_1, ..., K_q$ *such that:*

(a) $K_j \in C^\infty(\mathbb{R}^n - (0))$ *is homogeneous of degree* $m_j - n$

(b) *The support of* K_j *is contained in* Γ

(c) $$\sum_j P_j(D)K_j = \delta$$

The conjecture is known to be true in certain cases [9]. To prove the conjecture by cohomology with bounds methods as described here, much better estimates are needed (see Ref. [3]). For interesting applications of the known cases of the conjecture see Ref. [9].

Added in proof: For K.T. Smith's conjecture see also: ESKIN, M., SHAMIR, E., Systèmes elliptiques surdéterminés dans des cônes convexes et la conjecture de Smith, C.R. Acad. Sc. Paris, Sér. A **282** (1976) 879–882.

REFERENCES

[1] HÖRMANDER, L., An Introduction to Complex Analysis in Several Variables, Van Nostrand, Princeton (1966).

[2] KOMEČ, A.I., Vestn. Mosk. Univ. Ser. I. Mat. Mekh. **29** (1974) 14–20.

[3] PETERSEN, B.E., On the Laplace transform of a temperate distribution supported by a cone, Proc. Am. Math. Soc. **35** (1972) 123–128.

[4] SIU, Y.-T., Holomorphic functions of polynomial growth on bounded domains, Duke Math. J. **37** (1970) 77–84.

[5] NARASIMHAN, R., "Cohomology with bounds on complex spaces", Several Complex Variables I (Proc. Conf. Univ. Maryland, 1970), Springer Lecture Notes in Math. **155**, Springer Verlag, Berlin and New York (1970) 141–150.

[6] SKODA, H., Application des techniques L^2 à la théorie des idéaux d'une algèbre de fonctions holomorphes avec poids, Ann. Sci. Ecole Norm. Sup. (4) **5** (1972) 545–579.

[7] PETERSEN, B.E., Holomorphic functions with growth conditions, Trans. Am. Math. Soc. **206** (1975) 395–406.

[8] HÖRMANDER, L., L^2 estimates and existence theorems for the $\bar\partial$ operator, Acta Math. **113** (1965) 89–152.

[9] SMITH, K.T., Formulas to represent functions by their derivatives, Math. Ann. **188** (1970) 53–77.

[10] STEIN, E.M., Singular Integrals and Differentiability Properties of Functions, Princeton Math. Ser. No. 30, Princeton Univ. Press (1970).

IAEA-SMR-18/29

COMPLEX AND ALMOST COMPLEX FOUR-MANIFOLDS

H. PITTIE
Department of Mathematics,
University of Georgia,
Athens, Georgia,
United States of America

Abstract

COMPLEX AND ALMOST COMPLEX FOUR-MANIFOLDS.

A result of van de Ven is described which shows that there are topological obstructions to integrability for almost-complex structures on four-manifolds. A brief review is given of the salient definitions and properties and a theorem of Hirzebruch and Hopf is discussed which gives necessary and sufficient conditions for a compact, oriented four-manifold to have an almost-complex structure.

INTRODUCTION

A result of van de Ven [10] will be described which shows that there are topological obstructions to integrability for almost-complex structures on four-manifolds. If one is interested in the integrability of a particular almost-complex structure, then of course the vanishing of its torsion tensor is necessary and sufficient, by the Newlander-Nirenberg theorem (see the paper of Robertson in Vol.I of these Proceedings). Van de Ven's theorem concerns itself with the existence question of whether there is *any* almost-complex structure, on a given almost-complex manifold, which is integrable.

The statement and proof of the theorem involve characteristic classes, and so a brief review of the salient definitions and properties is given. Then, partly for illustration and partly because it fits in well with Prof. Robertson's chapters on almost-complex structures on spheres, we shall discuss a theorem of Hirzebruch and Hopf [6] which gives necessary and sufficient conditions for a compact, oriented four-manifold to have an almost-complex structure. The underlying principle in both these theorems is to define invariants associated to the tangent-bundle (the characteristic classes) and then to show that the existence of an almost-complex structure or an integrable almost-complex structure imposes algebraic conditions on these invariants; by looking at examples we shall see that these conditions are sometimes satisfied, sometimes not.

1. CONNECTIONS AND CURVATURE

Let M be a smooth manifold[1], TM its tangent-bundle and Γ(TM) the linear space of smooth sections, i.e. the linear space of (smooth) vector fields. A **connection** on TM is a real linear mapping

$$\nabla : \Gamma(TM) \times \Gamma(TM) \to \Gamma(TM)$$

[1] In applications, M is compact, oriented and four-dimensional: the general definitions, however, can be given for any manifold.

satisfying the following two conditions:

(i) $\nabla_{fX}(Y) = f\nabla_X(Y)$ for $f \in C^\infty(M)$

(ii) $\nabla_X(gY) = g\nabla_X(Y) + X(g)Y$ for $g \in C^\infty(M)$

These conditions say that ∇ is a "local" operator, and in fact a first-order differential operator. In local co-ordinates, ∇ is given by the classical Christoffel symbols.

Connections always exist: locally they are easy to define (see below) and then the local connections can be patched together by a partition of unity. The notation ∇_X in fact comes from the local situation; if we take $M = R^n$ (or an open subset in R^n) and choose co-ordinates $(x_1, \ldots, x_n)$ so that the vector fields $\partial/\partial x_i$ span TM, then $\nabla_{\partial/\partial x_i}$ is just the "directional derivative", i.e.

$$\nabla_{\partial/\partial x_i}(\partial/\partial x_j) = 0$$

and more generally

$$\nabla_{\partial/\partial x_i}(\textstyle\sum f_j(\partial/\partial x_j)) = \textstyle\sum_j (\partial f_j/\partial x_i)(\partial/\partial x_j)$$

Now let us go back to the case of a general connection. For each $X \in \Gamma(TM)$, ∇_X is a linear map from $\Gamma(TM)$ to $\Gamma(TM)$; the space $\Gamma(TM)$ is a Lie algebra under the bracket of vector fields and the set of linear maps from a vector space to itself is a Lie algebra under the "usual" bracket $[A, B] = AB-BA$. We can ask whether ∇ is a Lie algebra homomorphism; or more precisely, we can measure the deviation of ∇ from being one by setting

$$\tilde{k}_\nabla : \Gamma(TM) \times \Gamma(TM) \to \mathrm{Hom}\,(\Gamma(TM), \Gamma(TM))$$

to be

$$\tilde{k}_\nabla(X,Y)Z = \nabla_X\nabla_Y(Z) - \nabla_Y\nabla_X(Z) - \nabla_{[X,Y]}(Z)$$

One checks that $\tilde{k}_\nabla$ is linear over the C^∞-functions in each of the three arguments; hence it actually comes from a **tensor**

$$k_\nabla : TM \times TM \to \mathrm{Hom}\,(TM, TM)$$

In the classical language, this is the Ricci tensor of the connection; we shall call it the **curvature**[2]. Notice that k_∇ is skew-symmetric in the first two arguments, so it gives

$$k_\nabla : \Lambda^2(TM) \to \mathrm{Hom}\,(TM, TM)$$

Thus locally k_∇ is a "matrix-valued two-form". The definitions here can be found in any standard book on differential geometry, e.g. Kobayashi and Nomizu [7]; a very concise but illuminating treatment is given in Milnor and Stasheff [9].

---

[2] In this abstract setting, the reader is advised not to look too hard for an intuitive meaning of "curvature": this does have some justification, but it comes into its own only when one works with the Levi-Cività connection of a manifold embedded in R^n.

2. CHARACTERISTIC CLASSES

Consider now a manifold M, its tangent bundle TM equipped with a connection ∇, and the associated curvature tensor

$$k_\nabla : \Lambda^2(TM) \rightarrow \text{Hom}(TM, TM)$$

As remarked in Section1, locally k_∇ is a matrix-valued two-form. If we want to produce ordinary differential forms out of it locally we can apply any function from matrices to scalars. However, in order to get *global* differential forms, defined over M, we must restrict ourselves to functions which transform correctly with respect to the Jacobian matrix in the overlaps of co-ordinate patches: i.e. if ψ is the Jacobian, the functions must satisfy $f(\psi k_\nabla \psi^{-1}) = f(k_\nabla)$. We take invariant polynomials: these are polynomials P with entries in the matrices which satisfy $P(ABA^{-1}) = P(B)$ for all invertible matrices A. For example, the trace and determinant are such polynomials: more generally expanding

$$\det(tI+B) = \sum_0^n \sigma_i(B)\, t^{n-i},$$

the $\sigma_i(B)$ are such polynomials. The differential forms $\sigma_j(k_\nabla)$ will then be 2j-forms on the manifold, and the basic facts about them are embodied in the following two theorems, due to Chern [4].

Theorem 1. *Each* $\sigma_j(k_\nabla)$ *is a closed form of degree* 2j: *i.e.* $d\sigma_j(k_\nabla) = 0$.

Theorem 2. *If* ∇_1 *and* ∇_2 *are two connections on* TM, *with curvatures* k_1 *and* k_2 *then* $\sigma_j(k_1) - \sigma_j(k_2)$ *is an exact form, i.e. there is a form* η *of degree* $(2j-1)$ *such that* $d\eta = \sigma_j(k_1) - \sigma_j(k_2)$.

The first theorem allows us to look at the de Rham cohomology class of $\sigma_j(k_\nabla) \in H^{2j}(M:R)$. The second theorem says that this **cohomology class** is independent of the particular connection used to construct it. Thus it is an invariant of TM, and is the so-called j^{th} **characteristic class.** (Actually one has to multiply by some universal constant, such as $(1/2\pi)^j$, but we shall ignore this.)

To bring the almost-complex structure into the act, we need to look at a refinement of the above procedure. So suppose now that M is an almost-complex manifold. $J: TM \rightarrow TM$ a particular almost-complex structure, with $J^2 = -1_{TM}$. Then on the complexified bundle $TM \otimes C$, J has "±i-eigenbundles" TM′ and TM″ and TM = TM′ + TM″. Moreover, TM, TM′ and TM″ are all isomorphic as **real** vector bundles (see Robertson).

We pick a Hermitian metric $\langle\, ,\rangle$ on TM′. A **Hermitian connection** on TM′ is then a map

$$\nabla : \Gamma(TM') \times \Gamma(TM') \rightarrow \Gamma(TM')$$

satisfying the two conditions above (with respect to $C^\infty(M:C)$) and in addition

(iii) $\langle \nabla_X Y, Z\rangle + \langle Y, \nabla_X Z\rangle = X(\langle Y, Z\rangle)$

It is easily verified that Hermitian connections always exist: locally one simply performs the construction outlined above with a Hermitian-orthogonal basis for TM′ over trivializing open sets, and then patches together the local connections by a partition of unity.

As before, there is an associated tensor

$$k_\nabla : \Lambda^2_C(TM') \rightarrow \text{Hom}_C(TM', TM)$$

The condition (iii) says that for each pair $X, Y \in \Gamma(TM')$ $\kappa_\nabla(X,Y)$ is skew-Hermitian, or equivalently that $i\kappa_\nabla(X,Y)$ is Hermitian ($i = \sqrt{-1}$). The invariant polynomials in $i\kappa_\nabla$ will then provide cohomology classes c_j as before. Theorems 1 and 2 still hold, although in general they *do* depend on the choice of J.

We can now relate the characteristic classes c_j associated to J and those constructed earlier for real bundles. Of course, there are relations valid in all dimensions, but for computational simplicity we shall restrict ourselves to the four-dimensional case. Let us repeat the basic data. M is a compact, oriented *four*-dimensional manifold; TM is equipped with a J-operator; TM' is the + i-eigenbundle of J on $TM \otimes C$. We put a Hermitian metric $\langle\, ,\rangle$ on TM', and a Hermitian connection ∇. Then its curvature $i\kappa_\nabla$ will give two cohomology classes $c_1 \in H^2(M:R)$ and $c_2 \in H^4(M:R)$ which are represented by the forms trace($i\kappa_\nabla$) and det($i\kappa_\nabla$). (Notice that these forms are **real** because $i\kappa_\nabla$ is Hermitian: at any point $x \in M$, $i\kappa_\nabla(X,Y)$ is given by a Hermitian matrix, and trace and det are then given in terms of the eigenvalues which are real.)

Now TM' and TM are isomorphic as **real** vector bundles. If we ignore the complex structure on TM' then $\langle\, ,\rangle$ gives an orthogonal metric on TM, ∇ gives a connection on TM satisfying (iii), and its curvature k is skew-symmetric. We now establish

Proposition. *For every pair of vector fields* $X, Y \in TM' = TM$

$$(\mathrm{trace}(i\kappa_\nabla(X,Y)))^2 = 2\,\det(i\kappa_\nabla(X,Y)) + \sigma_2(k(X,Y))$$

Proof. It suffices to check the identity point by point. So fix a point $m \in M$ and a pair of tangent vectors $X, Y \in T'_mM$. Then at m, $\kappa_\nabla(X,Y)$ is a 2×2 Hermitian matrix, and $k(X,Y)$ is the corresponding 4×4 skew-symmetric matrix. Now the identity above becomes a matter of linear algebra. If U is the 2×2 unitary matrix which diagonalizes $i\kappa_\nabla(X,Y)$ to

$$\begin{pmatrix} \lambda_1 & 0 \\ 0 & \lambda_2 \end{pmatrix}$$

then as a real 4×4 matrix U is orthogonal and conjugates $k(X, Y)$ into

$$\left(\begin{array}{cc|cc} 0 & -\lambda_1 & & \\ \lambda_1 & 0 & \multicolumn{2}{c}{0} \\ \hline & & 0 & -\lambda_2 \\ \multicolumn{2}{c|}{0} & \lambda_2 & 0 \end{array}\right)$$

Thus one has

$$(\lambda_1 + \lambda_2)^2 = 2\,\lambda_1\lambda_2 + (\lambda_1^2 + \lambda_2^2) \qquad \square$$

Corollary. *For the particular choice of connections given above,*

$$c_1^2 = 2\,c_2 + p_1$$

at the level of differential forms: here $p_1 = \sigma_2(k)$.

Now if we had chosen different connections, we would no longer have the identity at the level of differential forms, but we would still have the identity on cohomology. Since we are dealing with forms in the top degree, this says then that in any case

$$\int_M c_1^2 = 2\int_M c_2 + \int_M p_1$$

3. THE HIRZEBRUCH-HOPF THEOREM

We begin by showing that in the integral identity of the previous section, the right-hand side can be interpreted in terms of global topological invariants of M. This will then lead to the theorem of Hirzebruch and Hopf.

Consider first an arbitrary **compact** manifold X of dimension n. Then the cohomology groups $H^p(X:R)$ are all finite dimensional, and zero for $p > n$. Thus the alternating sum of the Betti numbers is well defined:

$$\chi(X) = \sum_p (-1)^p \dim p\, H^p(X:R)$$

For $n = 2$ this is the well-known Euler characteristic of the surface X, and the Gauss-Bonnet theorem expresses $\chi(X)$ as the integral of the Gaussian curvature over X. For $n > 2$, there is a generalized Gauss-Bonnet theorem due to Chern and in the case of almost-complex four-manifolds it takes the following form:

Theorem 3. *For any compact almost-complex four-manifold* M,

$$\int_M c_2 = \chi(M)$$

Notice as a consequence of Theorem 1, the cohomology class of c_2 is a topological invariant of M.

To give the topological interpretation of the other integral, we need to recall the definition of the **signature** or **index** of a compact manifold X. Suppose that X is oriented and has even dimension 2m. Then the wedge product gives a bilinear pairing:

$$\beta : H^m(X) \times H^m(X) \to H^{2m}(X:R) = R$$

defined by

$$\beta(\omega_1, \omega_2) = \int_X \omega_1 \omega_2$$

Now

$$\beta(\omega_2, \omega_1) = (-1)^m \beta(\omega_1, \omega_2)$$

so when m itself is even, say $m = 2\ell$, then β is a symmetric, bilinear form on $H^m(X)$. The form β then has a signature or index, and we define[3]

sign X = sign β_X = (number of positive eigenvalues) − (number of negative eigenvalues)

[3] By Poincaré-duality (or Hodge theory) one knows that this form β_X is always non-singular, so there are no zero eigenvalues.

By our definition, the lowest-dimensional manifolds with an index are compact oriented four-manifolds, and here one has

Theorem 4 (Thom). *If* M *is a compact, oriented four-manifold then*

$$\int_M p_1 = 3 \text{ sign } M$$

Remark. The generalized Gauss-Bonnet theorem was proved by Chern about the same time that he introduced the classes c_i, and within the framework of differential geometry. In sharp contrast, Thom's result above, and its extension to higher dimensions by Hirzebruch [5] came some twenty years after Pontrjagin had defined the classes p_i. More important, the proofs of Thom and Hirzebruc were based on Thom's deep work in topology (Cobordism theory). It is only very recently that a purely differential-geometric proof of this result has been given (see Ref.[1]).

Using Theorems 3 and 4, we can now state the theorem of Hirzebruch and Hopf.

Theorem 5. *Let* M *be a compact, oriented four-manifold. A necessary condition for* M *to be almost complex is the existence of a closed two-form* γ *such that*

$$\int_M \gamma^2 = 2\chi(M) + 3 \text{ sign } (M)$$

Proof. If M has an almost-complex structure $J: TM \to TM$, then we can put a Hermitian connection on $T'M$ and take $\gamma = c_1$. The equation

$$\int_M c_1^2 = 2 \int_M c_2 + \int_M p_1$$

combined with Theorems 3 and 4 gives the result. □

Remark. The condition above, together with a mod 2 condition on the periods of the closed form γ, actually gives a sufficient condition as well for M to possess an almost-complex structure. This is certainly the deeper part of the Hirzebruch-Hopf theorem, but its precise formulation alone, quite apart from its proof, would require a long detour through the thick of algebraic topology, so we omit it. Note, however, that this will come into the proof of van de Ven's result in the next section.

Corollary. *The four-sphere* S^4 *has no almost-complex structure.*

Proof. $\chi(S^4) = 2$, and sign $(S^4) = 0$ because $H^2(S^4) = 0$. For the same reason, any closed two-form α on S^4 is exact, so

$$\int_{S^4} \alpha \wedge \alpha = 0$$

Thus

$$2\chi(S^4) + \text{sign}(S^4) \neq \int_{S^4} \alpha \wedge \alpha$$

for any closed two-form. □

One virtue of this proof is that it works for any manifold (compact) which has the same homology groups as S^4; of course, it is not known whether there are any such simply connected examples, but the proof at least is more general. Another point worth noting is that essentially the same type of argument, using numerical properties of characteristic classes, gave the first proof that S^{2n} has no almost-complex structure for $n > 3$. The point is that if there were, then the generalized Gauss-Bonnet theorem would imply

$$\int_{S^{2n}} c_n = \chi(S^{2n}) = 2$$

On the other hand, using deep properties of the cohomology of Lie groups (and a very different interpretation of the classes c_j) Borel and Serre [3] showed that

$$\int_{S^{2n}} c_n$$

is an integer which is divisible by every prime $p \leqslant n-1$. Thus, if $n > 3$, $p = 3$ would have to divide this integral which is 2 – contradiction! For $n = 3$, Robertson's paper in these Proceedings gives the construction of an explicit almost-complex structure J on S^6; it is known that this particular J is not integrable, but whether there is some other integrable J on S^6 is still an open question.

4. COMPLEX STRUCTURES ON FOUR-MANIFOLDS

We shall now see that characteristic classes also come into the question of whether an almost-complex four-manifold possesses an integrable almost-complex structure – or what is the same, whether it is a complex manifold (with a possibly different almost-complex structure).

For simplicity, we shall not discuss van de Ven's general theorems, but only give a couple of his examples of almost-complex four-manifolds on which no almost-complex structure is integrable. The methods used in these special cases are fairly representative of the methods employed in the general proofs.

To begin, let us formulate the integrability condition on J in terms of differential forms rather than in terms of vector fields. So consider the complexified cotangent bundle $T^*M \otimes C$, and $\Omega^1(M)$ its space of smooth sections – these are the smooth, complex-valued differential one-forms. The action of J on $T^*M \otimes C$ again breaks up the bundle into the $\pm i$-eigenbundles, and it is common to write the corresponding spaces of sections as $\Omega^1(M) = \Omega^{1,0}(M) \oplus \Omega^{0,1}(M)$. So the differential of a function $f \in C^\infty(M:C)$ can then be decomposed into two parts, one lying in $\Omega^{1,0}$ and the other in $\Omega^{0,1}$; thus $df = \partial f + \bar{\partial} f$ where ∂f is the projection into $\Omega^{1,0}$ and $\bar{\partial} f$ into $\Omega^{0,1}$. Similarly, the higher-order forms $\Omega^r(M)$ admit decompositions;

$$\Omega^r(M) = \sum_{p+q=r} \Omega^{p,q}(M)$$

when $\Omega^{p,q}(M)$ is the space of sections of

$$\Lambda^p(TM^{(1,0)}) \otimes_C \Lambda^q(TM^{(0,1)})$$

The integrability of J can be expressed by saying that if $\omega \in \Omega^{p,q}(M)$, then $d\omega$ only has components in $\Omega^{p+1,q}$ and $\Omega^{p,q+1}$, as we shall now show. This allows one to give a decomposition of d into ∂ and $\bar{\partial}$ in each $\Omega^{p,q}$ and from $d^2 = 0$ it follows that $\partial^2 = 0$, $\bar{\partial}^2 = 0$.

Proposition. *J is integrable (i.e.* $T_J(X, Y) = 0$) *if and only if for* $\omega \in \Omega^{p,q}$, $d\omega = \phi_1 + \phi_2$ *where* $\phi_1 \in \Omega^{p+1,q}$, $\phi_2 = \Omega^{p,q+1}$.

Proof. If we write $TM \otimes C = TM' \oplus TM''$ and let P, $\bar{P}$ be the projections on the summands, then $T_J(X, Y) = \bar{P}[PX, PY] + [\bar{P}X, \bar{P}Y]$. (This T_J differs in sign from the torsion in the paper by Robertson in these Proceedings.) The vanishing of T_J is then equivalent to $[PX, PY] \in \Gamma(TM')$ and $[\bar{P}X, \bar{P}Y] \in \Gamma(TM'')$. It remains only to translate this into the dual set-up.

Now suppose $T_J = 0$, $\omega \in \Omega^{1,0}$. Then $d\omega(X, Y) = X(\omega(Y)) - Y(\omega(X)) - \omega[X, Y]$. If X, Y are both in $\Gamma(TM'')$ then the (RHS) is zero, so $d\omega$ has components only in $\Omega^{2,0}$ and $\Omega^{1,1}$. By conjugation we get the result for forms in $\Omega^{0,1}$. The same procedure extends to higher degrees by induction; one writes $\omega \in \Omega^{p,q}$ locally as a linear combination of products of one-forms, and uses the derivation property of d, together with the result for $\Omega^{1,0}$ and $\Omega^{0,1}$.

In the other direction the argument is easier. Take $X, Y \in \Gamma(TM')$ and $\omega \in \Omega^{0,1}$. Then $d\omega$ only has components of type (1, 1) and (0, 2) so $d\omega(X, Y) = 0$. Hence $\omega[X, Y] = 0$ so $[X, Y] \in \Gamma(TM')$. Similarly if $X_1, Y_1 \in \Gamma(TM'')$, $[X_1, Y_1] \in \Gamma(TM'')$. □

We now define ∂ and $\bar{\partial}$ on $\Omega^{p,q}$ by $\partial\omega = (p+1, q)$ component of $d\omega$, $\bar{\partial}\omega = (p, q+1)$ component of $d\omega$. Since $0 = d^2 = \partial^2 + \bar{\partial}^2 + \partial\bar{\partial} + \bar{\partial}\partial$, and ∂^2, $\bar{\partial}^2$, $\partial\bar{\partial} + \bar{\partial}\partial$ are in different components, they are individually zero, thus $\partial^2 = 0$, $\bar{\partial}^2 = 0$ and $\partial\bar{\partial} = -\bar{\partial}\partial$.

Now this proposition allows us to define cohomology groups based on ∂ and $\bar{\partial}$; geometrically, this gives cohomology of holomorphic, antiholomorphic, or forms of given mixed type. For we know by Newlander-Nirenberg that the integrability of J means that M is a complex manifold; and a form ω satisfies $\bar{\partial}\omega = 0$ if and only if ω is holomorphic (Cauchy-Riemann equations). To give but one example, consider the complex

$$0 \longrightarrow A(M) \xrightarrow{\partial} \Omega^{1,0}(M) \xrightarrow{\partial} \Omega^{2,0}(M) \longrightarrow \cdots$$

Then since $\partial^2 = 0$ we can define $H^{p,0}(M) = \ker \partial$ on $\Omega^{p,0}/\partial(\Omega^{p-1,0})$. On compact, complex manifolds, these groups are also finite-dimensional, and one can consider numerical characters like

$$\chi^0(M) = \sum_j (-1)^j \dim_C H^{j,0}(M) \text{ or } \chi^q(M) = \sum (-1)^j \dim_C H^{j,q}(M)$$

It turns out that these numerical characters are also related to the integrals of characteristic classes: the expressions are in general much more complicated, but the example of Riemann surfaces illustrates the point.

If S is a compact Riemann surface, then the Gauss-Bonnet theorem says

$$\int_S c_1 = \chi(S) = 2 - 2g$$

The Riemann-Roch theorem implies that

$$\chi^{0}(S) = \int_S c_1 + (g-1) = 1 - g$$

The Riemann-Roch theorem has been generalized to all compact, complex manifolds by Atiyah and Singer [2], and it expresses the numbers $\chi^q(M)$, and many others, in terms of integrals of characteristic forms. Van de Ven's examples use this theorem in an essential way, and this was the point of bringing in the concept of ∂- and $\bar{\partial}$-cohomology.

We can now state the examples of van de Ven. The first we shall discuss is constructed as follows. We take P_2, the complex projective plane, and $S^1 \times S^3$, the Hopf manifold: as explained in the paper of Robertson, these are both complex manifolds. Now there is a general construction called "connected sum" – or more picturesquely "plumbing" – which *adds* manifolds of the same dimension in a certain way. It is just this: if M_1, M_2 are compact n-dimensional manifolds, we take a point $x_1 \in M_1$, $x_2 \in M_2$ and remove small open discs $D_1 \subseteq M_1$, $D_2 \subseteq M_2$ around x_1, x_2 respectively. The manifolds $M_1 - D_1$ and $M_2 - D_2$ both have S^{n-1} as a boundary, and we can then glue them together along S^{n-1} to get a new manifold M: in symbols,

$$M = M_1 \# M_2 = (M_1 \cup D_1) \bigcup_{S^{n-1}} (M_2 - D_2)$$

It can be shown that this construction is independent of all choices.

Van de Ven's first example then is $V_1 = P_2 \# (S^1 \times S^3) \# (S^1 \times S^3)$. We shall need to compute the Euler characteristic and signature of V_1 and so we compute the cohomology ring $H^*(V_1 : R)$. There are two steps in this computation: first, if we start with a compact, oriented manifold M and remove a small disc, this kills the top homology and leaves the other groups unchanged (this can be seen by triangulating M). Thus if we know $H^*(M : R)$ we know $H^*(M - D : R)$. Now one computes $H^*(M_1 \# M_2 : R)$ by applying the Mayer-Vietoris sequence to the triple $(M_1 - D_1, M_2 - D_2, S^{n-1} = (M_1 - D_1) \cap (M_2 - D_2))$. Applying this to V_1, one finds that

$$H^*(V_1 : R) = \frac{R[\alpha, \beta, \gamma]}{(\alpha^2 = \beta^2 = 0,\ \alpha\beta = 0,\ \gamma^3 = 0)} \quad \deg \alpha = \deg \beta = 1,\ \deg \gamma = 2$$

Thus

$$H^1(V_1 : R) = \{\alpha, \beta\}$$

$$H^2(V_1 : R) = \{\gamma\}$$

$$H^3(V_1 : R) = \{\alpha\gamma, \beta\gamma\}$$

$$H^4(V_1 : R) = \{\gamma^2\}$$

Therefore $\chi(V_1) = -1$, sign $(V_1) = 1$. Now V_1 is almost-complex: this can be seen either by keeping close track of the J-operator on P_2 and $S^1 \times S^3$ while one is plumbing or one can apply the sufficiency assertion of the Hirzebruch-Hopf theorem. Thus there must be a closed two-form ω with **integral** periods such that

(i) $$\int_{V_1} \omega^2 = 2\chi(V_1) + 3\mathrm{sign}(V_1)$$

(ii) ω must have the proper mod 2 reduction. These conditions are fulfilled by $\omega = \gamma$: the first can be read off from the information above, and the second depends on an explicit computation – which, of course, we cannot do here because we have really not discussed the second condition. In any case, taking this as established, we see that

$$\int_{V_1} c_1^2 = 1$$

So V_1 has an almost complex structure. We shall now see that *no* almost-complex structure on V_1 is integrable. Suppose one were integrable: then V_1 would be a compact, **complex** manifold of complex dimension 2. We now need to invoke deep results in the theory of these manifolds to show that there is no such manifold having the cohomological structure of V_1.

It was Kodaira who began and essentially completed the study of compact, complex manifolds of dimension 2. One of his basic results (Kodaira [8], Theorem 8), which depends in a very essential way on the Atiyah-Singer generalization of the Riemann-Roch theorem, is that if X is a compact surface and

$$\int_X c_1^2 > 0$$

then, X is a projective algebraic variety. The proof depends on deep work of Kodaira's spanning several years, and one cannot really describe it except to say that Kodaira's theorems together with the Riemann-Roch theorem make it possible to follow roughly the same kind of arguments as are used in the classical theory of Riemann surfaces to produce holomorphic differentials, and meromorphic maps into projective spaces. In our case,

$$\int_{V_1} c_1^2 = 1$$

so V_1 is projective algebraic.

We are now in a position to use the great wealth of information about algebraic surfaces, due largely to the Italian school. First a couple of general remarks. Since V_1 is projective algebraic, the $H^{p,q}$-cohomology groups are subspaces of de Rham cohomology groups and span it[4], and as one can show $H^{p,q} H^{q,p}$ are conjugate, one finds $H^{1,0}(V_1)$ is one-dimensional, or that V_1 has a unique (up to scalar multiples) holomorphic one-form ϕ. This ϕ gives a very classical map $\mathrm{alb}: V_1 \to E$ where E is an elliptic curve:

$$\mathrm{alb}\ (x) = \int_{x_0}^{x} \phi$$

where $x_0 \in V_1$ is a fixed point, and x is joined to x_0 by a path. The integral is of course not independent of path, and therefore the map is into a torus rather than C. At this point our task is completed by a theorem of Enriques and Campedelli. If an algebraic surface S admits a holomorphic map to a curve C whose generic fibre is connected, then $\chi(S) \geqslant 4$ (genus(fibre)-1) · ·(genus C-1). Applying this to V_1, E we get $\chi(V_1) \geqslant 0$. But $\chi(V_1) = -1$, so V_1 cannot be a complex manifold.

---

[4] This is true more generally for Kähler manifolds: $H^r(X) = \bigoplus_{p+q=r} H^{p,q}(X)$.

A similar argument can be used to give other examples, and we mention one. This example has the advantage that the manifold in question is simply connected, although the details of the arguments are more complicated. We start with the quartic

$$Q = \{[z_0, \ldots, z_4] \in P_3 : \textstyle\sum_0^4 z_j^4 = 0\}$$

Using the plumbing procedure, construct $V_k = Q \# Q \# \ldots \# Q$ (k copies). When k is odd, V_k satisfies the conditions of the Hirzebruch-Hopf theorem, and so it is an almost-complex manifold. Suppose it were complex: then by Kodaira's results again it would be projective algebraic, and by looking at arguments from algebraic geometry one shows that there cannot be an algebraic surface with the numerical characters of V_k. This set of examples is due to Alan Howard (unpublished as far as I know).

REFERENCES

[1] ATIYAH, M.F., BOTT, R., PATODI, V., On the heat equation and the index theorem, Inventiones Math. **19** (1973) 297–330.

[2] ATIYAH, M.F., SINGER, I.M., The index of elliptic operators III, Ann. Math. **87** (1968) 546–604.

[3] BOREL, A., SERRE, J.-P., Groupes de Lie et puissances réduites de Steenrod, Am. J. Math. **75** (1953) 409–448.

[4] CHERN, S., Characteristic classes of Hermitian manifolds, Ann. Math. **47** (1946) 85–121.

[5] HIRZEBRUCH, F., Topological Methods in Algebraic Geometry, 3rd enlarged edn, Springer, New York (1966).

[6] HIRZEBRUCH, F., HOPF, H., Felder von Flächenelementen in 4-dimensionalen Mannigfaltigkeiten, Math. Annalen **136** (1958) 156–172.

[7] KOBAYASHI, S., NOMIZU, K., Foundations of Differential Geometry **1**, Interscience, New York (1969).

[8] KODAIRA, K., On the structure of compact complex analytic surfaces I, Am. J. Math. **86** (1964) 751–798.

[9] MILNOR, J.W., STASHEFF, J.D., Characteristic Classes (Annals of Math. Studies 76), Princeton Univ. Press (1974).

[10] VAN DE VEN, A., On the Chern numbers of certain complex and almost complex manifolds, Proc. Natl Acad. Sci. USA **55** (1966) 1624–1627.

DEFORMATIONS AND CLASSIFICATIONS OF COMPACT COMPLEX MANIFOLDS

D. SUNDARARAMAN
The Ramanujan Institute,
University of Madras,
Madras, India

Abstract

DEFORMATIONS AND CLASSIFICATIONS OF COMPACT COMPLEX MANIFOLDS.

The paper deals with two basic problems concerning compact complex manifolds: the moduli problem and the classification problem.

Part I

THE MODULI PROBLEM

1. GENERALITIES

An n-dimensional complex manifold is a paracompact Hausdorff space M which has a covering by open sets U_i such that, for each U_i, there exists a homeomorphism h_i of U_i onto an open set Ω_i of $\mathbb{C}^n$ such that whenever $U_i \cap U_j \neq \emptyset$, the local co-ordinates transform by a holomorphic transformation. That is, for each pair of indices i,j such that $U_i \cap U_j \neq \emptyset$, the map $h_i \circ h_j^{-1}$ is a holomorphic map of $h_j(U_i \cap U_j)$ onto $h_i(U_i \cap U_j)$. We take the collection $\{U_i, h_i\}$ to be maximal with respect to these properties. M together with $\{U_i, h_i\}$ is called a complex manifold. If $(Z_i^1, ..., Z_i^n)$ and $(Z_j^1, ..., Z_j^n)$ are local co-ordinates in U_i and U_j respectively and if $U_i \cap U_j \neq \emptyset$, we have $Z_j^r = Z_j^r(Z_i^1, ..., Z_i^n)$, $1 \leqslant r \leqslant n$, as holomorphic functions of $(Z_i^1, ..., Z_i^n)$ and the Jacobian determinant $\partial(Z_j^1, ..., Z_j^n)/\partial(Z_i^1, ..., Z_i^n) \neq 0$. It is clear that a complex manifold has a natural orientation.

Let M be a complex manifold with local co-ordinate system $\{h_i\}$. Let W be an open subset of M. A continuous map $f: W \to C^1$ is said to be holomorphic if $f \circ h_i^{-1}$ is holomorphic for each i, where defined. Let N be another complex manifold with local co-ordinate system $\{\lambda_j\}$. A continuous map $f: M \to N$ is called holomorphic if λ_j of $\circ\, h_i^{-1}$ is holomorphic, for each i and j, where defined. A holomorphic map $f: M \to N$ is called biholomorphic if the inverse map f^{-1} is also holomorphic. Two complex manifolds are complex analytically isomorphic if there exists a biholomorphic map between them. Thus we can talk of distinct complex structures on a given paracompact Hausdorff topological space. But the existence of a complex structure itself is a non-trivial phenomenon.

Underlying a complex manifold, we have a differentiable (C^∞) manifold. In fact we have even an almost complex manifold. An almost complex manifold is a differentiable manifold X together with a C^∞ field of endomorphisms $J: T_x X \to T_x X$ such that $J_x^2 = -1$ where $T_x X$ denotes the tangent space of X at x. Not all differentiable manifolds are almost complex manifolds. The obvious necessary conditions are that the differentiable manifold be of even dimension and be orientable. But these conditions are sufficient only in dimension 2. Well-known examples of even-dimensional, orientable differentiable manifolds which are not almost complex are the spheres S^{2n} for $n \neq 1, 3$ (Ehresmann [46] – Hopf [90], Borel-Serre [17]; see also Section 13 in Part III of this paper and

Robertson [193] and Pittie [184] in these Proceedings). Underlying a complex manifold there is a unique almost complex structure given by the complex structures on the real tangent spaces to the underlying differentiable manifold. But not every almost complex structure arises this way. Only in real dimension 2 is this the case. If an almost complex structure arises from a complex structure, i.e. it is the underlying almost complex structure of a complex structure, we say it is an integrable almost complex structure. There are almost complex manifolds not admitting any integrable almost complex structures. Van de Ven was the first to give such examples. He showed [222] that the four-dimensional almost complex manifold $S^1 \times S^3 \# S^1 \times S^3 \# \underline{\mathbb{P}}^2$ (where # denotes the connected sum operation and $\underline{\mathbb{P}}^2$ denotes the differentiable manifold underlying the two-dimensional projective space $\mathbb{P}^2$ over the complex numbers) does not admit any integrable almost complex structures. For a detailed proof of this, see the paper by Pittie in these Proceedings. It is easy to see that on S^2 there is a unique almost complex structure and that it is integrable. It is known that on S^6 there is an almost complex structure but it is not integrable [109]. It is not known whether there are any integrable almost complex structures on S^6.

Even the existence of a differentiable structure is not to be taken for granted as there are topological manifolds which do not admit any differentiable structure. Kervaire [103] gave an example of a compact ten-dimensional topological manifold which cannot carry any differentiable structure. Other such examples in other dimensions were given subsequently by Smale, Wall, Eells and Kuiper. Also, it was discovered by Milnor [147] that exotic spheres exist. An exotic n-sphere is a compact n-dimensional differentiable manifold which is homeomorphic to S^n but not diffeomorphic to S^n with its standard differentiable structure. A beautiful result of Kervaire-Milnor [104] states that the number of isomorphism classes of differentiable structures on S^n is finite and the authors actually computed this number. The existence of a real analytic structure on a differentiable manifold can be taken for granted since every differentiable manifold admits a unique real analytic structure.

Just as exotic differentiable structures exist, so do "exotic complex structures": i.e. there exist complex structures on a given topological manifold which are distinct not only as complex manifolds but also as differentiable manifolds. The only known examples of this phenomenon are due to Brieskorn and Van de Ven [22]. They showed that for every homotopy sphere Σ of dimension $(2n-1)$, $n \neq 2$, bounding a parallelizable manifold, there exist complex structures on $S^1 \times \Sigma$ such that the underlying differentiable structures are exotic. Note that a homotopy n-sphere is homeomorphic to S^n, for $n \geqslant 5$ (Smale [208]).

We have the notion of affine structures on a complex manifold. An affine complex manifold is a complex manifold with a complex structure $\{U_i, Z_i\}$ whose transition functions are affine, i.e. if $(Z_i^1, ..., Z_i^n)$ and $(Z_j^1, ..., Z_j^n)$ are local co-ordinates in U_i and U_j respectively and if $U_i \cap U_j \neq \emptyset$, then letting $Z^{(i)}$ be the column vector ${}^t(Z_i^1, ..., Z_i^n)$ and $Z^{(j)}$ be the column vector ${}^t(Z_j^1, ..., Z_j^n)$, we have

$$Z^{(i)} = A_{ij}Z^{(j)} + b_{ij} \quad \text{with } A_{ij} \in GL(n, C) \text{ and } b_{ij} \in \mathbb{C}^n$$

Not every compact complex manifold admits affine structures. Among the one-dimensional compact complex manifolds, only the tori admit affine structures. There exist countably many distinct affine structures on a complex one-dimensional torus [74]. Thus a fixed compact complex manifold may have many distinct affine structures on it. The affine structures can be characterized by the fact that there is a one-to-one correspondence between the affine structures on a complex manifold and its holomorphic linear connections with zero curvature and zero torsion (Matsushima [145], Vitter [223]).

A complex projective structure is a complex structure whose transition functions are projective transformations. Affine structures are special projective structures. Not every compact complex manifold admits projective structures. But every one-dimensional compact complex manifold of genus greater than one does admit projective structures [74].

Differentiable structures and complex structures can be regarded as special cases of more general structures, called **Γ-structures.** Let D be an open set in R^n.

Definition 1.1. *A pseudogroup of transformation in* D *is a set* Γ *of local diffeomorphisms of* D *such that: (1)* $f \in \Gamma \Rightarrow f^{-1} \in \Gamma$; *(2)* $f \in \Gamma$ *and* $g \in \Gamma \Rightarrow g \circ f \in \Gamma$ *if defined; (3)* $f \in \Gamma \Rightarrow f|W \in \Gamma$, *for every open set* W *in* D; *(4) let* f *be any local diffeomorphism of* D. *Let* $D = \cup D_i$, *and* $f|D_i \in \Gamma$, *for each* i, *then* $f \in \Gamma$; *(5) the identity map* $\in \Gamma$.

Definition 1.2. *Let* Γ *be a pseudogroup on* D. *Let* X *be a paracompact Hausdorff space. By a system of local* Γ *co-ordinates we mean a collection* $\{Z_j\}_{j \in I}$ *of local topological homeomorphisms* Z_j *of* X *into* D *such that* $Z_j \circ Z_k^{-1} \in \Gamma$ *whenever it is defined. Two systems* $\{Z_j\}$ *and* $\{W_\lambda\}$ *of local* Γ *co-ordinates are said to be* Γ*-equivalent if* $W_\lambda \circ Z_j^{-1} \in \Gamma$, *whenever defined. A* Γ*-structure on* X *is an equivalence class of systems of local* Γ *co-ordinates on* X. *A* Γ*-manifold is a paracompact Hausdorff space* X *together with a* Γ*-structure on* X.

Let $D = \mathbb{R}^n$ and Γ_d = all local diffeomorphisms of $\mathbb{R}^n$. Then a Γ_d-structure is a differentiable structure.

Let $D = \mathbb{C}^n$ and $\Gamma_{\mathbb{C}}$ = all local biholomorphic maps of $\mathbb{C}^n$. Then a $\Gamma_{\mathbb{C}}$-structure is a complex structure.

The notion of Γ-structures is one of the unifying general concepts in differential geometry and these were extensively studied by E. Cartan [27]. One of his important results is that there are only six classes of primitive infinite continuous complex pseudogroups, one of which is the pseudogroup of all local biholomorphic maps in $\mathbb{C}^n$.

2. RIEMANN SURFACES

As we have already remarked, every orientable C^∞ surface is a complex manifold of dimension 1. This is easily seen by introducing isothermal co-ordinates x, y so that locally we can define a positive definite Riemannian metric by $dS^2 = \lambda^2(dx^2 + dy^2) = \lambda^2 dZ d\bar{Z}$ where $Z = x + iy$, the orientation being given by $dx \wedge dy = (\sqrt{-1}/2) dZ \wedge d\bar{Z}$. If W is another local co-ordinate defining the same orientation, we have $dS^2 = \mu^2 dW d\bar{W}$ so that dW is a multiple of dZ and hence W is a holomorphic function of Z. A one-dimensional complex manifold is called a **Riemann surface.** The theory of Riemann surfaces has been developed in the last 125 years, and Riemann surfaces are still actively studied from various viewpoints (see Ref. [3]). We mention here only those facts which are very important for us.

There is only one compact Riemann surface of genus zero: the **Riemann sphere** S^2 but it is known there exist countably many distinct complex structures on $S^2 \times S^2$; see e.g. Ref. [84]). A compact Riemann surface of genus 1 is a complex structure on the two-dimensional real torus $\underline{M} = R^2/L$, L being the standard lattice generated by (1,0) and (0,1). The orientation on $\underline{M}$ is given as mentioned above. Let $w = dz + \alpha d\bar{z}$ where α is a complex number. w is a complex-valued 1-form on $\underline{M}$ and $w \wedge \bar{w} = (1 - |\alpha|^2)\, dz \wedge d\bar{z}$. Hence each α with $|\alpha| < 1$ gives a complex structure M_α on $\underline{M}$. Conversely any complex structure on $\underline{M}$ is a M_α for α belonging to the unit disc Δ. Δ can be mapped on to the upper-half plane by the transformation $\beta = \{(1 - \alpha)/(1 + \alpha)\}\sqrt{-1}$, $|\alpha| < 1$, and the torus M_α is mapped onto the torus $\mathbb{C}/L_\beta$ where L_β is the lattice generated by 1 and β. It is easy to check that $M_\beta \cong M_{\beta'}$ if and only if $\beta' = (a\beta + b)/(c\beta + d)$ where $\begin{pmatrix} a & b \\ c & d \end{pmatrix} \in SL(2, Z)$. A compact Riemann surface of genus $g \geqslant 2$ has the unit disc Δ as its universal covering surface and hence it is of the form $M = \Delta/G$ where G is a properly discontinuous subgroup of the group of automorphisms of Δ. (Let G be a subgroup of the group Aut M of automorphisms of a complex manifold M; G is said to act properly discontinuously if, for any two compact sets K_1

and K_2 of M, the set $\{g \in G | g K_1 \cap K_2 \neq \emptyset\}$ is finite.) Each element of G is of the form $g(z) = e^{i\theta}(z - \alpha)/(\alpha z - 1)$, $|\alpha| < 1$.

No such concrete description exists in general for higher dimensional complex manifolds. There are also other striking differences between Riemann surfaces and higher dimensional manifolds. On every compact Riemann surface there exist non-constant global meromorphic functions; however, there are higher dimensional compact complex manifolds with no non-constant global meromorphic functions (see e.g. Calabi-Rosenlicht [26]). On every open Riemann surface there exist non-constant global holomorphic functions; but this is not necessarily so in higher dimensions (see e.g. Calabi-Eckmann [25]).

3. STEIN MANIFOLDS

Given a complex manifold, one of the natural questions to ask is whether it can be embedded in $\mathbb{C}^N$ for some N? This question does not arise for a compact complex manifold as there are no non-trivial connected submanifolds of any $\mathbb{C}^N$ (**maximum-modulus principle**). Let us recall what we know about the corresponding question for differentiable manifolds and real analytic manifolds. A differentiable map $f: X \to Y$ between two differentiable manifolds is called an **immersion** if the rank of f is equal to the dimension of X at all points of X. An immersion is called an embedding if it is a homeomorphism onto its image in the induced topology. An **embed**[ding] is a one-to-one immersion but not every one-to-one immersion is an embedding. A standard probl[em] in differential topology is to find the least integers l, m such that a differentiable manifold X of dimension n can be immersed in $\mathbb{R}^{n+l}$ and embedded in $\mathbb{R}^{n+m}$. Whitney was the first to consider such questions. He proved that a differentiable manifold of dimension n, compact or non-compac[t] can be differentiably immersed in $\mathbb{R}^{2n-1}$ and embedded in $\mathbb{R}^{2n}$. The embedding theorem of Morrey [155] and Grauert [58] says that the existence of C^1-immersion (embedding) implies the existence of real analytic immersion (embedding). An important result of Hirsh [83] states that a non-compact differentiable manifold of dimension n can be differentiably immersed in $\mathbb{R}^n$ itself if its tangent bundle is trivial.

The complex manifolds, necessarily non-compact, which admit embeddings in complex Euclidean spaces, are the Stein manifolds. The embedding theorem of R. Narasimhan [173] (see also Bishop [15] and Remmert [192(a)]), states that a Stein manifold of dimension n can be holomorphically embedded in $\mathbb{C}^{2n+1}$. Forster improved this result as follows. He showed [49] that if $n \geqslant 2$ the Stein manifold can be embedded in $\mathbb{C}^{2n}$ and if $n \geqslant 6$ it can be embedded in $\mathbb{C}^{2n-k}$ where $k = [(n-2)/3]$. It is conjectured that the complex analogue of the theorem of Hirsh is true:

Conjecture 3.1. *Let* M *be a Stein manifold of dimension* n *with trivial tangent bundle. Then* M *can be holomorphically immersed in* $\mathbb{C}^n$ *itself.* Gunning and R. Narasimhan have proved [76] that this conjecture is true for an open Riemann surface, i.e. for n = 1.

The concept of a Stein manifold is very important in modern complex analysis. The theory of **Stein manifolds, Stein spaces** and their generalizations has been extensively developed in the last 25 years. We shall now define a Stein manifold and state the important theorems.

Definition 3.1. *A complex manifold* M *is called a Stein manifold if: (1)* M *is holomorphically convex; (2) the global holomorphic functions of* M *separate points of* M; *and (3) for each point there exist global holomorphic functions giving local co-ordinates of that point.*

Holomorphic convexity of M means the following. Let K be any compact set of M and let $\hat{K}$ denote the set

$$\left\{x \in M \,\middle|\, |f(x)| \leqslant \sup_{x \in K} f(x) \text{ for any holomorphic function } f \text{ on } M\right\}$$

$\hat{K}$ is called the holomorphic hull of K. If for each compact K, $\hat{K}$ is also compact, we say that M is holomorphically convex. Note that a Stein manifold is necessarily non-compact. A domain of holomorphy in $\mathbb{C}^n$ is Stein, and in fact the definition of a Stein manifold is given in such a way that it abstracts the properties of domains of holomorphy. With the powerful tools of sheaf theory and cohomology theory, H. Cartan and Serre reformulated the pioneering work of Oka and we have the following celebrated Theorems A and B. Let θ be the sheaf of germs of holomorphic functions on a Stein manifold M and let φ be any coherent sheaf of θ-modules (for the notion of coherence refer to Section 7 in Part II of this paper). Let $H^q(M,\varphi)$ be the cohomology groups with coefficients in φ. Then

Theorem A. $H^0(M,\varphi)$ *generate the stalk* φ_x *for each* $x \in M$.

Theorem B. $H^q(M,\varphi) = 0$ *for all* $q \geqslant 1$.

Moreover Theorem B characterizes Stein manifolds. In fact, if $H^1(M,\varphi) = 0$ for any coherent sheaf φ of θ-modules, M must be a Stein manifold. The various nice properties possessed by Stein manifolds are due to these Theorems A and B. Some of these important properties are: (a) every meromorphic function on a Stein manifold is the quotient of two global holomorphic functions; (b) the additive Cousin problem always has a solution on a Stein manifold; and (c) the multiplicative Cousin problem has a solution on a Stein manifold M if $H^2(M, Z) = 0$ (for these details refer to Ch.V of Hörmander [92]).

4. ALGEBRAIC MANIFOLDS

Among the non-compact complex manifolds, the Stein manifolds (those admitting embeddings in $\mathbb{C}^n$ for some n) are the most important; the algebraic manifolds (those admitting embeddings in $\mathbb{P}^n$ for some n) are the most important among the compact complex manifolds. First we define the complex projective spaces $\mathbb{P}^n$ and state some of the important problems concerning them.

Definition of $\mathbb{P}^n$. Consider $\mathbb{C}^{n+1} - \{0\}$. Define an equivalence relation in it by defining two points equivalent if their co-ordinates differ from each other by a non-zero complex number. The resulting quotient space is $\mathbb{P}^n$. There is a natural projection map $\pi : \mathbb{C}^{n+1} - \{0\} \to \mathbb{P}^n$. With the quotient topology induced by π, $\mathbb{P}^n$ is a compact Hausdorff space. If $Z = (Z^0, ..., Z^n) \in \mathbb{C}^{n+1} - \{0\}$, we denote the point $\pi(Z)$ by $[Z]$ and call $(Z^0, ..., Z^n)$ the homogeneous co-ordinates of $[Z]$. If $(W^0, ..., W^n)$ is another set of homogeneous co-ordinates for $[Z]$, we have $W^r = \lambda Z^r$, $0 \leqslant r \leqslant n$, where λ is a non-zero complex number. Using homogeneous co-ordinates, we define a complex structure on $\mathbb{P}^n$ as follows. Let $U_i = \{p \in \mathbb{P}^n \mid \text{the } i^{th} \text{ homogeneous co-ordinate of } p \text{ is} \neq 0\}$. Then the U_i form an open covering of $\mathbb{P}^n$. Define $h_i : U_i \to \mathbb{C}^n$ by

$$h_i(Z^0, ..., Z^n) = (Z^0/Z^i, ..., Z^{i-1}/Z^i, Z^{i+1}/Z^i, ..., Z^n/Z^i)$$

Then h_i maps U_i biholomorphically onto $\mathbb{C}^n$ and it is easy to check that $h_i \circ h_j^{-1}$ is biholomorphic for each i and j. Thus we have prescribed a complex structure on $\mathbb{P}^n$. Now we ask a basic question. Is this the only way of prescribing a complex structure on $\mathbb{P}^n$ (i.e. are there complex structures on $\mathbb{P}^n$ different from the one we have prescribed above)? So far no other complex structure has been found to exist on $\mathbb{P}^n$. There is a long-standing conjecture:

Conjecture 4.1. $\mathbb{P}^n$ *has a unique complex structure.*

Note that $\mathbb{P}^1$ has a unique complex structure. A number of important partial results are known relating to this conjecture, and we shall state them in some detail.

On a complex manifold we can always introduce a hermitian metric. Associated to this metric there is a real (1, 1) form, called the fundamental form of the metric. This form is in general not d-closed, d being the exterior derivative. If it is, we say that the metric is a Kähler metric. A complex manifold is Kähler if there is a Kähler metric on it. Every Riemann surface is Kähler; $\mathbb{P}^n$ are Kähler. There are topological restrictions for a complex manifold to admit a Kähler metric. Necessarily, for a Kähler manifold the odd Betti numbers must be even numbers. A conjecture of Kodaira is that for a complex analytic surface to be Kähler it is sufficient that the first Betti number is even. Recently, Y. Miyaoka [149] has proved that this conjecture is true for elliptic surfaces (for definition of an elliptic surface see Section 19 (Part V)). It is easy to check that submanifolds of a Kähler manifold are Kähler and therefore submanifolds of $\mathbb{P}^n$ are Kähler.

Hirzebruch and Kodaira [87] proved that the only Kähler complex structure on $\mathbb{P}^n$, when n is odd, is the standard one. When n is even, only if further conditions are satisfied do we have a similar assertion. In precise terms their theorem is

Theorem 4.1 **(Hirzebruch-Kodaira):** *Let* M *be a compact connected Kähler of complex manifold of dimension* n *such that* M *is homeomorphic to* $\mathbb{P}^n$. *Then: (a) If* n *is odd,* M *is complex analytically isomorphic with* $\mathbb{P}^n$. *(b) Let* n *be even; let* $g \in H^2(M, Z)$ *generate* $H^2(M, Z)$ *and belong to the cohomology class of a Kähler metric on* M; *then if the first Chern class* $C_1(M)$ *of* M *is not equal to* $-(n+1)g$, *then* M *is complex analytically isomorphic with* $\mathbb{P}^n$. (For the notion of Chern class, see Section 13 of this paper.)

A similar result is true for n-dimensional quadrics in $\mathbb{P}^{n+1}$:

Theorem 4.2 **(Brieskorn-Van de Ven [20]).** *Let* M *be a compact connected Kähler complex manifold of dimension* n *such that* M *is homeomorphic to an n-dimensional quadric* Q_n *in* $\mathbb{P}^{n+1}$. *Let* $n > 2$. *Then: (a) if* n *is odd,* M *is complex analytically isomorphic with* Q_n; *(b) if* n *is even, let* $g \in H^2(M, Z)$ *belonging to the cohomology class of a Kähler metric on* M, *generate* $H^2(M, Z)$. *Then if* $C_1(M) \neq -ng$, M *is complex analytically isomorphic with* Q_n.

There are also important results characterizing $\mathbb{P}^n$ in terms of its curvature. One of the important problems in Riemannian geometry is to determine all compact connected Riemannian manifolds, of a given dimension, with positive sectional curvature (for the notion of sectional curvature see e.g. Ref. [109]). As a special case of this problem, Andreotti-Frankel [53] proved that if M is a compact Kähler surface of positive holomorphic sectional curvature, M is biholomorphic with $\mathbb{P}^2$. Frankel conjectured the following

Conjecture 4.2. *A compact connected* n*-dimensional Kähler manifold of positive holomorphic sectional curvature is biholomorphic with* $\mathbb{P}^n$.

Kobayashi and Ochiai proved that this conjecture is true for n = 3. The status of this conjecture is not known for $n \geqslant 4$.

It is well known that the tangent bundle of $\mathbb{P}^n$ is ample (for the notion of ample vector bundles see Ref. [78]). An important result of Hartshorne ([78], Theorem 2.2, page 87) states that for n = 1, 2, $\mathbb{P}^n$ is the only compact complex manifold whose tangent bundle is ample. This gives rise to

Conjecture 4.3. *A compact connected complex manifold of dimension* n *with ample tangent bundle is biholomorphic with* $\mathbb{P}^n$.

Kobayashi and Ochiai [110] proved that this conjecture is true under an additional condition. They showed that the only compact connected homogeneous complex manifold with ample tangent bundle is $\mathbb{P}^n$. Recall that a complex manifold is said to be homogeneous if its holomorphic automorphism group acts transitively. There are other results in this direction; we refer the reader to Berger [13], Goldberg-Kobayashi [57], Yau [228].

Now we ask a basic question. Does every compact complex manifold admit an embedding in $\mathbb{P}^N$ for some N? If a compact complex manifold admits an embedding in a complex projective space, it is called a projective algebraic manifold or simply an algebraic manifold. A fundamental theorem of Chow [33] says that any subvariety of $\mathbb{P}^N$ is algebraic, meaning that it is given by a finite number of homogeneous polynomials in homogeneous co-ordinates. Every compact Riemann surface is algebraic. The Grassmann manifolds are algebraic (the set $G_{k,N}$ of all k-dimensional subspaces of $\mathbb{C}^{N+1}$ can be given the structure of a complex manifold, called a Grassmann manifold. $G_{1,N}$ is isomorphic with $\mathbb{P}^N$). Algebraic manifolds are necessarily Kähler. But not every compact Kähler complex manifold is algebraic as it is well known that not every complex torus is algebraic (see De la Harpe [37] in these Proceedings for a non-algebraic torus). Only a restricted class of compact complex Kähler manifolds, called the Hodge manifolds, are algebraic. A **Hodge manifold** is a compact Kähler complex manifold with a positive line bundle on it (for the notion of positive line bundles see Section 11 (Part III)). The celebrated embedding theorem of Kodaira [111] is that a Hodge manifold is algebraic. It is not difficult to prove that an algebraic manifold is Hodge.

A well known theorem of Thimm [216] (see also Remmert [192], Siegel [206]) says that the field $\mathbb{C}(M)$ of meromorphic functions on a compact complex connected manifold M is finitely generated over $\mathbb{C}$ and the transcendence degree of $\mathbb{C}(M)$ cannot exceed the dimension of M (for a proof of this theorem see the paper by Cornalba [36] in these Proceedings). The transcendence degree of $\mathbb{C}(M)$ is called the algebraic dimension of M. Compact complex manifolds M of algebraic dimension exactly equal to the dimension of M form a very important class and this class was extensively studied by Moishezon. A compact complex connected manifold M of algebraic dimension equal to the dimension of M is called a **Moishezon manifold.** A Moishezon manifold of dimension n is algebraic if and only if it is Kähler [150]. A theorem of Kodaira [117] (also, see Chow-Kodaira [34]) says the assumption of Kählerity is unnecessary for n = 2.

For a survey on the topology of an algebraic surface, we refer the reader to notes on a Seminar by Moishezon [152] presented during this Course (unfortunately, not included in these Proceedings).

5. NON-ALGEBRAIC MANIFOLDS

There are many non-Kähler manifolds which are also of interest, e.g. the Hopf manifolds. Recall the theorem of H. Cartan that if G is a properly discontinuous subgroup of the group of the holomorphic automorphisms of a complex manifold M, then M/G, the quotient space, has the structure of a complex analytic space, with singularities at the fixed points of G. Let $W = \mathbb{C}^n - \{0\}$. Let G be the infinite cyclic group of holomorphic automorphisms of W generated by $g : (z_1, ..., z_n) \to (\alpha z_1, ..., \alpha z_n)$ where $|\alpha| \neq 1$. It is easy to verify that G acts on W properly discontinuously and fixed point free. Hence M = W/G is a complex manifold. We can show that M is diffeomorphic to $S^1 \times S^3$. These compact complex manifolds (called **Hopf manifolds)** were first introduced by Hopf [90]. They are non-Kähler since they do not satisfy the necessary condition for Kählerity that the odd Betti numbers must be even. Kodaira [117] has studied Hopf surfaces in great detail. He has shown that every complex structure on $S^1 \times S^3$ must be a Hopf surface $\mathbb{C}^2 - \{0\}/G$, for a suitable G. It is not known whether every complex structure on

$S^1 \times S^{2n-1}$ for $n \geq 3$ is an n-dimensional Hopf structure. Kodaira has given a topological characterization of Hopf surfaces as follows:

Theorem 5.1 **(Kodaira** [117]**).** *Let S be a complex analytic surface such that its second Betti number is zero and its fundamental group contains an infinite cyclic subgroup of finite index. Then S is a Hopf surface.*

Generalizing the construction of Hopf, Calabi-Eckmann [25] constructed distinct complex structures on $S^{2p+1} \times S^{2q+1}$, all of which are non-Kähler. The Brieskorn manifolds previously referred to are still more general than the Calabi-Eckmann manifolds.

A number of interesting results have become known in the last few years on complex structures on a product of two odd-dimensional spheres (see Kato [100], Maeda [137], Morita [154]

6. THE MODULI PROBLEM

From the foregoing, it must be clear that the existence of a complex structure on a given compact differentiable manifold M is something very special. There may not be any complex structure on M; there may be countably many or uncountably many distinct complex structures on M; there may also be **exotic complex structures** on M. To determine all the complex structures on a given M is a very difficult problem.

Let M be a compact connected oriented differentiable manifold of even dimension. Let Σ(M) denote the set of all distinct (isomorphism classes of) complex structures on M consistent with the given differentiable structure M and orientation. The **problem of moduli** (also called the **fine classification problem**) is the problem of prescribing a natural complex structure[1] on the set Σ(M). This is a very difficult problem. Examples show that it is too much to expect a complex manifold structure on Σ(M); we can only hope to introduce a complex analytic space structure (a complex structure with singularities) on Σ(M).

This problem has its origin in Riemann's work. Riemann considered the set of all conformal equivalence classes of compact Riemann surfaces of fixed genus $g \geq 2$ and observed that these classes can be considered in some sense a continuum described by $(3g-3)$ complex parameters. He found that the number of independent parameters on which compact Riemann surfaces of genus g depend is $(3g-3)$, 1 or 0 according as $g > 1$, $g = 1$ or $g = 0$. He called these parameters "moduli". Riemann's ideas were made precise after a long time by Teichmüller [215], Rauch [191] Ahlfors [2] and Bers [14]. We have the following central theorem:

Theorem 6.1 **(Riemann-Teichmüller-Rauch-Ahlfors-Bers).** *The set of all isomorphism classes of compact Riemann surfaces of genus* $g \geq 2$ *carries a natural structure of a complex analytic space of dimension* $(3g-3)$.

We have seen that the set of all isomorphism classes of compact Riemann surfaces of genus 1 is isomorphic with the upper half plane modulo SL(2, Z) and hence has a nice complex structure. And there is only one (isomorphism class of) compact Riemann surface of genus 0.

No global theorem such as the above is true in general for higher dimensional compact complex manifolds. In some very special cases we have such results on the existence of **moduli spaces.** We mention here some important results in this direction.

Theorem 6.2 **(Kodaira** [117]**).** $\Sigma(S^1 \times S^3)$ *carries a natural complex analytic structure (in fact the punctured disc is the space of moduli).*

[1] Natural in the sense of Mumford ([159], p.96).

Remark. We have already mentioned the result of Kodaira that every complex structure on $S^1 \times S^3$ is a Hopf surface.

Theorem 6.3 **(Matsusaka-Mumford** [143], **Narasimhan-Simha** [176]). *The set of all isomorphism classes of complex structures on* $\underline{M}$ *with ample canonical line bundle carries a natural structure of a complex analytic space.*

Theorem 6.4 **(Popp** [187]). *Canonically polarized algebraic manifolds have moduli spaces as algebraic spaces (complex analytic spaces with sufficiently many meromorphic functions* [8]). For the notion of polarization see Ref. [144] .

Theorem 6.5 **(Douady** [41]). *The set of all compact complex analytic subspaces of a complex analytic space carries a natural structure of a complex analytic space.*

Remark. Douady's theorem (the proof is very difficult) is considered to be a landmark in this direction. It generalizes the already known result that the set of all compact submanifolds of $\mathbb{P}^n$ carries a natural structure of a complex analytic space (Chow variety, Hilbert scheme).

The moduli problem can be divided naturally into two parts: local theory and global theory. We have a reasonably complete local theory due to Kodaira, Spencer and Kuranishi, called the **theory of deformations.** This is one of the two main topics of this paper, and a detailed account of the theory is given in Part IV. One approach to global theory of moduli is due to Griffiths [69–72].

The second main topic of this paper is the **rough classification** of compact complex manifolds, i.e. classification of compact complex manifolds of a given dimension by certain important bimeromorphic invariants and then the study of each of these classes in detail. We have a well developed theory of classification of surfaces. The classification theory of algebraic surfaces is mainly due to Castelnuovo and Enriques, that of analytic surfaces to Kodaira. A summary of the theory of classification of surfaces is given in Part V. Recently Iitaka and Ueno have proposed a classification of higher dimensional manifolds. An account of this is given in Part VI.

Part II

COMPLEX SPACES, FLAT MAPS, MEROMORPHIC MAPS

Part II contains the basic facts on **complex analytic spaces, flat maps** and **meromorphic maps.** For more details and proofs, the reader is referred to Malgrange [138] for general complex analytic spaces, to R. Narasimhan [174] for reduced complex analytic spaces, to Douady [44] for flat maps and to Remmert [192] and Stein [211] for meromorphic maps. Throughout, by complex spaces we mean complex analytic spaces.

7. COMPLEX ANALYTIC SETS

Let $z \in \mathbb{C}^n$. Consider the set of pairs (U,f) where U is an open set in $\mathbb{C}^n$, $z \in U$, and f is holomorphic in U. We say two such pairs (U,f) and (V,g) are equivalent if there exists an open set $W \subset U \cap V$, $z \in W$, such that $f|W = g|W$. This is an equivalence relation, and an equivalence class is called a germ of a holomorphic function at z; the germ to which f belongs is denoted by $\underline{f}_z$. The germ of a holomorphic function at a point depends on the behaviour of the function in a full open neighbourhood of the point and not merely on the value of the function at that point. However, all functions belonging to a germ have the same value at that point and this common value is called the value of the germ at that point. Let O_z denote the set of all germs of holomorphic functions at z. It is easy to check the following facts (see e.g. Ref. [75]). O_z is a commutative ring with identity; it is isomorphic with the ring of convergent power series centred at that point; it is an integral domain (its quotient field is called the field of germs of meromorphic functions at z); it is a local ring, the non-units forming the unique maximal ideal; it is also Noetherian: every ideal in O_z has a finite basis;and it is further a unique factorization domain. For local study it suffices to consider only the ring O_0 at the origin 0. Let

$$O = \bigcup_{z \in \mathbb{C}^n} O_z$$

We define a topology on O as follows. An element of O is a germ $\underline{f}_b$ at some point $b \in C^n$. Let (U,f) define $\underline{f}_b$. Let $N(U,f) = \{\underline{f}_c | c \in U\}$ where $\underline{f}_c$ is the germ at c defined by (U,f). We define the sets N(U,f), as (U,f) runs through all the pairs defining $\underline{f}_a$, to be the fundamental systems of neighbourhoods of $\underline{f}_a$. We have the natural projection map $p: O \to \mathbb{C}^n$ defined by $p(\underline{f}_a) = a$. One can check that p is continuous, that the topology on O is Hausdorff and that p is a local homeomorphism. Moreover, letting

$$O \underset{p}{\times} O = \{(x,y) \in O \times O | p(x) = p(y)\}$$

we can check that the maps

$$O \underset{p}{\times} O \to O \quad \text{defined by} \quad (x,y) \mapsto x-y, (x,y) \mapsto xy$$

are continuous in the topology of O. O is a typical example of a sheaf of rings over $\mathbb{C}^n$. More generally, the notions of sheaves of algebraic structures over a Hausdorff topological space and morphisms between them are easily formulated (see Ch. IV of Ref. [75]). One of the important concepts in function theory of several complex variables is the concept of a **coherent analytic sheaf.** An analytic sheaf over a domain D in $\mathbb{C}^n$ is a sheaf of O-modules over D.

Definition 7.1. *An analytic sheaf* S *over an open set* D in $\mathbb{C}^n$ *is said to be coherent if in some open neighbourhood* U_a *of each point* a *in* D *there is an exact sequence of analytic sheaves over* U_a *of the form*

$$(O_D|U_a)^p \to (O_D|U_a)^q \to (S|U_a) \to 0$$

for some positive integers p *and* q.

Note that coherence is a local property. When an analytic sheaf is coherent it has nice properties. For example, a general theorem of Cartan-Serre says that the cohomology groups of a compact complex space with coefficients in a coherent analytic sheaf are finite-dimensional vector spaces. But some of the difficult theorems in several complex variables are in proving that certain analytic sheaves are coherent. It is evident from the definition that the structure sheaf O_D of an open set D in $\mathbb{C}^n$, considered as an analytic sheaf over O_D itself, is coherent.

The following are two important theorems on coherence:

Theorem 7.1 **(Oka [181]).** *For any analytic sheaf homomorphism* $\phi: O_D^r \to O_D^s$, *the kernel and the image are coherent analytic sheaves.*

Theorem 7.2 (**Serre** [202]). *For any exact sequence of analytic sheaves of the form*

$$0 \to R \to S \to T \to 0$$

if any two of them are coherent so is the third.

An important coherent sheaf is the **ideal sheaf of an analytic set.** We now define this concept, after giving some basic facts on complex analytic sets. (By an analytic set we mean a complex analytic set.)

Definition 7.2. *An analytic set* A *in an open set* D *is a subset* A *of* D *having the following property: to each point* $a \in A$, *there exists a neighbourhood* U_a *in* D *and holomorphic functions* $f_1, f_2, \ldots, f_r$ *in* U_a *such that* $U_a \cap A = \{x \in U_a | f_1(x) = 0 = f_2(x) = \ldots = f_r(x)\}$.

It can be proved that the set of common zeros of a collection of holomorphic functions defined in an open set is an analytic subset. Consider the set of pairs (A_i, D_i) where D_i is an open neighbourhood of the origin in $\mathbb{C}^n$ and A_i is an analytic subset of D_i. Two such pairs (A_1, D_1) and (A_2, D_2) are called equivalent if there is an open neighbourhood W of the origin, $W \subseteq D_1 \cap D_2$ such that $W \cap A_1 = W \cap A_2$. This is an equivalence relation, and an equivalence class is called a germ of an analytic set at the origin in $\mathbb{C}^n$. For brevity, we call a germ of an analytic set an **analytic germ** and denote the germ of an analytic set A at the origin by $\underline{A}_0$.

Let $\underline{f}_0$ be the germ of a holomorphic function f at the origin. Let Z(f) be the zero set of f. If $\underline{Z(f)}_0 \supseteq \underline{A}_0$, we say that f vanishes on $\underline{A}$. Define $id(A) = \{f \in O_0 | f \text{ vanishes on } A\}$. id(A) is an ideal in O_0. Thus to each analytic germ $\underline{A}_0$ there is a canonically associated ideal in O_0, called the ideal of $\underline{A}$. Now, given an ideal I in O_0, we can associate an analytic germ at the origin, called its **locus,** as follows: $loc(I) = \underline{Z(g_1, \ldots, g_r)}_0$, where $g_1, \ldots, g_r$ are in O_0 and generate the ideal I. This is well defined. The most important relation connecting an ideal I and its locus is the Hilbert basis theorem: id loc I = radical of I. This is one of the basic theorems in local theory of several complex variables and is an important consequence of the local parametrization theorem ([75], p. 93). Using the fact that O_0 is Noetherian, we can prove that any analytic germ can be uniquely written as an irredundant union of finitely many irreducible analytic germs. We call an analytic germ irreducible if and only if it cannot be expressed as the union of two proper subanalytic germs. It is easy to check that an analytic germ is irreducible if and only if its ideal is prime. A set of co-ordinates $Z_1, \ldots, Z_n$ at the origin in $\mathbb{C}^n$ is called a regular system of co-ordinates for a prime ideal $I \subseteq {}_nO_0$ if for some integer k, $0 \leqslant k < n$, we have (i) ${}_kO_0 \cap I = 0$ and (ii) ${}_{j-1}O_0[Z_j] \cap I$ contains a Weierstrass polynomial in Z_j for $j = k+1, \ldots, n$. It is a basic fact that every prime ideal has a regular system of co-ordinates ([75], p. 93). The integer k is called the dimension of the ideal. The dimension of a prime ideal depends not only on the ideal but also on the choice of co-ordinates. However, it can be proved that if there is a regular system of co-ordinates for a prime ideal with respect to which the ideal has dimension k, then a dense open subset of a sufficiently small neighbourhood of the origin in any analytic set representing the germ of its locus is a k-dimensional complex manifold. Hence we can speak of the dimension of a prime ideal. For any analytic germ $\underline{A}$, its dimension is defined as the maximum of the dimensions of its irreducible components. If all the irreducible components of an analytic germ have the same dimension, then the analytic germ is said to have pure dimension.

Let A be an analytic set in a domain D in $\mathbb{C}^n$. A point $a \in A$ is called a regular point of A of dimension p if there exists a neighbourhood U_a of a in D, such that $A \cap U_a$ is a complex submanifold of U_a of dimension p. It follows that $a \in A$ is a regular point of dimension p if and only if there exist functions $f_{p+1}, \ldots, f_n \in O_a$ such that in a neighbourhood of a, $A = \{x | f_{p+1}(x) = 0 = f_{p+2}(x) = \ldots = f_n(x)\}$ and $(df_{p+1})_a, \ldots, (df_n)_a$ are linearly independent. A point $a \in A$ is called a singular point if it is not a regular point. One of the difficulties with singularities is that a complex analytic set can never be a smooth manifold throughout a neighbourhood of a singular point (Milnor [148], p. 13). Regarding the structure of regular and singular points we have the following

Theorem 7.3. *Let A be an analytic set in a domain D in $\mathbb{C}^n$. Then: (a) Let $a \in A$ and dimension $\underline{A}_a$ be p. Then any neighbourhood of a contains points at which A is regular of dimension p. In particular, the set of regular points of A is dense in A. (b) The set of singular points of A is an analytic set in D.*

Let A be an analytic subset in a domain D in $\mathbb{C}^n$. To every $z \in D$ associate the ideal $\mathrm{id}(\underline{A}_z)$ and write

$$g(A) = \bigcup_{z \in D} \mathrm{id}(\underline{A}_z)$$

Then g(A) is an open subset of the ring O_D, and it is a sheaf of ideals on D. It is called the sheaf of ideals of the analytic set A. It is known that g(A) is coherent (see e.g. [75], p. 138). Hence the quotient sheaf ${}_AO_D = O_D/g(A)$ is a coherent analytic sheaf. Since g(A) is a sheaf of ideals, ${}_AO_D$ is actually a sheaf of rings with support A. Let ${}_AO = {}_AO_D|A$. ${}_AO$ is called the sheaf of germs of holomorphic functions on A. This definition is motivated by the following. Let f be a continuous complex-valued function on A. f is said to be holomorphic at $z \in A$ if there exist an open neighbourhood W of z in D and a holomorphic function F in W such that $F|W \cap A = f|W \cap A$. Then one has the notion of the ring of germs of holomorphic functions on A and the sheaf O_A of germs of holomorphic functions on A. It can be checked that ${}_AO = O_A$. We take the pairs (A, O_A) to be the local models for reduced analytic spaces.

8. COMPLEX ANALYTIC SPACES

Definition 8.1. *A reduced complex analytic space (complex analytic space in the sense of Cartan-Serre) is a pair (X, O_X) where X is a Hausdorff space and O_X is a sheaf of subalgebras of the sheaf $\mathscr{C}$ of germs of continuous functions, which is locally isomorphic to a local model, i.e. for each $x \in X$ there is a neighbourhood U of x in X, a local model (A, O_A) and a homeomorphism $\phi: U \to A$ with the property that for $y \in U$, $f \in \mathscr{C}_{U,y}$ belongs to $O_{U,y}$ if and only if $f = g \circ \phi$ for some germ $g \in O_{A,\phi(y)}$.*

A morphism between one reduced complex space (X, O_X) into another (Y, O_Y) is a continuous map $f: X \to Y$ such that $f^*(O_{Y,f(x)}) \subset O_{X,x}$ for all $x \in X$. Note that complex manifolds are special types of reduced complex space.

To define non-reduced complex spaces, we define their local models first.

Let D be open in $\mathbb{C}^n$, and let I be any coherent sheaf of ideals in O_D. Let $V = \mathrm{Supp}(O_D/I)$. Then V is an analytic set in D. The restriction of O_D/I to V is denoted by O_V. In general it is not a subsheaf of $\mathscr{C}_V$. We define (V, O_V) to be a local model of non-reduced type. It is a local model of reduced type if and only if I is the sheaf of all germs of holomorphic functions vanishing on V. In the non-reduced case the local model (V, O_V) is not determined by V alone; the structure sheaf also has to be specified. For an example of a non-reduced model, take $D = \mathbb{C}$, I being the sheaf of ideals generated by Z^2, where Z denotes the co-ordinate function in $\mathbb{C}$. Then $V = \mathrm{Supp}\, O_{\mathbb{C}}/(Z^2) = \{0\}$ and $O_{V,0} = \mathbb{C}\{Z\}/(Z^2)$ is the space of "dual numbers" represented by $a + b\epsilon$, where $a, b \in \mathbb{C}$ and $\epsilon^2 = 0$. Certainly $O_{V,0}$ cannot be a subring of the ring of continuous functions on $\{0\}$.

Definition 8.2. *A non-reduced complex analytic space (complex analytic space in the sense of Grothendieck) is a pair* (X, O_X), *where* X *is a Hausdorff topological space and* O_X *is a sheaf of local* $\mathbb{C}$*-algebras, which is locally isomorphic to a local model of non-reduced type.*

Theorem 8.1. *A non-reduced complex space* (X, O_X) *is a reduced complex space if and only if the local rings* $O_{X,x}$ *have no nilpotent elements for any* $x \in X$.

Given a non-reduced complex space (X, O_X), we can associate to it a reduced complex space as follows. Let N_x be the ideal in $O_{X,x}$ consisting of all nilpotent elements. Then

$$N = \bigcup_{x \in X} N_x$$

is a coherent sheaf: for in a local model (V, O_V) for (X, O_X) we have $N_X = (I'/I)_X$ where I' is the sheaf of germs of holomorphic functions vanishing on V, and I is the sheaf of ideals defining the structure sheaf O_V. The sheaf I' is coherent (Oka-Cartan) and I is coherent by our assumption. Hence the quotient sheaf I'/I is coherent. Now define $(X_{red}, O_{X\,red})$ by $X_{red} = X$ and $O_{X\,red} = O_X/N$.

One of the significant differences between reduced and non-reduced complex spaces is that for a non-reduced complex space, decomposition into irreducible components has no meaning.

The Zariski tangent space at a point x of any complex space is defined to be the $\mathbb{C}$-dual of $(m_x | m_x^2)$ where m_x denotes the maximal ideal of $O_{X,x}$. If X is defined by the ideal $I \subset O_D$, D open in $\mathbb{C}^n$, the tangent space may be identified with the linear variety defined by the linear parts of all germs $\in I_x$. The Zariski tangent space of X_{red} may be strictly contained in that of X.

A coherent analytic sheaf on any complex space (X, O_X) is a sheaf S of O_X-modules such that for each $x \in X$ there exists an open neighbourhood over which there exists an exact sequence of the form

$$(O_X | U)^p \to (O_X | U)^q \to (S|U) \to 0$$

for some positive integers p and q.

Let (X, O_X) be any complex space and S be any coherent sheaf of O_X-modules. The cohomology groups $H^q(X,S)$ are well defined, with a topology of a quotient of a Fréchet space, and hence in general this topology is not separated. If X is compact, we have the following finiteness theorem:

Theorem 8.2 (Cartan-Serre [29]). *Let* X *be any compact complex space and* S *a coherent analytic sheaf on* X. *Then for every* $q \geqslant 0$ *the cohomology groups* $H^q(X,S)$ *are separated and finite dimensional.*

Let (X, O_X) be any complex space and $x \in X$. Let (Y, O_Y) be another complex space with $y \in Y$. We say (X, x) is equivalent to (Y, y) if there exists some open set U containing x and a biholomorphic map between U and an open set V containing y, mapping x into y. This is an equivalence relation, and an equivalence class is called a germ of a complex space. An analytic algebra $\mathscr{A}$ is a quotient $\mathbb{C}(x_1, ..., x_n)/I$ where $\mathbb{C}(x_1, ..., x_n)$ is the ring of convergent power series in the n-variables $x_1, ..., x_n$ and I is a non-trivial ideal. An analytic algebra is a local $\mathbb{C}$-algebra. Let $m(\mathscr{A})$ be its maximal ideal. Then $\mathscr{A}/m(\mathscr{A}) \approx \mathbb{C}$. Also, an analytic algebra is Noetherian, and is therefore separated in the Krull topology. If $\mathscr{A}$ and $\mathscr{B}$ are two local algebras and $f: \mathscr{A} \to \mathscr{B}$ is a homomorphism then f is local and is continuous in the Krull topology. The category of analytic algebras is dual to the category of complex spaces, as seen from the following theorem (Malgrange [138], p. 20).

Theorem 8.3. *To any germ* (X, x) *of a complex space there is associated an analytic ring* $O_{X,x}$. *Every analytic ring is obtained in this way. Every morphism* $(X, x) \to (Y, y)$ *of germs of complex* *spaces induces a homomorphism* $O_{Y,y} \to O_{X,x}$ *of analytic rings. Conversely, every homomorphism* $\mathscr{B} \to \mathscr{A}$ *of analytic rings is obtained from a morphism of corresponding germs of complex spaces, and the latter is unique.*

9. FLAT MORPHISMS

First we give some elementary properties of **flat modules.** Let A be a commutative ring with unit and let E be a unitary A-module. We consider only unitary modules.

Definition 9.1. *E is said to be flat if for every exact sequence of A-modules* $0 \to F' \to F \to F'' \to 0$ *the sequence* $0 \to E \otimes F' \to E \otimes F \to E \otimes F'' \to 0$ *is also exact.*

Definition 9.2. *A free resolution of E is an exact sequence* $\cdots \to L_n \to L_{n-1} \to \cdots \to L_0 \to E \to 0$ *where all the* L_i *are free A-modules.*

It is well known that every module has a free resolution. Let F be any other A-module. Then forming the tensor product, we get an exact sequence
$\cdots \to L_n \otimes F \to L_{n-1} \otimes F \to \cdots \to L_1 \otimes F \to L_0 \otimes F \to 0.$

Definition 9.3. *We define for* $n \geqslant 1$

$$\mathrm{Tor}_n^A(E,F) = \frac{\mathrm{Ker}(L_n \otimes F \to L_{n-1} \otimes F)}{\mathrm{Im}(L_{n+1} \otimes F \to L_n \otimes F)}$$

and

$$\mathrm{Tor}_0^A(E,F) = E \otimes F$$

The two basic properties of Tor which can be checked easily are that it is independent of the choice of the free resolution and that it is symmetric:

$$\mathrm{Tor}_n^A(E,F) = \mathrm{Tor}_n^A(F,E)$$

The following two theorems give various conditions equivalent to flatness.

Theorem 9.1. *Let E be an A-module. Then the following conditions are equivalent:*
(a) *E is flat;*
(b) *For all A-modules F, and for all* $n \geqslant 1$, $\mathrm{Tor}_n^A(E,F) = 0$;
(c) *For all A-modules F,* $\mathrm{Tor}_1^A(E,F) = 0$.

Theorem 9.2. *Let A be a Noetherian local ring with maximal ideal m and let* $k = A/m$. *Let E be any finitely generated A-module. Then the following conditions are equivalent:*
(a) *E is free;*
(b) *E is flat;*
(c) $\mathrm{Tor}_1^A(E,k) = 0$.

Definition 9.4. *Let* $\pi : X \to S$ *be a holomorphic map between two complex spaces. Then* π *induces a map* π^* *between the local rings* $O_{S,s} \to O_{X,x}$; $s = \pi(x)$ *by* $\pi^*(f) = f \circ \pi$. $O_{X,x}$ *can be naturally considered as an* $O_{S,s}$*-module. We say* π *is flat at x if* $O_{X,x}$ *is a flat* $O_{S,s}$*-module for*

$s = \pi(x)$. *π is flat if it is flat at every point of* X. *If π is a local isomorphism near* x, *then it is easy to see that π is flat at* x. *Let* X *be the closed subspace of* $\mathbb{C}^2$ *defined by* $y^2 - x = 0$ *where* x, y *are the co-ordinates in* $\mathbb{C}^2$. *Let* $S = \mathbb{C}$. *Let π be the projection* $X \to \mathbb{C}$ *to the first co-ordinate. Then* $\pi^{-1}(s)$ = *two simple points if* $s \neq 0$. $\pi^{-1}(s)$ = *double point if* $s = 0$.

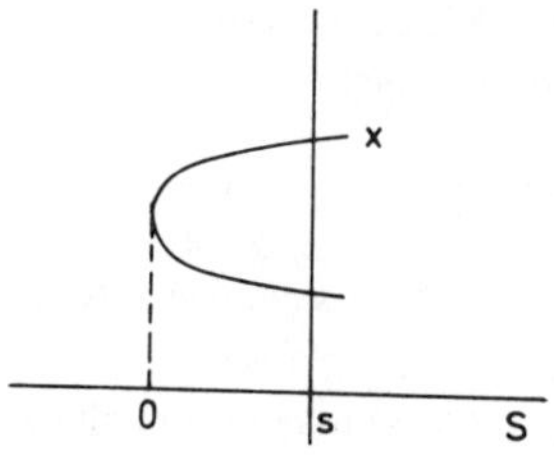

That flatness is a reasonable condition follows from the following two theorems:

Theorem 9.3 **(Frish [52], Kiehl [105])**
(a) *For any holomorphic map* $\pi: X \to S$ *of complex spaces, the set* $\{x \in X | \pi \text{ is flat at } x\}$ *is open, and it is the complement of an analytic set.*
(b) *If π is flat it is open; conversely, if π is open,* S *is non-singular and the fibres of π are all reduced complex spaces, then π is flat.*

Theorem 9.4 **(Douady [44]).** Let S, X *be complex analytic spaces and* $\pi : S \times X \to S$ *be the projection morphism. Then π is flat.*

10. MEROMORPHIC MAPS

Meromorphic maps are fundamental for the classification of compact complex manifolds. We adopt the definition of a meromorphic map due to Remmert, and state only those properties we need. For proofs and more details the reader is referred to Remmert [192], Stein [211]. The complex spaces considered in this section are all reduced and irreducible.

Definition 10.1. *A proper surjective holomorphic map* $f: X \to Y$ *between complex spaces is called a* **proper modification** *if there exist nowhere dense analytic subsets* A *of* X *and* B *of* Y *such that* f *is a biholomorphic map of* $X - A$ *onto* $Y - B$.

Definition 10.2. *Let* X *and* Y *be complex spaces. A mapping φ from* X *into the power set of* Y *is called a* **meromorphic mapping** *of* X *into* Y *if the following two conditions are satisfied:*
(a) The graph G_φ of $\varphi : G_\varphi = \{(x,y)\ X \times Y | y \in \varphi(x)\}$ is an irreducible analytic subset of $X \times Y$;
(b) The projection map $p_1 : G_\varphi \to X$ is a proper modification.

A meromorphic mapping φ of X into Y is also denoted by (the usual notation $\varphi: X \to Y$. By the definition a meromorphic map $\varphi: X \to Y$ determines an irreducible analytic subset of $X \times Y$. Conversely, every irreducible analytic subset G of $X \times Y$ such that the projection (to the first factor) $p_1 : G \to X$ is a proper modification defines a meromorphic map φ (we have to only set $\varphi(x) = p_2 \circ p_1^{-1}(x)$) whose graph G_φ is precisely the given G.

It can be checked that a meromorphic map $\varphi : X \to Y$ is a holomorphic map if and only if p_1 is biholomorphic. **Note:** a meromorphic function f on X is nothing but a meromorphic map

$f: X \to \mathbb{P}^1$, such that $f(X) \neq \infty$. The following theorem is important. Recall that X is said to be normal if the local ring $O_{X,x}$ is integrally closed in its complete ring of quotients, for every $x \in X$.

Theorem 10.1 (Remmert). *Let $\varphi : X \to Y$ be a meromorphic map. Then there exists a smallest nowhere dense analytic subset $S(\varphi)$ in X such that φ is a holomorphic map of $X - S(\varphi)$ into Y. If X and Y are both normal, then the co-dimension of $S(\varphi)$ is at least two.*

One of the difficulties of meromorphic maps is that composition of two meromorphic maps is not defined in general: if $\varphi : X \to Y \psi : Z$, $\psi \circ \varphi$ need not be defined. However, if the projection $p_2 : G_\varphi \to Y$ is surjective, then $\psi \circ \varphi$ is defined as follows.

If $x \in X' = X - (S(\varphi) \cup \varphi^{-1}(S(\psi))$, define $\psi \circ \varphi(x) = \psi(\varphi(x))$.

If $x \in S(\varphi) \cup \varphi^{-1}(S(\psi))$, define $\psi \circ \varphi(x)$ to consist of all points $z \in Z$ such that there exist a point $y \in Y$ and a sequence $\{x_\nu\}$ in X^1 such that $\{x_\nu\}$, $\{\varphi(x_\nu)\}$, $\{(\psi(\varphi(x_\nu))\}$ converge respectively to x, y, z (see Stein [211]). A meromorphic mapping $\varphi : X \to Y$ is a bimeromorphic mapping if the projection $p_2 : G_\varphi \to Y$ is also a proper modification. In this case we can define a mermorphic mapping φ^{-1} from Y into X such that $\varphi \circ \varphi^{-1} = id_Y$ and $\varphi^{-1} \circ \varphi = id_X$. Two complex analytic spaces are bimeromorphically equivalent if there exists a bimeromorphic mapping between them.

Remark. If X and Y are complete algebraic varieties, the meromorphic mappings from X into Y are exactly the rational mappings from X into Y (see e.g. Lang [135]).

Meromorphic mappings arise naturally:

(a) Let $f_1, \ldots, f_n$ be meromorphic functions on a compact complex space X. Then there exists an analytic set S in X outside which $f_1, \ldots, f_n$ are holomorphic. Let $X^1 = X - S$ and let G' be the graph of the holomorphic mapping:

$$f : X^1 \to \mathbb{C}^n$$

$$x \mapsto (f_1(x), \ldots, f_n(x))$$

Let $\overline{G}$ be the closure of G' in $X \times \mathbb{P}^n$. Then $\overline{G}$ is an irreducible analytic set in $X \times \mathbb{P}^n$ such that the projection $p_1 : \overline{G} \to X$ is a proper modification. Hence $\overline{G}$ determines a meromorphic map $X \to \mathbb{P}^n$, which we denote by

$$x \mapsto (1; f_1(x); \quad \cdots \quad ; f_n(x))$$

(b) Let $L \to X$ be a holomorphic line bundle on a compact complex space X. Let $f_0, f_1, \ldots, f_n$ be linearly independent global sections of this line bundle. Then

$$\frac{f_1}{f_0}, \frac{f_2}{f_0}, \ldots, \frac{f_n}{f_0}$$

are meromorphic functions and hence, as explained above, these give rise to a meromorphic mappi

$$L : X \to \mathbb{P}^n$$

$$x \mapsto (f_0(x);\ f_1(x);\ \ldots;\ f_n(x))$$

Part III

ALMOST COMPLEX STRUCTURES, CHERN CLASSES

11. HARMONIC THEORY ON A COMPACT COMPLEX MANIFOLD

Let M be a compact complex manifold. Let $\underline{\Omega}^p$ be the sheaf over M of holomorphic p-forms. Let $\underline{A}^{p,q}$ be the sheaf of smooth (p,q) forms on M, with coefficients in complex numbers. $\bar{\partial}$ stands as usual for the exterior differential operator with respect to the conjugate of the local complex co-ordinates. We denote by Ω^p the complex vector space of global sections of $\underline{\Omega}^p$, i.e. $\Omega^p = H^0(M,\underline{\Omega}^p)$; similarly $A^{p,q} = H^0(M,\underline{A}^{p,q})$. We introduce a hermitian scalar product $\langle\, ,\rangle$ in $A^{p,q}$; $A^{p,q}$ is an incomplete inner product space. With respect to this metric there exists the adjoint operator δ of $\bar{\partial}$, characterized by $\langle\bar{\partial}\alpha,\beta\rangle = \langle\alpha,\delta\beta\rangle$ for $\alpha \in A^{p,q-1}$, $\beta \in A^{p,q}$. Note that $\bar{\partial}$ takes a form of type (p,q) into a form of type (p,q+1) while δ takes a form of type (p,q) into a form of type (p,q−1). Define the Laplace-Beltrami operator $\Box = \bar{\partial}\delta + \delta\bar{\partial}$. $\Box$ maps $A^{p,q}$ into itself. We checked that $\Box$ is a strongly elliptic self-adjoint second-order partial differential operator. Using this fact, we establish the existence of the harmonic projection operator $\mathbb{P}$ and the corresponding Green's operator G yielding the Hodge decomposition: every $\varphi \in A^{p,q}$ has a unique representation $\varphi = \mathbb{P}\varphi + \Box G\varphi$. A form $\varphi \in A^{p,q}$ is called harmonic if $\Box\varphi = 0$; or, equivalently, $\Box$ is harmonic if both $\bar{\partial}\varphi = 0$ and $\delta\varphi = 0$. Let $H^{p,q}$ be the space of harmonic forms in $A^{p,q}$. Then we have the fundamental **theorem of harmonic theory** that $H^{p,q}$ is finite dimensional. We have to extend the above theory to forms with values in any holomorphic vector bundle over M.

Definition 11.1. *A holomorphic vector bundle of rank* r *over* M *(not necessarily compact) is a complex manifold* E *together with a surjective holomorphic map* $\pi : E \to M$ *such that:*
(a) $E_p := \pi^{-1}(p)$, $p \in M$, *is a complex vector space of dimension* r;
(b) *For every* $p \in M$ *there exists a neighbourhood* U *of* p *and a biholomorphic map* $h : \pi^{-1}(U) \to U \times \mathbb{C}^r$ *such that* $h(E_p) \subset \{p\} \times \mathbb{C}^r$ *and the composition* $h^p : E_p \to \{p\} \times \mathbb{C}^r \xrightarrow{\text{projection}} \mathbb{C}^r$ *is a* $\mathbb{C}$ *vector space* $\cong$.

E_p is called the **fibre** over p and (U,h) is called a **local trivialization.** Note that for two local trivializations (U_α, h_α) and (U_β, h_β) the map $h_\alpha \circ h_\beta^{-1} : (U_\alpha \cap U_\beta) \times \mathbb{C}^r \to (U_\alpha \cap U_\beta) \times \mathbb{C}^r$ induces a map $g_{\alpha\beta} : U_\alpha \cap U_\beta \to GL(r,\mathbb{C})$ where $g_{\alpha\beta}(p) = h_\alpha^p \circ (h_\beta^p)^{-1}$. The functions $g_{\alpha\beta}$ are called the transition functions of the holomorphic vector bundle. They satisfy the compatibility conditions: on $U_\alpha \cap U_\beta \cap U_\gamma$, $g_{\alpha\beta} \circ g_{\beta\gamma} \circ g_{\gamma\alpha} = I_r$ where the product is a matrix product and I_r is the identity matrix of r rows. The bundle is determined by the transition functions. Given a covering $\{U_\alpha\}$ of M and functions $g_{\alpha\beta}$ satisfying the compatibility conditions, we can construct a holomorphic vector bundle $\pi : E \to M$ whose transition functions are precisely these.

A section of the bundle over an open set $U \subset M$ is a holomorphic map $f : U \to E$ such that $\pi \circ f = 1_M$ where 1_M is the identity map of M. Since holomorphic vector bundles are locally of the forms $U \times \mathbb{C}^n$, we can regard sections of a vector bundle as vector-valued functions (locally) where two different local representations are related by the transition functions of the bundle. Hence sections can be thought of as twisted vector-valued functions. Given two vector spaces, we can form new vector spaces by familiar algebraic operations and we can extend all these algebraic constructions to bundles. A holomorphic vector bundle of rank 1 is called a **holomorphic line bundle.**

Definition 11.2 (positive line bundle). *Let* M *be a complex manifold and* A *a subset of* M. *We say* A *can be blown down to a point if there exists a complex analytic space* X, *a point*

$x_0 \in X$, *and a holomorphic map* $f: M \to X$ *such that* $f(A) = x_0$ *and* $f: M - A \to X - x_0$ *is biholomorphic.*

Let F be a holomorphic line bundle over a compact complex manifold. F is defined to be negative (or weakly negative) if the zero cross-section of F can be blown down to a point. F is said to be positive (or weakly positive) if its dual bundle is negative. This notion is due to Grauert.

A compact complex manifold is called a **Hodge manifold** if there is a positive line bundle on it. It can be easily proved that $\mathbb{P}^n$ is a Hodge manifold.

Now we state again the famous **embedding theorem of Kodaira.** *A compact complex manifold is algebraic if and only if it is a Hodge manifold.* This is the generalization of Riemann's theorem that a compact Riemann surface is algebraic. Grauert [61] generalized this theorem to compact complex analytic spaces, i.e. he proved that a compact analytic space is algebraic if and only if it carries a positive line bundle. A well-known example of a holomorphic vector bundle over a complex manifold M is its holomorphic tangent bundle $TM \to M$. Let $\{U_j\}$ be a covering of M with local co-ordinates $(Z_j^1, ..., Z_j^n)$ on U_j. A holomorphic tangent vector at Z is an element of the form

$$v = \sum_{\alpha=1}^{n} \xi_j^\alpha (\partial / \partial Z_j^\alpha)$$

The set of all complex tangent vectors at Z is a complex vector space $T_Z(M) \cong \mathbb{C}^n$. The set

$$TM = \bigcup_{Z \in M} T_Z(M)$$

can be made into a complex manifold and $TM \to M$ is a holomorphic vector bundle with transition functions $(\partial Z_j^\alpha / \partial Z_\kappa^\beta)$. $\overline{TM}$ is called the **conjugate bundle** of M and $\mathcal{T}M = TM \oplus \overline{TM}$ is called the **complexified** tangent bundle of M. The sheaf of germs of holomorphic sections of TM is called the **sheaf of germs of holomorphic vector fields** and is denoted by Θ.

Let $\underline{M}$ be the underlying differentiable manifold of M, $T\underline{M}$ its (real) tangent bundle, and $T\underline{M} \otimes_{\mathbb{R}}$ the complexified tangent bundle of $\underline{M}$. Then it is easy to see that $\mathcal{T}M = T\underline{M} \otimes_{\mathbb{R}} \mathbb{C}$.

Let $T^*(M)$ be the dual bundle of TM. Then a differential form φ of type (p,q) over an open set U in M is a differential section of $(\otimes TM)^p \otimes (\otimes \overline{T^*M})^q$, such that the fibre co-ordinates $\varphi j; \alpha_1, ..., \alpha_p, \bar\beta_1, ..., \bar\beta_q$ are skew symmetric with respect to $\alpha_1; ... \alpha_p, \beta_1; ... \beta_q$, i.e. φ is a section of $\Lambda^p T^* M \otimes \Lambda^q \overline{T^*M} = \Lambda^{p,q} T^*M$.

$$H^{p,q}(M) = H_\square(\Lambda^{p,q} T^*M)$$

We have the following isomorphism:

$$\textbf{Dolbeault:}\ H^q(M, \Omega^p) \cong \frac{\mathrm{Ker}\,(A^{p,q} \to A^{p,q+1})}{\mathrm{Im}\,(A^{p,q-1} \to A^{p,q})} \left\{ =: H_{\bar\partial}^{p,q}(M) \right\}$$

Hodge-Kodaira: $H^{p,q}_{\bar\partial}(M) \cong H^{p,q}(M)$

Now let $E \to M$ be any holomorphic vector bundle over M. Let

$$\underline{A}^{p,q}(E) = \underline{E} \otimes_{O} \underline{A}^{p,q}, \quad A^{p,q}(E) = H^0(M, \underline{A}^{p,q}(E))$$

$$\underline{\Omega}^p(E) = \underline{E} \otimes_{O} \underline{\Omega}^p \; ; \qquad \Omega^p(E) = H^0(M, \underline{\Omega}^p(E))$$

where O is the sheaf of germs of holomorphic functions on M. $\varphi \in A^{p,q}(E)$ is called a differential form of type (p,q) with coefficients in E. $\bar\partial$ can be extended to $A^{p,q}(E)$. Corresponding to the above isomorphisms, we have the following:

Dolbeault: $H^q(M, \underline{\Omega}^p(E)) \cong H^{p,q}_{\bar\partial}(M, E)$

Hodge-Kodaira: $H^{p,q}_{\bar\partial}(M, E) \cong H^{p,q}(M, E)$

Using these isomorphisms, we get the following **duality theorem** due to Serre [200]. *Let* M *be a compact complex manifold and* $E \to M$ *a holomorphic vector bundle over* M. *Then there is a conjugate linear isomorphism* $H^q(M, \underline{\Omega}^p(M)) \to H^{n-q}(M, \underline{\Omega}^{n-p}(E))$ *and hence these spaces are dual to one another.*

The main step in proving the embedding theorem of Kodaira is the **vanishing theorem of Kodaira.** *Let* X *be a compact connected complex manifold;* F *a positive line bundle on* X; *and* S *a coherent analytic sheaf on* X. *Then there exists an integer* k_0, *depending on* S *and* F, *such that for all* $k > k_0$, $H^q(X, S \otimes F^k) = 0$ *for all* $q > 1$.

For deformation theory of M, we have to consider differentiable forms with values in the holomorphic tangent bundle TM. Let A^q be the (0,q) forms with values in TM. Then we have the following isomorphism, as stated above:

$$H^q(M, \Theta) \cong H^{0,q}_{\bar\partial}(M, TM) \cong H^{0,q}(M, TM)$$

The cohomology groups $H^0(M,\Theta)$, $H^1(M,\Theta)$ $H^2(M,\Theta)$ and the space A^1 play important roles in the deformation theory of M, as will be clear in the sequel. Under suitable conditions, elements of A^1 represent complex structures on the differentiable manifold $\underline{M}$ underlying M. We study this condition in detail in the next section.

12. ALMOST COMPLEX STRUCTURE

Let $\underline{M}$ be an orientable differentiable manifold of dimension 2n, $T(\underline{M})$ its tangent bundle, and $\mathcal{T}(\underline{M})$ its complexified tangent bundle. An almost complex structure on $\underline{M}$ can be defined in any of the following three equivalent ways:

Definition 12.1. *An almost complex structure on* $\underline{M}$ *is a differentiable vector bundle isomorphism* $J: T(\underline{M}) \to T(\underline{M})$ *such that* $J^2 = -I$ *where* I *is the identity vector bundle isomorphism.*

Definition 12.2. *An almost complex structure on* $\underline{M}$ *is a differentiable sub-bundle* T'' *of* $\mathcal{T}(M)$ *such that* $\mathcal{T}(\underline{M}) = T'' \to \overline{T}''$ *where* $\overline{T}''$ *denotes the conjugate bundle of* T''. *We usually write* $\overline{T}''$ *as* T'.

Definition 12.3. *Regarding* GL(n, $\mathbb{C}$) *as a subgroup of* GL(2n, R) *(in its real representation), an almost complex structure on* $\underline{M}$ *is a reduction of* GL(2n, R), *the structure group of the bundle* L(M) *of linear frames of* $\underline{M}$, *to* GL(n, $\mathbb{C}$).

As remarked already, an orientable differentiable manifold of even dimension need not admit any almost complex structure on it. There are many methods known in the theory of fibre bundles to find necessary conditions for a differentiable manifold to admit an almost complex structure.

A complex structure M on $\underline{M}$ naturally induces an almost complex structure on $\underline{M}$ given by the holomorphic tangent bundle TM of M. But not every almost complex structure is induced by a complex structure. If an almost complex structure is induced by a complex structure, it is called an integrable almost complex structure.

Let M be a complex structure on $\underline{M}$ and T″ be an almost complex structure on $\underline{M}$. Then we know $\mathscr{T}(\underline{M}) = TM \oplus \overline{TM} = T''M \oplus T'M = T'' \oplus T'$.

Let P″(M) (or P′(M)) be the projection map from $\mathscr{T}(\underline{M})$ to TM (or $\overline{TM}$). We say that the almost complex structure T″ is of finite distance from the complex structure M if P″(M) induces an isomorphism of T″ onto TM = T″M. We can prove the basic fact:

Theorem 12.1. *There is a bijective correspondence between the set of all almost complex structures on* $\underline{M}$ *of finite distance from the given complex structure* M *on* $\underline{M}$ *and the set of all* T′M *valued* C^∞ *differential forms of type* (0, 1) *such that at each point* $x \in M$, $\overline{\omega} \circ \overline{\omega} : T''_x M \to T''_x M$ *does not have eigenvalue 1.*

Remark. According to our previous notation, the space of all T′M valued C^∞ differential forms of type (0, 1) is A^1. An element $\omega \in A^1$ can be regarded as a C^∞ bundle homomorphism $\omega : T''M \to T'M$. $\overline{\omega}$ is defined as $\overline{\omega(L)}$ for $L \in T''M$. If $\omega \in A^1$ is sufficiently near zero in the C^0-topology, we can see that ω determines an almost complex structure, denoted by M_ω on $\underline{M}$.

Theorem 12.2. *Let* M *be a complex structure on* $\underline{M}$. *Let* $\omega \in A^1$ *give rise to an almost complex structure* M_ω. *If* M_ω *is integrable, then*

$$\overline{\partial}\omega - \tfrac{1}{2}[\omega, \omega] = 0$$

Remark. We have the usual bracket operator [,] for sections of T′M. This can be extended to differential forms with values in T′M. The converse of the above theorem is of fundamental importance.

Theorem 12.3 **(Newlander-Nirenberg).** *Let* M *be a complex structure on* $\underline{M}$. *Let* $\omega \in A^1$ *satisfy the condition that* $\overline{\partial}\omega - \frac{1}{2}[\omega, \omega] = 0$. *Then the almost complex structure* M_ω *is integrable.*

Remark. The first proof of the above theorem was given by Newlander-Nirenberg [177]. In subsequent years other proofs were given by Nijenhuis-Woolf [179], Kohn [127], Hörmander [91]. Recently Malgrange [139] has proved the theorem in a general context which is considered to be very significant.

The condition $\overline{\partial}\omega - \frac{1}{2}[\omega, \omega] = 0$ is called the **integrability condition.** In view of the importan of this equation in deformation theory, it is also referred to as the **deformation equation.** The integrability condition can be exhibited in different forms. This equation is important as it opens up the techniques of partial differential equations to the study of complex structures. In fact, deformation theory of complex manifolds can be regarded as geometric applications of partial differential equations [180]. For a global version of the integrability condition see the recent work of Hamilton [77].

As already remarked, there is no almost complex structure on the spheres S^{2n} for $n \geqslant 4$. This was proved first by Borel-Serre; Ehresman and Hoff proved there is no almost complex structure on S^4. A simpler proof of the theorem of Borel can be given by applying a theorem of Bott in K-theory. To state this theorem we have to introduce the concept of **Chern classes** for a C^∞ complex vector bundle over a differentiable manifold.

13. CHERN CLASSES

Chern classes are topological cohomology classes in the base manifold and they measure how far the given bundle deviates from the product bundle. If $E \to X$ is a C^∞ complex vector bundle over the C^∞ manifold X, of fibre dimension m, the definition of its Chern classes $C_r(E)$; $r = 1, 2, m$, are given such that $C_r(E) \in H^{2r}(X, R)$. The definition is rather involved. One approach is to define these in terms of connections.

Definition 13.1 (horizontal subspaces). *Let* $P = P(X,G)$ *be a differentiable principal bundle over a differentiable manifold with structure group* G *a Lie group. Let* $p: P \to X$ *be the projection. For* $u \in P$, *let* F_u *be the fibre through* u. *Let* TP *be the tangent bundle of* P *and* $T_u(F_u)$ *be the space of tangent vectors to* F_u *at* u. *Suppose in* $T_u(P)$ *we can choose a space* $\underline{T_u(P)}$ *such that:*

(a) $T_u(P)$ *is the direct sum of* $T_u(P)$ *and* $T_u(F)$;

(b) The correspondence $u \to T_u(P)$ *is invariant under* G;

(c) $\underline{T_u(P)}$ *depends differentiably on* u.

$\underline{T_u(P)}$ *is called* a *horizontal subspace of* $T_u(P)$ *at* u. $T_u(F_u)$ *is called* the *vertical subspace of* $T_u(P)$ *at* u. *Given* $T_u(F_u)$ *and* $T_u(P)$, *every vector* $X_u \in T_u(P)$ *admits a unique decomposition* $X_u = {}^{\perp}X_u + \underline{X_u}$ where ${}^{\perp}X_u \in T_u(F_u)$ and $\underline{X_u} \in \underline{T_u(P)}$.

Definition 13.2. *Given a principal bundle* $P = P(X,G)$, *if we can define a field of horizontal subspaces in* T(P) *we say we have a connection* Γ *in* P.

Given a connection Γ in P, we associate with it a 1-form ω on P with values in the Lie algebra $\mathcal{G}$ of G, as follows.

For each vector field $X \in T(P)$, we define $\omega(X)$ to be the unique $A \in \mathcal{G}$ such that $A^* = {}^{\perp}X$. (G acts on P on the right; consider $A \in \mathcal{G}$. Associate to A the set $a_t = \exp tA$, t real; this is a one-parameter subgroup of G and its action on P induces a vector field A^*.) The form ω is called the connection form of Γ. (This ω is not to be confused with the notation for a (0, 1) form given in the previous section.) Let θ be the canonical 1-form on G, i.e. θ is the left invariant $\mathcal{G}$-valued 1-form satisfying $\theta(A) = A$, $\forall A \in \mathcal{G}$.

Definition 13.3 (covariant differentiation). *Given a connection* Γ *in* $P = P(X,G)$, *we can associate to the exterior differentiation operator* d *an operator* ∇ *as follows. For any* α *on* P, $\nabla\alpha = (d\alpha)h$ *where* h *is the projection* $T_u(P) \to \underline{T_u(P)}$. ∇ *is called the exterior covariant differentiation and the form* $\nabla\alpha$ *is called the exterior covariant derivative of* α.

Definition 13.4 (curvature and torsion of a connection). *Let a connection* Γ *be given in* $P = P(X,G)$; *let the connection form be* ω *and the canonical form on* G *be* θ. *Set* $\Omega = \nabla\omega$, $\Theta = \nabla\theta$. Ω *is called the curvature form of the connection and* Θ *is called the torsion form of the connection.* (This Θ is not to be confused with the notation for the sheaf of germs of holomorphic vector fields on a complex manifold used in the previous sections.)

Relating these we have the following structure equations:

Theorem 13.1 **(E. Cartan).** $d\omega = -\frac{1}{2}[\omega, \omega] + \Omega$.

Remark. Note the resemblance of this equation to the deformation equation.

Weil homomorphism

Let G be a Lie group with Lie algebra $\mathcal{G}$. Consider the space $S^k(G)$ of k-linear symmetric maps

$$\underbrace{\mathcal{G} \times \ldots \times \mathcal{G}}_{\text{(k factors)}} \to \mathbb{R}$$

which are invariant under G, i.e. for $\forall\, a \in G$ and $\forall\, (t_1, \ldots, t_k) \in \mathcal{G} \times \mathcal{G} \ldots \times \mathcal{G}$

$$f((\text{ad } a)t_1, \ldots, (\text{ad } a)t_k) = f(t_1, \ldots, t_k)$$

Set

$$S(G) = \sum_{k \geqslant 0} S^k(G)$$

S(G) can be made into a commutative algebra by defining multiplication in a familiar way.

Let now P = P(X,G) be a principal bundle with a given connection Γ in P. Let Ω be the curvature form of Γ. Define for $f \in S^k(G)$ and $X_i \in T_u(P)$, $1 \leqslant i \leqslant 2k$:

$$F(\Omega)\,(X_1, \ldots, X_{2k}) = 1/(2k)! \quad \sum_{\sigma} \pm f(\Omega(X_{\sigma(1)}, X_{\sigma(2)}), \ldots, \Omega(X_{\sigma(2k-1)}, X_{\sigma(2k)})$$

where the summation is taken over all permutations σ of $(1, 2, \ldots, 2k)$. $F(\Omega)$ is a 2k-form on P.

With these preliminary definitions and notations we state a basic theorem in the theory of characteristic classes.

Theorem 13.2 **(Chern-Weil).** *Let* P = P(X,G) *be a principal bundle on* X, *with group* G *and projection* p. *Let* Γ *be a connection in* P *and* Ω *its curvature form. Then:*

(a) For each $f \in S^k(G)$, *the* 2k*-form* $F(\Omega)$ *on* P *projects into a unique closed* 2k *form, say* $\gamma(\Omega)$ *on* X, *i.e.* $F(\Omega) = p^*(\gamma(\Omega))$.

(b) Let W(f) *be the element of the de Rham cohomology group* $H^{2k}(X, \mathbb{R})$ *defined by the closed* 2k*-form* $\gamma(\Omega)$. *Then* W(f) *is independent of the choice of the connection* Γ *and* $W : S(G) \to H^*(X, R)$ *is an algebra homomorphism, called the Weil homomorphism.*

Definition 13.5 **(Chern classes).** *Let* E *be a complex vector bundle over* X *with fibre* $\mathbb{C}^m$ *and group* $G\ell(m, \mathbb{C})$ *and let* P *be its associated principal bundle.*

Given a connection Γ on P with its curvature form Ω, define polynomial functions $f_1, \ldots, f_m$ on the Lie algebra $\mathcal{G}\ell(m, \mathbb{C})$ by

$$\det(\lambda I_m - \left(\frac{1}{2\sqrt{-1}\,\pi}\right)\Omega) = \sum_{0 \leqslant k \leqslant m} f_k(\Omega)\,\lambda^{m-k}$$

These are invariant under $\mathrm{ad}(G\ell(m,\mathbb{C}))$. Hence by the above theorem of Weil, there exists for each $k, 0 \leqslant k \leqslant m$ a unique closed 2k-form γ_k on X such that $p^*(\gamma_k) = f_k(\Omega)$, where $p : P \to X$ is the projection, so that we can write

$$\det(I_m - \left(\frac{1}{2\sqrt{-1}\,\pi}\right)\Omega) = p^*(1 + \gamma_1 + \ldots + \gamma_m)$$

Definition 13.6. *The* k^{th} *Chern class* $C_k(E)$ *of* E *is represented by the* 2k*-closed forms* γ_k *(and thus* $C_k(E) \in H^{2k}(X,\mathbb{R})$*).* $C(E) = C_1(E) + \ldots + C_m(E)$ *is called the total Chern class of* E.

We now state the obstruction nature of the Chern classes.

Theorem 13.3. *Let* $E \to X$ *be a differential vector bundle of rank* m. *Then:*
(a) $C_0(E) = 1$;
(b) If $E \cong X \times \mathbb{C}^m$ (trivial), $C_j(E) = 0$, for $j = 1, \ldots, m$;
(c) If $E \cong F + F'$ where F' is a trivial bundle of rank r, $C_j(E) = 0$ for $j = m - r + 1, \ldots, m$.

Now we come to the theorem of Bott referred to:

Theorem 13.4 (Bott [19]). *Let* E *be any complex vector bundle of rank* n *over the sphere* S^{2n}. *Then* $C_n(E) \cdot S^{2n}$ *is divisible by* $(n-1)!$ *(factorials).*

Remark. $C_n(E) \cdot S^{2n}$ stands for the value of $C_n(E)$ over the fundamental cycle S^{2n}.

If S^{2n} admits an almost complex structure, its tangent bundle $T(S^{2n})$ is a complex vector bundle of rank n. Then we must have $C_n(T(S^{2n})) \cdot S^{2n} =$ Euler characteristic of $S^{2n} = 2$. But according to the above theorem of Bott, $C_n(T(S^{2n})) \cdot S^{2n}$ must be divisible by $(n-1)!$. Hence if S^{2n} were almost complex, 2 is divisible by $(n-1)!$. Hence n must be 1, 2, 3. This proves the non-existence of almost complex structures on S^{2n} for $n \geqslant 4$.

By a different method we can prove that there is no almost complex structure on S^{4k} (see Ref. [109]) and, in particular, there is no almost complex structure on S^4 (see Pittie in these Proceedings). On S^6 there is an almost complex structure but it is non-integrable (see Kobayashi-Nomizu [109]). It is now conjectured that there is no integrable almost complex structure on S^6.

Remark. We have given the differential geometric approach to the theory of Chern classes: another approach is through the **universal bundle theorem**, and a third way is the axiomatic development of the theory of Chern classes (for a detailed account see Ref. [109]).

Part IV

DEFORMATION THEORY OF COMPACT COMPLEX MANIFOLDS

The theory of deformations of compact complex manifolds, due to Kodaira-Spencer-Kuranishi, studies complex structures "close to" a given one. Let M be a complex structure on a compact connected differentiable manifold $\underline{M}$ and let $\Sigma(\underline{M})$ be the set of all isomorphism classes of complex structures on $\underline{M}$ consistent with the given differentiable structure. Deformation theory studies $\Sigma(\underline{M})$ in a "neighbourhood" of the point which represents the given complex structure M. Part IV gives a survey of the theory.

14. DEFINITIONS AND THE THEOREM OF KODAIRA-NIRENBERG-SPENCER

Definition 14.1. *A holomorphic family of compact complex manifolds parametrized by a connected complex manifold* S *is a complex manifold* X *together with a proper surjective holomorphic map* $\pi : X \to S$ *of maximal rank.*

From the definition it follows that the fibres $\pi^{-1}(s)$, $s \in S$, are all compact complex manifolds of the same dimension. It can be proved that if $f : M \to N$ is a proper surjective holomorphic map between two complex manifolds, there exists a nowhere dense complex analytic set A of M such that f is of maximal rank at any point of M-A and f(A) is a nowhere dense complex analytic subset of N.

Definition 14.2. *A differentiable family of compact complex manifolds parametrized by a connected differentiable manifold* S *is a differentiable manifold* X *together with a map* $\pi : X \to S$ *which is a proper surjective differentiable map such that:*
(a) There exists a covering $\{U_i\}$ *of* X *and diffeomorphism* $h_i : U_i \to U_i \times V_i$ *where* U_i *is open in* $\mathbb{C}^n$, V_i *is open in* S, *such that the following diagram commutes:*

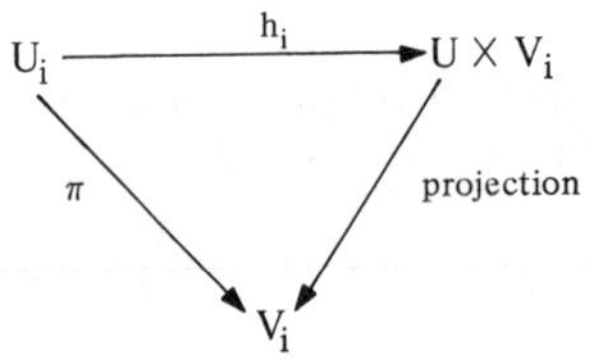

(b) $\forall s \in S$, $\pi^{-1}(s)$ *is a complex manifold and* $h_i | U_i \cap \pi^{-1}(s)$ *is a complex analytic chart of* $\pi^{-1}(s)$.

Theorem 14.1. *Let* (X, S, π) *be a family of compact complex manifolds (as for any of the definitions above). Then the fibres* $\pi^{-1}(s)$ *are all diffeomorphic to each other.*

Remark. Hence, in a family the fibres can be regarded as a family of complex structures on a compact differentiable manifold. In general the complex structure of $\pi^{-1}(s)$ depends on s.

Definition 14.3. *Let* (X, S, π) *be a holomorphic family of compact manifolds. Let* M *be a given compact complex manifold. We say* (X, S, π) *is a holomorphic family of deformations of* M *if there exists a point* $o \in S$ *and a holomorphic isomorphism* $\pi^{-1}(o) \approx M$.

Definition 14.4. *Let* (X, S, π, o), (Y, S, σ, o) *be two holomorphic families of deformations of* M. *They are equivalent if there exists a neighbourhood* S' *of* o *in* S *such that* $\pi^{-1}(s) \cong \sigma^{-1}(s)$ *complex analytically for all* $s \in S'$. *This is an equivalence relation. Hence, we have the notion of the germ of a family of deformations of* M. *By deforming* M *locally we mean to consider the germ of a family of deformations of* M.

It becomes necessary to consider holomorphic families parametrized by a complex space which may be reduced or non-reduced. Also, for studying the local deformations of a compact complex manifold M, it is sufficient to consider germs of families of deformation of M. These considerations lead us to formulate the definition of deformation in the following form:

Definition 14.5. *Let* M *be a compact complex manifold. Let* (S, s_0) *be a germ of a complex space. A deformation of* M *over* S *is a complex space* X *together with a proper flat holomorphic mapping* $\pi : X \to S$ *and an embedding* $M \hookrightarrow X$ *which induces an isomorphism* $\alpha : M \xrightarrow{\sim} \pi^{-1}(s_0) = M$.

Remarks

(1) We have already mentioned (Section 8 (Part II)) that flatness is a reasonable condition.
(2) Let S_1, S_2 be two representatives of the germ (S, s_0). Let X_1, X_2 be two complex spaces and $\pi_1 : X_1 \to S_1$, $\pi_2 : X_2 \to S_2$ be proper flat holomorphic maps. They are said to be equivalent if there exist open neighbourhoods V_1, V_2 of s_0, $V_1 \subset S_1$, $V_2 \subset S_2$ such that $V_1 = V_2$, $\pi_1^{-1}(V_1) = \pi_2^{-1}(V_2)$ and $\pi_1|\pi_1^{-1}(V_1) = \pi_2|\pi_2^{-1}(V_1)$. In particular, $\pi_1^{-1}(s_0) = \pi_2^{-1}(s_0) =: \pi^{-1}(s_0)$. Hence a deformation $\pi : X \to S$ of M is an equivalence class of flat proper holomorphic maps.
(3) The flatness of $\pi : X \to S$, when the fibre $\pi^{-1}(s_0)$ is a complex manifold, is equivalent to the following property: for any $x \in \pi^{-1}(s_0)$ there exist a neighbourhood U of x in X and an isomorphism $\beta : \alpha^{-1}(U) \times S \to U$ such that β restricted to $\alpha^{-1}(U) \times s_0$ is α, and the following diagram is commutative:

$$\begin{array}{ccc} \alpha^{-1}(U) \times S & \xrightarrow{\ \beta\ } & U \\ & {\scriptstyle pr_S}\searrow \quad \swarrow{\scriptstyle \pi} & \\ & S & \end{array}$$

(4) When both X and S are complex manifolds, the above definition is equivalent to Definition 14.1.
(5) The fibres $\pi^{-1}(s_0)$, $s_0 \in U$, where U is a small neighbourhood of s_0, are all compact complex manifolds and they are all diffeomorphic to each other. The complex structure of $\pi^{-1}(s)$ depends in general on s.

Definition 14.6. *We say that a compact complex manifold* M *is rigid if for any holomorphic family* (X, S, π, s_0) *of deformations of* M *we can find a neighbourhood* S' *of* s_0 *in* S *such that* $\pi^{-1}(s) \approx \pi^{-1}(s_0)$ $(\approx M)$ *complex analytically for all* $s \in S'$.

Theorem 14.2. *If* $H^1(M, \Theta) = 0$, M *is rigid* (Frolicher-Nijenhuis [55]).

Example. $\mathbb{P}^n$ is rigid since $H^1(\mathbb{P}^n, \Theta) = 0$ (Bott). This gives strength to the conjecture that on $\mathbb{P}^n$ there is only one complex structure.

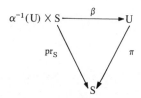

Local triviality. We have remarked that any family (X, S, π) of compact complex manifolds is a differentiable fibre bundle. But it need not be a holomorphic fibre bundle. However, if all the fibres are complex-analytically isomorphic to each other, (X, S, π) is a holomorphic fibre bundle according to a theorem of Grauert-Fisher [48]. If (X, S, π) is a holomorphic fibre bundle, then in particular it is locally trivial complex analytically. This means that for each $s \in S$ there exists a neighbourhood U of s and a biholomorphic map f of $\pi^{-1}(U)$ onto $U \times M_s$ such that the following diagram commutes:

$$\begin{array}{ccc} \pi^{-1}(U) & \xrightarrow{\ f\ } & U \times M_s \\ & \searrow \quad \swarrow {\scriptstyle pr_U} & \\ & U & \end{array}$$

Hence, in a locally trivial family the complex structures of the fibres are complex analytically the same.

Jumping of structures. If in a family (X,S,π) all the fibres except at one point are biholomorphic to each other, we say there is a jumping of complex structures in the family.

For example, consider the family of Hopf surfaces constructed as follows:

A Hopf surface M_t is defined by

$$M_t = \frac{\mathbb{C}^2 - \{0\}}{G_t}$$

where $G_t = \{g^m \,|\, m \in Z\}$

and

$$g : \begin{pmatrix} Z_1 \\ Z_2 \end{pmatrix} \rightarrow \begin{pmatrix} \alpha & t \\ 0 & \alpha \end{pmatrix} \begin{pmatrix} Z_1 \\ Z_2 \end{pmatrix}$$

where $0 < |\alpha| < 1$ and $t \in \mathbb{C}$. Then it can be proved that $\{M_t | t \in \mathbb{C}\}$ is a complex analytic family and $M_t = M_1$ complex analytically for $t \neq 0$ and $M_0 \neq M_1$.

Remark. Because of jumping of complex structures, one is unable to generalize the concept of distance between two compact Riemann surfaces. This is the main difficulty in constructing "global moduli space" for a compact complex manifold.

Kodaira-Spencer map. Let (X,S,π) be a holomorphic family of compact complex manifolds parametrized by a connected complex manifold S. Then for each $s \in S$ there exists a canonical complex linear map $P_s : T_sS \rightarrow H^1(M_s, \Theta_s)$ where T_sS represents the complex tangent space of S at s; M_s is the fibre $\pi^{-1}(s)$ over s, and Θ_s is the sheaf of germs of holomorphic vector fields over M_s. This map is called the Kodaira-Spencer map and is of fundamental importance in the study of deformations as it measures the magnitude of the dependence of the complex structure of the fibre M_s on the parameter s. For a tangent vector $v \in T_sS$, the image $P_s(v)$ is called the infinitesimal deformation M_s along v. We now outline the construction of P_s. By definition there exists a covering $\{\mathscr{U}_i\}$ of X with the associated biholomorphic maps $h_i : \mathscr{U}_i \rightarrow U_i \times V_i$. Let $h_i(p) = (Z_i^1, ..., Z_i^n, s)$, $s = \pi(p)$; for any $p \in \mathscr{U}_i$ on $U_i \cap U_k$ we have the transition functions

$$g_{ik} = h_i \circ h_k^{-1} :$$

$$g_{ik} : (Z_k, s) \rightarrow (Z_i^1, ..., Z_i^n, s), \quad Z_i = g_{ik}^{\alpha}(Z_k, s)$$

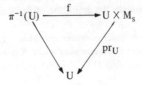

where $Z_k = (Z_k', \ldots, Z_k^n)$ and the $g_{ik}^{\alpha}(Z_k, s)$ are differentiable functions of (Z_k, s) in $\mathscr{U}_i \cap \mathscr{U}_k$ and holomorphic in Z_k for fixed s.

Let $(s^1, \ldots, s^m)$ be local co-ordinates of s on S. For a tangent vector $v = \sum v^r (\partial/\partial s^r)$ of S at s we define

$$\theta_{ik}(s) = \sum_{\alpha=1}^{n} v \cdot g_{ik}^{\alpha}(z_k, s) \frac{\partial}{\partial z_i^{\alpha}}$$

$\theta_{ik}(s)$ is a holomorphic vector field on $M_s \cap \mathscr{U}_i \cap \mathscr{U}_k$. From the identity $g_{ik} = g_{ij} \circ g_{jk}$ we get

$$\theta_{ik}(s) = \theta_{ij}(s) + \theta_{jk}(s) \quad \text{on} \quad M_s \cap \mathscr{U}_i \cap \mathscr{U}_j \cap \mathscr{U}_k$$

Hence $\{\theta_{ik}(s)\}$ forms a 1-cocycle of the nerve of the covering $\{M_s \cap \mathscr{U}_1\}$ of M_s with coefficients in Θ_s and hence it determines an element of $H^1(M_s, \Theta_s)$ which we denote by $P_s(v)$. We can prove that $P_s(v)$ is independent of the choice of the covering $\{\mathscr{U}_i\}$ and of the maps h_i. Thus we get the map

$$P_s : T_s S \rightarrow H^1(M_s, \Theta_s)$$

Remarks

(1) In the case of a differentiable family (X, S, π), we can construct in a similar way P_s, which will be a linear map over the reals.

(2) In the case of a holomorphic family (X, S, π) parametrized by a complex space S, P_s is to be interpreted as the Zariski tangent space of S at s. In this case also, the existence of P_s can be proved (see e.g. Forster-Knorr [50], Section 5.16).

(3) If P_s is injective at every point s, we say that the family is effectively parametrized. Let

$$\theta_{ik|r}(s) = \sum_{\alpha=1}^{n} \frac{\partial}{\partial s^r} g_{ik}^{\alpha}(z_k, s) \left(\frac{\partial}{\partial z_i^{\alpha}}\right)$$

This defines a cohomology class in $H^1(M_s, \Theta_s)$ which we denote by $(\partial M_s/\partial s^r)$. Define

$$\frac{\partial M_s}{\partial s} = \sum_{r=1} v^r \frac{\partial M_s}{\partial s^r} \quad \text{and} \quad \left(\frac{\partial M_s}{\partial s}\right)_{s=0}$$

to be the cohomology class in $H^1(M_0, \Theta_0)$ given by the cocycle

$$\theta_{ik} = \sum_{\alpha=1}^{n} \left(\frac{\partial}{\partial s} g_{ik}^{\alpha}(z_k, s)\right)\Bigg|_{s=0} \left(\frac{\partial}{\partial z_i^{\alpha}}\right)$$

Theorem 14.3. *If* (X, S, π) *is locally trivial,* $(\partial M_s/\partial s^r) = 0$ *for all* s *and* r. *Conversely if* $\dim H^1(M_s, \Theta_s)$ *is independent of* s *and if* $(\partial M_s/\partial s^r) = 0$ *for all* s *and* r, *the family* (X, S, π) *is locally trivial.*

Obstructions. If M is a given compact complex manifold, an element η is said to be unobstructed if there exists a holomorphic family (X, S, π, o) of deformation of $M \cong M_o$ such that $\eta \in P_o(T_o(S))$. If no such family exists, η is said to be obstructed. An example of obstruction is given by $M = T^n \times \mathbb{P}^1$ where T^n is a complex torus of $\dim n \geqslant 2$. A necessary condition for η to be in the image of the Kodaira-Spencer map is that $[\eta, \eta] = 0$. But this is not sufficient. There are "higher order" obstructions but all these obstructions lie in $H^2(M, \Theta)$. If all these obstructions vanish, we can formally construct a family of deformation of M. In case $H^2(M, \Theta) = 0$, Kodaira-Spencer-Nirenberg proved that we can actually construct a family of deformation of M. Precisely, we have

Theorem 14.4 (Kodaira-Spencer-Nirenberg [124]). *Let* M *be a compact complex manifold with* $H^2(M, \Theta) = 0$. *Then there exists a holomorphic family* (X, B_ϵ, π) *where* $B_\epsilon = \{t \mid |t| < \epsilon\} \subset \mathbb{C}^m$, $m = \dim H^1(M, \Theta)$ *such that:*

(a) $M_o = \pi^{-1}(0) \cong M$.

(b) *The map* $P_o : T_o B_\epsilon \to H^1(M, \Theta)$ *is an isomorphism.*

Remarks

(1) If moreover $H^0(M, \Theta) = 0$, the family (X, B_ϵ, π) is effectively parametrized in a neighbourhood of the reference point.

(2) Recently Forster and Knorr [50] have given a new proof of Theorem 14.4.

Let M now be such that $H^2(M, \Theta) \neq 0$. In Ref. [129] Kuranishi constructed a decreasing filtration of $H^1(M, \Theta) = H^{(1)}$.

$$H^{(1)} \supseteq H^{(2)} \supseteq H^{(3)} \supseteq \ldots \supseteq H^{(n)} = H^{(n+1)} = \ldots$$

denoted by

$$H^*(M) = \bigcap_{n=1}^{\infty} H^{(n)}$$

Kuranishi proved that there exists a holomorphic family (X, S, π) of deformations of $M = M_{s_o}$ which is "normal" at s_o and such that the map $P_{s_o} : T_{s_o} S \to H^1(M, \Theta)$ is an isomorphism onto $H^*(M)$. For details relating to this result see Refs [129, 212].

15. STABILITY OF STRUCTURES

It is always interesting and useful to know whether a certain important property possessed by a fibre in a family is enjoyed by neighbouring fibres. We now give three examples: in the first, a certain important property, being Kähler, is locally preserved; in the second, another important property, being algebraic, is not in general preserved locally; and for the third it is not known whether the important property of being hyperbolic is locally preserved or not.

(A) *Kählerity is locally preserved*

One of the important theorems in deformation theory is the following.

Theorem 15.1 Upper semi-continuity theorem (Kodaira-Spencer)

Let (X,S,π) be a family of compact complex manifolds. Then the function $s \mapsto \dim H^r(M_s,\Theta_s)$ is upper-semicontinuous, i.e.

$$\dim H^r(M_s,\Theta_s) \leqslant \dim H^r(M_{s_0}, \Theta_{s_0})$$

if s is in a sufficiently small neighbourhood of s_0. The proof of this theorem follows again from the theory of elliptic differential equations. As an application of this theorem, we get the following difficult theorem, on the stability of Kähler metrics.

Theorem 15.2 (Kodaira-Spencer). *If* (X,S,π) *is a differentiable family of compact complex manifolds and if* $M_{s_0} = \pi^{-1}(s_0)$ *is a Kähler manifold,* $M_s = \pi^{-1}(s)$ *is Kähler for* $|s-s_0|$ *small enough.*

Remark. The theorem is true only for $|s-s_0|$ small. It was originally conjectured by Kodaira-Spencer that any deformation of a Kähler manifold is Kähler. But Hironaka gave an example of a Kähler complex manifold of dimension 3 having non-Kähler deformations [79].

Problem. Is any deformation of a Kähler surface Kähler?

Problem. Is any deformation of $\mathbb{P}^n$, $n > 2$, $\mathbb{P}^n$? (**Known**: any deformation of $\mathbb{P}^2$ is $\mathbb{P}^2$ ([122], II, Theorem 20.1).)

(B) *Algebricity is not locally preserved*

Let (X,S,π) be a family. Assume $M_{s_0} = \pi^{-1}(s_0)$ is an algebraic manifold. Then in general we cannot expect M_s to be algebraic in some neighbourhood of s_0 as the family of complex tori shows.

Let T^n be an n-dimensional complex torus. It is defined by 2n vectors $\omega_1, \ldots, \omega_{2n}$ in $\mathbb{C}^n$ which are linearly independent over the reals. Let $\omega_{i1}, \ldots, \omega_{in}$ be the components of the vector ω_i. Form the period matrix $\Omega = (\omega_{ij})$, $1 \leqslant i \leqslant 2n$, $1 \leqslant j \leqslant n$. Suppose there exists a non-singular skew symmetric matrix of rank 2n such that

(1) $\Omega\, A^t\, \Omega = 0$
(2) $-\sqrt{(-1)}\, \Omega\, A^t\, \overline{\Omega} = M > 0$ where $A = Q^{-1}$.

Then Ω is called a Riemannian matrix. An algebraic torus is called an abelian variety. Not every torus is an abelian variety. The following theorem is well known.

Theorem 15.3. *An n-dimensional complex torus is an abelian variety if and only if any one of the following three equivalent conditions holds (and hence all hold):*
(a) The periods defining the torus give rise to a Riemannian matrix;
(b) There exists a positive line bundle on the torus;
(c) The torus is a Moishezon manifold.

It can be proved that, in a family (X,S,π), if any one fibre is a torus then every fibre is a torus (see Andreotti and Stoll [6], p. 339).

We construct a family of complex tori as follows. Let S be the space of $n \times n$ matrices $s = (s^\alpha_\beta)$ with $\det \operatorname{Im}(s) > 0$; form the $n \times 2n$ matrix $\omega(s) = (I,s)$ where I is the identity $n \times n$ matrix. Let G be the group of analytic automorphisms of $\mathbb{C}^n \times S$ generated by $g_j : (Z,s) \mapsto (Z + \omega_j(s),s)\ (Z + \omega_j(s),s)$, $j = 1, \ldots, 2n$ where $\omega_j(s)$ is the jth column vector of

$\omega(s)$. G acts properly discontinuously without fixed points and hence $X = \mathbb{C}^n \times S/G$ is a complex manifold. The canonical projection $\mathbb{C}^n \times S \to S$ induces a proper surjective holomorphic map $\pi : X \to S$ and each fibre $\pi^{-1}(s) = M_s$ is an n-torus with periods $\omega_1(s), ..., \omega_{2n}(s)$. This family (X, S, π) is effectively parametrized and in fact at every point $s \in S$, the Kodaira-Spencer map P_s is an isomorphism. Suppose M_{s_o} is an abelian variety; then in every neighbourhood of s_o there exists a point s such that the period matrix of M_s is not a Riemannian matrix and hence M_s is not algebraic.

The following theorems are of interest in this connection.

Theorem 15.4 (Moishezon-Tjurin [196]). *Let (X, S, π) be a holomorphic family and let $M_s = \pi^{-1}(s_0$ be an algebraic manifold.*

(1) *Then in some neighbourhood U of s_0 in S there exists an analytic set B, with co-dimension not greater than the dimension of the space of two-dimensional holomorphic forms on M_{s_0}, such that for all $s \in B$, M_s is algebraic. The set of points A in S, such that M_s is algebraic for every $s \in A$, is contained in the union of not more than a countable number of such analytic sets.*

(2) *Let M_0 be a Hodge manifold with $H^2(M, \Theta) = 0$; then in any holomorphic family (X, S, π_{s_0}) of deformations of M_0 there exists a neighbourhood U of s_0 in S such that M_s is Hodge for $s \in U$.*

Theorem 15.5 (Kodaira)

(1) Any small deformation of a rational surface is rational.

(2) Let M_0 be an algebraic surface with $C_1^2(M_0) > 0$. Then any small deformation of M_0 is an algebraic surface.

(3) Let M_0 be an algebraic surface with no exceptional curve of the first kind. If $C_1^2(M_0) \neq 0$, any small deformation of M_0 is an algebraic surface. If $C_1^2(M_0) = 0$, M_0 can be deformed into a nonalgebraic surface by small deformations.

(4) Let M_0 be birationally equivalent to a ruled surface, then any small deformation M_s of M_0 is also an algebraic surface which is birationally equivalent to a ruled surface.

(5) Every compact Kähler surface is a deformation of an algebraic surface.

Remarks. For the notions of ruled surfaces, rational surfaces and exceptional curves of the first kind, see Sections 18 and 19 (Part V).

In the above $C_1(M_0)$ represents the first Chern class of M_0, and $C_1^2(M_0)$ represents the value of C_1^2 on the 4-cycle M_0. It can be proved that C_1^2 is a deformation invariant. Also if $C_1^2(M_0) > 0$ for an analytic surface, then M_0 must be algebraic.

(C) *Not known whether "hyperbolicity" is locally preserved.*

It is not known whether hyperbolicity is locally preserved. We now define a hyperbolic complex manifold.

Definition 15.1. Let $D = \{z \in \mathbb{C} \mid |z| < 1\}$; let P be the Poincaré-Bergman metric of D; let M be any complex manifold; let p, q be any two points of M. Choose points $p = p_0, p_1, ..., p_k = q$ in M and points $a_1, ..., a_k$, $b_1, ..., b_k$, in D and holomorphic maps $f_1, ..., f_k$ of D into M such that $f_i(a_i) = p_{i-1}$ and $f_i(b_i) = p_i$, $i = 1, ..., k$. Define

$$d_M(p, q) = \inf \sum_{i=1}^{k} P(a_i, b_i)$$

where inf is taken over all possible choices of points and maps. Then $d_M : M \times M \to R$ is a pseudodistance; d_M is a generalization of the Poincaré-Bergman metric P of D.

We say M is hyperbolic if d_M is a distance function. Every compact Riemann surface is hyperbolic; every bounded domain in $\mathbb{C}^n$ is hyperbolic and $\mathbb{C} - \{a, b\}$, where a, b are two distinct points of ϵ, is also hyperbolic. But $\mathbb{C}^n$ is not hyperbolic as d_M is trivial for $M = \mathbb{C}^n$, i.e. d, $\mathbb{C}^n(Z_1, Z_2) = 0$ for any two $Z_1, Z_2 \in \mathbb{C}^n$. It can be proved that for a compact hyperbolic manifold M, the automorphism group Aut(M) is finite.

Problem. If in a holomorphic family (X, S, π), a fibre $M_s = \pi^{-1}(s)$ is hyperbolic, does this imply that M_t is hyperbolic for t sufficiently near s?

Problem. If in a holomorphic family (X, S, π) all the fibres except one M_0 are hyperbolic, does it imply that M_0 is also hyperbolic?

16. LOCALLY COMPLETE FAMILIES AND THE THEOREM OF KURANISHI

Definition 16.1 (induced family). Let (X, S, π) be a holomorphic family of compact complex manifolds. Let W be a complex space and $f : W \to S$ be a holomorphic map. Then f induces a unique family over W as follows. Define $X_W = \{(w, x) \in W \times X | \, f(w) = \pi(x)\}$. This is an analytic set in $W \times X$. Define $\widetilde{\pi} : X_w \to W$ by taking $\widetilde{\pi} = (\text{projection to } W) \times \pi$. Then it can be checked that $(X_w, W, \widetilde{\pi})$ forms a holomorphic family of deformations. The induced family is also denoted by $(X_f, W, \widetilde{\pi})$.

Definition 16.2 (locally complete family). Let (X, S, π) be a holomorphic family of deformations with reference point s_0, of a given compact complex manifold. This family is said to be **complete** at s_0, (or **versal** at s_0) if for any other holomorphic family (Y, W, P) of deformation of M with reference point w_0 there exists a neighbourhood W' of w_0 in W and a holomorphic map $f : W' \to S$ with $f(w_0) = s_0$ such that the restricted family $Y|W'$ is holomorphically isomorphic with the induced family $(X_{W'}, W', \widetilde{\pi})$.

Remarks

(1) It can be proved that if a family is complete at one point s_0, it is complete in a neighbourhood of s_0.

(2) We could have formulated the definition of versality to families parametrized by complex manifolds. However, examples show that if a compact complex manifold M is such that there are obstructed elements in $H^1(M, \Theta)$, then in any versal family of M the parameter space must have a singularity at the reference point. This is the main reason why one has to consider families parametrized by complex analytic spaces.

(3) Suppose in a holomorphic family (X, S, π) parametrized by a complex manifold S is such that at $s_0 \in S$, the Kodaira-Spencer map P_{s_0} is surjective. Then a theorem of Kodaira-Spencer [125] states that the family must be holomorphically complete at s_0. Hence the family of complex tori that we constructed is complete at every point of the parameter space.

Definition 16.3 (local space of moduli). Let (X, S, π, s_0) be a locally complete family of deformation of M, as in the above definition. If the germ of f is unique, i.e. if M_f and M_g are isomorphic, then f = g, and we say that the family (X, S, π, s_0) is a universal family or a modular family for M and (S, s_0) is called a local space of moduli for M.

Theorem 16.1 (fundamental theorem of deformation theory – Kuranishi). *For any compact complex manifold* M, *there exists a versal family of deformations.*

More precisely, Kuranishi proved

Theorem 16.2. *Let* A^1 *be the space of* $(0,1)$ *forms with values in the holomorphic tangent bundle of* M. *Then there exists a neighbourhood* W *of the origin in* $H^1(M,\Theta)$ *and a holomorphic map* $\Phi : W \to A^1$ *such that if* K *is the analytic set in* W *defined by*

$$K = \{t \in W | \mathbb{P}[\Phi(t), \Phi(t)] = 0\}$$

then the family $\{\Phi(t)\}_{t \in K}$ *represents a locally complete family* (X, K, π) *of deformation of* M *at the reference point* 0, *and the Kodaira-Spencer map* $P_0 : T_0K \to H^1(M,\Theta)$ *is an isomorphism.*

Remarks

(1) The versal family (X, K, π) constructed by Kuranishi is called the **Kuranishi family** for M and the parameter space K is called the **Kuranishi space** of M.

(2) If $H^0(M,\Theta) = 0$, the Kuranishi family is in fact a modular family and the Kuranishi space is a local space of moduli. More generally, if in the Kuranishi family (X, K, π), $\dim H^0(M_t, \Theta_t)$ is independent of t, and if K is reduced, then it can be proved that the Kuranishi family is a modular family and the Kuranishi space is a local space of moduli [133].

(3) It is not necessary that $H^0(M,\Theta)$ should be zero for M to have a local space of moduli.

(4) There are examples of complex manifolds not having a space of moduli.

(5) If a local space of moduli exists for a compact complex manifold, it must be the Kuranishi space of that manifold [224].

(6) Mumford [157] and Griffiths [67] gave examples of complex manifolds for each of which the Kuranishi space is nowhere reduced.

(7) If $H^1(M,\Theta) = 0$, the Kuranishi space K reduces to a point so that M is locally rigid.

(8) If $H^2(M,\Theta) = 0$, K is a complex manifold and $\dim K = \dim H^1(M,\Theta)$. The Kuranishi family reduces to the family constructed by Kodaira-Nirenberg-Spencer.

(9) If M is a compact Riemann surface of genus g, the Kuranishi space has dimension equal to the dimension of $H^1(M,\Theta)$, which is $3g-3$ if $g \geqslant 2$; 1 if $g = 1$ and 0 if $g = 0$.

(10) The Kuranishi family is effectively parametrized at the reference point but in general it need not be effectively parametrized in any neighbourhood of the reference point even if $H^0(M,\Theta) = 0$.

(11) If $H^1(M,\Theta)$ contains obstructed elements, the Kuranishi space of M must have a singularity at the reference point.

(12) The difficult part of the proof of Kuranishi's theorem is in proving that the family $\{\Phi(t)\}_{t \in K}$ represents a locally complete family.

Analogous to the above theory of deformations of compact complex manifolds, there are "deformation theories" for other structures. For deformation theory of singularities and complex spaces, see e.g. Grauert [62,63], Douady [42, 43], Milnor [148], and Brieskorn [21]. For algebra-geometric deformation theory, see e.g. Grothendieck [73], Schlessinger [198, 199], Mumford [159, 160] and Artin [7]. For deformations of holomorphic vector bundles, see e.g. Forster and Knorr [51] and Sundararaman [214]. For deformation theory of G-structures and Γ-structures, see e.g. Griffiths [65], Kumpera-Spencer [128], Ngo Van Que [188], Spencer [210] and Moolgavkar [153]. For deformations of Lie groups, Lie algebras and abstract rings and algebras, see e.g. Nijenhuis-Richardson [178] and Gerstenhaber [56].

For the importance of these theories to the general problem of structural stability in mathematics, the reader is referred to the recent book, especially the first five chapters, of R. Thom [216(a)].

Part V

CLASSIFICATION THEORY OF COMPACT COMPLEX SURFACES

The classical theory of classification of algebraic surfaces is due to the Italian geometers [30, 47]. For a detailed account of this classification see Safarevich et al. [196]. Beginning in 1960, Kodaira in a series of papers [116 , 117], has extended this theory to complex surfaces (throughout, by a complex surface we mean a compact connected complex manifold of dimension two). This is a vast field and we content ourselves with stating the main results of Kodaira. For details and proofs see Kodaira [117], Bombieri [16(a), (b)], Safarevich et al. [196]. In the four papers of Kodaira [117], there are 57 theorems and we refer to these theorems as Kodaira's theorems 21, 22, ...

It is well known that if two compact Riemann surfaces (curves) are bimeromorphic, they are complex analytically isomorphic. But this is not true in higher dimensions: two complex surfaces may be bimeromorphically isomorphic without being complex analytically isomorphic. The theory of relatively minimal models [229] is motivated to overcome this difficulty. According to this theory, any complex surface is obtained from a relatively minimal model by a finite number of blow-ups. Except for rational and ruled surfaces, two relatively minimal models are bimeromorphic to each other if and only if they are complex analytically isomorphic. Hence it is sufficient to classify relatively minimal models.

17. BIMEROMORPHIC INVARIANTS

Complex surfaces are classified in terms of certain fundamental numerical invariants associated with them. We now define these and state the relations connecting them. Let S be a surface. $b_r(S)$ will denote its rth Betti number; $c_r(S)$ its rth Chern class. We represent any cohomology class $c \in H^4(S, Z)$ by the value $c(S)$ of c on the fundamental cycle of the surface oriented in the natural way with respect to the complex structure of S. c_1^2 and c_2 are thus considered as integers. Let θ_S be the structure sheaf of S and $\Omega^r(S)$ be the sheaf of germs of holomorphic r forms. Let $q(S): = \dim H^1(S,\theta_S)$, $p_g(S): = \dim H^2(S,\theta_S)$, $h^{r,s}(S): = \dim H^s(S,\Omega^r(S))$. q(S) is called the **irregularity** of S; $p_g(S)$ is called the **geometric genus** of S and $h^{r,s}(S)$ are called the **Hodge numbers** of S. The arithmetic genus of S, $P_a(S)$ is the Euler-Poincaré characteristic of S $\chi(S)$ with coefficients in θ_S ([85], p. 151).

The Riemann-Roch theorem ([85], Section 20) gives

$$p_a(S) = \chi(S) = 1 - q(S) + p_g(S) \qquad \{ = (1/12)\ (c_1^2(S) + c_2(S)) \quad \text{Noether's formula}\}$$

Serre duality gives $h^{0,2} = h^{2,0} (= p_g)$. Also $q = h^{0,1}$.

A divisor on S is a finite sum $\sum n_i E_i$, $n_i \in Z$, where E_i is an irreducible curve on S. The divisor is called non-negative if all the n_i are non-negative and it is called positive if it is non-negative and not zero. For any pair of divisors D and E, the symbol $D \circ E$ will denote the intersection number of their homology classes. The projective space of non-negative divisors linearly equivalent to D is denoted by $|D|$. Let K_S denote the canonical line bundle of S, i.e. $K_S : = \Lambda^2 T^*(S)$ where $T^*(S)$ denotes the cotangent bundle of S. Let $P_m(S) : = \dim|mK_S| + 1$. $P_m(S)$ is called the mth plurigenus of S. $P_m(S) = \dim H^0(S, mK_S)$. Note $P_1(S) = p_g(S)$ by duality. If $P_{12}(S)$ is equal to zero, all $P_m(S)$ are equal to zero (Kodaira's theorem 57).

Let $N(S,K_S): = \{\text{integers } m \geq 1 \mid P_m(S) \geq 1\}$. Assume $N(S,K_S) \neq \emptyset$. Let $m \in N(S,K_S)$. Let $\phi_0, ..., \phi_N$ be a basis of $H^0(S, mK_S)$. With respect to this choice of basis, we have a meromorphic mapping (see Section 9 (Part II)):

$$\theta_{mK_S} : S \to P^N$$

θ_{mK_S} is called the mth pluricanonical map of S;

$$R[S, K_S] := \bigoplus_{m \geq 0} H^0(S, mK_S)$$

is called the canonical ring of S. It is important to know when θ_{mK_S} is holomorphic and when the canonical ring is finitely generated. It is known that θ_{mK_S} is holomorphic when the complex linear system $|mK_S|$ associated to mK_S has no base points and no fixed components (see e.g. Lemma 4.20.1 of Ref. [220]). The canonical ring is finitely generated when S is a non-singular algebraic surface (Mumford [158], Kodaira [116]). This is not true in general in higher dimensions.

The Kodaira dimension of S (also called the canonical dimension of S), denoted by k(S), is defined as follows:

$$k(S) := \begin{cases} \operatorname{Max}_{m} \dim \theta_{mK_S}(S) & \text{if } N(S, K_S) \neq \emptyset \\ -\infty \text{ if } N(S, K_S) = \emptyset \end{cases}$$

Note that there are only four possible values for k(S): 0, 1, 2 and $-\infty$.

The algebraic dimension of S, denoted by a(S), is the transcendence degree of the field of meromorphic functions of S (see Section 4 (Part I).) Note a(S) = 0, 1 or 2, and $k(S) \leq a(S)$ always.

Associated to a complex surface S there exists a complex torus A(S) and a holomorphic map $\alpha : S \to A(S)$ such that for any holomorphic map $\beta : S \to T$ of S into a complex torus T, there exists a unique Lie group homomorphism $h : A(S) \to T$ and a unique element $t \in T$ such that $\beta(x) = h(\alpha(x)) + t$, $x \in S$. $(A(S), \alpha)$ is called an Albanese torus of S. (For any compact complex manifold M an Albanese torus A(M) exists (see Blanchard [16].) If $(A_1(S), \alpha_1)$ and $(A_2(S), \alpha_2)$ are two Albanese tori for S, then $A_1(S)$ and $A_2(S)$ are isomorphic as Lie groups and there exists a uniquely determined $a_1 \in A_1(S)$ such that $\alpha_1(x) = \alpha_2(x) + a_1$, $x \in S$. Thus an Albanese torus is uniquely determined up to translations and hence we can say **the** Albanese torus of S. The Albanese dimension of S is defined to be the dimension of A(S) and is denoted by t(S). From the construction of the Albanese, it follows that $t(S) \leq h^{1,0}(S)$ and if S is Kähler, we have the equality: $t(S) = h^{1,0}(S) = 1/2\, b_1(S)$. It can be proved that a complex surface S, the numerical characters q(S), $p_g(S)$, $p_a(S)$, $P_m(S)$, k(S), a(S), t(S) and r(S) are all bimeromorphic invariants of the surface.

We write $b_r, h^{r,s}, p_g, \ldots\ldots$ for $b_r(S)$, $h^{r,s}(S)$, $p_g(S)$ where there is only one surface S under consideration.

18. BLOW-UPS AND BLOW-DOWNS

Let M be any complex manifold of dimension n. Let x be any point of M. Blowing up M at x means "replacing" x by the projective space P^{n-1}, resulting in a new complex manifold, denoted by $\sigma_x M$. This process (also called σ-process, quadratic transformation) is carried out as follows. Let U be a co-ordinate neighbourhood of x in M with local co-ordinate $Z = (Z_1, \ldots, Z_n) : U \to C^n$ such that $Z(x) = 0$. Consider the map $f : U - \{x\} \to P^{n-1}$ given by $f(x) = [Z_1(x), \cdots, Z_n(x)]$. Let Γ be the graph of f and let $M_x = \{x\} \times P^{n-1}$. Let $N = \Gamma \cup Mx$. Then N is a non-singular submanifold of $U \times P^{n-1}$. In fact if $\omega_1, \ldots, \omega_n$ are homogeneous co-ordinates in P^{n-1}, let V_i be the open subset of $U \times P^{n-1}$ given by $\omega_i \neq 0$. Then V_i cover $U \times P^{n-1}$. We can assume $\omega_i = 1$ in V_i and consider $Z_1, \ldots, Z_n, \omega_1, \ldots, \omega_{i-1}, \omega_{i+1}, \ldots, \omega_n$ to be the local co-ordinates in V_i.

With respect to these co-ordinates, N is given by $Z_j = Z_i\omega_j$ $(1 \leqslant j \leqslant n,\ j \neq i)$ so that $\omega_1, ..., \omega_{i-1}, Z_i, \omega_{i+1}, ..., \omega_n$ give a system of local co-ordinates in $N \cap V_i$. Using the projection $\Gamma \to U - \{x\}$, we identify $U - \{x\}$ with $\Gamma = N - M_x$ in the disjoint union of $M - \{x\}$ and N to get the new manifold $\sigma_x M$. $\sigma_x M$ does not depend on any of the choices we have made but depends only on M and x. We have a projection map $\pi_x : \sigma_x M \to M$ which maps M_x onto x and maps $\sigma_x M - M_x$ biholomorphically onto $M - \{x\}$. This blowing-up process can be iterated. Let $x_1 \in M$. Consider $\sigma_{x_1} M$. Pick a point x_2 in $M_{x_1} = \pi_{x_1}^{-1}(x_1)$. Now blow up $\sigma_{x_1} M$ at this point to get $\sigma_{x_1 x_2} M := \sigma_{x_2}\sigma_{x_1}$ M. M_{x_1} and M_{x_2} intersect exactly at one point and the projection

$$\pi_{x_1 x_2} := \pi_{x_2} \cdot \pi_{x_1} : \sigma_{x_1 x_2} M \to M \text{ maps } M_{x_1} \cup M_{x_2}$$

onto x. We now blow up at a point $x_3 \in M_{x_1} \cup M_{x_2}$ and this process can be continued. After s number of blow-ups we get a complex manifold $\overline{M} = \sigma_{x_1 \ldots x_s} M$ and projection $\overline{\pi} : \overline{M} \to M$ with $\pi^{-1}(x_1) = M_1 \cup M_2 \cup \ldots \cup M_s$. M_i and M_j are either disjoint or intersect at only one point. Let us now consider the case of a complex surface S. Let $x \in S$. Let Z_1, Z_2 be the local co-ordinates in U centred at x. In the blown-up surface $\sigma_x S$ these co-ordinates are replaced by two systems u,v and $\overline{u}, \overline{v}$ such that $Z_1 = u$, $Z_2 = uv$ and $Z_1 = \overline{u}\overline{v}$, $Z_2 = \overline{v}$. M_x is given by u = 0 and v = 0. M_x is the 2-sphere embedded in $\sigma_x M$ and represents a cocycle with self intersection number -1. A non-singular rational curve (isomorphic with P^1) is called an exceptional curve of the first kind if its self intersection number is -1. Hence blowing up a point on the surface means replacing that point by an exceptional curve of the first kind, resulting in a non-singular complex surface. Conversely, an exceptional curve of the first kind can be blown down (see Section 11 (Part III), for the notion of blowing down), i.e. it can be "replaced" by a point such that the resulting surface is again a non-singular complex surface. The converse was first proved for algebraic surfaces by Castelnuovo and it is well known as Castelnuovo's criterion for contractability. For complex surfaces this follows from Grauert [61] (see Kodaira [116] for details). More generally, we can ask the following question: given a complex-analytic space X and a closed complex analytic set A in X, when can we blow down A? In recent years a number of interesting results have become known in this direction (see Grauert [61], Moishezon [150], Markoe-Rossi [140], Siu [207], Knorr-Schneider [106], Nakano [168]). An algebraic surface remains algebraic after blowing up or down (Kodaira [116, I]).

A complex surface is called a relatively minimal model (or relatively minimal surface) if and only if it does not contain any exceptional curve of the first kind. Every complex surface can be obtained from a relatively minimal model S by a finite number of blow-ups. A surface S is a minimal surface (model) if every surface in the bimeromorphic class of S can be obtained from S by a finite number of blow-ups.

We have the following basic fact:

Theorem 18.1 (Kodaira's theorem 56, Castelnuovo-Enriques-Zariski-Kodaira). *If the bimeromorphic class of a surface* S *has no minimal model, then* S *is a ruled surface.*

19. SPECIAL AND GENERAL SURFACES

(a) Ruled surface

A surface S is a ruled surface of genus g if S is birationally equivalent to a product of P^1 and a non-singular curve of genus g. A ruled surface is rational if and only if its genus is equal to zero. A minimal ruled surface of genus $g \geqslant 1$ is a P^1 bundle over a non-singular curve of genus g (for details see Nagata [165], Maruyama [141]).

(b) Rational surface

A surface S is rational if it is birationally equivalent to P^2. Hence for any rational surface S, $\chi(S) = 1$ and $P_m = 0$ for all m. A minimal rational surface is either P^2 or a P^1 bundle over P^1 (see Nagata [165]). To find a criterion for rationality is a very important problem in algebraic geometry. Castelnuovo [30] was the first to give a criterion for rationality of algebraic surfaces (see also Safarevich [196], Zariski [230]). We give a list of important results (let S be any non-singular algebraic surface):

(1) If $q = P_2 = 0$, then there exists on S a non-singular rational curve E with $E^2 \geqslant 0$ (Kodaira's theorem 48);

(2) If $q = P_2 = 0$, then S is rational (Castelnuovo's criterion for rationality);

(3) If $q = P_2 = 0$, then S is either P^2 or a rational ruled surface (Castelnuovo-Andreotti, Kodaira's theorem 49);

(4) If $q = 0$ and there exists on S a non-singular rational curve E with $E^2 \geqslant 0$, then S is rational (Proposition 1.2 of Ref. [88]).

(5) If $q = 0$ and there exists on S an irreducible curve E with $K \cdot E < 0$ and $E^2 \geqslant 0$, then S is rational (Proposition 1.4 of Ref. [88]).

(6) If $q = 0$ and there exist two exceptional curves of the first kind which intersect, then S is rational (Proposition 1.6 of Ref. [88]).

In this connection, we must mention the important result of Clemens and Griffiths on cubic threefolds. A cubic threefold is a non-singular hypersurface in P^4 of degree 3. It was a longstanding problem to decide whether cubic threefolds are rational or not. Clemens and Griffiths [35] proved that cubic threefolds are not rational. For a discussion of the fundamental work of Griffiths and Clemens see Tjurin [217] (see also Artin and Mumford [9], Murre [164], Iskovoski and Manin [97] and Roth [194]).

(c) K3 surfaces

A complex surface S is called a K3 surface if and only if its irregularity q is equal to zero and its canonical bundle K is trivial. Equivalently, S is a K3 surface if and only if q and the first Chern class c_1 are equal to zero. It is known that any deformation of a K3 surface is a K3 surface; Kodaira proved (Kodaira's theorem 13) the Weil-Andreotti conjecture that any K3 surface is a deformation of a non-singular quartic surface in P^3 (see also Grauert [60]). Hence any K3 surface is simply connected and there is a unique diffeomorphism type of K3 surface. In Ref. [121], Kodaira constructed all complex surfaces which have the same homotopy type as a K3 surface. The problem of determining all complex surfaces which have the same homeomorphism type as a K3 surface remains open. The existence of moduli space for algebraic K3 surfaces has been proved by Pjateckij-Sapiro and Safarevich [185] (for Kähler K3 surfaces see Burns and Rapport [23]).

(d) Elliptic surfaces

A complex surface is an elliptic surface if it admits at least one elliptic fibring, i.e. a holomorphic map of S onto a non-singular curve such that all but a finite number of fibres are non-singular elliptic curves. Kodaira [116] has described in detail all possible types of such fibring. This has stimulated further studies of "degeneration" (for some of the aspects of this see Namikawa [171], Namikawa-Ueno [172], Mumford [163]). If for a surface S, $a(S) = 1$, then S is elliptic (Kodaira's theorem 4). If $k(S) = 1$, then S is an elliptic surface of general type. An elliptic surface of general type is elliptic.

(e) Enriques surface

A surface S is an Enriques surface if and only if $q = 0$, $P_2 = 1$ and $p_g = 0$. It is known that an Enriques surface is elliptic and its universal covering surface is a K3 surface (for details see Enriques [47], Safarevich [196]).

(f) Hyperelliptic surface

A surface S is a hyperelliptic surface if $q = 1$ and 12K is trivial (remember K represents the canonical bundle of S). Any hyperelliptic surface has a finite unramified covering surface which is a product of two elliptic surfaces.

(g) Surfaces of class VII

A surface S is of class VII if and only if its first Betti number b_1 is equal to 1. For a surface of class VII, its geometric genus p_g is equal to zero (Kodaira's theorem 26). The class of minimal surfaces with $b_1 = q = 1$ is denoted by VII_0. Kodaira has shown that all Hopf surfaces and a certain type of elliptic surfaces belong to VII_0 (Kodaira's theorems 27 and 30). In 1974, Inoue [96] found new examples of surfaces of class VII_0. It is not known whether there are surfaces of class VII_0 other than those given by Kodaira and Inoue.

(h) Surfaces of general type

A complex surface S is said to be of general type if $k(S) = 2$. A surface of general type S is also characterized by $P_2(S) \geqslant 1$ and $C_1^2(S) > 0$. It is known that a surface of general type is algebraic (Kodaira [120]). From the classification theorem of Kodaira it follows that a minimal algebraic surface which is not of general type must be one of the following three classes: (1) P^2 and ruled surfaces; (2) surfaces with trivial canonical bundle; (3) elliptic surfaces. Conversely, no surface of any one of these classes can be a surface of general type. It is also known that any deformation of a surface of general type is a surface of general type. For studying the structure of surfaces of general type it is necessary to study the finer properties of the map θ_{mK}. On a minimal surface S of general type there exists only a finite number of rational curves with self intersection equal to -2. Let E be the set of all such curves and E_r, $r = 1, 2, \ldots, p$, be the connected components of E.

Definition. $\theta_{mK} : S \to P^N$ is said to be biholomorphic modulo E if: (i) θ_{mK} is everywhere defined on S and is holomorphic; (ii) θ_{mK} is biholomorphic on $S - E$; and (iii) $\theta_{mK}^{-1}\theta_{mK}(E_r) = E_r$, for $r = 1, \ldots, p$.

We have the following important theorems of Bombieri [16(a), (b)]:

Theorem 19.1 (Bombieri). *Let* S *be a surface of general type. Then*

(i) θ_{mK} *is holomorphic for* $m \geqslant 4$ *and for* $m = 3$ *if* $C_1^2 > 1$;

(ii) θ_{mK} *is biholomorphic modulo* E *for* $m \geqslant 5$ *and for* $m \geqslant 4$ *if* $C_1^2 > 1$ *and for* $m = 3$ *if* $p_g = 4$, $C_1^2 > 2$.

Bombieri also obtained information on the nature of possible singularities of $\theta_{mK}(S)$. From the above theorem it follows that θ_{mK} is birational for $m \geqslant 5$. This is an improvement of the earlier results of Safarevich-Moishezon [196] and Kodaira [120]. Using the above theorems of Bombieri, Popp [187] has proved that moduli space of surfaces of general type exists as an algebraic space. The problem of finer classification of surfaces within the class of surfaces of general type remains open.

TABLE I. RELATIVELY MINIMAL SURFACES

Class	b_1	p_g	C_1	C_1^2	Structure
I_o	Even	0			Algebraic
II_o	0	+	0	0	K3 surface
III_o	4	+	0	0	Complex tori
IV_o	Even	+	$\neq 0$	0	Elliptic surface of general type
V_o	Even	+		+	Algebraic surface of general type
VI_o	Odd	+		0	Elliptic
VII_o	1	0			Certain elliptic surfaces + All Hopf surfaces + Inoue surfaces + ?

20. CLASSIFICATION THEOREMS

Classification theorem 1 (Kodaira's theorem 21). *Relatively minimal surfaces can be classified into the following seven classes (see Table I):*

(I_o) The class of minimal algebraic surfaces with $p_g = 0$
(II_o) The class of K3 surfaces
(III_o) The class of complex tori of complex dimension 2
(IV_o) The class of minimal elliptic surfaces with $b_1 \equiv 0(2)$, $p_g \geqslant 1$, $C_1^2 = 0$, $C_1 \neq 0$
(V_o) The class of minimal algebraic surfaces with $p_g \geqslant 1$ and $C_1^2 > 0$
(VI_o) The class of minimal elliptic surfaces with $b_1 \equiv 1(2)$, $p_g \geqslant 1$ and $C_1^2 = 0$
(VII_o) The class of minimal surfaces with $b_1 = 1 = q$ and $p_g = 0$

We define classes I to VII to be the classes of those surfaces which are birationally equivalent to surfaces belonging to the classes I_o to VII_o, respectively.

Classification theorem 2 (Kodaira's theorem 22). *Complex surfaces can be classified into the following classes I to VII characterized by the following conditions:*

(I) $b_1 \equiv 0(2)$ and $p_g = 0$
(II) $b_1 = 0$, $p_g = 1$ and $p_m \sim 1$
(III) $b_1 = 4$, $p_g = 1$ and $p_m \sim 1$
(IV) $b_1 = 0(2)$, $p_g > 0$ and $p_m \sim (\frac{1}{2} C_1^2)m$, $C_1^2 > 0$
(V) $b_1 = 0(2)$, $p_g > 0$ and $p_m \sim (\frac{1}{2} C_1^2) m^2$, $C_1^2 > 0$
(VI) $b_1 = 1(2)$ and $p_g > 0$
(VII) $b_1 = 1$

The classes II_o to VI_o of surfaces are closed under deformations and all the classes I to VII of surfaces are closed under deformations (Kodaira's theorem 24). Any deformation of any Hopf surface is a Hopf surface and any deformation of an elliptic surface of class VII_o is either an elliptic surface of class VII_o or a Hopf surface (Kodaira's theorems 36 and 37). Note that all Hopf surfaces belong to class VII_o (Kodaira's theorem 30).

The following theorem of Kodaira can be considered an extension of the classical classificatio theory of algebraic surfaces.

TABLE II. OVERALL CLASSIFICATION OF SURFACES

b_1	P_{12}	P_2	K	c_1^2	Structure
Even	0	0			P^2 or ruled
0	1	1	Trivial	0	K3 surface
4	1	1	Trivial	0	Complex torus
Even	+		Non-trivial	0	Elliptic surface
Even	+	+		+	Algebraic surface of general type
Odd	+			0	Elliptic surface
1	0	0			Certain elliptic surface + Hopf surface + Inoue surface + ?

TABLE III. STRUCTURES OF SURFACES WITH $k(S) = 0$ and $k(S) = -\infty$

k	p_g	P_{12}	q	b_1	Structure
0	1	1	2	4	Complex torus
0	1	1	2	3	Elliptic surface with K trivial
0	0	1	1	2	Hyperelliptic surface
0	0	1	1	1	Elliptic surface belonging to class VII with mK trivial, $m > 0$
0	1	1	0	0	K3 surface
0	0	1	0	0	Enriques surface
$-\infty$	0	0	0	0	Rational surface
$-\infty$	0	0	$\geqslant 1$	2q	Ruled surface of genus q
$-\infty$	0	0	1	1	Surface of class VII

Classification theorem 3 **(Kodaira's theorem 55**; see also Theorem ROC in Ref. [88]). *Relatively minimal surfaces can be classified into the following seven classes (see Table II):*

(1) The class of projective plane and ruled surfaces
(2) The class of K3 surfaces
(3) The class of complex tori
(4) The class of minimal elliptic surfaces with $b_1 \equiv 0(2)$, $P_{12} > 0$, $K \neq 0$
(5) The class of minimal algebraic surfaces with $P_2 > 0$, $c_1^2 > 0$
(6) The class of minimal elliptic surfaces with $b_1 \equiv 1(2)$, $P_{12} > 0$
(7) The class of minimal surfaces with $b_1 = 1$, $P_{12} = 0$

Using the above classification theorems, Iitaka [94] proved the important fact that all the plurigenera and hence the Kodaira dimension of a complex surface are deformation invariants.

Using the above classification theorems, we give a classification of surfaces in terms of Kodaira dimension. For a surface S, $k(S) = 2, 1, 0$ or $-\infty$. By definition, if $k(S) = 2$, S is of general type and if $k(S) = 1$, S is an elliptic surface of general type. The structures of surfaces with $k(S) = 0$ and $k(S) = -\infty$ are given in Table III.

Complex surfaces can be classified in terms of their Kodaira dimension into three big classes: a surface S is said to be hyperbolic, parabolic, or elliptic, respectively, if $k(S) = 2, 0,$ or $-\infty$, respectively. The class of surfaces of hyperbolic type is the same as the class of surfaces of general type. Table III gives finer classification of surfaces of parabolic and elliptic type. According to this classification, curves of genus $\geqslant 2$ are of hyperbolic type, elliptic curves are of parabolic type and the projective line P^1 is of elliptic type!

Part VI

CLASSIFICATION OF HIGHER DIMENSIONAL COMPACT COMPLEX MANIFOLDS

Part VI contains a brief introduction to the work of Iitaka and Ueno (for details and proofs see Ueno [220]). All complex manifolds considered here are assumed to be compact and connected; all algebraic varieties are assumed to be complete, irreducible and defined over complex numbers. By a complex variety we mean a compact irreducible reduced complex space. An algebraic variety can be regarded as a complex variety (see e.g. Safarevich [195], Ch. VIII).

21. KODAIRA DIMENSION OF A COMPLEX VARIETY

Let M be a complex manifold of dimension n. As in the case of a surface, the Kodaira dimension of M is defined as follows. Let $K = \overset{n}{\Lambda} T^*M$ be the canonical line bundle of M. The m-genus of M, denoted by $P_m(M)$, is the dimension of $H^0(M, \underline{mK})$ where $mK = K \otimes \ldots \otimes K$ (m times). Set $N(M,K) = \{\text{integers } m \geqslant 1 \mid P_m(M) \geqslant 1\}$. Assume $N(M,K) \neq \emptyset$. Let $m \in N(M,K)$. Then with respect to a choice of basis of $H^0(M, \underline{mK})$, we have a meromorphic mapping, called the mth pluricanonical map, $\theta_{mk} : M \to \mathbb{P}^N$. The Kodaira dimension of M, denoted by k(M), is defined by

$$k(M) = \begin{cases} \text{Max dim } \theta_{mk}(M), & \text{if } N(M,K) \neq \emptyset \\ -\infty & \text{if } N(M,K) = \emptyset \end{cases}$$

For a smooth algebraic variety, the m-genus and the Kodaira dimension are similarly defined. The m-genus and the Kodaira dimension of complex manifolds (smooth algebraic varieties) are bimeromorphic (birational) invariants.

Let V be a complex variety (algebraic variety) and V* be a non-singular (smooth) model for V (such models exist, Hironaka [80, 81]). Since any two non-singular (smooth) models of a complex variety (an algebraic variety) are bimeromorphic (birational), we define the m-genus and the Kodaira dimension of V by $P_m(V) = P_m(V^*)$ and $k(V) = k(V^*)$.

Note

(1) There are (n + 2) possible values for $k(M) : k(M) = -\infty$ and $0 \leqslant k(M) \leqslant n$.

(2) $k(M) \leqslant a(M)$ always, where a(M) denotes the algebraic dimension of M. If $a(M) = 0$, then k(M) must be either 0 or $-\infty$. If $k(M) = n$, then $a(M) = n$ and hence M must be Moishezon.

(3) Rational and ruled varieties have Kodaira dimension $-\infty$. More generally, if the tangent bundle of an algebraic variety is ample, then its Kodaira dimension is $-\infty$.
(4) Complex tori have Kodaira dimension zero. More generally, if the canonical bundle of a complex manifold is trivial, its Kodaira dimension is zero.

Two important properties of Kodaira dimension are the following:

Asymptotic behaviour. In the classification theory it is of great importance to know the existence and nature of the limit $P_m(M)/m^{k(M)}$ as m ranges over N(M, K). The following two results give information in this direction. Let M be a complex manifold and d the largest common divisor of the integers in N(M, K). Then

(i) There exist positive numbers α and β and a positive integer m_0 such that for any integer $m \geqslant m_0$, we have

$$\alpha \cdot m^{k(M)} \leqslant P_{md}(M) \leqslant \beta \cdot m^{k(M)}$$

(ii) For any positive integer p, there exist a positive number δ and a positive integer m_1 such that for any integer $m \geqslant m_1$ we have

$$P_{md}(M) - P_{(m-p)d}(M) \leqslant \delta \cdot m^{k(M)-1}$$

Addition formula. The following important theorem holds:

Theorem. *Let* $\pi : V \to B$ *be a holomorphic fibre bundle over a complex manifold* B *whose fibre and structure group are respectively a Moishezon manifold* M *and its automorphism group* Aut M. *Then* k(V) = k(M) + k(B).

This theorem is not true without the assumption on M. In this special case it affirms the following conjecture of Iitaka:

Conjecture C_n: *Let* $f : V \to B$ *be a fibre space where* V *and* B *are algebraic manifolds. Then* $k(V) \geqslant k(V_b) + k(B)$, *where* $V_b = \pi^{-1}(b)$, $b \in B$, *is a general fibre of* f.

Using the classification theory of surfaces given in Part V, it can be checked that Conjecture C_2 is true for algebraic as well as complex surfaces. But Conjecture C_n is not necessarily true for fibre spaces of complex manifolds. Ueno has shown that Conjecture C_3 is true in some special cases.

22. CLASSIFICATION OF COMPLEX VARIETIES IN TERMS OF KODAIRA DIMENSION

Definition. A complex variety V is called a variety of hyperbolic, parabolic or elliptic type if k(V) = dim V, 0 or $-\infty$, respectively.

If $k(V) > 0$, then according to the fundamental theorem on the pluricanonical fibrations, given below, there exists a projective manifold V*, bimeromorphically equivalent to V, which has the structure of a fibre space whose general fibres are of Kodaira dimension zero. Consider the algebraic variety $W_m = \theta_{mK}(V)$, $m \in N(V,K)$. Let $\mathbb{C}(W_m)$ be the function field of W_m. Then it can be proved that there exists an integer m_0 such that for any integer $m \geqslant m_0$,

$m \in N(V,K)$, $\mathbb{C}(W_m) = \mathbb{C}(W_{m_0})$ and $\mathbb{C}(W_{m_0})$ is algebraically closed in $\mathbb{C}(V)$. Now we state the main theorem of Part VI.

Fundamental theorem on the pluricanonical fibrations (Iitaka [95]). Let V be an algebraic variety (complex variety) of positive Kodaira dimension. Then there exist a projective (complex) manifold V^*, a projective manifold B and a surjective morphism $f: V^* \to B$, such that:

(1) V^* is birationally (bimeromorphically) equivalent to V;

(2) $\dim W = k(V)$;

(3) For a dense subset U of B (in the complex topology), each fibre $V_b^* = \pi^{-1}(b)$, $b \in U$, is irreducible and non-singular;

(4) $k(V_b^*) = 0$ for each $b \in U$;

(5) The fibre space $f: V^* \to B$ is unique up to birational (bimeromorphic) equivalence.

One natural question that arises regarding the above theorem is whether we can take the dense set U to be open. From the proof of the theorem it can be seen that if Kodaira dimension is deformation-invariant then U can be taken to be open. We already stated the result of Iitaka that Kodaira dimension is deformation-invariant for complex surfaces. But contrary to the conjecture of Moishezon [151], the Kodaira dimension for manifolds of dimension $\geqslant 3$ are not necessarily deformation-invariant (see Nakamura [166]). For U to be taken to be open, it is sufficient if the Kodaira dimensions are upper-semicontinuous under small deformations (see Libermann-Serenese [136]).

From the fundamental theorem it is clear that the study of classification of complex varieties reduces to (a) the study of complex varieties of hyperbolic, parabolic and elliptic type and (b) the study of fibre spaces whose general fibres are of parabolic type. Associated with the pluricanonical map we have a fibre space; associated with the algebraic dimension we can introduce a fibre space;and associated with the Albanese dimension we can introduce a fibre space. Using these fibre spaces, classification of varieties can be studied. For a detailed account of this programme and for open problems in this area of active current research, the reader is referred to Ueno [220] and the references given there. We conclude by stating three open problems pertaining to complex manifolds of hyperbolic type.

Problem 1. Is any deformation of a complex manifold of hyperbolic type a complex manifold of hyperbolic type? (Recall the theorem of Kodaira that any deformation of a surface of general type is a surface of general type.)

Problem 2. Let M be a complex manifold of hyperbolic type. Does there exist a positive integer m_0 depending only on the dimension of M, such that for any integer $m \geqslant m_0$, the pluricanonical map θ_{mK} is bimeromorphic? (Recall the corresponding theorem of Bombieri-Kodaira for surfaces of general type.)

Problem 3. Does there exist a moduli space for complex manifolds of hyperbolic type? If it exists is it an algebraic space? (Recall the corresponding theorem of Popp for surfaces of general type.)

ACKNOWLEDGEMENTS

The author would like to thank Professor J. Eells for continuous encouragement and Professor Raghavan Narasimhan for his interest in the work and for his critical comments.

REFERENCES

[1] ABHYANKAR, S., Local Analytic Geometry, Academic Press (1964).
[2] AHLFORS, L., "The complex analytic structure of the space of closed Riemann surfaces", Analytic Functions, Princeton Univ. Press (1960).
[3] AHLFORS, L., et al., Advances in the Theory of Riemann Surfaces, Ann. Math. Studies 66, Princeton Univ. Press (1971).
[4] ANDREOTTI, A., Recherches sur les surfaces irrégulières, Acad. R. Belg., Cl. Sci., Mem., Coll. 8°4 and 8°7 (1952).
[5] ANDREOTTI, A., "On the complex structure of a class of simply connected manifolds", Algebraic Geometry and Topology, Princeton Univ. Press (1957).
[6] ANDREOTTI, A., STOLL, W., Analytic and Algebraic Dependence of Meromorphic Functions, Lecture Notes 234, Springer Verlag (1971).
[7] ARTIN, M., "Algebraization of formal moduli I, II", Global Analysis, Princeton Univ. Press (1970) 88–135.
[8] ARTIN, M., Algebraic Spaces, Yale Univ. Press (1970).
[9] ARTIN, M., MUMFORD, D., Some elementary examples of unirational varieties which are not rational, Proc. London Math. Soc. Ser. 3 **25** (1972) 75–95.
[10] ATIYAH, M.F., Some examples of complex manifolds, Bonner Math. Schriften **6** (1958).
[11] ATIYAH, M.F., Complex analytic connections in fibre bundles, Trans. Am. Math. Soc. **85** (1957) 181–207.
[12] BAILY, W.L., On the moduli of Jacobian varieties, Ann. Math. **71** (1960) 303–314.
[13] BERGER, M., Les variétés riemanniennes à courbure positive, Bull. Soc. Math. France **87** (1959) 285–292.
[14] BERS, L., Uniformization, Moduli and Kleinian Groups, Colloquium Lectures, Am. Math. Soc. (1971).
[15] BISHOP, E., Mappings of partially analytic spaces, Am. J. Math. **83** (1961) 209–242.
[16] BLANCHARD, A., Sur les variétés analytiques complexes, Ann. Sc. Ecole Norm. Sup. **73** (1956) 157–202.
[16(a)] BOMBIERI, E., "The pluricanonical map of a complex surface", Lecture Notes 155, Springer Verlag (1970) 35–87.
[16(b)] BOMBIERI, E., Canonical models of surfaces of general type, Publ. Math. IHES, Bûres-sur-Yvette **42** (1973) 171–219.
[17] BOREL, A., SERRE, J.P., Groupes de Lie et puissances réduites de Steenrod, Am. J. Math. **75** (1953) 409–448.
[18] BOTT, R., Homogeneous vector bundles, Ann. Math. **66** (1957) 203–248.
[19] BOTT, R., The space of loops on a Lie group, Mich. Math. J. **5** (1958) 35–61.
[20] BRIESKORN, E., Ein Satz über die komplexen Quadriken, Math. Ann. **155** (1964) 187–193.
[21] BRIESKORN, E., Beispiele zur Differentialtopologie von Singularitäten, Invent. Math. **2** (1966) 1–14.
[22] BRIESKORN, E., VAN DE VEN, A., Some complex structures on product of homotopy spheres, Topology **7** (1968) 389–393.
[23] BURNS, D., RAPPORT, M., On the Torelli theorem for Kählerian K3 surfaces, Ann. Sci. ENS (1975) 235–274.
[24] CALABI, E., "On Kähler manifolds with vanishing canonical class", Algebraic Geometry and Topology, Princeton Univ. Press (1957).
[25] CALABI, E., ECKMANN, B., A class of compact complex manifolds, Ann. Math. **58** (1953) 494–500.
[26] CALABI, E., ROSENLICHT, M., Complex analytic manifolds without countable basis, Proc. Am. Math. Soc. (1953) 335–340.
[26(a)] CALABI, E., VESENTINI, E., On compact locally symmetric manifolds, Ann. Math. **71** (1960) 472–507.
[27] CARTAN, E., Les groupes de transformations continus, infinis, simples, Ann. Sci. ENS (1909) 93–161.
[28] CARTAN, H., "Quotient of complex analytic spaces", Function Theory, Tata Inst. and Oxford Univ. Press (1960).
[29] CARTAN, H., SERRE, J.P., Un théorème de finitude concernant les variétés analytiques compactes, C.R.Acad. Sci. **237** (1953) 128–130.
[30] CASTELNUOVO, G., Memorie scelte, Zanichelli, Bologna (1937).
[31] CHERN, S.S., Complex Manifolds Without Potential Theory, Van Nostrand (1967).
[32] CHERN, S.S., The geometry of G-structures, Bull. Am. Math. Soc. **72** (1966) 167–219.
[33] CHOW, W.L., On compact complex varieties, Am. J. Math. **71** (1949) 893–914.
[34] CHOW, W.L., KODAIRA, K., On analytic surfaces with two independent meromorphic functions, Proc. Natl Acad. Sci. USA **38** (1952) 319–325.
[35] CLEMENS, H., GRIFFITHS, P., The intermediate Jacobian of the cubic threefold, Ann. Math. **96** (1972) 281–356.
[36] CORNALBA, M., "Complex tori and Jacobians", these Proceedings.
[37] DE LA HARPE, P., "Introduction to complex tori", these Proceedings.
[38] DELIGNE, P., Théorie de Hodge I, II, III, Proc. Int. Congr. Nice, 1970; Publ. IHES, Bûres-sur-Yvette **40** (1972) 5–58; **45** (1974) 5–78.

[39] DELIGNE, P., MUMFORD, D., The irreducibility of the space of curves of given genus, Publ. IHES, Bûres-sur-Yvette **36** (1969) 75–110.

[40] DOUADY, A., Le problème des modules pour les variétés analytiques complexes (d'après M. Kuranishi), Séminaire Bourbaki, Exposé 277, 1964.

[41] DOUADY, A., Le problème des modules pour sous-espaces analytiques compacts d'un espace analytique donné, Ann. Inst. Fourier, Grenoble **16** (1966) 1–95.

[42] DOUADY, A., Les problèmes des modules locaux pour les espaces C-analytiques compacts, Ann. Sc. ENS (1974) 569–602.

[43] DOUADY, A., "Quelques problèmes des modules en géométrie analytique complexe", Proc. Int. Congr. Moscow, 1966.

[44] DOUADY, A., Flatness and privilege, L'Enseignement Math. **14** (1968).

[45] EARLE, C.J., EELLS, J., "Deformations of Riemann surfaces", Modern Analysis and Applications I, Lecture Notes 103, Springer Verlag (1969).

[46] EHRESMANN, C., Sur les variétés presque complexes, Proc. Int. Congr. Math. Cambridge, 1950.

[47] ENRIQUES, F., Le superficie algebriche, Zanichelli, Bologna (1949).

[48] FISHER, W., GRAUERT, H., Lokal-triviale Familien kompakter komplexer Mannigfaltigkeiten, Nachr. Akad. Göttingen Math.-Phys. 2 (1965) 89–94.

[49] FORSTER, O., Comm. Math. Helv. **45** (1970) 170–184.

[50] FORSTER, O., KNORR, K., Ein neuer Beweis des Satzes von Kodaira-Nirenberg-Spencer, Mat. Z. **139** (1974) 257–291.

[51] FORSTER, O., KNORR, K., Über die Deformationen von Vektorraumbündeln auf kompakten komplexen Räumen, Math. Ann. **209** (1974) 291–346.

[52] FRISH, J., Points de platitude d'un morphisme d'espaces analytiques, Invent. Math. **4** (1967) 118–138.

[53] FRANKEL, T., Manifolds with positive curvature, Pac. J. Math. **11** (1961) 165–174.

[54] FROLICHER, A., NIJENHUIS, A., A theorem on the stability of complex structures, Proc. Natl Acad. Sci.USA **43** (1957) 229–241.

[55] FROLICHER, A., KOBAYASHI, S., NIJENHUIS, A., Deformation theory of complex manifolds, Techn. Rep. 10, Univ. Washington (1960).

[56] GERSTENHABER, M., On the deformations of rings and algebras I, II, III: Ann. Math. **79** (1964) 59–104; **84** (1966) 1–16; **88** (1968) 1–34.

[57] GOLDBERG, S.I., KOBAYASHI, S., On holomorphic bisectional curvature, J. Diff. Geom. **1** (1967) 225–233

[58] GRAUERT, H., On Levi's problem and the embedding of real analytic manifolds, Ann. Math. **68** (1958) 460–472.

[59] GRAUERT, H., Ein Theorem der analytischen Garbentheorie und die Modulräume komplexer Strukturen, Publ. IHES, Bûres-sur-Yvette **5** (1960).

[60] GRAUERT, H., "On the number of moduli of complex structures", Function Theory, Tata Inst.,Oxford Univ. Press (1960).

[61] GRAUERT, H., Über Modifikationen und exzeptionelle analytische Mengen, Math. Ann. **146** (1962) 331–36

[62] GRAUERT, H., Über die Deformation isolierter Singularitäten analytischer Mengen, Invent. Math. **15** (1972) 171–198.

[63] GRAUERT, H., Der Satz von Kuranishi für kompakte komplexe Räume, Invent. Math. **25** (1974) 107–142.

[64] GRIFFITHS, P., Some geometric and analytic properties of homogeneous complex manifolds, Acta Math. **11** (1963) 115–208.

[65] GRIFFITHS, P., On the existence of a locally complete germ of deformation of certain G-structures, Math. Ann. **159** (1966) 151–171.

[66] GRIFFITHS, P., "The extension problem in complex analysis I", Proc. Conf. Complex Analysis, Minneapolis Springer Verlag (1966).

[67] GRIFFITHS, P., Some remarks and examples of continuous systems and moduli, J. Math. Mech. **16** (1967) 789–802.

[68] GRIFFITHS, P., "Deformation of complex structures", Global Analysis, Am. Math. Soc. (1970).

[69] GRIFFITHS, P., Periods of integrals on algebraic manifolds I, II; Am. J. Math. **90** (1968) 586–626, 805–86

[70] GRIFFITHS, P., Periods of integrals on algebraic manifolds III, Publ. IHES, Bûres-sur-Yvette **38** (1970) 125–180.

[71] GRIFFITHS, P., Periods of integrals on algebraic manifolds: summary of main results and discussion of open problems, Bull. Am. Math. Soc. **76** (1970) 228–296.

[72] GRIFFITHS, P., SCHMID, W., "Recent developments in Hodge theory", Proc. Int. Coll. Discrete Subgroups of Lie Groups and Applications to Moduli, 1973, Tata Inst. and Oxford Univ. Press (1975).

[73] GROTHENDIECK, A., Techniques de construction en géométrie analytique, I à X, Cartan Seminar, 1960/6 Secrétariat Mathématique, Paris (1962).

[73(a)] GUILLEMIN, V., STERNBERG, S., Deformation theory of pseudogroup structures, Memoirs AMS 64 (1966).
[74] GUNNING, R.C., Lectures on Riemann Surfaces, Princeton Univ. Press (1965).
[75] GUNNING, R.C., ROSSI, H., Analytic Functions of Several Complex Variables, Prentice Hall (1965).
[76] GUNNING, R., NARASIMHAN, R., Immersions of open Riemann surfaces, Math. Ann. **174** (1967) 103–108.
[77] HAMILTON, R.S., Deformation of complex structures on pseudoconvex domains, Cornell Univ. preprint (1972).
[78] HARTSHORNE, R., Ample Subvarieties of Algebraic Varieties, Lecture Notes 156, Springer Verlag (1970).
[79] HIRONAKA, H., An exmple of a non-Kählerian complex analytic deformation of Kählerian complex structures, Ann. Math. **75** (1962) 642–648.
[80] HIRONAKA, H., Resolution of singularities of an algebraic variety over a field of characteristic zero, Ann. Math. **79** (1964) 109–306.
[81] HIRONAKA, H., Bimeromorphic smoothing of a complex space, Math. Inst., Warwick Univ. preprint (1971).
[82] HIRONAKA, H., Flattening theorem in complex analytic geometry, Am. J. Math. **97** (1975) 503–537.
[83] HIRSH, M.W., On embedding differentiable manifolds in Euclidean space, Ann. Math. **67** (1958) 566–571.
[84] HIRZEBRUCH, F., Über eine Klasse von einfachzusammenhängenden komplexen Mannigfaltigkeiten, Math. Ann. **124** (1951) 77–86.
[85] HIRZEBRUCH, F., Topological Methods in Algebraic Geometry, Springer Verlag (1966).
[86] HIRZEBRUCH, F., "Hilbert modular surfaces", L'Enseignement Math. **19** (1972) 183–281.
[87] HIRZEBRUCH, F., KODAIRA, K., On complex projective spaces, J. Math. Pure Appl. **36** (1957) 201–216.
[88] HIRZEBRUCH, F., VAN DE VEN, A., Hilbert modular surfaces and classification of algebraic surfaces, Invent. Math. **23** (1974) 1–29.
[89] HODGE, W.V.D., The Theory and Applications of Harmonic Integrals, Cambridge Univ. Press (1952).
[90] HOPF, H., "Zur Topologie der komplexen Mannigfaltigkeiten", Courant Volume, Interscience (1948) 167–185.
[91] HÖRMANDER, L., Linear Partial Differential Operators, Springer Verlag (1963).
[92] HÖRMANDER, L., An Introduction to Complex Analysis in Several Variables, Van Nostrand (1966).
[93] IGUSA, J., Fibre systems of Jacobian varieties I, II, III, Am. J. Math. **78** (1956) 171–199, 745–760; **81** (1959) 453–476.
[94] IITAKA, S., "Deformations of compact complex surfaces I, II, III", Global Analysis, Princeton Univ. Press and Tokyo Univ. Press (1969) 267–272; J. Math. Soc. Jap. **22** (1970) 247–261; **23** (1971) 692–705.
[95] IITAKA, S., On D-dimensions of algebraic varieties, J. Math. Soc. Jap. **23** (1971) 356–373.
[96] INOUE, M., On surfaces of class VII_0, Invent. Math. **24** (1974) 269–310.
[97] ISKOVOSKI, V.A., MANIN, J.U., Three-dimensional quartics and counter-examples to the Luroth problem, Math. USSR-Sb. **15** (1971) 141–166.
[98] KAS, A., On obstructions to deformations of analytic surfaces, Proc. Natl Acad. Sci. USA **58** (1967) 402–404.
[99] KAS, A., On deformations of certain type of irregular algebraic surfaces, Am. J. Math. **90** (1968) 789–804.
[100] KATO, M., Topology of Hopf surfaces, J. Math. Soc. Jap. **27** (1975) 222–238.
[101] KATO, M., Complex structures on $S^1 \times S^5$, Proc. Jap. Acad. **49** (1973) 575–577.
[102] KAWAI, S., On compact complex analytic manifolds of complex dimension 3, I and II, J. Math. Soc. Jap. **17** (1965) 438–442; **21** (1969) 604–616.
[103] KERVAIRE, M., A manifold which does not admit any differentiable structure, Comm. Math. Helv. **34** (1960) 257–270.
[104] KERVAIRE, M., MILNOR, J., Groups of homotopy spheres I, Ann. Math. **77** (1963) 504–537.
[105] KIEHL, R., Points de platitude d'un morphisme d'espaces analytiques, Invent. Math. **4** (1967) 139–141.
[106] KNORR, K., SCHNEIDER, M., Relativexzeptionelle analytische Mengen, Math. Ann. **193** (1971) 238–254.
[107] KLEIMAN, S.L., Completeness of characteristic systems, Adv. Math. **11** (1973) 304–310.
[108] KOBAYASHI, S., Hyperbolic Manifolds and Holomorphic Maps, Marcel Dekker (1970).
[109] KOBAYASHI, S., NOMIZU, K., Foundations of Differential Geometry **1**, **2**, Wiley (1969).
[110] KOBAYASHI, S., OCHIAI, I., On complex manifolds with positive tangent bundles, J. Math. Soc. Jap. (1970) 499–525.
[111] KODAIRA, K., On Kähler varieties of restricted type (an intrinsic characterization of algebraic varieties), Ann. Math. **60** (1954) 28–48.
[112] KODAIRA, K., Characteristic linear systems of complete continuous system, Am. J. Math. **78** (1956) 716–744.
113] KODAIRA, K., A theorem of completeness of characteristic system for analytic families of compact submanifolds of complex manifolds, Ann. Math. **84** (1962) 146–162.
114] KODAIRA, K., On stability of compact submanifolds of complex manifolds, Am. J. Math. **85** (1963) 79–94.
115] KODAIRA, K., On characteristic systems of families of surfaces with ordinary singularities in projective spaces, Am. J. Math. **87** (1965) 227–256.

[116] KODAIRA, K., On the structure of compact complex analytic surfaces I, II, III, Ann. Math. **71** (1960) 111–152; 77 (1963) 563–626; **78** (1963) 1–40.
[117] KODAIRA, K., On the structure of compact complex analytic surfaces I, II, III, IV, Am. J. Math. **86** (1964) 751–798; 88 (1966) 682–721; **90** (1968) 55–83, 1048–1066.
[118] KODAIRA, K., Complex structures on $S^1 \times S^3$, Proc. Natl Acad. Sci. USA **55** (1966) 240–243.
[119] KODAIRA, K., A certain type of irregular algebraic surfaces, J. Anal. Math. **19** (1967) 207–215.
[120] KODAIRA, K., Pluricanonical systems of algebraic surfaces of general type, J. Math. Soc. Jap. **20** (1968) 170–192.
[121] KODAIRA, K., "On homotopy K3 surfaces", Mémoires dédiés à G. de Rham, Springer Verlag (1970) 58–69.
[122] KODAIRA, K., SPENCER, D.C., On deformations of complex structures I, II, III, Ann. Math. **67** (1958) 328–466; **71** (1960) 43–76.
[123] KODAIRA, K., SPENCER, D.C., Existence of complex structures on a differentiable family of deformations of compact complex manifolds, Ann. Math. **70** (1959) 145–166.
[124] KODAIRA, K., NIRENBERG, L., SPENCER, D.C., On the existence of deformation of complex analytic structures, Ann. Math. **67** (1958) 450–459.
[125] KODAIRA, K., SPENCER, D.C., A theorem of completeness for complex analytic fibre spaces, Acta Math. **100** (1958) 281–294.
[126] KODAIRA, K., MORROW, J., Complex Manifolds, Holt, Rinehart and Winston (1971).
[127] KOHN, J.J., Harmonic integrals on strongly pseudoconvex manifolds I, II, Ann. Math. **78** (1963) 112–148.
[128] KUMPERA, A., SPENCER, D.C., Lie Equations – **1**: General Theory, Ann. Math. Studies, Princeton Univ. Press (1972).
[129] KURANISHI, M., On a type of family of complex structures, Ann. Math. **74** (1961) 262–328.
[130] KURANISHI, M., On the locally complete families of complex structures, Ann. Math. **75** (1962) 536–577.
[131] KURANISHI, M., "New proof for the existence of locally complete families of complex structures", Proc. Conf. Complex Analysis, Minneapolis, 1964, Springer Verlag (1965) 142–154.
[132] KURANISHI, M., Deformations of Compact Complex Manifolds, Univ. Montreal Press (1969).
[133] KURANISHI, M., "A note on families of complex structures", Global Analysis, Princeton Univ. Press and Tokyo Univ. Press (1969).
[134] KURANISHI, M., Deformations of isolated singularities and $\bar{\partial}_b$, Columbia Univ. preprint (1974).
[135] LANG, S., Introduction to Algebraic Geometry, Interscience (1958).
[136] LIBERMANN, D., SERENESE, E., Semicontinuity of Kodaira dimension, Bull. Am. Math. Soc. (1975).
[137] MAEDA, H., Some complex structures on product of spheres, J. Fac. Sci. Univ. Tokyo, Sec. IA **21** (1974) 161–165.
[138] MALGRANGE, B., "Analytic spaces", L'Enseignement Math. **14** (1968) 1–28.
[139] MALGRANGE, B., Equations de Lie I, II, J. Diff. Geom. **6** (1972) 503–522; **7** (1972) 117–142.
[140] MARKOE, A., ROSSI, H., Families of Strongly Pseudoconvex Manifolds, Lecture Notes 184, Springer Verla (1970).
[141] MARUYAMA, M., On Classification of Ruled Surfaces, Lecture Notes, Kyoto Univ. (1970).
[142] MATSUSAKA, T., On canonically polarized varieties, Coll. Algebraic Geometry, Tata Inst. (1969) 265–306
[143] MATSUSAKA, T., MUMFORD, D., Two fundamental theorems on deformations of polarized varieties, Am. J. Math. **86** (1964) 668–684.
[144] MATSUSAKA, T., Polarized varieties and fields of moduli, Am. J. Math. **80** (1958).
[145] MATSUSHIMA, Y., Affine complex manifolds, Osaka J. Math. **5** (1968) 215–222.
[146] MATSUSHIMA, Y., On Hodge manifolds with zero first Chern class, J. Diff. Geom. **3** (1969) 477–480.
[147] MILNOR, J., On manifolds homeomorphic to the 7-sphere, Ann. Math. **64** (1956) 394–405.
[148] MILNOR, J., Singular points of complex hypersurfaces, Ann. Math. Studies 61, Princeton Univ. Press (1968).
[149] MIYAOKA, Y., Kähler metrics on elliptic surfaces, Proc. Jap. Acad. Sci. **50** (1974) 533–536.
[150] MOISHEZON, B.G., On n-dimensional compact varieties with n algebraically independent meromorphic functions I, II, III, Am. Math. Soc. translations, Ser. 2, No.63, p.51–177 (1967).
[151] MOISHEZON, B.G., in Proc. Int. Congr. Math., Nice, 1970.
[152] MOISHEZON, B.G., Seminar presented at this Course (not in these Proceedings).
[153] MOOLGAVKAR, S.H., The existence of a universal germ of deformations for elliptic pseudogroup structur on compact manifolds, Ph D. Thesis, Johns Hopkins Univ. (1974).
[154] MORITA, S., Topological classification of complex structures on $S^1 \times \Sigma^{2n-1}$, Topology (1975).
[155] MORREY, C.B., Jr., The analytic embedding of abstract real analytic manifolds, Ann. Math. **68** (1958) 159–201.
[155(a)] MORROW, J., "Survey of some results on compact Kähler manifolds", Global Analysis, Princeton Univ. Press and Tokyo Univ. Press (1969).

[156] MUMFORD, D., The topology of normal singularities of an algebraic surface and a criterion for simplicity, Publ. Math. IHES, Bûres-sur-Yvette **89** (1961) 5–22.
[157] MUMFORD, D., Further pathologies in algebraic geometry, Am. J. Math. **85** (1962) 642–648.
[158] MUMFORD, D., The canonical ring of an algebraic surface, Ann. Math. **76** (1962) 612–615.
[159] MUMFORD, D., Geometric invariant theory, Springer-Verlag (1965).
[160] MUMFORD, D., Lectures on Curves on an Algebraic Surface, Ann. Math. Studies 59, Princeton Univ. Press (1966).
[161] MUMFORD, D., "Introduction to the theory of moduli", Nordic Summer School, Oslo, 1970.
[162] MUMFORD, D., Abelian Varieties, Tata Inst. and Oxford Univ. Press (1970).
[163] MUMFORD, D., An analytic construction of degenerating abelian varieties over complete rings, Comp. Math. **24** (1972) 239–272.
[164] MURRE, J.P., "Some results on cubic threefolds", Lecture Notes 412, Springer Verlag (1974) 140–164.
[165] NAGATA, M., On rational surfaces I, II, Coll. Sci. Univ. Kyoto **32** (1960) 351–370; **33** (1961) 271–293.
[166] NAKAMURA, I., Complex parallelizable manifolds and their small deformations, J. Diff. Geom. **10** (1975) 85–112.
[167] NAKAMURA, I., UENO, K., An addition formula for Kodaira dimensions of analytic fibre bundles whose fibres are Moishezon manifolds, J. Math. Soc. Jap. **25** (1973) 363–371.
[168] NAKANO, S., On the inverse monoidal transformation, Publ. Res. Inst. Math. Sci. Kyoto Univ. **6** (1971) 483–502.
[169] NAMBA, M., On maximal families of compact complex submanifolds of complex manifolds, Tohoku Math. J. **24** (1972) 581–609.
[170] NAMBA, M., On deformations of automorphism groups of compact complex manifolds, Tohoku Math. J. **26** (1974) 237–283.
[171] NAMIKAWA, Y., "Studies of degenerations", Lecture Notes 412, Springer Verlag (1974) 165–210.
[172] NAMIKAWA, Y., UENO, K., The complete classification of fibres in pencils of curves of genus two, Manuscripta Math. **9** (1973) 163–186.
[173] NARASIMHAN, R., Embedding of holomorphically complete complex spaces, Am. J. Math. **82** (1960) 917–934.
[173(a)] NARASIMHAN, R., Analysis on Real and Complex Manifolds, North-Holland, Amsterdam (1968).
[174] NARASIMHAN, R., Introduction to the Theory of Analytic Spaces, Lecture Notes 25, Springer Verlag (1966).
[175] NARASIMHAN, M.S., SESHADRI, C.S., Stable and unitary vector bundles on a compact Riemann surface, Ann. Math. **82** (1965) 540–567.
[176] NARASIMHAN, M.S., SIMHA, R., Manifolds with ample canonical class, Invent. Math. **5** (1968) 120–126.
[177] NEWLANDER, A., NIRENBERG, L., Complex analytic coordinates in almost complex manifolds, Ann. Math. **65** (1957) 391–404.
[178] NIJENHUIS, A., RICHARDSON, R., Cohomology and deformations in graded Lie algebras, Bull. Am. Math. Soc. **72** (1966) 1–29.
[179] NIJENHUIS, A., WOOLF, J., Some integration problems in almost complex manifolds, Ann. Math. **77** (1963) 424–483.
[180] NIRENBERG, L., Partial differential equations with applications to geometry, Lectures on Modern Mathematics 2, Wiley (1964).
[181] OKA, K., Sur les fonctions analytiques de plusieurs variables, Iwanami Shoten (1961).
[182] PALAMODOV, V.P., On the existence of versal deformations of complex spaces, Sov. Math. – Dokl. **13** (1972) 1246–1250.
[183] PFLUGER, A., Lectures presented at this Course (not published in these Proceedings).
[184] PITTIE, H., "Complex and almost complex four-manifolds" (these Proceedings).
[185] PJATECKIJ-SAPIRO, I.I., SAFAREVICH, I.R., A Torelli theorem for algebraic surfaces of type K3, Math. USSR-Izv. **5** (1971) 547–588.
[186] POURCIN, J., Théorème de Douady au-dessus de S, Ann. Scuola Sup. Pisa **23** 3 (1969).
[187] POPP, H., On moduli of algebraic varieties I, II, Invent. Math. **22** (1973) 1–40; Comp. Math. **28** (1974) 51– 81.
[188] QUE, Ngo Van, Non-abelian Spencer cohomology and deformation theory, J. Diff. Geom. **3** (1969) 165–211.
[189] RAMANUJAM, C.P., Remarks on the Kodaira vanishing theorem, J. Indian Math. Soc. **36** (1972) 41–51.
[190] RAMANUJAM, C.P., Supplement to "Remarks on the Kodaira vanishing theorem", J. Indian Math. Soc. **38** (1974) 121–124.
[191] RAUCH, H.E., A transcendental view of the space of algebraic Riemann surfaces, Bull. Am. Math. Soc. **71** (1965) 1–39.
[192] REMMERT, R., Holomorphe und meromorphe Abbildungen komplexer Räume, Math. Ann. **133** (1957) 328–360.

[192(a)] REMMERT, R., Habilitationsschrift, Münster (1956).

[193] ROBERTSON, S.A., "Elementary geometry of complex manifolds" (these Proceedings).

[194] ROTH, L., Algebraic threefolds, Springer Verlag (1955).

[195] SAFAREVICH, I.R., Basic Algebraic Geometry, Springer Verlag (1974).

[196] SAFAREVICH, I.R., et al., Algebraic surfaces, Proc. Steklov Inst., AMS Transl. (1967).

[197] SCHMID, W., Variation of Hodge structures: the singularities of the period mapping, Invent. Math. **22** (1973) 213–319.

[198] SCHLESSINGER, M., Infinitesimal deformations of singularities, PhD. Thesis, Harvard Univ. (1964).

[199] SCHLESSINGER, M., Functors of Artin rings, AMS Transl. **130** (1968) 208–222.

[199(a)] SCHWARTZ, L., Complex Manifolds, Tata Institute Lecture Notes (1955).

[200] SERRE, J.P., Un théorème de dualité, Comm. Math. Helv. **29** (1955) 9–26.

[201] SERRE, J.P., Géométrie algébrique et géométrie analytique, Ann. Inst. Fourier **6** (1956) 1–42.

[202] SERRE, J.P., Faisceaux algébriques cohérents, Ann. Math. **61** (1955) 197–278.

[203] SESHADRI, C.S., Space of unitary vector bundles on a compact Riemann surface, Ann. Math. **85** (1967) 303–336.

[204] SESHADRI, C.S., Quotient spaces modulo reductive algebraic groups, Ann. Math. **95** (1972) 511–556.

[205] SESHADRI, C.S., "Theory of moduli", Proc. Conf. Algebraic Geometry, Arcata, Calif., Am. Math. Soc. (1975).

[206] SIEGEL, C.L., Analytic Functions of Several Complex Variables, Inst. Advanced Study, Princeton (1948).

[207] SIU, Y.T., The 1-convex generalization of Grauert's direct image theorem, Math. Ann. **193** (1971) 203–214.

[208] SMALE, S., Generalized Poincaré conjecture in dimension greater than four, Ann. Math. **74** (1961) 391–406

[209] SPENCER, D.C., "Some remarks on homological analysis and structures", Differential Geometry, Am. Math. Soc. (1961).

[210] SPENCER, D.C., Deformations of structures on manifolds defined by transitive continuous pseudo groups I, Ann. Math. **76** (1962) 306–445.

[211] STEIN, K., Meromorphic mappings, L'Enseignement Math. II, **14** (1968) 29–46.

[212] SUNDARARAMAN, D., Normal filtration of $H^1(M, \Theta)$, J. Diff. Geom. **8** (1973) 225–248.

[213] SUNDARARAMAN, D., Normal families of complex structures, J. Indian Math. Soc. **39** (1975) 149–154.

[214] SUNDARARAMAN, D., On the Kuranishi space of a holomorphic principal bundle over a compact complex manifold (to appear in Adv. Math.).

[215] TEICHMÜLLER, O., Bestimmung der extremalen quasikonformen Abbildungen bei geschlossenen orientierten Riemannschen Flächen, Preuss. Akad. Ber. **4** (1943).

[216] THIMM, W., Meromorphe Abbildungen von Riemannschen Bereichen, Mat. Z. **60** (1954) 435–457.

[216(a)] THOM, R., Structural Stability and Morphogenesis, Benjamin (1975).

[217] TJURIN, A.N., Five lectures on three-dimensional varieties, Russian Math. Surveys **27** (1972) 1–53.

[218] TJURIN, A.N., Locally semi-universal flat deformation of isolated singularities of complex spaces, Math. USSR-Izv. **3** (1969) 967–999.

[219] UENO, K., Classification of algebraic varieties I, II, Comp. Math. **27** (1973) 277–342.

[220] UENO, K., Classification Theory of Algebraic Varieties and Compact Complex Spaces, Lecture Notes 439, Springer Verlag (1975).

[221] UENO, K., On the pluricanonical systems of algebraic manifolds, Math. Ann. **216** (1975) 173–179.

[222] VAN DE VEN, A., Chern numbers of complex and almost complex manifolds, Proc. Natl. Acad. Sci. USA 5 (1966) 1624–1627.

[223] VITTER, A., Affine structures on compact complex manifolds, Invent. Math. **17** (1972) 231–244.

[224] WAVRIK, J.J., "Obstructions to the existence of a space of moduli", Global Analysis, Princeton Univ. Press (1969).

[225] WEIL, A., Introduction à l'étude des variétés Kähleriennes, Hermann (1958).

[226] WELLS, R.O., Jr., Differential Analysis on Complex Manifolds, Prentice Hall (1973).

[226(a)] WHITNEY, H., Complex Analytic Varieties, Addison-Wesley (1972).

[227] WU, W.T., Sur les classes caractéristiques de structures fibrées sphériques, Actualités Sci. Ind. (1952) 5–89.

[228] YAU, S.T., On the curvature of compact Hermitian manifolds, Invent. Math. **25** (1974) 213–239.

[229] ZARISKI, O., Introduction to the problem of minimal models in the theory of algebraic surfaces, Publ. Math. Soc. Jap. **4** (1958).

[230] ZARISKI, O., Algebraic Surfaces, 2nd edn, Springer Verlag (1971).

IAEA-SMR-18/107

ANALYTIC FUNCTIONS IN QUANTUM FIELD THEORY
An introduction

J. TARSKI*
International Centre for Theoretical Physics,
Trieste, Italy

Abstract

ANALYTIC FUNCTIONS IN QUANTUM FIELD THEORY: AN INTRODUCTION.

A short introduction to the applications of functions of several complex variables in quantum field theory is presented. Simple examples relating to the Wightman axioms and to dispersion relations are included.

1. PRELIMINARIES

Analytic functions have been utilized for a long time for the solution of physical problems. However, the use of functions of several complex variables in physics is of relatively recent origin. Such functions first appeared some twenty years ago, in the attempts to study quantum field theory (and elementary particle interactions) by other means than a perturbation expansion. Two lines of investigation of this kind became prominent. One dealt with the Wightman axioms and the other with dispersion theory. These axioms provided a general framework for describing interacting fields, at a time when non-trivial models were not available. Dispersion theory, on the other hand, led to relations which could be tested experimentally and which were independent of the detailed assumptions about the interaction.

Various notions which were developed in the course of those investigations retain their usefulness, even though the research interest in field-theoretic applications of several complex variables has declined. The present article is intended as a short introduction to these notions. We include in particular the Wightman axioms (in § 3) and an example of a dispersion relation (in § 4). Of the mathematical tools, we discuss the Laplace transform (in § 2) and the edge-of-the-wedge theorem (in § 5).

This article contains no new material, nor a systematic presentation of old results. Rather, our goal was to give a glimpse of a few "highlights", while keeping the article reasonably short. For further details, we refer to the standard treatments of these subjects in Refs [1–3]. A more recent review of dispersion theory is also available [4]. A few other references will be given later.

We hoped to make this article accessible to those mathematicians whose knowledge of quantum field theory may be fragmentary: we therefore summarize now the relativistic transformation laws and the construction of the free scalar field. (On the other hand, we presuppose elements of functional analysis as background knowledge.)

The Minkowski space M^4 is an R^4, but equipped with indefinite scalar product. We adopt the following notations and conventions, where $a, b \in M^4$, and the spatial parts are in boldface:

$$a \cdot b = ab = a^0 b^0 - \mathbf{a} \cdot \mathbf{b} = a^0 b^0 - \sum_{j=1}^{3} a^j b^j \tag{1.1}$$

* Present address: Fakultät für Physik, Universität Bielefeld, Bielefeld, Federal Republic of Germany

A Lorentz transformation Λ is a linear transformation on M^4 which leaves the product $a \cdot b$ invariant. We also assume (unless otherwise stated) that

$$\det \Lambda = 1, \qquad \Lambda^0_0 \geqslant 1, \qquad \Lambda \text{ real} \tag{1.2}$$

The inhomogeneous group consisting of such Lorentz transformations and of translations is the (proper) Poincaré group. In § 3 we shall also consider transformations violating each of the conditions of (1.2).

A free field φ has a definite mass μ and satisfies the Klein-Gordon equation (as usual, we set the physical constants c and $\hbar$ equal to one),

$$(-\partial_0^2 + \nabla^2 - \mu^2)\varphi = 0 \tag{1.3a}$$

or, upon taking the Fourier transform,

$$[(k^0)^2 - \mathbf{k}^2 - \mu^2]\widetilde{\varphi} = 0 \tag{1.3b}$$

We suppose for definiteness that $\mu > 0$. In view of the last equation, we shall always assume the following relation for energy-momentum when working with the free field:

$$k^0 = \sqrt{\mathbf{k}^2 + \mu^2} \tag{1.4}$$

In this article we shall consider only scalar fields (also pseudoscalar fields, in § 4). However, our discussion could be readily adapted to fields with spin.

The free (scalar, hermitian) field φ can now be expressed as follows:

$$\varphi(x) = \frac{1}{(2\pi)^{3/2}} \int d^3k \frac{1}{\sqrt{2k^0}} [a^{(+)}(\mathbf{k}) e^{ikx} + a^{(-)}(\mathbf{k}) e^{-ikx}] \tag{1.5}$$

The quantum features of φ are assured by the commutation relation,

$$[a^{(-)}(\mathbf{k}), \; a^{(+)}(\boldsymbol{\ell})] = \delta(\mathbf{k} - \boldsymbol{\ell}) \tag{1.6}$$

This is a distribution-theoretic relation. Upon multiplying both members by $f^*(\mathbf{k}) f(\boldsymbol{\ell})$ and integrating, where f is in L_2 and normalized, we obtain a relation $[a^-, a^+] = 1$. (The function f need not be continuous.) The operators $a^{\pm}$ can be represented as follows:

$$a^- = \begin{pmatrix} 0 & 1 & & 0 \\ 0 & 0 & \sqrt{2} & \\ & & 0 & \sqrt{3} \\ 0 & & & \ddots & \ddots \end{pmatrix} \qquad a^+ = \begin{pmatrix} 0 & 0 & & 0 \\ 1 & 0 & & \\ & \sqrt{2} & 0 & \\ 0 & & \ddots & \ddots \end{pmatrix} \tag{1.7}$$

(For an example of a non-hermitian field, see § 4.)

The one-particle space of the theory is the following Hilbert space:

$$\mathscr{H} = L_2(R^3, \; d^3k/\sqrt{\mathbf{k}^2 + \mu^2}) \tag{1.8}$$

The Fock space now contains scalar multiples of the normalized vacuum vector (or state) Ψ_0 and also symmetrized n-fold tensor products of $\mathscr{H}$, describing states of n particles:

$$\mathscr{H}_{\Phi OK} = \{\lambda\Psi_0\} \dot{+} \sum_{n=1}^{\infty} \mathscr{H}^{\otimes n}_{sym} \tag{1.9}$$

The above operators $a^{\pm}$ act on $\mathscr{H}_{\Phi OK}$ and, more explicitly, on the component spaces, as follows:

$$a^{\pm}: \mathscr{H}^{\otimes n}_{sym} \to \mathscr{H}^{\otimes(n\pm 1)}_{sym}, \qquad a^{-}\Psi_0 = 0 \tag{1.10}$$

We identified here $\mathscr{H}^{\otimes 0}$ with $\{\lambda\Psi_0\}$. In view of (1.10), a^{+} is an operator which creates a particle or is a creation operator, while a^{-} is an annihilation operator. (However, some authors use plus for annihilation operators and minus for creation operators.)

Later we shall be concerned with vacuum expectation values of fields. The simplest example is the following:

$$\langle\Psi_0, \varphi(x)\varphi(y)\Psi_0\rangle = \frac{1}{(2\pi)^3}\int \frac{d^3k}{2k^0}\, e^{-ik(x-y)} \tag{1.11}$$

The equality is a consequence of (1.5), (1.6) and (1.10); the indicated Fourier transform exists in the sense of distribution theory.

For future reference it will be useful to elaborate on the steps leading to (1.11). The action of the Poincaré group extends in a natural way to $\mathscr{H}_{\Phi OK}$, with the translation by $a \in M^4$ and the Lorentz transformation Λ inducing, respectively, U_a and U_Λ. Then the action of the field φ is,

$$U_a\varphi(x)U_a^{-1} = \varphi(x+a), \qquad U_\Lambda\varphi(x)U_\Lambda^{-1} = \varphi(\Lambda x) \tag{1.12}$$

Now, in (1.11) we can insert a complete orthonormal set of vectors Ω between the fields. Then

$$\langle\Psi_0, \varphi(x)\varphi(y)\Psi_0\rangle = \sum_{\Omega} \langle\Psi_0, \varphi(x)\Omega\rangle\langle\Omega, \varphi(y)\Psi_0\rangle \tag{1.13}$$

and

$$\langle\Psi_0, \varphi(x)\Omega\rangle = \langle\Psi_0, U_x\varphi(0)U_x^{-1}\Omega\rangle \tag{1.14a}$$

We may, moreover, express the U_a in terms of the generators $P = (P^{\nu})$ of the translations: $U_a = \exp(iP^{\nu}a_{\nu})$. These generators have an extensive continuous spectrum, and if Ω_{k_j} are vector-valued distributions with the eigenvalues $k_j = (k_j^{\nu})$, then

$$\langle\Omega_{k_1}, \varphi(x)\Omega_{k_2}\rangle = e^{i(k_1-k_2)x}\langle\Omega_{k_1}, \varphi(0)\Omega_{k_2}\rangle \tag{1.14b}$$

In the sum (1.13) only vectors $\Omega \in \mathscr{H} = \mathscr{H}^{\otimes 1}$ contribute, in view of (1.10). If we use the distributions from this space, and if we observe that the vacuum Ψ_0 corresponds to the eigenvalue $k = 0$ of P, we obtain Eq. (1.11).

We remark, finally, that an interacting field satisfying rather general conditions will become a free field in the asymptotic limits, $t \to \pm\infty$. Hence the field φ is also called an asymptotic field.

2. THE LAPLACE TRANSFORM

If a function f(u) vanishes for $u < 0$ and is in L_1, and

$$\tilde{f}(k) = \frac{1}{(2\pi)^{1/2}} \int_0^\infty du\, e^{iku} f(u) \tag{2.1}$$

then one sees immediately that $\tilde{f}$ is the boundary value of a function holomorphic in the upper half plane. The conclusion remains valid if f is a tempered distribution rather than a function. (See [1], § 2–3. See also [3], p. 231, for the terminology: "holomorphic" means analytic and single-valued.)

These considerations extend to the case of several variables, say n. Then, however, one is interested in functions f (or distributions) whose support is not necessarily a product of n half-lines, but more generally, is included in a cone. So, let $\hat{C}$ be a cone in R^n with vertex at the origin. We define the conjugate cone by

$$\hat{C}' = \{x \in R^n : \langle x, y\rangle \geqslant 0 \text{ for } \forall y \in \hat{C}\} \tag{2.2}$$

We assume for definiteness that $\hat{C}$ is closed and convex, and such that the interior of $\hat{C}'$, denoted by int $\hat{C}'$, is not empty.

Now, if g is a tempered distribution whose support is included in $\hat{C}$, then its Laplace transform is

$$(Lg)(x + iy) = \frac{1}{(2\pi)^{1/2n}} \int_{\hat{C}} d^n v\; e^{iv(x + iy)} g(v) \tag{2.3}$$

This function is holomorphic in the tubular domain

$$T_{\hat{C}'} = R^n + i(\text{int } \hat{C}') \subset C^n \tag{2.4}$$

For Minkowski-type spaces, with an indefinite scalar product, it is clear from (2.3) that the definition (2.2) remains the appropriate one to use. Physically the most important example is of course the future or the past part of the light cone in M^4 together with the interior. Either part is self-conjugate. Let us consider the future part:

$$\bar{V}_+ = \bar{V}'_+ = \{x \in M^4 : x^0 \geqslant 0, (x^0)^2 - \sum_{j=1,2,3} (x^j)^2 \geqslant 0\} \tag{2.5}$$

We denote the corresponding tube, but complex-conjugated, by $\mathscr{T}_1$, and the n-fold Cartesian product of such tubes by $\mathscr{T}_n$:

$$\mathscr{T}_1 = (T_{\overline{V}_+})^*, \quad \mathscr{T}_n = \mathscr{T}_1 \times \ldots \times \mathscr{T}_1 \text{ (n times)} \tag{2.6}$$

Each $\mathscr{T}_n$ is also a tube in the sense of (2.4), and is called a **future tube.**

These simple facts about the Laplace transform suffice for our needs. It may be worth noting, however, that the theory of functions which are holomorphic in domains such as (2.4) has been developed in its own right. An account of this theory can be found in Ref. [5]. In particular, this reference contains the proof of the correspondence between tempered distributions on $\hat{C}$ and functions which are holomorphic in $T_{\hat{C}'}$ and satisfy a growth condition. This correspondence is also discussed briefly in Ref. [6], together with other criteria for a function to be a Laplace transform.

3. THE WIGHTMAN AXIOMS

These axioms describe those features of the free field φ, which are expected to remain valid for fields in interaction. We consider, as before, a single scalar and hermitian field Φ. In view of the distribution-theoretic character of Φ, we construct operators by "smearing" with a test function $f \in \mathscr{S}^{\otimes 4}$:

$$\Phi(f) = \langle \Phi, f \rangle = \int d^4x \, f(x) \, \Phi(x) \tag{3.1}$$

[For the distributions $a^{(\pm)}$ of § 1, as well as for φ, it suffices to "smear" in three dimensions, with a test function $f(\mathbf{x})$ or $\tilde{f}(\mathbf{k})$. However, Φ may be a more singular object.]

The following axioms are given in an outline form (see [1, 2]).

(A) Domain and continuity of field operators. The operator $\Phi(f)$, in general unbounded, acts on a complex Hilbert space $\mathscr{H}$. This space contains a vacuum vector Ψ_0. If each $f_j \in \mathscr{S}^{\otimes 4}$ then

$$\Phi(f_{n-1}) \ldots \Phi(f_1)\Psi_0 \in D(\Phi(f_n)) \tag{3.2}$$

where D denotes the domain. Such vectors depend continuously on the f_j, and span a dense subset D_0 of $\mathscr{H}$.

(B) Relativistic invariance. In particular, Ψ_0 is the only vector in $\mathscr{H}$, up to scalar multiples, which is invariant under transformations of the Poincaré group (we do not elaborate further).

(C) Causality. Let $\Omega \in D_0$, and let $f, g \in \mathscr{S}^{\otimes 4}$ be such that their supports are spacelike separated, i.e. $(x-y)^2 < 0$ whenever $x \in \text{supp } f$, $y \in \text{supp } g$. Then

$$[\Phi(f), \ \Phi(g)]\Omega = 0 \tag{3.3}$$

(D) Spectral condition. The action of the Poincaré group on $\mathscr{H}$ is such that the generators of translations (P^ν) have spectral values (q^ν) lying in the forward light cone $\overline{V}_+$, i.e. satisfying $(q^0)^2 - q^2 \geqslant 0$, $q^0 \geqslant 0$.

These axioms deserve some comments. The first two are in the nature of a definition. With regard to (B), we note that theories with non-unique vacua have also been considered. Next, (3.3) has the interpretation that spacelike separated measurements do not influence each other, and so this equation is an expression of causality. The last axiom expresses non-negativity of energy (i.e. of the component P^0) in a Lorentz-invariant way. Finally, we note that these axioms are now known to be valid for certain non-trivial models in a two-dimensional space-time (cf. [6]).

We proceed with simple deductions from the axioms.

(1) The following is a distribution in $(\mathscr{S}^{\otimes 4(n-1)})'$:

$$W_n(x_1 - x_2, \ldots, x_n - x_{n+1}) = \langle \Psi_0, \Phi(x_1) \ldots \Phi(x_{n+1}) \Psi_0 \rangle \tag{3.4}$$

[cf. (1.11)]. Such vacuum expectation values are called **Wightman functions.**

(2) We use the rule $e^{iPa}\Phi(x)\,e^{-iPa} = \Phi(x+a)$, an argument such as in Eqs (1.13) – (1.14), and the axiom (D) to conclude the following: The Fourier transform $\widetilde{W}_n$, defined by

$$W_n(\xi_1, \ldots, \xi_n) = \int d^4q_1 \ldots d^4q_n \; \widetilde{W}_n(q_1, \ldots, q_n) \exp(-i \sum q_j \xi_j) \tag{3.5}$$

has support in the Cartesian product $\overline{V}_+ \times \ldots \times \overline{V}_+$. Thus § 2 applies.

(3) $W_n(\xi_1, \ldots, \xi_n)$ is the boundary value of a function $W_n(\zeta_1, \ldots, \zeta_n)$ holomorphic when $(\zeta_1, \ldots, \zeta_n) \in \mathscr{T}_n$, i.e. for

$$\zeta_j = \xi_j - i\eta_j, \qquad \eta_j \in \text{int } \overline{V}_+ = V_+ \tag{3.6}$$

(4) Consider complex Lorentz transformations, satisfying $\det \Lambda = 1$ (and leaving $a \cdot b$ invariant). They form a connected group, containing $\Lambda = -I$. The W_n, as holomorphic functions, can be continued to the extended tubes $\mathscr{T}_n'$ defined by applying complex Lorentz transformations to vectors in $\mathscr{T}_n$. Moreover, the W_n are invariant under complex Lorentz transformations.

(5) Suppose $\zeta = \xi - i\eta \in \mathscr{T}_1$ and ζ^2 is real. Then

$$\zeta^2 = \xi^2 - \eta^2 - 2i\xi\cdot\eta = \xi^2 - \eta^2, \qquad \text{so that } \xi\cdot\eta = 0 \tag{3.7}$$

and ξ is spacelike ($\xi^2 < 0$). Thus $\zeta^2 < 0$. One can also easily verify that if ζ is real and $\zeta^2 < 0$, then a complex Lorentz transformation can bring ζ into $\mathscr{T}_1$. Thus $\zeta \in \mathscr{T}_1'$. More generally, one can show:

A real point $(\zeta_1, \ldots, \zeta_n) \in \mathscr{T}_n'$ if and only if all linear combinations $\sum \lambda_j \zeta_j$ with $\sum \lambda_j > 0$, each $\lambda_j \geqslant 0$, are spacelike, i.e. satisfy $(\sum \lambda_j \zeta_j)^2 < 0$.

(6) The Lorentz group (or the Poincaré group) can be enlarged by adjoining the parity transformation, $(x^0, \mathbf{x}) \to (x^0, -\mathbf{x})$, and time reversal, $(x^0, \mathbf{x}) \to (-x^0, \mathbf{x})$. These transformations induce operations P and T on $\mathscr{H}$, and on Φ. There is also an operation C of charge (or hermitian) conjugation which, however, is the identity for Φ. Various arguments were given at various times that a quantum field theory should be invariant under the combined transformation PCT. In terms of the Wightman functions for Φ, this invariance takes the following form:

$$\langle \Psi_0, \Phi(x_1) \ldots \Phi(x_{n+1}) \Psi_0 \rangle = \langle \Psi_0, \Phi(-x_{n+1}) \ldots \Phi(-x_1) \Psi_0 \rangle \tag{3.8}$$

Theorem. *The Wightman axioms imply the PCT condition (3.8).*

Proof. We shall use the following special case of axiom (C): If $(\zeta_1, \ldots, \zeta_n)$ is a real point of $\mathscr{T}'_n$, and $\zeta_j = x_j - x_{j+1}$, then

$$\langle\Psi_0, \Phi(x_1) \ldots \Phi(x_{n+1})\Psi_0\rangle = \langle\Psi_0, \Phi(x_{n+1}) \ldots \Phi(x_1)\Psi_0\rangle \tag{3.9}$$

This condition is also known as weak local commutativity. This equation on one hand, and the invariance of the W_n under complex Lorentz transformations including $\Lambda = -I$ on the other, imply

$$W_n(\zeta_1, \ldots, \zeta_n) = W_n(-\zeta_n, \ldots, -\zeta_1) = W_n(\zeta_n, \ldots, \zeta_1) \tag{3.10}$$

This equality holds in a real neighbourhood (more precisely, in a real environment), hence it extends to the entire region of holomorphy and to the boundary values. Since the members of (3.8) are boundary values which are approached from the same tube $\mathscr{T}_n$, Eq. (3.8) follows.

Note that in the above, the invariance under real (proper) Lorentz transformations alone would not ensure invariance under $\Lambda = -I$.

4. DISPERSION THEORY

This section is devoted to another branch of quantum field theory, one that has a closer connection with experimentally measurable quantities. Some of the results of this branch, in particular some dispersion relations, have also been deduced from the Wightman axioms. However, such a deduction requires an extensive development, and we shall therefore consider the present subject as independent. The reader will perhaps observe that the techniques of this section do not appear mathematically as neat and intuitive as those of § 3. But it will be satisfying to encounter from a new angle the notions that we have ready discussed.

For definiteness, we shall consider the elastic scattering of charged π-mesons, or pions, with mass μ and four-momenta p, etc:

$$\pi^+(p) + \pi^-(k) \to \pi^+(p') + \pi^-(k') \tag{4.1}$$

This reaction cannot as yet be carried out directly in a laboratory, but is nonetheless of fundamental importance. We note that pions exist in three charge states, $\pi^\pm$ and π^0, and the pion field has three corresponding components. We shall usually leave π^0 out of consideration, and sometimes suppress the charge label.

4.1. Asymptotic states

The particles in (4.1) are free in the asymptotic limit $t \to \pm$, and an assumption about the space of asymptotic vectors, or states, has to be made. We assume for simplicity that this space is $\mathscr{H}_{\Phi OK}(\pi^+) \otimes \mathscr{H}_{\Phi OK}(\pi^-)$. But this assumption is not crucial for what follows, and can be modified. Now, in (4.1), the particles have definite momenta, and so should be described in terms of vector-valued distributions rather than normalizable vectors. We shall refer to such distributions and to vectors as states, and denote them by $|p, k\rangle$, $|p\rangle$, $|\mathbf{p}\rangle$, $|\Omega\rangle$, etc., also by $\langle p, k|$ to form scalar products, etc.

The initial state $|p, k\rangle^{in}$ can be constructed with the help of the creation parts of the free field $\varphi_{\pi^\pm}$. We choose a reference frame (i.e. a co-ordinate system for M^4) and write

$$|p, k\rangle^{in} = |\mathbf{p}, \mathbf{k}\rangle^{in} = a^{(+)}_{\pi^+}(\mathbf{p})\, a^{(+)}_{\pi^-}(\mathbf{k})\, \Psi_0 \tag{4.2}$$

The final state $|p', k'\rangle^{out}$ can also be constructed in terms of φ. However, one then has to use a representation of φ which is equivalent to but not identical with the representation in (4.2). The equivalence is given by the S-matrix, which contains the quantum-theoretic amplitudes for processes like (4.1):

$$^{out}\langle p', k'|p, k\rangle^{in} = {}^{in}\langle p', k'|S|p, k\rangle^{in} \tag{4.3}$$

It is convenient to introduce another matrix, T, by

$$^{out}\langle p', k'|p, k\rangle^{in} = \delta(p-p')\,\delta(k-k') - 2\pi i\,\delta(p'+k'-p-k)\,T(p', k';\ p, k) \tag{4.4}$$

4.2. A dispersion relation and crossing

We shall consider the T-matrix only for forward scattering, T(p, k; p, k). [Forward scattering is defined as the limit when the deflection angle tends to zero. In particular, the term $\delta(p-p') \times \delta(k-k')$ should not contribute.] Then T depends only on the energy of the system, taken in any convenient frame of reference. We shall use the frame where $p = p' = (\mu, \mathbf{0})$, and write ω for k^0.

We have therefore the function $T(\omega)$. It has an extensive region of holomorphy, and satisfies a dispersion relation of the form

$$T(\omega) = \frac{1}{\pi} \lim_{\epsilon \downarrow 0} \left(\int_{-\infty}^{-\mu} + \int_{\mu}^{\infty} \right) d\omega' \frac{\mathrm{Im}\, T(\omega')}{\omega' - \omega - i\epsilon} \tag{4.5}$$

(One integrates here over the energies, or frequencies. In the case of light, different frequencies correspond to different colours, and hence the name "dispersion".) A crossing relation and the optical theorem allow an independent determination of Im T:

$$\mathrm{Im}\, T_{\pi^+\pi^-}(-\omega) = -\mathrm{Im}\, T_{\pi^+\pi^+}(\omega) \tag{4.6a}$$

$$\mathrm{Im}\, T_{\pi^+\pi^\pm}(\omega) = (\omega/4\pi)\sigma^{tot}_{\pi^+\pi^\pm}(\omega) \tag{4.6b}$$

where σ^{tot} indicates the total cross-section. One can now, in principle, compare (4.5) with the scattering data. If the integrals do not converge, then a simple modification can be introduced. (Such dispersion relations for other processes have yielded satisfactory agreement with experiment.

The integral in (4.5) defines a holomorphic function F(z) which has $T(\omega)$ as a boundary value:

$$T(\omega) = T_{\pi^+\pi^-}(\omega) = \lim_{\epsilon \downarrow 0} F(\omega + i\epsilon) \tag{4.7a}$$

Moreover, in place of (4.6a), one can say more precisely:

$$T_{\pi^\pm\pi^\pm}(\omega) = \lim_{\epsilon \downarrow 0} F(-\omega - i\epsilon) \tag{4.7b}$$

Thus (4.5) exhibits the amplitudes for different processes as different boundary values of the same holomorphic function. This conclusion, called a **crossing property** (it has been generalized to arbitrary scattering processes [4, 7]), is based on the fact that the same field component, i.e. φ_{π^+}, can annihilate a π^- and create a π^+. In other words, by using different Fourier coefficients of the same field component, one can exchange $\pi^{-,\,\mathrm{in}}$ with $\pi^{+,\,\mathrm{out}}$, etc.

In particular, the components $\varphi_{\pi^\pm}$ are not hermitian, but rather, $(\varphi_{\pi^\pm})^* = \varphi_{\pi^\mp}$. The commutation rule (1.6) continues to hold between the hermitian-conjugate parts, but should be completed as follows. We consider the decomposition:

$$\varphi_{\pi^\pm}(x) = \frac{1}{(2\pi)^{3/2}} \int d^3k \frac{1}{\sqrt{2k^0}} [a^{(+)}_{\pi^\pm}(k)e^{ikx} + a^{(-)}_{\pi^\mp}(k)e^{-ikx}] \tag{4.8}$$

Then all the commutators of the a's vanish except two:

$$[a^{(-)}_{\pi^\pm}(k), a^{(+)}_{\pi^\pm}(\ell)] = \delta(k-\ell), \qquad \text{otherwise } [a^{\cdot}_{\cdot}, a^{\cdot}_{\cdot}] = 0 \tag{4.9}$$

In the remainder of this section and in the next we shall establish the existence of a holomorphic function T^h of a complex four-vector, whose boundary values include the amplitudes of (4.7a–b). However, we shall not establish the existence of the holomorphic function F.

4.3. Assumptions concerning the S-matrix

We base our arguments on assumptions imposed directly on the S-matrix (cf. also [8]). We first assume an expansion

$$S = \sum_{n=0}^{\infty} \int \left(\prod_1^n d^4x_j d^4y_j\right) : \prod_1^n \varphi_{\pi^+}(x_j)\varphi_{\pi^-}(y_j) : \rho_n(x_1, y_1, \ldots, x_n, y_n) \tag{4.10}$$

The $\varphi_{\pi^\pm}$ occur in pairs as shown, to ensure charge conservation. While the creation and the annihilation parts separately could give a more general expansion for S, the form (4.10) is needed for the locality condition below. The double dots indicate that the annihilation parts should follow the creation parts. We assume moreover that S is unitary, and that it leaves the vacuum Ψ_0 and the one-particle states $|p\rangle$ invariant.

We next introduce the current j which describes, so to say, the tendency of the particles to interact:

$$j_{\pi^\pm}(x) = i[\delta S/\delta\varphi_{\pi^\mp}(x)]S^* \tag{4.11}$$

(The corresponding current for a non-interacting theory vanishes.) We assume that j is local, i.e. that for $(x-y)^2 < 0$,

$$[j_{\pi^\pm}(x), j_{\pi^\pm}(y)] = [j_{\pi^\pm}(x), j_{\pi^\mp}(y)] = 0 \tag{4.12}$$

Another assumption about j is the following: Let Ω_q be a state with four-momentum q. Then

$$\langle p|j_{\pi^\pm}(x)|\Omega_q\rangle = 0 \quad \text{whenever} \quad q^2 < (2\mu)^2 \tag{4.13}$$

This condition means that an interaction must affect at least four different pionic states. This condition has an empirical basis, but it can also be weakened without changing our conclusions. (We remark that $\langle p|j|p'\rangle = 0$ follows from the pseudoscalar nature of φ, i.e. from $P\varphi P = -\varphi$ where P was introduced in § 3.)

4.4. Consequences of these assumptions

We return to the matrix element ${}^{in}\langle p',k'|S|p,k\rangle^{in}$. It can be investigated with the help of the expansion (4.10) of S and thc commutation rules (4.9). It is reasonable to expect that the interacting part of S, i.e. the T-matrix, can be expressed in terms of matrix elements of the current, and this turns out to be the case. If we set

$$T^r(k) = -i \int d^4x\, e^{ikx}\, \theta(x^0)\, \langle p|\,[j_{\pi^+}(\tfrac{1}{2}x), j_{\pi^-}(-\tfrac{1}{2}x)]\,|p\rangle \tag{4.14}$$

where $\theta(x^0) = 1$ for $x^0 > 0$, and $= 0$ for $x^0 < 0$, then in view of (4.12), T^r is holomorphic for $\mathrm{Im}\,k \in V_+$, i.e. for $k \in \mathscr{T}_1^*$, and one can show that

$$T_{\pi^+\pi^-}(\omega) = \lim_{\eta \to 0, \eta \in V_+} T^r((\omega, \mathbf{k}) + i\eta) \tag{4.15}$$

Here **k** can be any real vector satisfying $\mathbf{k}^2 + \mu^2 = \omega^2$. [Note that the integrand of (4.14) is a product of distributions. As a result, there may be an ambiguity in the asymptotic behaviour of T^r, but not in its analytic properties.]

Similarly, we introduce a function holomorphic in $\mathscr{T}_1$:

$$T^a(k) = i \int d^4x\, e^{ikx}\, \theta(-x^0)\, \langle p|\,[j_{\pi^+}(\tfrac{1}{2}x), j_{\pi^-}(-\tfrac{1}{2}x)]\,|p\rangle \tag{4.16}$$

[Here a stands for "advanced", as implied by $\theta(-x^0)$, and r above, for "retarded".] In order to bring the last integral to the form (4.14), we have to let $x \to -x$ and to exchange the two terms of the commutator. The resulting matrix element $\langle \ldots \rangle$ will yield an amplitude for $\pi^+ - \pi^+$ scattering, and

$$T_{\pi^+\pi^+}(\omega) = \lim_{\eta \to 0, \eta \in V_+} T^a((-\omega, \mathbf{k}) - i\eta) \tag{4.17}$$

It is important for us also to examine the following difference:

$$(T^r - T^a)(k) = -i \int d^4x\; e^{ikx} \langle p|[j_{\pi^+}(\tfrac{1}{2}x), j_{\pi^-}(-\tfrac{1}{2}x)]|p\rangle \tag{4.18}$$

From the assumption (4.13), from the rule

$$\langle p|j(x)|\Omega_q\rangle = e^{i(p-q)x} \langle p|j(0)|\Omega_q\rangle \tag{4.19}$$

and from manipulations such as in (1.13) – (1.14), we conclude that there is a real environment E of k = 0 such that

$$(T^r - T^a)(k) = 0 \quad \text{when} \quad k \in E \tag{4.20}$$

We return to the functions $T^{r,a}$ in the next section.

It is worth noting at this point, however, that the presence of π^0 and of other particles in the theory would not upset the arguments, as long as (4.13) remains valid.

5. THE EDGE-OF-THE-WEDGE THEOREM

This theorem can be described as a generalization of the Schwarz reflection principle. We first state a special case. Suppose that f_1 and f_2 are two functions, holomorphic in regions above and below an interval $(a, b) \subset R^1$ respectively, that

$$\lim_{\epsilon \downarrow 0} f_1(x + i\epsilon) = \lim_{\epsilon \downarrow 0} f_2(x - i\epsilon) \quad \text{for} \quad a < x < b \tag{5.1}$$

and that the boundary function here defined is continuous. Then f_1 and f_2 are branches of the same holomorphic function, which is also holomorphic on (a, b).

The foregoing special case can be generalized as follows: (i) the f_j may be functions of several complex variables; (ii) instead of holomorphy in upper and lower half-planes we may have it in cones; and (iii) instead of continuous boundary values we may have distributions. Explicitly: Let S be a region of R^n, let $\hat{C} \subset R^n$ be an open convex cone with vertex at 0, and let D be an open set of C^n containing S. Let $F_\pm$ be two functions holomorphic in $(R^n \pm i\hat{C}) \cap D$ respectively. Suppose that the boundary values satisfy

$$\lim_{y \to 0,\, y \in \hat{C}} F_+(x + iy) = \lim_{y \to 0,\, y \in \hat{C}} F_-(x - iy), \qquad x \in S \tag{5.2}$$

the equality being in the sense of distributions.

The conclusion now is: $F_\pm$ are branches of the same holomorphic function F, which is also holomorphic in a complex neighbourhood of S (including S itself). In particular, this neighbourhood will include some complex points where f was not assumed to be holomorphic.

An easy-to-follow proof of this theorem can be found in Ref. [1], where the above special case and successive generalizations are established in turn. A discussion of global aspects of this theorem can be found in Ref. [9]. (We also remark that the reader who is acquainted with the theory of functions of several complex variables will recognize this theorem as related to the construction of envelopes of holomorphy.)

It is a direct consequence of this theorem that the functions T^r and T^a of § 4 are branches of the same function $T^h(\kappa)$, which is holomorphic in $\mathcal{T}_1 \cup \mathcal{T}_1^* \cup E'$. Here E′ is a complex neighbourhood of E. The function T^h is such as we promised in §4.2.

This function is clearly invariant under rotations in R^3, and it can be expressed in terms of the rotational invariants ω and k^2, as indicated in Ref. [10]. It is tempting to set

$$F(z) = T^h(z, z^2 - \mu^2) \tag{5.3}$$

but then we find that the above region of holomorphy of T^h is incompatible with the restriction $\kappa^2 = \mu^2$ implied in (5.3). E.g., if κ is purely imaginary then it takes the form $i(\omega, \mathbf{e}\sqrt{\omega^2 + \mu^2})$ where $\mathbf{e}$ is any unit three-vector, and so $\kappa \notin \mathcal{T}_1, \mathcal{T}_1^*$.

Nevertheless, the function F of (5.3) can be proved holomorphic in the cut plane, as is needed for the dispersion relation (4.5). A proof can be constructed by exploiting further the techniques that we have described (cf. [10]). Certain integral representations, however, provide a more direct approach to dispersion relations.

As another application of the edge-of-the-wedge theorem, we prove a converse of the PCT theorem of § 3. Explicitly, we show that the Wightman axioms (A), (B) and (D) and the PCT condition (3.8) imply weak local commutativity, i.e. these imply (3.9) for points such that the differences $(x_1 - x_2, \ldots)$ constitute a point of $\mathcal{T}'_n$.

We use the following easy corollary to the edge-of-the-wedge theorem: If a function F_+ is holomorphic as described above, and its boundary value on S vanishes, then F_+ vanishes identically. Now, in view of (3.8),

$$F_+(\zeta_1, \ldots, \zeta_n) = W_n(\zeta_1, \ldots, \zeta_n) - W_n(\zeta_n, \ldots, \zeta_1) \tag{5.4}$$

satisfies this condition, and hence $F_+ = 0$. Invariance under complex Lorentz transformations then implies (3.10). Moreover, if the differences $(x_1 - x_2, \ldots)$ constitute a point of $\mathcal{T}'_n$, (3.9) also follows. Note that if the differences $x_j - x_{j+1}$ are arbitrary, then the two boundary values in (3.9) are approached from different regions (or tubes) of holomorphy, and so need not be equal.

REFERENCES

[1] STREATER, R.F., WIGHTMAN, A.S., PCT, Spin and Statistics, and All That, Benjamin, New York (1964).

[2] JOST, R., The General Theory of Quantized Fields, Am. Math. Soc., Providence, R.I. (1965).

[3] (DeWITT, C., OMNES, R., Eds) Relations de dispersion et particules élémentaires, Hermann, Paris (1960).

[4] SOMMER, G., Fortschr. Phys. **18** (1970) 577–688.

[5] VLADIMIROV, V.S., "The Laplace transform of tempered distributions", Global Analysis and its Applications (Proc. Int. Course, Trieste, 1972) **III**, IAEA, Vienna (1974) 243–270.

[6] SIMON, B., The $P(\phi)_2$ Euclidean (Quantum) Field Theory, Princeton Univ. Press (1974), especially pp. 53–59 and Ch. VIII.

[7] BROS, J., EPSTEIN, H., GLASER, V., Commun. Math. Phys. **1** (1965) 240.

[8] BOGOLUBOV, N.N., MEDVEDEV, B.V., POLIVANOV, M.K., Problems of the Theory of Dispersion Relations, Gos. Izd., Fiz.-Mat. Lit., Moscow (1958), in Russian.

[9] BROS, J., EPSTEIN, H., GLASER, V., STORA, R., in Hyperfunctions and Theoretical Physics (PHAM, F., E Lecture Notes in Mathematics N° 449, Springer-Verlag, Berlin-Heidelberg-New York (1975) 185–218.

[10] BREMERMANN, H.J., OEHME, R., TAYLOR, J.G., Phys. Rev. **109** (1958) 2178.

RECENT RESULTS ON FEYNMAN-TYPE INTEGRALS

J. TARSKI*
International Centre for Theoretical Physics,
Trieste, Italy

Abstract

RECENT RESULTS ON FEYNMAN-TYPE INTEGRALS.

Feynman-type integrals are discussed on the basis of the definition of Itô. The previous (rigorous) results are summarized and extended slightly. A formula for integration by parts is established.

1. INTRODUCTION

Not long ago the present author had occasion to review the available rigorous material on Feynman-type integrals (i.e. path integrals and their modifications) [1]. We cited some ten definitions, which accumulated over a period of some ten years. The particular definition due to Itô [2] has several appealing features, and in this note we discuss various properties of the integral on its basis. We start by summarizing this definition, or construction, for the convenience of the reader.

Consider a real, separable Hilbert space $\mathscr{H}$, and the following class of linear operators $T: \mathscr{H} \to \mathscr{H}$:

$$\mathscr{T} = \{T : T > 0,\ T = T^*,\ T \text{ of trace class}\} \tag{1.1}$$

Corresponding to each such T and to a vector $\alpha \in \mathscr{H}$, there exists a gaussian measure $\mu_{T,\alpha}$ on $\mathscr{H}$ having T as the covariance operator and α as the mean vector. Let a function (or functional) $f: \mathscr{H} \to C^1$ be in $L_1(\mathscr{H}, \mu_{T,\alpha})$. Then we set

$$I_{T,\alpha}(f) = c_T^{-1} \int_{\mathscr{H}} d\mu_{T,\alpha}(\xi) \exp(\tfrac{1}{2} is\langle\xi,\xi\rangle) f(\xi) \tag{1.2a}$$

$$c_T = \int_{\mathscr{H}} d\mu_{T,0}(\xi) \exp(\tfrac{1}{2} is\langle\xi,\xi\rangle) \tag{1.2b}$$

and here $s \in R^1$, $s \neq 0$. In typical applications $s = m/\hbar$, m being the mass of a particle, and $\hbar$ is Planck's constant divided by 2π. We shall sometimes set $s = 1$, and often suppress the dependence of $I_{T,\alpha}$ etc. on s.

The set $\mathscr{T}$ is partially ordered by the relation $\geqslant$, where

$$T_1 \geqslant T_2 \Leftrightarrow T_1 - T_2 \geqslant 0 \tag{1.3}$$

(Inequalities like $T > 0$, $T \geqslant 0$ are defined, of course, in terms of quadratic forms $\langle\beta, T\beta\rangle$, $\beta \in \mathscr{H}$.)

---

* Present address: Fakultät für Physik, Universität Bielefeld, Bielefeld, Federal Republic of Germany.

The partial ordering allows us to define

$$\hat{I}(f) = \lim_{T\to\infty} I_{T,\alpha}(f) \tag{1.4}$$

with the provision that the limit be independent of α. We shall also use the notation

$$\hat{I}(f) = \hat{I}^{(s)}(f) = \int \mathscr{D}(\xi)\exp(\tfrac{1}{2}\, is\langle\xi,\xi\rangle)f(\xi) \tag{1.5}$$

We observe that this definition depends on taking a limit of measure-theoretic integrals, and so defines a kind of generalized measure. After Itô's definition in Ref. [2], the present author put this notion into a broader context [3]. We expect that several of the subsequent propositions can be readily adapted to other examples of generalized measures.

In particular, the factor $\exp(\frac{1}{2}\, is\langle\xi,\xi\rangle)$ characterizes the preceding integral, and such factors were called weight factors in Ref. [3]. We introduce later (in Eq. (3.3) and in Proposition 10) integrals with different weight factors, but otherwise defined in complete analogy with (1.2)--(1.5).

Later, when we speak of integrability of a function, without further qualification, we refer to the existence of the limit (1.4) and to its independence of α. Or, if a different weight factor is used, we refer to the existence and independence of the analogous limit.

In various applications of Feynman-type integrals, the scalar product is the same one that is associated with the Wiener integral. Thus, if $\eta: [0,t] \to R^n$, then we set

$$\langle\eta,\eta\rangle_W = \langle\dot{\eta},\dot{\eta}\rangle = \int_0^t d\tau \sum_{j=1}^{n} \left(\frac{d\eta^j}{d\tau}\right)^2, \quad \text{assuming } \eta(0) = 0 \tag{1.6}$$

The Green's function $G(t,x;\, t_0,x_0)$ for the Schrödinger equation with a potential V can now be expressed as follows:

$$G(t,x;\,0,0) = \int_{\eta(0)=0} \mathscr{D}(\eta)\exp(\tfrac{1}{2}\, i(m/\hbar)\langle\dot{\eta},\dot{\eta}\rangle)\ \exp\left[-(i/\hbar)\int_0^t d\tau\, V(\eta(\tau))\right]\delta(\eta(t)-x) \tag{1.7}$$

Since the functions $\eta:[0,t] \to R^n$ can be thought of as paths, the term **path integral** is often used for functional integrals of this kind.

The quantity $\eta(\sigma)$, $\sigma \in [0,t]$ can be expressed as a scalar product:

$$\eta(\sigma) = \langle\dot{\eta},\dot{\beta}_\sigma\rangle \quad \text{where} \quad \beta_\sigma(\tau) = \min(\sigma,\tau) \tag{1.8}$$

Thus the functional integral of (1.7) reduces to Hilbert space concepts. In particular, the change of variable $\dot{\eta} = \xi$ brings the integral to the form (1.5) (with $s = m/\hbar$). However, the δ-function deserves a comment.

We recall, also for future reference, a general result on decomposition of measures [4]. This result states (as a special case) that a sufficiently regular measure λ on the direct sum of two linear spaces $\mathscr{L}_j$ can be decomposed as follows:

$$d\lambda(\eta_1,\eta_2) = d\lambda_1(\eta_1)\, d\lambda_{\eta_1}(\eta_2), \quad \eta_j \in \mathscr{L}_j \tag{1.9}$$

We may in particular consider the linear span L of functions of the form $\mathbf{a}\beta$ where $\mathbf{a} \in R^n$, and write

$$\mathscr{H}_W = L^\perp + L \tag{1.10}$$

Then, for each approximating measure $\mu_{T,\alpha}$ the decomposition (1.9) yields a gaussian measure on L, i.e. on R^n. The integration of $\delta(\eta(t) - x)$ now has an obvious meaning.

In this article we present twelve propositions, which summarize a good part of what is known about the integral $\hat{I}$ defined above. The integration theory for $\hat{I}$, in fact, has barely begun, and many elementary properties remain to be established. To give an example, let us consider Fubini's theorem for $\hat{I}$, which is still an open question: If the functions $f_j(\xi_j)$ are defined for $\xi_j \in \mathscr{H}_j$ and are integrable, and if f is defined on $\mathscr{H}_1 \dot{+} \mathscr{H}_2$ by

$$f(\xi_1, \xi_2) = f_1(\xi_1)\, f_2(\xi_2) \tag{1.11}$$

then, is f also integrable? [For the special case, when both f_j are of the form (2.2a) below, integrability is evident. Another special case is given in Proposition 4.]

Some of our propositions are new. Some are based on Ref. [2] and on a recent note by Buchholz and the present author [5]. One proposition is adapted from the work of Albeverio and Höegh-Krohn [6]. We also cite some related studies of C. DeWitt-Morette [7].

In § 2 we consider the preliminary questions of integrability and of evaluating the integrals. We also include examples of asymptotic estimates. Section 3 contains a brief discussion of some foundational problems, like path integrals over phase spaces, the action principle, and its justification by integration by parts. Some proofs are relegated to the Appendix.

The author gratefully acknowledges useful discussions with Dr. P. de Mottoni concerning the connection between path integrals and the action principle, and with Professor W.H.J. Fuchs concerning the asymptotic behaviour of integrals.

2. EXISTENCE, EVALUATION AND ESTIMATION OF INTEGRALS

A basic problem in any theory of integration is that of integrability of functions. In the case of (measure-theoretic) gaussian integrals, there are a few functions whose evaluation in closed form is familiar, in particular polynomials, linear exponentials, and gaussian functions. To evaluate the corresponding integral $\hat{I}$, one can find the approximations $I_{T,\alpha}$ explicitly and then investigate the limit $T \to \infty$. For instance, if $\beta \in \mathscr{H}$ then

$$f_\beta(\xi) = \exp i\langle\beta,\xi\rangle \Rightarrow \hat{I}^{(s)}(f_\beta) = \exp[-i(2s)^{-1}\langle\beta,\beta\rangle] \tag{2.1}$$

Our first three propositions are due to Itô [2], and the first provides a significant extension of (2.1). The measure ν below is to be defined on the σ-algebra generated by the strongly open sets of $\mathscr{H}$ (or equivalently, by the weakly open sets [8]).

Proposition 1. *Let ν be a complex measure of bounded absolute variation on $\mathscr{H}$ (and defined on subsets as specified), and let*

$$f(\xi) = \int_{\mathscr{H}} d\nu(\theta) \exp(i\langle\theta,\xi\rangle) \tag{2.2a}$$

Then f *is integrable, and*

$$\hat{I}^{(s)}(f) = \int_{\mathscr{H}} d\nu(\theta)\ \exp[-i(2s)^{-1}\langle\theta,\theta\rangle] \tag{2.2b}$$

The functions of the form (2.2a) can be handled with relative ease. In Ref. [2] several useful rules may be found for integrating such functions.

In connection with the next proposition, we call a (linear) operator A: $\mathscr{H}\to\mathscr{H}$ nearly orthogonal if it is one-to-one and if

$$\|(A^*A)^{\frac{1}{2}} - I\|_p < \infty \quad \text{for some} \quad 0<p<1 \tag{2.3a}$$

where

$$\|M\|_p = [\mathrm{tr}(M^*M)^{p/2}]^{1/p} \tag{2.3b}$$

and we call B nearly isometric if for some $\alpha \in \mathscr{H}$ and for some A nearly orthogonal

$$B\xi = \alpha + A\xi \qquad (\forall\xi\in\mathscr{H}) \tag{2.4}$$

Proposition 2. *Let* f *be integrable, let* B *be nearly isometric, and let* $f_B : \mathscr{H}\to\mathscr{H}$ *be defined by*

$$f_B(\xi) = \exp(-\tfrac{1}{2}is\langle\xi,\xi\rangle)\ \exp(\tfrac{1}{2}is\langle B\xi,B\xi\rangle)\ f(B\xi) \tag{2.5}$$

Then f_B *is also integrable and, if* J *denotes the Jacobian,*

$$\hat{I}(f_B) = J(B)^{-1}\hat{I}(f) \tag{2.6}$$

We note that it is sometimes convenient to combine the weight factor $\exp(\frac{1}{2}is\langle\xi,\xi\rangle)$ with the function f. If this were done here, and if we set $F = f\ \exp(\frac{1}{2}is\langle\,.\,,\,.\,\rangle)$, then (2.5) would take the simple form $F_B(\xi) = F(B\xi)$. We also observe that, for $r \geqslant 1$ and $\kappa_i, \lambda_j \geqslant 0$,

$$(d/d\kappa_2)\,[\kappa_1^r + \kappa_2^r - (\kappa_1+\kappa_2)^r] \leqslant 0, \qquad \text{hence } \kappa_1^r + \kappa_2^r \leqslant (\kappa_1+\kappa_2)^r \tag{2.7a}$$

from which follows

$$\sum \lambda_j \leqslant \left(\sum \lambda_j^{1/r}\right)^r \tag{2.7b}$$

This implies in turn $\|M\|_1 \leqslant \|M\|_p$ in the above, so that J(A) exists [9], and then J(B) = J(A).

We now come to integrals of the form (1.7). Our way of handling the endpoint restriction $\eta(t) = x$, as we explained in the Introduction ,differs from that of Ref. [2]. This difference does not affect the essentials of the proofs of [2] but requires the elimination of the factors with square roots in Eq. (22) of *loc. cit.* (Examples of handling the decomposition of measures can be found in the Appendix.)

Proposition 3. *The Green's function for the Schrödinger equation in one dimension can be represented as in Eq. (1.7) for the following potentials:*

$$V(q) = \int_{-\infty}^{\infty} d\nu_1(y)\; e^{iy(q-b)} \tag{2.8a}$$

$$V(q) = c_1(q-b), \qquad c_1 \in R^1 \tag{2.8b}$$

$$V(q) = c_2(q-b)^2, \qquad c_2 \geqslant 0 \tag{2.8c}$$

Here $b \in R^1$ *is arbitrary, and* ν_1 *is a complex Borel measure of bounded absolute variation.*

The number b was included in order to compensate for the restriction $x_0 = 0$ in (1.7). Integrability for (2.8a) and (2.8b) follows from Proposition 1, while Proposition 2 was used for (2.8c). The identification of $\hat{I}$ with the Green's function was based on detailed calculations.

A representation similar to (1.7) was established in Ref. [6] for wave operators in scattering theory.

The next proposition is elementary but basic [5]. It can be easily established by decomposing the measures $\mu_{T,\alpha}$, as in (1.9).

Proposition 4. *Let* $f_1 : \mathcal{H}_1 \to C^1$ *be integrable. Extend* f_1 *to* $f_0 : \mathcal{H}_1 \dot{+} \mathcal{H}_2 \to C^1$ *by*

$$f_0(\xi_1, \xi_2) = f_1(\xi_1), \qquad \xi_j \in \mathcal{H}_j \tag{2.9}$$

Then f_0 *is also integrable, and the respective integrals are equal.*

This proposition states in particular the following. Cylinder functions, i.e. those which depend on only a finite number k of co-ordinates, can be integrated by restricting $\mathcal{H}$ to the appropriate k-dimensional subspace. Now, integration over R^k is substantially easier than over $\mathcal{H}$ of dimension ∞, and integrability for a few classes of unbounded cylinder functions has been established [5].

Proposition 5. *If a function* $f : R^k \to C^1$ *satisfies one of the two following conditions, then it is integrable: (a)* f *is the restriction to* R^k *of an entire (holomorphic) function of order less than* 2; *(b) the derivatives of* f *satisfy an equation of the form*

$$(1-\Delta)^N f(x) = (1+x^2)^M g(x) \tag{2.10}$$

where Δ *is the Laplacian,* $g \in L_1$, *and* N, M *are non-negative integers such that* $N - M > \frac{1}{2}k$.

In the finite-dimensional case, integrability relates also to Tauberian theorems. Let f be defined on R^k and be locally L_1. We introduce polar co-ordinates $x = (\rho, \Omega)$, and set

$$F(\rho) = \rho^{k-1} \int d^{k-1}\Omega\, f(\rho, \Omega) \tag{2.11}$$

Proposition 6. *Let* f *and* F *be related by (2.11). Suppose that* f *is integrable and that* $(\rho + \rho^{-1})F(\rho)$ *is bounded. Then*

$$\left(\frac{s}{2\pi i}\right)^{k/2} \lim_{R\to\infty} \int_0^R d\rho\, \exp(\tfrac{1}{2} is\, \rho^2) F(\rho) = \hat{I}^{(s)}(f) \tag{2.12}$$

This proposition follows e.g. from the analysis given in Ref. [10]. Since the integrability of f is assumed, we may set $\alpha = 0$, $T^{-1} = \epsilon I$, then do the angular integration, and let $\epsilon \downarrow 0$.

The converse of this proposition, i.e. the integrability of f under the assumption that the limit $R \to \infty$ exists, is a reasonable conjecture. The case of one dimension is elementary, and was included in the preprint version of Ref. [5].

We now turn to the estimates of the integral $\hat{I}^{(s)}$. One kind of estimate which has been considered on a number of occasions is the asymptotic behaviour as $s \to \infty$. (The case $s \to -\infty$ is analogous.) We restrict ourselves here only to the leading term of a presumed asymptotic expansion i.e. to the term independent of s.

The elementary asymptotic estimate for the case of k dimensions is:

$$\lim_{s \to \infty} \left(\frac{s}{2\pi i}\right)^{k/2} \int d^k u \exp(\tfrac{1}{2} isu^2) f(u) = f(0) \tag{2.13}$$

If f is in L_1 and continuous at 0, then one may try to establish this relation by the method of stationary phase. There are many discussions of this method, e.g. in [11–13], under various additional hypotheses. Furthermore, by Proposition 1 the Fourier transform $\tilde{f}$ is integrable, and

$$\left(\frac{s}{2\pi i}\right)^{k/2} \int d^k u \exp(\tfrac{1}{2} isu^2) f(u) = \frac{1}{(2\pi)^{k/2}} \int d^k v \exp(-\tfrac{1}{2} is^{-1} v^2) \tilde{f}(v) \tag{2.14}$$

(Note that in the r.h.s. one has the parameter $-s^{-1}$ in place of s.) If in addition $\tilde{f} \in L_1$, then the bounded convergence theorem provides an immediate proof of (2.13).

It seems difficult to establish a relation like (2.13) under the general assumptions of integrability of a function and of its continuity at 0. However, for particular classes of integrable functions this is easy.

Proposition 7. *If* $f: R^k \to C^1$ *satisfies one of the two conditions (a), (b) of Proposition 5, then* f *also satisfies the relation (2.13).*

Proof. In view of the integrability of f, we may take $T^{-1} = \epsilon I$ and $\alpha = 0$. For (a), a rotation of the contours of integration $u \to u(1 + ia/s)$ where $a > 0$ (as in [5]) reduces the problem to the above case, with f, $\tilde{f} \in L_1$. For (b), the Fourier transform $\tilde{f}$ is in general a distribution which, after some obvious rearrangements, can be expressed as follows:

$$\tilde{f}(p) = (1 - \Delta_p)^M (1 + p^2)^{-N} \; h(p) \tag{2.15}$$

the function h being continuous and bounded. Now, the integral $\hat{I}^{(-s^{-1})}(\tilde{f})$ is well defined (cf. [5]) and (2.14) remains valid. The r.h.s. of (2.14) becomes

$$\lim_{\epsilon \downarrow 0} \frac{1}{(2\pi)^{k/2}} \int d^k p \; \frac{h(p)}{(1 + p^2)^N} (1 - \Delta_p)^M \exp(-\tfrac{1}{2}(is^{-1} + \epsilon)p^2) \tag{2.16}$$

The bounded convergence theorem allows both limits $\epsilon \downarrow 0$, $s \to \infty$ to be taken inside the integral. results

$$\frac{1}{(2\pi)^{k/2}}\int d^k p\,\frac{h(p)}{(1+p^2)^N} = \frac{(1+x^2)^M}{(2\pi)^{k/2}}\int d^k p\,\frac{h(p)e^{-ipx}}{(1+p^2)^N}\Bigg|_{x=0} = f(0) \tag{2.17}$$

We come finally to functions f on $\mathscr{H}$ which are Fourier transforms of bounded measures (Proposition 1). Then the evaluation of $\hat{I}^{(s)}(f)$ in (2.2b) and the bounded convergence theorem yield at once f(0) in the limit $s \to \infty$. A more interesting result is the following [6], where s is allowed to be complex, and where use is made of the Fréchet derivatives ∇V and $\nabla\nabla V$ (a vector and an operator on $\mathscr{H}$ respectively).

Proposition 8. *Consider two measures λ, ν on $\mathscr{H}$ (and defined on subsets as in Proposition 1), whose absolute variations $|\lambda|$ and $|\nu|$ satisfy*

$$\int_{\mathscr{H}} d|\lambda|(\zeta)\,\exp(\sqrt{2}\|\zeta\|) < 1, \qquad \int_{\mathscr{H}} d|\nu|(\theta)\,\exp(\sqrt{2}\|\theta\|) < \infty \tag{2.18a, b}$$

We set

$$V(\xi) = \int_{\mathscr{H}} d\lambda(\zeta)\,\exp(i\langle\zeta,\xi\rangle), \qquad F(\xi) = \int_{\mathscr{H}} d\nu(\theta)\,\exp(i\langle\theta,\xi\rangle) \tag{2.19a, b}$$

and suppose that $V(0) = 0$, $\nabla V(0) = 0$. *Then*

$$\hat{I}^{(s)}(e^{-isV}F) = \int \mathscr{D}(\xi)\,\exp\{is[\tfrac{1}{2}\langle\xi,\xi\rangle - V(\xi)]\}\,F(\xi) \tag{2.20}$$

is holomorphic in s *for* Im $s > 0$ *and is* $\mathscr{C}^\infty$ *in* s^{-1} *for* $-\infty < s^{-1} < \infty$, *and in addition*

$$\lim_{|s|\to\infty,\ \mathrm{Im}\, s \geq 0} \hat{I}^{(s)}(e^{-isV}F) = F(0)\,\det[I - \nabla\nabla V(0)]^{-\frac{1}{2}} \tag{2.21}$$

We comment on the conditions on V. First, the strong restriction (2.18a) on λ ensures that the exponent is[. . .] in (2.20) has only one critical point, at $\xi = 0$. If $\nabla V \neq 0$, then the critical point would be elsewhere. Furthermore, (2.18a) also implies the convergence of the expansion of the determinant (= exp tr log) in $\nabla\nabla V$.

The proof proceeds by expanding e^{-isV} and by estimating the terms [6]. Several extensions of this proposition are also included in *loc. cit.*

3. PHASE SPACES, ACTIONS AND INTEGRATION BY PARTS

The Green's function for the Schrödinger equation was given in Eq. (1.7) as an integral over paths on the co-ordinate space. Alternative expressions can be constructed in terms of paths on the phase space. Such expressions are discussed extensively in Ref. [14] in connection with commutation rules, variational methods, etc.

Let us consider the following forms for the Lagrangian and for the action:

$$L(p,q) = p\dot{q} - H = p\dot{q} - (p^2/2m) - V(q) \tag{3.1a}$$

$$A(p(\cdot), q(\cdot)) = \int_0^t d\tau L(p(\tau), q(\tau)) \tag{3.1b}$$

instead of the Lagrangian

$$L(q) = \tfrac{1}{2} m\dot{q}^2 - V(q) \tag{3.2}$$

presupposed in (1.7). Then the new path integral becomes

$$\bar{I}^{(m)}(f) = \int_{\eta \in \mathscr{H}_q, \xi \in \mathscr{H}_p} \mathscr{D}(\eta, \xi) \exp\left(-i\langle\xi,\xi\rangle/2m + i \int_0^t d\tau \xi \dot{\eta}\right) f(\eta) \tag{3.3}$$

The function f should include the effect of the potential V and an endpoint condition (if one is desired). The Hilbert space $\mathscr{H}_q$ is as in (1.6), while $\mathscr{H}_p$ is determined by

$$\langle \xi, \xi \rangle = \int_0^t d\tau \sum_{j=1}^{n} (\xi^j(\tau))^2 \tag{3.4}$$

The integral $\bar{I}^{(m)}$ is defined as before, but with the exponential of (3.3) being the new weight factor. [See Eqs (1.2) – (1.5) and the subsequent remarks. Note also the different way that m enters in (1.7) and in (3.3), and compare with (2.14).] Heuristically, an integration with respect to ξ reduces the integral to an integral $\hat{I}^{(m)}$ over $\mathscr{H}_q$, in the standard form. Such a conclusion can also be established rigorously:

Proposition 9. *Let* $f: \mathscr{H}_q \to C^1$ *be as in Proposition 1. Then* $\bar{I}^{(m)}(f)$ *exists and*

$$\bar{I}^{(m)}(f) = \hat{I}^{(m)}(f) \tag{3.5}$$

Of course, for $\bar{I}^{(m)}$ we extend the definition of f to $\mathscr{H}_q \dotplus \mathscr{H}_p$, as in Eq. (2.9).

The proof depends on the decomposition of measures, and is a direct adaptation of the proof given in [2] and in [15] (see Appendix).

We remark that a modified definition of the phase space integral and some additional discussion is given in Ref. [16].

Now, the Lagrangian L in (3.1a–b) can be modified by adding a total derivative, without changing the content of the theory. For instance, let us set

$$L_0 = L - d(pq)/dt = -\dot{p}q - H \tag{3.6a}$$

$$A_0 = A - p(t)q(t) + p(0)q(0) \tag{3.6b}$$

and one may ask if a path integral determined by A_0 will be equal to the corresponding integrals $\bar{I}$ and $\hat{I}$. We give the following heuristic argument for equality. In general, one supposes $q(0) = 0$ and $q(t) \neq 0$. However, the functions $\xi \in \mathscr{H}_p$ in Eq. (3.3) are not restricted at either endpoint (and in general they are not continuous). Hence $p(t)$ as well as $p(0)$ should have zero as the average value, and in this way A and A_0 should yield the same integrals and the same quantum dynamics.

The foregoing discussion also raises the question whether path integrals are invariant under canonical transformations. We shall not consider this question, except for the following example. In mechanical systems it is generally possible to find co-ordinates such that the Hamiltonian H in (3.1a) vanishes, so that $L = p\dot{q}$. But $H = 0$ implies a static situation, and this fact lends support to the heuristic evaluation:

$$\int \mathscr{D}(\xi) \exp\left(i \int_0^t d\tau \xi \dot{\eta}\right) = \delta(\dot{\eta}) \tag{3.7a}$$

$$\int_{\eta(0)=0} \mathscr{D}(\eta) \delta(\dot{\eta}) f(\eta) = f(0) \tag{3.7b}$$

The integrals have not yet been defined, but the last integral should be over paths satisfying $\eta(\tau) = \text{const} = 0$.

We are also led to these relations by letting $m \to \infty$ in (3.3) and (3.5), and by taking note of the discussion in the last part of § 2. However, we can formulate (3.7) in a way which is independent of the limit $m \to \infty$. The proof of the following proposition is somewhat like the proof of Proposition 9, and the details are given in the Appendix.

Proposition 10. *Let* $f: \mathscr{H}_q \to C^1$ *be bounded and continuous (for the strong topology). We extend the definition of* f *to* $\mathscr{H}_q \dotplus \mathscr{H}_p$, *as in (2.9). Let* $\bar{\bar{I}}$ *be the integral defined as in (1.2), (1.4), but over* $\mathscr{H}_q \dotplus \mathscr{H}_p$ *and with the weight factor*

$$\exp\left(i \int_0^t d\tau \xi \dot{\eta}\right)$$

Then

$$\bar{\bar{I}}(f) = f(0) \tag{3.8}$$

The next proposition is a first step towards establishing a rigorous connection between path integrals and variational principles. We give there an infinite-dimensional generalization of the formula

$$\int_{-\infty}^{\infty} du \frac{d}{du} [e^{iu^2} f(u)] = 0 \tag{3.9}$$

This equality is expected for any translation-invariant integral, independently of its precise definition and of the behaviour of f at $\pm\infty$. Upon expanding the derivative, the usual formula for integration by parts is found.

Proposition 11. *Let $\mathscr{H} = L_2(S, \lambda)$ and consider the integral over $\mathscr{H}$ defined by (1.2), (1.4). Let $\zeta \in \mathscr{H}$, and assume that the following are integrable, as functions of $\xi \in \mathscr{H}$:*

$$\langle \zeta, \xi \rangle f(\xi), \qquad \left[\int_S d\lambda(v) \zeta(v) \frac{\delta}{\delta \xi(v)} \right] f(\xi) \tag{3.10}$$

The differential operator, to be denoted by $\langle \zeta, \delta/\delta\xi \rangle$, is in the sense of Gâteaux. Then

$$\int \mathscr{D}(\xi) \langle \zeta, \delta/\delta\xi \rangle [\exp(\tfrac{1}{2} i \langle \xi, \xi \rangle) f(\xi)] = 0 \tag{3.11}$$

This proposition is proved in the Appendix. Its extension to multicomponent functions ξ is immediate. It has in particular the following consequence:

Proposition 12. *Let $\sigma \in (0, t)$, and let $f \in \mathscr{H}_q$ be a function of class $\mathscr{C}^2$ and vanishing in neighbourhoods of 0 and t. Assuming that the following integrand is integrable, one has*

$$\int_{\eta(0)=0} \mathscr{D}(\eta) \exp(\tfrac{1}{2} i \langle \dot{\eta}, \dot{\eta} \rangle) \exp \left[-i \int_0^t d\tau V(\eta(\tau)) \right] \delta(\eta(t) - x)$$

$$\times \int_0^t d\sigma f(\sigma) [\ddot{\eta}^j(\sigma) + (\partial^j V)(\eta(\sigma))] = 0 \tag{3.12}$$

The quantity $\ddot{\eta}$ should be interpreted in the sense of distributions.

The last equation is a quantum-mechanical form of Newton's law of motion.

Proof. Let β_v be as in (1.8). Then in addition to $\langle \dot{\beta}_v, \dot{\eta} \rangle = \eta(v)$ one has also

$$(-d^2/d\sigma^2) \langle \dot{\beta}_\sigma, \delta/\delta\dot{\eta} \rangle = \delta/\delta\eta(\sigma) \tag{3.13}$$

This equation may be verified by noting that each member yields $\delta(\sigma - v)$ when applied to $\eta(v)$. Next, we take the integral of (1.7), and Proposition 11 implies that

$$\int_0^t d\sigma f(\sigma)(-d^2/d\sigma^2) \int_{\eta(0)=0} \mathscr{D}(\eta) \langle \dot{\beta}_\sigma, \delta/\delta\dot{\eta} \rangle (\ldots) = 0 \tag{3.14}$$

One may now try to justify the interchange of integrations, which would give (3.12). However, such an interchange is not necessary, since the combined operator (after integration by parts),

$$-\int_0^t d\sigma f''(\sigma) \int_0^t d\tau \dot{\beta}_\sigma(\tau) \frac{\delta}{\delta \dot{\eta}(\tau)} \tag{3.15}$$

can be expressed in the form $\langle \zeta, \delta/\delta\dot{\eta} \rangle$. Therefore it can be applied directly inside the integral, and (3.12) follows.

Now, in classical physics the equations of motion are obtained by a variation of the action, and the last proposition shows how this procedure carries over to the quantum domain. We may also obtain a more general relation by a similar argument. Let A be the action of a system, and we introduce the notation:

$$\langle F \rangle = \int \mathscr{D}(\eta)\, e^{iA(\eta)} F(\eta) \tag{3.16}$$

Then (3.11) yields the following (heuristic) action principle:

$$\langle \delta F \rangle + i \langle (\delta A) F \rangle = 0 \tag{3.17}$$

Here δ indicates a small increment or, if one wishes to be more precise, a derivative like $\langle \zeta, \delta/\delta\eta \rangle$.

APPENDIX

(a) INTEGRATION OF EXPONENTIAL FUNCTIONS

We need to integrate linear exponentials and Gaussians. For this purpose it is convenient to write the measure $d\mu_{T,\alpha}$ as

$$d\mu_{T,\alpha}(\zeta) = \mathscr{D}_T(\zeta) \exp\left[\tfrac{1}{2} \langle \zeta - \alpha, T^{-1}(\zeta - \alpha) \rangle\right] \tag{A.1}$$

We remark that $\mathscr{D}$ can also be interpreted as an invariant generalized measure [3], in a similar way as for Feynman-type integrals. Conceptually $\mathscr{D}_T(\zeta) \exp[\ldots]$ would then differ from the measure $d\mu_{T,\alpha}$, even though the corresponding integrals agree in typical cases.

For a symbol $\mathscr{D}$ a certain normalization must be presupposed, and we let $\mathscr{D}_0$ be such that

$$\int \mathscr{D}_0(\zeta) \exp\left(-\tfrac{1}{2} \langle \zeta, Q_0 \zeta \rangle\right) = 1 \tag{A.2}$$

The following evaluation will be basic for us:

$$\int \mathscr{D}_0(\zeta) \exp\left[-\tfrac{1}{2} \langle \zeta, (Q_0 + Q)\zeta \rangle + \langle \beta, \zeta \rangle\right] = \det\left[I + Q_0^{-\frac{1}{2}} Q Q_0^{-\frac{1}{2}}\right]^{-\frac{1}{2}} \exp\left[\tfrac{1}{2} \langle \beta, (Q_0 + Q)^{-1} \beta \rangle\right] \tag{A.3}$$

For integrating polynomials one can now use the rule,

$$\int \mathscr{D}_0(\zeta)\exp(-\tfrac{1}{2}\langle\zeta, Q_0\zeta\rangle + \langle\beta,\zeta\rangle)P(\zeta) = P(\delta/\delta\beta)\exp(\tfrac{1}{2}\langle\beta, Q_0^{-1}\beta\rangle) \tag{A.4}$$

We shall not discuss the conditions on Q_0 and Q except to note that Q_0 and Q should be symmetric and that, moreover,

$$\mathrm{Re}\, Q_0 \geqslant 0, \qquad \mathrm{Re}\,(Q_0 + Q) \geqslant 0 \tag{A.5}$$

In particular, Q_0, Q and β may be complex. The Hilbert space then becomes complexified, but the product $\langle\cdot\, ,\cdot\rangle$ remains symmetric. We have allowed ourselves here a certain abuse of notation.

In an application we might start with Q_0 and $\mathscr{D}_0$ as in (A.2). Next we may supply Q and a compensating factor $[c(Q)]^{-1}$, so that $\beta = 0$ in (A.3) would yield unity. [Cf. Eqs (1.2), with $\alpha = 0$.] Then (A.3) will simplify:

$$[c(Q)]^{-1} \int \ldots \exp[\ldots + \langle\beta,\zeta\rangle] = \exp[\tfrac{1}{2}\langle\beta,(Q_0 + Q)^{-1}\beta\rangle] \tag{A.6}$$

In particular, the square root of (A.3) is cancelled by $[c(Q)]^{-1}$. (Thus the problem of its correct choice does not arise.)

(b) COVARIANCE OPERATORS AND RESTRICTIONS

In the proofs that follow we consider measures $d\mu_{T,\alpha}$ on $\mathscr{H}_1 \dotplus \mathscr{H}_2$, with $T \in \mathscr{T}$. We are then led to consider the restriction of T and of T^{-1} to $\mathscr{H}_j$, and we note some useful definitions and relations (these are adapted from the preprint version of [5]). Let P_j denote the orthogonal projection $\mathscr{H} \to \mathscr{H}_j$. For convenience we now make the assumption $P_j D(T^{-1}) \subseteq D(T^{-1})$ (D denotes the domain), but see the remarks below. We set

$$T_j = P_j T P_j, \qquad T_{0j} = ((P_j T^{-1} P_j \restriction \mathscr{H}_j)^{\sim})^{-1} \tag{A.7}$$

where ~ denotes the Friedrichs extension. This extension is selected on the basis of domain considerations.

If R is symmetric and non-negative, then

$$(aP_1 - bP_2)\, R\, (aP_1 - bP_2) \geqslant 0 \tag{A.8a}$$

which is equivalent to (if $a, b > 0$ and $v^{-1} = 1 + b/a$)

$$(1 - v)^{-1} P_1 R P_1 + v^{-1} P_2 R P_2 \geqslant R \tag{A.8b}$$

By setting in turn $R = T^{-1}$ and $R = T$, and also $a = b$, and by taking inverses, we obtain

$$\tfrac{1}{2}(T_{01} + T_{02}) \leqslant T \leqslant 2(T_1 + T_2) \tag{A.9a, b}$$

$$\tfrac{1}{2}(T_1^{-1} + T_2^{-1}) \leqslant T^{-1} \leqslant 2(T_{01}^{-1} + T_{02}^{-1}) \tag{A.9c, d}$$

In particular, it follows that $T_{0j} \in \mathscr{T}(\mathscr{H}_j)$.

By decomposing the measure $d\mu_{T,0}$ in accordance with (1.9) and by evaluating the integral of $\exp(i\langle\zeta,\cdot\rangle)$, $\zeta \in \mathscr{H}_1$, in different ways, we obtain a relation between T_{01}^{-1} and T_1^{-1}:

$$T_{01}^{-1} = (T_1^{-1} + T^{-1}T_{02}T^{-1} \restriction \mathscr{H}_1)^{\sim} \tag{A.10}$$

Let us return to the assumption $P_jD(T^{-1}) \subseteq D(T^{-1})$. This assumption does not restrict the applications of (A.9) – (A.10) that we make, for the following reason. In the functional integrals T^{-1} appears first in quadratic forms. Then the relevant domain is $D(T^{-\frac{1}{2}})$, and it suffices to assume that $P_jD(T^{-\frac{1}{2}})$ is dense in $\mathscr{H}_j$. However, for symmetric operators there is the implication (cf. [2] and [15]),

$$0 < R_1 \leqslant R_2 \Rightarrow D(R_1^{-\frac{1}{2}}) \subseteq D(R_2^{-\frac{1}{2}}) \tag{A.11}$$

It follows easily that $P_jD(T^{-\frac{1}{2}})$ is dense in $\mathscr{H}_j$ for all $T \in \mathscr{T}$ sufficiently large. [We also note: For some manipulations of integrals it is more natural to use T^{-1} than $T^{-\frac{1}{2}}$, but in such cases the restriction to $D(T^{-1})$ is normally unnecessary.]

(c) PROOF OF PROPOSITION 9

This proof and the following one (of Proposition 10) are only outlined.

We start by decomposing the measure $d\mu_{T,\alpha}$ on $\mathscr{H}_q \dotplus \mathscr{H}_p$ (as in (1.9)) and by interchanging integrations,

$$\frac{1}{c_T}\int d\mu_{T,\alpha}(\eta,\xi)f(\eta)W(\xi,\eta) = \int d\nu(\theta)\int d\lambda(\eta)\,\frac{1}{c_T}\,\exp(i\langle\theta,\dot{\eta}\rangle)\int d\lambda_\eta(\xi)W(\xi,\eta) \tag{A.12a}$$

$$W(\xi,\eta) = \exp\left(-i\langle\xi,\xi\rangle/2m + i\int_0^t d\tau\,\xi\dot{\eta}\right) \tag{A.12b}$$

The measure $d\lambda_\eta$ is gaussian, with the covariance operator T_{0p} defined by (A.7), and $d\lambda$ is likewise gaussian. The integrals over ξ and η can therefore be done in closed form. We show below that the result is bounded, so that we may take the limit $T \to \infty$ inside the integral over θ. Taking the limit means, essentially, replacing T^{-1} by 0, but various details like those of domain must be verified. Since similar manipulations and arguments are described in Ref. [2], in [15], and elsewhere in this Appendix, we shall not give the details for the present case. The result is as in (2.2b), with s replaced by m.

We still have to establish a bound on the θ-integrand. We translate the variables of integration:

$$\int d\mu_{T,\alpha}(\eta,\xi)\exp(i\langle\theta,\eta\rangle)W(\xi,\eta) = \int d\mu_{T,0}(\eta,\xi)\exp(i\langle\theta,\dot{\eta}+\dot{\alpha}_q\rangle)W(\xi+\alpha_p,\eta+\alpha_q) \tag{A.13}$$

Upon expressing $d\mu_{T,0}$ as in (A.1) and $W(\xi + \ldots)$ as in (A.12b), we are led to an evaluation as in (A.6), with β purely imaginary and $\mathrm{Re}(Q_0 + Q) > 0$. Under these conditions

$$\mathrm{Re}\langle\beta,(Q_0+Q)^{-1}\beta\rangle < 0, \qquad |\exp\tfrac{1}{2}\langle\beta\ldots\rangle| < 1 \tag{A.14}$$

(This way of evaluating the integral, however, is not so convenient for investigating the limit $T \to \infty$.)

(d) PROOF OF PROPOSITION 10

We consider (A.12), but we leave out the term $i\langle\xi,\xi\rangle/2m$ in the exponent, and also the integration over θ. Thus $f(\eta) = \exp(i\langle\theta,\dot\eta\rangle)$. We carry out the ξ-integration, and recognize the resulting expression as the Fourier transform of a probability measure on $\mathcal{H}_q$, aside from a factor depending on α. For brevity we now restrict ourselves to the case $\alpha = 0$. (If $\alpha \neq 0$, one always has $\alpha \in D(T^{-\frac{1}{2}})$ for T sufficiently large, and there are no particular complications. See [15], App. A.) The Fourier transform $S_T(\theta)$ then becomes

$$S_T(\theta) = \exp\{-\tfrac{1}{2}\langle\theta, [T_{0q}^{-1} - ((-T^{-1} + iJ)T_{0p}(-T^{-1} + iJ)) \upharpoonright \mathcal{H}_1]^{-1}\theta\rangle\} \tag{A.15}$$

Here J is an operator such that

$$\int_0^t d\tau\xi\dot\eta = \tfrac{1}{2}\langle\xi + \dot\eta, (P_pJP_q + P_qJP_p)(\xi + \dot\eta)\rangle \tag{A.16}$$

In other words, the last integral depends on an identification between $\mathcal{H}_q$ and $\mathcal{H}_p$, and J expresses this identification in an abstract way.

We denote $JT_{0p}J \upharpoonright \mathcal{H}_1$ by $T_{[p]}$, and Eq. (A.10) implies

$$S_T(\theta) = \exp\{-\tfrac{1}{2}\langle\theta, [T_q^{-1} + T_{[p]} + i(\ldots)]^{-1}\theta\rangle\} \tag{A.17}$$

Now, the proposition in effect asserts the weak convergence (called in Ref. [4] "étroite") of the probability measures over $\mathcal{H}_q$ to the δ-measure at the origin. A criterion for weak convergence can be given with the help of the normal or isotropic integral over $\mathcal{H}_q$ [8], in the following way:

$$I = \lim_{T\to\infty} \int \mathcal{D}(\theta)\exp(-\tfrac{1}{2}\langle\theta,\theta\rangle)\,|S_T(\theta) - 1| = 0 \tag{A.18}$$

One way of estimating this integral depends on the following relation, which is a consequence of convexity and of $|\sin x| \leqslant |x|$:

$$|e^{F_1} - e^{F_2}| \leqslant 2|F_1 - F_2| \max(|e^{F_1}|, |e^{F_2}|) \tag{A.19}$$

In our case $F_2 = 0$, $\max(\ldots) = 1$, and $|F_1|$ may be majorized by dropping the imaginary part in (A.17) (cf. [15], p. 115). The integral can then be evaluated in closed form, following (A.4):

$$I \leqslant \lim_{T\to\infty} \int \mathcal{D}(\theta)\exp(-\tfrac{1}{2}\langle\theta,\theta\rangle)\langle\theta,(T_q^{-1} + T_{[p]})^{-1}\theta\rangle = \lim_{T\to\infty} \mathrm{tr}(T_q^{-1} + T_{[p]})^{-1} \tag{A.20}$$

The last operator is of trace class, since $(\ldots)^{-1} \leqslant T_q$. Moreover, $T \to \infty$ implies $T_{[p]} \to \infty$. It is now easy to show, e.g. with the help of (A.11), that the limit in (A.20) is indeed 0.

(e) PROOF OF PROPOSITION 11

We start with the expression (A.1) for $d\mu_{T,\alpha}$, and it will suffice to consider only $\alpha = 0$, in view of the integrability assumed in the hypothesis. The invariance of $\mathscr{D}$ in (A.1) under translation has the consequence that, whenever the integrand is integrable,

$$\frac{1}{c_T}\int \mathscr{D}(\xi)\left\langle \zeta, \frac{\delta}{\delta\xi}\right\rangle [\exp(-\tfrac{1}{2}\langle\xi, T^{-1}\xi\rangle)\exp(\tfrac{1}{2}i\langle\xi,\xi\rangle)f(\xi)] = I_T^1 + I_T^2 = 0 \qquad \text{(A.21)}$$

Here

$$I_T^1 = \frac{1}{c_T}\int d\mu_{T,0}(\xi)(-\langle T^{-\frac{1}{2}}\zeta, T^{-\frac{1}{2}}\xi\rangle)\exp(\tfrac{1}{2}i\langle\xi,\xi\rangle)f(\xi) \qquad \text{(A.22a)}$$

$$I_T^2 = \frac{1}{c_T}\int d\mu_{T,0}(\xi)\exp(\tfrac{1}{2}i\langle\xi,\xi\rangle)\left[i\langle\zeta,\xi\rangle + \left\langle \zeta, \frac{\delta}{\delta\xi}\right\rangle\right]f(\xi) \qquad \text{(A.22b)}$$

By the assumed integrability, I_T^2 exists for all $T \in \mathscr{T}$ sufficiently large, and $\lim_{T\to\infty} I_T^2$ also exists. We shall show that this limit equals zero by considering a sequence $\{T(n)\}$ of operators in $\mathscr{T}$ such that: (a) $T(n) \to \infty$; (b) $I^1_{T(n)}$ exists for each n sufficiently large; and (c)

$$\lim_{n\to\infty} I^1_{T(n)} = 0 \qquad \text{(A.23)}$$

Let $\{\bar{T}^{[n]}\}$ be any sequence of operators in $\mathscr{T}$ tending to ∞. We use (A.9b), with $\mathscr{H}_2$ the linear span of ζ, and $\mathscr{H}_1 = \mathscr{H}_2^\perp$. The operator $T(n) = 2(\bar{T}^{[n]})_1 + 2(\bar{T}^{[n]})_2$ now satisfies $T(n) \in \mathscr{T}$, $T(n) \geqslant \bar{T}^{[n]}$, and $T(n)^{-1}\zeta = a_n\zeta$. Since $T^{[n]} \to \infty$, one also has $T(n) \to \infty$ and $a_n \downarrow 0$. But

$$I^1_{T(n)} = -a_n\left[\frac{1}{c_{T(n)}}\int d\mu_{T(n),0}(\xi)\langle\zeta,\xi\rangle\exp(\tfrac{1}{2}i\langle\xi,\xi\rangle)f(\xi)\right] \qquad \text{(A.24)}$$

By hypothesis, [. . .] tends to a limit as $n \to \infty$ (*a fortiori,* $I^1_{T(n)}$ exists for all n sufficiently large), hence $I^1_{T(n)} \to 0$, and the proposition follows.

REFERENCES

[1] TARSKI, J., in Functional Integration and its Applications (ARTHURS, A.M., Ed.), Oxford Univ. Press, London (1975) 169.
[2] ITÔ, K., in Proc. 5th Berkeley Symp. on Mathematical Statistics and Probability **II**, Part I, Univ. California Press, Berkeley (1966) 145.
[3] TARSKI, J., Ann. Inst. H. Poincaré **A17** (1972) 313.
[4] BOURBAKI, N., Eléments de mathématique **XXXV**: Intégration, Ch. IX, Hermann, Paris (1969) 39ff.
[5] BUCHHOLZ, D., TARSKI, J., Ann. Inst. H. Poincaré **A24** (1976) 323 (preprint: DESY 74/35).
[6] ALBEVERIO, S., HÖEGH-KROHN, R., two Univ. of Oslo preprints (1974–75).

[7] DeWITT-MORETTE, C., Commun. Math. Phys. **28** (1972) 47; **37** (1974) 63.
[8] GROSS, L., Harmonic Analysis on Hilbert Space, Mem.Am. Math. Soc. No. 46 (1963).
[9] SHALE, D., Trans. Am. Math. Soc. **103** (1962) 149.
[10] DUNFORD, N., SCHWARTZ, J.T., Linear operators Part II, Interscience, New York (1963) 1003 ff.
[11] ERDELYI, A., Asymptotic Expansions § 2.8–2.9, Dover Publications (1956).
[12] MASLOV, V.P., Théorie des perturbations et méthodes asymptotiques Part 2, Ch. 6, Dunod, Paris (1972).
[13] FUCHS, W.H.J., "Asymptotic evaluation of integrals, Wiman-Valiron theory", these Proceedings.
[14] KATZ, A., Classical Mechanics, Quantum Mechanics, Field Theory, Academic Press, New York (1965).
[15] TARSKI, J., Ann. Inst. H. Poincaré **A15** (1971) 107.
[16] GAWĘDZKI, K., Reports on Math. Phys. **6** (1974) 327.

Added in proof: We include three further references that appeared recently. The first is the published form of one of the preprints in Ref. [6], while the other two discuss the asymptotic behaviour of path integrals.

ALBEVERIO, S.A., HØEGH-KROHN, R.J., Mathematical theory of Feynman path integrals, Lecture Notes in Mathematics No. 523, Springer-Verlag, Berlin-Heidelberg-New York (1976).
DeWITT-MORETTE, C., Ann. Phys. (New York) **97** (1976) 367.
TRUMAN, A., J. Math. Phys. **17** (1976) 1852.

COHOMOLOGY OF THE LIE ALGEBRA OF (0,1)-TYPE TANGENT FIELDS ON COMPLEX MANIFOLDS

N. TELEMAN
Istituto Matematico "G. Castelnuovo",
University of Rome,
Rome, Italy

Abstract

COHOMOLOGY OF THE LIE ALGEBRA OF (0,1)-TYPE TANGENT FIELDS ON COMPLEX MANIFOLDS.
One constructs on any analytic manifold an elliptic complex which contains the Dolbeault complex, and determines its cohomology.

1. INTRODUCTION

The well-known theorem of G. de Rham affirms that if M is a paracompact C^∞-manifold, the cohomology of the complex of differential forms over M is $H^*(M,\mathbb{R})$.

On the other hand, Dolbeault's theorem – which affirms that the cohomology of the complex of differential forms of type (0, *) over a complex analytic manifold N is $H^*(N,\mathcal{O})$, $\mathcal{O}$ being the structural sheaf of N – can be considered an analogue in the analytic case of de Rham's theorem.

A de Rham form and a Dolbeault form can be considered as a skew-symmetric differential operator of order zero over $\Lambda^* T(M)$ and $\Lambda^* T^{0,1}(N)$, respectively, T(M) being the real tangent bundle of M and $T^{0,1}(N)$ the antiholomorphic tangent bundle of N with values in the trivial one-dimensional $\mathbb{R}$-, and C-vector bundle over M and N, respectively.

M. Losik [1] considered an extension of the de Rham complex; the enlarged complex of Losik is constituted by all (not only of order zero!) skew-symmetric differential operators over $\Lambda^*T(M)$ with values in the trivial one-dimensional $\mathbb{R}$-vector bundle over M.

Losik proved that the cohomology of his enlarged complex is isomorphic with $H^*(\mathcal{E}, \mathbb{R})$, $\mathcal{E}$ being the principal unitary bundle associated with the complexified tangent bundle of M.

We intend to discuss the cohomology of an enlarged Dolbeault complex (for more details, see Teleman [2]).

2. RESULTS

Let $\mathcal{X}^{(0,1)}(N)$ denote the complex Lie algebra of smooth tangent fields of type (0,1) over the complex manifold N of dimension n, and let $\mathcal{F}^{\mathbb{C}}(N)$ denote the commutative algebra of smooth complex functions over N. Clearly, $\mathcal{F}^{\mathbb{C}}(N)$ is an $\mathcal{X}^{(0,1)}$-module.

Let $C^*(\mathcal{X}^{(0,1)}(N), \mathcal{F}^{\mathbb{C}}(N))$ denote the standard cohomology complex of the Lie algebra $\mathcal{X}^{(0,1)}(N)$ with values in $\mathcal{F}^{\mathbb{C}}(N)$.

Let $(U:z^1,..., z^n)$, $U\subset N$, be a local holomorphic chart in N. An antiholomorphic tangent field over U can be written

$$X = \sum_{i=1}^{n} v_i \cdot \partial/\partial \bar{z}^i, \quad v_i \in \mathcal{F}^{\mathbb{C}}(U)$$

We define the first-order forms ω_A^i over U by

$$\omega_A^i(X) = \partial^{|A|} v_i / \partial \bar{z}^A, \quad A = (a,\dots,a_n), \quad a_i \in N, \quad |A| = \sum a_i$$

The differential of the form ω_A^i is given by

$$d\,\omega_0^i = 0$$

$$d\,\omega_A^i = \sum_{\substack{A_1 + A_2 = A \\ A_2 \neq 0}} C_A^{A_1}\, \omega_{A_1 + I_j}^i \wedge \omega_{A_2}^j \quad \text{for } |A| > 0$$

where $I_j = (0,\dots,\overset{1}{\underset{j}{,}}\dots,0)$, and $C_{A_1}^A$ is a combinatorial symbol.

Let A_∞^* (N) denote the subcomplex of the standard cohomology complex C^* $(\mathscr{X}^{(0,1)}(N), \mathscr{F}^{\mathbb{C}}(N))$ which is constituted by all forms ω which can be described locally as:

$$\omega|_U = \sum \varphi_{i_1,\dots,i_k}^{A_1,\dots,A_k}\, \omega_{A_1}^{i_1} \wedge \dots \wedge \omega_{A_k}^{i_k}$$

Let A_I^*(N) denote the subcomplex in A_∞^* (N) of all forms which have in the upper local description $|A_i| \leqslant 1$, for all $i = 1, \dots, k$.

As in the real case, we have

Theorem A. *The inclusion of the complex* A_I^* (N) *in the complex* A_∞^* (N) *induces isomorphism in cohomology.*

Let $\mathscr{E}(N) \xrightarrow{p} N$ denote the unitary principal bundle associated with the antiholomorphic tangent bundle of N.

Theorem B. *If* N *is a compact analytic manifold, the cohomology of the complex* A_I^*(N) *is isomorphic with* $H^*(\mathscr{E}(N), p^*\mathscr{O})$, *$\mathscr{O}$ being the structural sheaf of* N.

Proof. Let $E \subset T(\mathscr{E}) \otimes C$ denote the complex subbundle of the complexified tangent bundle $T(\mathscr{E}) \otimes \mathbb{C}$ of $\mathscr{E}$ which is filled by these tangent vectors $X \in T(\mathscr{E}) \otimes \mathbb{C}$ which have the property that their projections $p_* X$ belong to $T^{(0,1)}$(N). The bundle E is an involutive subbundle and is right invariant in respect of the action of the structural group on $\mathscr{E}$(N).

Let $B^* = C^\infty(\mathscr{E}(N), \Lambda^* E)$; clearly B^* is a subcomplex of the complexified de Rham complex of $\mathscr{E}$(N).

Let C^* denote the subcomplex in B^* of all right invariant forms.

It can be proved that the complex A_I^*(N) is isomorphic with the complex C^*. On the other hand, it can be proved that the inclusion of C^* in B^* induces isomorphism in cohomology. Hence the cohomology of the complex A_I^*(N) is isomorphic with the cohomology of the complex B^*. Now it is easy to prove that the differential sheaf of germs of forms of B^* is a fine resolution of the sheaf $p^*\mathscr{O}$, which proves the assertion.

REFERENCES

[1] LOSIK, M., On the cohomology of the Lie algebra of tangent fields, Funct. Analiz Priloj **4** 2 (1970) (in Russian).

[2] TELEMAN, N., "Fibre bundles and cohomology of Lie algebras", Proc. Symposia Mathematica **10**, Academic Press, New York (1972) 173–197.

TOPOLOGY OF SOME SPECIAL ALMOST COMPLEX AND COMPLEX MANIFOLDS

G. TSAGAS*
Department of Mathematics,
University of Patras,
Patras, Greece

Abstract

TOPOLOGY OF SOME SPECIAL ALMOST COMPLEX AND COMPLEX MANIFOLDS.

Let M be an almost complex manifold. We assume that M admits a special hermitian metric; this influences the topological structure of M. Contents: introduction; riemannian geometry and topology; holomorphic and Kähler sectional curvatures; pinching for Kähler manifolds; cohomology structure of a pinched Kähler manifold; homotopy structure of a pinched Kähler manifold; the complex projective space theorem; manifolds diffeomorphic to $P^n(\mathbb{C})$; existence of an almost complex structure on a special manifold.

1. INTRODUCTION

Let (M, J) be an almost complex manifold. It is known that this can carry a hermitian metric, provided that M is paracompact.

An almost complex manifold and a complex manifold, with hermitian metric, are called respectively an almost hermitian manifold and a hermitian manifold.

Let M be a hermitian manifold with the property $\nabla_X(J)Y = 0$ where X, Y are any two vector fields on M and ∇ is the riemannian connection defined by the hermitian metric. Then M is called a Kähler manifold and the metric is called Kähler.

We assume that the Kähler metric on M has some properties, then these influence the topological structure of M.

In the final section of this paper, the existence is studied of an almost complex structure on a particular compact orientable four-dimensional manifold.

2. RIEMANNIAN GEOMETRY AND TOPOLOGY

Let (M, g) be a riemannian manifold. If we assume that the metric g is a special one, this gives some restrictions on the topology of M. Some examples are given to clarify these restrictions.

Example 2.1. *Prove that the manifold* $S^1 \times S^k$, $k \geqslant 1$, *cannot carry a riemannian metric with strictly positive sectional curvature.*

Proof. It is known that $\pi_1(S^1 \times S^k) = \pi_1(S^1) \times \pi_1(S^k) = Z \times Z$ if k=1 or $Z \times \{0\}$ if $k \geqslant 2$. The manifold $S^1 \times S^k$ is compact. If this can carry a metric with strictly positive sectional curvature, then its first homotopy group must be finite [21], which is not true. Thus the manifold $S^1 \times S^k$ cannot carry a riemannian metric with strictly positive sectional curvature.

---

* Present address: Department of Mathematics, University of Thessaloniki, Thessaloniki, Greece

Example 2.2. *Let* M_1, M_2 *be two compact riemannian manifolds whose sectional curvature is strictly negative. Then the manifold* $M_1 \times M_2$ *cannot carry a metric with strictly negative sectional curvature.*

Proof. Every element of $\pi_1(M_i)$, i = 1,2, has infinite order and every abelian subgroup of the same groups is cyclic [25]. From these two facts we conclude that the manifold $M_1 \times M_2$ cannot carry a riemannian metric with strictly negative sectional curvature.

Problem 2.3. *Let* S^2 *be a two-dimensional sphere. We do not know if the manifold* $S^2 \times S^2$ *can carry a metric with strictly positive sectional curvature.*

For expositions of riemannian manifolds with positive sectional curvature or negative sectional curvature we refer to Refs [1], [17] and [25].

3. HOLOMORPHIC AND KÄHLER SECTIONAL CURVATURES

Let M be a Kähler manifold. The sectional curvature $\sigma(\lambda)$ of the plane $\lambda \in T_P(M)$ is given by

$$\sigma(\lambda) = -\frac{\langle R(u,v)u,v \rangle}{\|u\|^2 \, \|v\|^2 - \langle u, v \rangle^2} \tag{3.1}$$

where u, v are vectors which span the plane λ. If the plane λ is invariant by J_P, then $\sigma(\lambda)$ is called th holomorphic sectional curvature of the plane λ. If u, v form an orthonormal base for λ, then (3.1) takes the form

$$\sigma(\lambda) = -\langle R(u,v)u, v\rangle \tag{3.2}$$

If λ is invariant by J_P and u is a unit vector in λ, then u, $J_P(u)$ form an orthonormal base of λ and therefore Eq. (3.2) becomes

$$\sigma(\lambda) = \langle R(u, J_P(u))u, J_P(u)\rangle \tag{3.3}$$

If $\sigma(\lambda)$ is constant for all planes λ in $T_P(M)$, which are invariant by J_P, and for all points $P \in M$, then M is called a space of constant holomorphic sectional curvature.

For such a Kähler manifold we have ([17], p. 168)

Theorem 3.1. *Let* M *be a connected Kähler manifold of complex dimension* $n \geqslant 2$. *We assume that the holomorphic sectional curvature* $\sigma(\lambda)$ *(where* λ *is a plane in* $T_P(M)$*) is invariant by* J_P *and depends only on P; then* M *is a space of constant holomorphic sectional curvature.*

If M is a Kähler manifold of constant holomorphic sectional curvature, then its sectional curvature belongs to an interval. This can be expressed by ([11], p. 209)

Theorem 3.2. *The general sectional curvature* $\sigma(\lambda)$ *of a Kähler manifold of constant holomorphic sectional curvature* k *satisfies the inequalities:*

$$0 < \tfrac{1}{4}k \leqslant \sigma(\lambda) \leqslant k \text{ if } k > 0 \tag{3.4}$$

$$k \leqslant \sigma(\lambda) \leqslant \tfrac{1}{4}k < 0 \text{ if } k < 0 \tag{3.5}$$

where the upper limit in (3.4) and lower limit in (3.5) are attained when the plane λ *is invariant by* J_p.

We now give some examples of Kähler manifolds with constant holomorphic sectional curvature.

Example 3.3. *Let* $P^n(\mathbb{C})$ *be the complex projective space. Then there is a Kähler metric on* $P^n(\mathbb{C})$ *such that it becomes a space of constant holomorphic curvature 1.*

Proof. It is known that $P^n(\mathbb{C})$ is defined by identifying pairs of antipodal points of the sphere:

$$S^{2n-1} = \{(z^0, z^1, \dots, z^n) \in \mathbb{C}^{n+1} : \sum_{i=0}^{n} z^i \bar{z}^i = 1\}$$

For any index $j = 0,1,\dots,n$ we obtain an open subspace U_j of $P^n(\mathbb{C})$ defined by $t^j \neq 0$, where $t^0, t^1, \dots, t^n$ are the homogeneous co-ordinates of the points of $P^n(\mathbb{C})$.
We consider the mapping

$$f_j : U_j \to f_j(U_j) \subseteq \mathbb{C}^{n+1}$$

$$f_j : (t^0, t^1, \dots t^n) \to (z_j^0, z_j^1, \dots, \hat{z}_j^j, \dots z_j^n)$$

where $z_i^i = t^i/t^j$, which is a holomorphic mapping. It can be easily seen that (U_j, f_j), $j = 0, 1, \dots, n$, define a complex atlas on $P^n(\mathbb{C})$.
On the open subset U_0 of $P^n(\mathbb{C})$ we define the following metric:

$$ds^2 = 2\,\frac{\sum_{i=0}^{n} |dz_0^i|^2 + \sum_{i=0}^{n} |z_0^i|^2 \sum_{i=0}^{n} |dz_0^i|^2 - \sum_{i=0}^{n} \bar{z}_0^i\, dz_0^i}{1 + \sum_{i=0}^{n} |z_0^i|^2}$$

which can be extended on the whole manifold $P^n(\mathbb{C})$. ds^2 is called a Fubini-study metric, which is a Kähler metric of constant holomorphic sectional curvature 1. Therefore its sectional curvature belongs to the interval $[1/4, 1]$.

Example 3.4. *The complex euclidean* n*-space* $\mathbb{C}^n$ *with the metric*

$$ds^2 = \sum_{\alpha=1}^{n} dz^\alpha\, d\bar{z}^\alpha$$

(where $(z^1, \dots, z^n)$ *is the natural complex co-ordinate system in* $\mathbb{C}^n$*) is a complex flat Kähler manifold.*

Proof. If we make some estimates, we obtain that the holomorphic sectional curvature of ds^2, which is a Kähler metric, is constant and equal to zero. Hence the sectional curvature of ds^2 is zero, which implies that the Kähler manifold $(\mathbb{C}^n, ds^2)$ is flat.

Example 3.5. *Let B_n be the unit open ball of $\mathbb{C}^n$ defined by*

$$B_n = \{(z^1,\ldots,z^n) \in \mathbb{C}^n : \sum_{\alpha=1}^{n} z^\alpha \bar{z}^\alpha < 1\}$$

on which we consider the following metric:

$$ds^2 = -\frac{4(1 - \sum_{\alpha=1}^{n} z^\alpha\bar{z}^\alpha)(\sum_{\alpha=1}^{n} dz^\alpha d\bar{z}^\alpha) - (\sum_{\alpha=1}^{n} z^\alpha d\bar{z}^\alpha)(\sum_{\alpha=1}^{n} z^\alpha d\bar{z}^\alpha)}{(1 + \sum_{\alpha=1}^{n} z^\alpha\bar{z}^\alpha)^2}$$

Then (B_n, ds^2) *is a Kähler manifold with negative constant holomorphic sectional curvature −1.*

Proof. It can be easily seen that $(g_{\alpha\bar{\beta}})$ is given by

$$\tfrac{1}{2}(1 + \sum_{\gamma=1}^{n} z^\gamma\bar{z}^\gamma)g_{\alpha\bar{\beta}} = (1 + \sum_{\gamma=1}^{n} z^\gamma\bar{z}^\gamma) - \bar{z}^\alpha z^\beta \tag{3.6}$$

We differentiate (3.6) with respect to $\partial/\partial z^\gamma$ and $\partial^2/\partial z^\gamma \partial\bar{z}^\delta$ and set $z^1=\ldots=z^n=0$. Then we obtain

$$g_{\alpha\bar{\beta}} = 2\delta_{\alpha\beta} \quad , \quad \frac{\partial g_{\alpha\bar{\beta}}}{\partial z^\gamma} = 0 \tag{3.7}$$

$$\frac{\partial^2 g_{\alpha\bar{\beta}}}{\partial z^\gamma \partial\bar{z}^\delta} = -2(\delta_{\alpha\beta} + \delta_{\gamma\delta} + \delta_{\alpha\delta} + \delta_{\beta\gamma}) \tag{3.8}$$

It can be easily proved by means of (3.7) and (3.8) that the holomorphic sectional curvature of B_n at origin is constant −1. Since we know that B_n admits a transitive group of holomorphic isometric transformations, we may conclude that ds^2 is of constant holomorphic sectional curvature −1 everywhere and is complete. The sectional curvature of (B_n, ds^2) belongs to the interval $[-1, -1/4]$.

Let $T_P(M)$ be the tangent space of a Kähler manifold at its point P. We consider two planes λ and λ' of $T_P(M)$. Let $(u,u') = w(u,u')$ be the angle of a vector u in λ and a vector u' in λ'. The infimum of $w(u,u')$ over u and u' is called the angle between λ and λ' and denoted by $\alpha(\lambda,\lambda')$. If we denote by $\alpha(\lambda)$ the angle between λ and $J_P(\lambda)$, then by analytic geometry we obtain

$$\cos\alpha(\lambda) = |\, g(u, J_P(v))\, |$$

where u, v is an orthonormal basis for λ.

The sectional curvature of a space of constant holomorphic sectional curvature 1 is given by $\frac{1}{4}(1+3\cos^2\alpha(\lambda))$, where $\alpha(\lambda)$ is the angle between λ and $J_P(\lambda)$. Therefore we set

$$\sigma^*(\lambda) = \frac{4\sigma(\lambda)}{1+3\cos^2\alpha(\lambda)}$$

We shall call $\sigma^*(\lambda)$ the Kähler sectional curvature of the plane λ.

4. PINCHING FOR KÄHLER MANIFOLDS

Let (M,g) be a riemannian manifold. We assume that the sectional curvature $\sigma(\lambda)$ of M satisfies the inequalities

$$\delta \leqslant \sigma(\lambda) \leqslant 1 \quad \text{where} \quad 0 < \delta \leqslant 1 \tag{4.1}$$

for every plane $\lambda \in T_P(M)$ and for every $P \in M$; then M is called positively δ-pinched manifold or δ-pinching with $\delta > 0$.

If the sectional curvature $\sigma(\lambda)$ of a riemannian manifold satisfies the inequalities

$$-1 \leqslant \sigma(\lambda) \leqslant -\delta \text{ for } \forall\ \lambda \in T_P(M) \text{ and } \forall\ P \in M \tag{4.2}$$

where $0 < \delta \leqslant 1$, then it is called negatively δ-pinched or δ-pinching with $\delta < 0$.

For a Kähler manifold M we consider three kinds of pinching. We say that M is δ-pinched if it is so as a riemannian.

The Kähler manifold M is called positively δ-Kähler pinched or Kähler pinching $\delta > 0$ if there is a positive number $\delta \leqslant 1$ such that

$$\delta \leqslant \sigma^*(\lambda) \leqslant 1, \forall\ \lambda \in T_P(M), \forall P \in M \tag{4.3}$$

We say that M is positively δ-holomorphically pinched or holomorphic pinching $\delta > 0$, if the following inequalities are satisfied:

$$\delta \leqslant \sigma^*(\lambda) \leqslant 1 \tag{4.4}$$

for all planes $\lambda \in T_P(M)$ which are invariant by J_P and $\forall\ P \in M$.

There are some relations between the three pinchings induced above. We mention only the following [5]:

Proposition 4.1. *If* M *is a positively* δ*-holomorphically pinched Kähler manifold, the sectional curvature* $\sigma(\lambda)$ *satisfies the inequalities*

$$\tfrac{1}{4}(3\delta-2) \leqslant \sigma(\lambda) \leqslant 1, \forall\lambda \in T_P(M), \forall P \in M \tag{4.5}$$

Proof. This is obtained by using the above definitions and Theorem 3.2.

In a similar way we can define negatively δ-Kähler pinched and negatively δ-holomorphically pinched manifolds.

5. COHOMOLOGY STRUCTURE OF A PINCHED KÄHLER MANIFOLD

Let M be a compact Kähler manifold. The existence of the Kähler metric on M has an influence on the cohomology structure of the manifold. This is expressed by the fact that $H^{2k}(M, \mathbb{R})$,

$k = 1, \ldots, [n/2]$, where n=dim M, are not trivial. This has a consequence that some complex manifold cannot carry a Kähler metric.

Example 5.1. *Let* M *be the Hopf manifold. Then* M *cannot carry a Kähler metric.*

Proof. It is known that the Hopf manifold M is diffeomorphic to $S^1 \times S^{2n-1}$. If $n > 1$, then $b_{2k}(S^1 \times S^{2n-1}) = 0$ for $0 < k < n$. Therefore the Hopf manifold cannot carry a Kähler structure.

Let M be any Kähler manifold on which we can define the vector space $\Lambda^{p,q}(M,\mathbb{C})$ of complex differential forms of bi-degree (p,q). Let $H^{p+q}(M,\mathbb{R})$ be the p+q cohomology group of M. Then we define

$$H^{p,q}(M,\mathbb{C}) = \Lambda^{p,q}(M,\mathbb{C}) \cap \{H^{p+q}(M,\mathbb{R}) \otimes C\} \tag{5.1}$$

It is important to study the groups $H^{p,q}(M,\mathbb{C})$ on a Kähler manifold. From Eq. (5.1) we obtain

$$H^{p+q}(M,\mathbb{C}) = H^{p+q}(M,\mathbb{R}) \otimes \mathbb{C} = H^{p+q,0}(M,\mathbb{C}) \oplus H^{p+q-1,1}(M,\mathbb{C}) \oplus \ldots$$
$$\ldots \oplus H^{1,p+q-1}(M,\mathbb{C}) \oplus H^{0,p+q}(M,\mathbb{C}) = \bigoplus_{\substack{r,s=0 \\ r+s=p+q}}^{p+q} H^{r,s}(M,\mathbb{C}) \tag{5.2}$$

Therefore, to obtain information for the group $H^{p+q}(M,\mathbb{C})$ we must know for its subgroups $H^{r,s}(M,\mathbb{C})$ that r+s = p+q; r,s = 0,p+q.

The following theorem is known [28]:

Theorem 5.2. *Let* M *be a compact Kähler manifold with positive definite Ricci tensor. Then on* M *there exists a non-zero holomorphic p-form for* $p \geqslant 1$; *in other words* $H^{p,0}(M,\mathbb{C}) = 0$.

Proof. If $\alpha \in \Lambda'(M,\mathbb{C})$, then we have ([19], p.3):

$$\tfrac{1}{2}\Delta(|\alpha|)^2 = \langle\alpha, \Delta\alpha\rangle - \frac{1}{p!}|\nabla\alpha|^2 + \frac{1}{2(p-1)!}Q_p(\alpha) \tag{5.3}$$

where

$$|\nabla\alpha|^2 = \nabla_i\alpha_{j_1\ldots j_p}\nabla^i\alpha^{j_1\ldots j_p} \tag{5.4}$$

$$Q_p(\alpha) = (p-1)R_{k\ell,mn}\alpha^{k\ell j_3\ldots j_p}\alpha^{mn}{}_{j_3\ldots j_p} - 2R_{k\ell}\alpha^{kj_2\ldots j_p}\alpha^{\ell}_{j_2\ldots j_p} \tag{5.5}$$

The fact that α is a harmonic p-form implies $\Delta\alpha = 0$, and Eq. (5.3) becomes

$$\tfrac{1}{2}\Delta(|\alpha|^2) = -\frac{1}{p!}|\nabla\alpha|^2 + \frac{Q_p(\alpha)}{2(p-1)!} \tag{5.6}$$

Since the manifold M is compact and its metric is Kähler with Ricci tensor positive definite, we obtain

$$\Delta(|\alpha|^2) = k > 0 \quad \text{or} \quad 0 = \int_M \Delta(|\alpha|^2)\,\upsilon = \int_M k\upsilon > 0 \tag{5.7}$$

which implies $\alpha = 0$, where υ is the volume element of M, q.e.d.

Let $K^{p,o}(M,\mathbb{C})$ be the vector space of all holomorphic antisymmetric contravariant tensor fields of type (p,o) on M. By the duality of the metric and the conjugation we obtain the mapping:

$$f : K^{p,o}(M,\mathbb{C}) \to \Lambda^{p,o}(M,\mathbb{C}) \tag{5.8}$$

$$f : T = (T^{j_1 \cdots j_p}) \to f(T) = (f(T^{j_1 \cdots j_p})) = S = (S_{\ell_1 \ldots \ell_p}) \tag{5.9}$$

where

$$S_{\ell_1 \ldots \ell_p} = g_{j_1 \bar{\ell}_1} \cdots g_{j_p \bar{\ell}_p} \overline{T^{j_1 \cdots j_p}}$$

and $(T^{j_1 \cdots i_p})$, $(S_{\ell_1 \ldots \ell_p})$ and $(g_{\alpha\bar{\beta}})$ are the components of the tensor fields T, S and g, respectively, on an open subset U of M with local complex co-ordinate system $(z^1,\ldots,z^n)$.

Theorem 5.3. *Let* M *be a compact Kähler manifold. If the first Chern class* $c_1(M)$ *of M is semi-positive, then* $\dim_{\mathbb{C}} T^{P,o}(M,\mathbb{C}) \geqslant \dim_{\mathbb{C}} H^P(M,\mathbb{C})$.

Proof. Let U be an open subset of the manifold M on which we consider a local complex co-ordinate system $(z^1,\ldots,z^n)$. Let g_U be the restriction of the metric g on U. Therefore g_U can be written $g_U = 2g_{\alpha\bar{\beta}} dz^\alpha dz^{\bar{\beta}}$. The components $\{R_{\alpha\bar{\beta}}\}$ of the Ricci tensor are given by

$$R_{\alpha\bar{\beta}} = - \partial_\alpha \partial_{\bar{\beta}} \log \sqrt{|g_U|} \tag{5.10}$$

where $|g_U|$ is the determinant which is obtained by g_U.

From (5.10) we obtain the closed 2-form τ defined by

$$\tau = (2\pi)^{-1}\, iR_{\alpha\bar{\beta}}\, dz^\alpha \Lambda dz^{\bar{\beta}} \tag{5.11}$$

which defines a global closed 2-form on M. Therefore it represents a cohomology class which is called the first Chern class of M and denoted by $c_1(M)$. We say that $c_1(M) \geqslant 0$ or $c_1(M) \leqslant 0$ if the Ricci tensor of M is semi-positive or semi-negative, respectively. Since $c_1(M)$ is semi-positive we can prove, using formulas similar to (5.3), that the mapping f is surjective, and from this we conclude that $\dim_{\mathbb{C}} T^{p,o}(M,\mathbb{C}) \geqslant \dim_{\mathbb{C}} H^{p,o}(M,\mathbb{C})$, q.e.d.

Theorem 5.4. *Let* M *be a compact Kähler manifold whose first Chern class is semi-negative. Then* $\dim_{\mathbb{C}} H^{p,o}(M,\mathbb{C}) \geqslant \dim_{\mathbb{C}} T^{p,o}(M,\mathbb{C})$.

Proof. We use the same formula (5.3), and from the fact that $c_1(M) \leqslant 0$ we conclude that the mapping f is injective. This proves our assertion, i.e. $\dim_{\mathbb{C}} H^{p,o}(M,\mathbb{C}) \geqslant \dim_{\mathbb{C}} T^{p,o}(M,\mathbb{C})$, q.e.d.

From these two theorems we have

Corollary 5.5 *We consider a compact Kähler manifold* M *whose first Chern class is equal to zero. Then* $\dim_{\mathbb{C}} H^{p,o}(M,\mathbb{C}) = \dim_{\mathbb{C}} T^{p,o}(M,\mathbb{C})$.

Proof. From Theorem 5.3 we have

$$\dim_{\mathbb{C}} T^{p,o}(M,\mathbb{C}) \geqslant \dim_{\mathbb{C}} H^{p,o}(M,\mathbb{C}) \tag{5.12}$$

and from Theorem 5.4 we obtain

$$\dim_{\mathbb{C}} T^{p,o}(M,\mathbb{C}) \leqslant \dim_{\mathbb{C}} H^{p,o}(M,\mathbb{C}) \tag{5.13}$$

The inequalities (5.12) and (5.13) imply $\dim_{\mathbb{C}} H^{p,o}(M,\mathbb{C}) = \dim_{\mathbb{C}} T^{p,o}(M,\mathbb{C})$. The cohomology ring of a special Kähler manifold can be described by

Theorem 5.6. *Let* M *be a compact Kähler manifold with Kähler pinching* $\delta > 0.8$. *Then* $H^*(M, Z_2) \cong H^*(p^n(\mathbb{C}), Z_2)$.

Proof. This was obtained by using a Kähler analogue of Rauch's comparison theorem ([9]).

Theorem 5.7. *Let* M *be a complete Kähler manifold either* δ*-pinched with* $\delta > 0$ *or holomorphicall pinching* $\delta > \frac{1}{2}$. *Then* $\dim H^2(M,\mathbb{R}) = 1$.

Proof. We know that

$$H^2(M,\mathbb{R}) = H^{2,0}(M,\mathbb{R}) \oplus H^{1,1}(M,\mathbb{R}) \oplus H^{0,2}(M,\mathbb{R})$$

It was proved that $\dim H^{2,0}(M,\mathbb{R}) = \dim H^{0,2}(M,\mathbb{R}) = 0$ and $\dim H^{1,1}(M,\mathbb{R}) = 1$, which impli $\dim H^2(M,\mathbb{R}) = 1$ [6], q.e.d.

From Theorem 5.7 we have

Corollary 5.8. *Let* $M = N_1 \times N_2$ *be the topological product of two compact Kähler manifolds. Then the product* M *cannot carry a Kähler metric of positive sectional curvature or holomorphic pinching* $\delta > \frac{1}{2}$.

Proof. For the manifold $M = N_1 \times N_2$ we have

$$b_2(M) = b_2(N_1)b_0(N_2) + b_1(N_1)b_1(N_2) + b_0(N_1)b_2(N_2) > 1 \tag{5.14}$$

Since N_1, N_2 are compact Kähler manifolds, we have $b_2(N_1) \neq 0$ and $b_2(N_2) \neq 0$, which implies (5.14), q.e.d.

6. HOMOTOPY STRUCTURE OF A PINCHED KÄHLER MANIFOLD

Let M be a complex manifold. If M can carry a pinched Kähler metric, this influences the homotopy groups of such a manifold.

Theorem 6.1. *Let* M *be a complete positively* δ*-holomorphically pinched manifold. Then* M *is compact and* $\pi_1(M) = \{0\}$.

Proof. The method is essentially the same as that for the theorem of Myers, as proved in Ref.[26].

Myers' theorem can be improved in the Kähler case as follows [15]:

Theorem 6.2. *We consider a compact Kähler manifold with positive definite Ricci tensor. Then* $\pi_1(M) = \{0\}$.

Proof. We use Myers' theorem [21], the Riemann-Roch theorem of Hirzebruch [13], and the results of Theorem 5.2.

Now we describe the whole homotopy structure of a special pinched Kähler manifold.

Theorem 6.3. *Let* M *be a compact* n*-dimensional Kähler manifold which is positively* δ*-Kähler pinched with* $\delta > 9/16$. *Then* M *has the same homotopy type as the complex projective space* $P^n(\mathbb{C})$.

Proof. This was proved [16] by reducing the problem to the sphere theorem by establishing the following result. If M is a compact Kähler manifold with Kähler-pinching $> \delta$, then there exists a principal circle bundle P over M with riemannian metric whose pinching is greater than $\delta/(4\text{-}3\delta)$.

7. THE COMPLEX PROJECTIVE SPACE THEOREM

The following problem, in the general case, is open. Let M be a compact Kähler manifold whose sectional curvature is positive. Determine the conditions for M to be holomorphically homeomorphic to $P^n(\mathbb{C})$. Theorems 5.6 and 6.3 offer one way to attack the problem.

This problem has been solved in the following cases [10, 18]:

Theorem 7.1. *Let* M *be an* n*-dimensional compact Kähler manifold* n = 2,3, *with positive sectional curvature. Then* M *is holomorphically homeomorphic to the complex projective space* $P^n(\mathbb{C})$, n = 2,3.

Proof. If n = 2, it is obtained because the classification of algebraic surfaces is known. If n = 3, the technique is described in Ref. [18].

We also have

Theorem 7.2. *We consider a compact Kähler manifold* M *with constant scalar curvature and positive sectional curvature. Then* M *is holomorphically isometric to* $P^n(\mathbb{C})$ *with the canonical metric, where* n = dim M.

Proof. If M is a compact Kähler manifold with constant scalar curvature, then the so-called Ricci form is harmonic. From Theorem 5.7 we obtain that a compact Kähler manifold with constant scalar curvature and positive sectional curvature is an Einstein manifold. These two facts imply the proof of the theorem [23], q.e.d.

Another theorem for the problem is

Theorem 7.3. *Let* M *be an* n*-dimensional compact Kähler manifold with constant scalar curvature and holomorphic pinching* $> 1/2$. *Then* M *is holomorphically isometric to* $P^n(\mathbb{C})$ *with the canonical metric.*

Proof. This is obtained by analysing better the proof of Theorem 7.2. [7], q.e.d.

Theorem 7.4. *Let* g *be a Kähler metric on* $P^n(\mathbb{C})$ *compatible with the standard complex structure. We assume that the distance to the first conjugate point in each direction from each point on* $P^n(\mathbb{C})$ *is* $(1/2)\pi$. *Then, at least if* g *is sufficiently near the canonical metric* g_0 *in the* C^0 *topology,* $(P^n(\mathbb{C}), g)$ *is isometric to* $(P^n(\mathbb{C}), g_0)$.

Proof. This is proved by the study of the volume of C_L-manifolds [27]. A riemannian manifold (M, g) is called a C_L-manifold if all geodesics on M are closed and have length $2\pi L$. $(P^n(\mathbb{C}), g_0)$ is a C_L-manifold. q.e.d.

8. MANIFOLDS DIFFEOMORPHIC TO $P^n(\mathbb{C})$

It is known that on a given topological manifold there is generally more than one differentiable structure [25].

Let $(P^n(\mathbb{C}), g_0)$ be the complex projective space with the standard Fubini-study metric g_0, whose holomorphic sectional curvature is const 1. We now consider another riemannian manifold (M, g), where M is compact and simply connected. The problem arises: how close must the riemannian metric g be to g_0 such that the manifold M is diffeomorphic to $P^n(\mathbb{C})$?

First we describe some properties of the complex projective space $(P^n(\mathbb{C}), g_0)$. Let C(P) be the cut locus of any point P of $P^n(\mathbb{C})$. Then the distance between P and any point in C(P) is constant. Every closed geodesic on $(P^n(\mathbb{C}), g_0)$ is simply closed and has the same length and the same index 1. Moreover, for every point P on $(P^n\mathbb{C}), g_0)$ the cut locus coincides with the first conjugate locus. Therefore C(P) is a compact submanifold of $P^n(\mathbb{C})$ of dimension 2(n-1).

We assume that the riemannian manifold (M, g) has all the properties that are described above for $(P^n(\mathbb{C}), g_0)$. Let L(P, x) be a subset of M defined as follows:

$$L(P,x) = \{y \in M: d(P,y) + d(y,x) = d(P,x),\ x \in C(P)\}$$

where d denotes the distance function on M. Let $T_L(P,x)$ be the tangent bundle of the submanifolc L(P, x) of M.

We consider the sets A_1, A_2 defined by

$$A_1 = \{\text{plane section } (X,Y): X, Y \in TL(P,x),\ \forall P \in M,\ \forall x \in (P)\}$$

$$A_2 = \{\text{plane section } (X,Y): X \in TL(P,x),\ Y \in NL(P,x),\ \forall P \in M,\ \forall x \in (P)\}$$

where NL(P, x) is the normal bundle on L(P, x).

The theorem for such a manifold can be stated as follows.

Theorem 8.1. *Let* M *be a compact simply connected riemannian manifold. We assume:*
(i) For every $P \in M$, *there exists* $\ell(P) \in \mathbb{R}$ *such that* $d(P,x) = \ell(P)$ *for all* $x \in C(P)$.
(ii) The index for any geodesic loop is equal to 1. Then there exist sequences

$$\{\delta_i\},\ \{k_i\},\ \delta_1 \leqslant \delta_2 \leqslant \ldots \leqslant \delta_m \leqslant, \ldots, k_1 \leqslant k_2 \leqslant \ldots \leqslant k_m \leqslant \ldots$$

such that

(iii) $$\delta = \frac{\operatorname{Min}\{\sigma(\lambda) : \lambda \in A_1\}}{\operatorname{Max}\{\sigma(\lambda) : \lambda \in A_2\}} > \delta_m$$

(iv) $$k = \frac{\operatorname{Min}\{\sigma(\lambda) : \lambda \in A_2\}}{\operatorname{Max}\{\sigma(\lambda) : \lambda \in A_2\}} > k_m$$

then these imply M *diffeomorphic to* $P^n(\mathbb{C})$ [23] .

Proof. First of all it has been proved [22] that the cut locus $C(P)$ is diffeomorphic to $P^{n-1}(\mathbb{C})$. For this reason we introduce a differentiable S^1 action on S^{2n-1} as follows:

$$\Psi : S^{2n-1} \times S^1 \to S^{2n-1}, \qquad \Psi : (u, s) \to \Psi(u, s) = us$$

$$\Psi(u, 1) = u \text{ for } 1 \in S^1 (\text{identity element of } S^1)$$

$$\Psi(\Psi(u,s), t) = \Psi(u, st) \text{ for } s, t \in S^1, u \in S^{2n-1}$$

Therefore from this action we obtain a fibre bundle

$$S^1 \to S^{2n-1} \to S^{2n-1} / \Psi = P^{n-1}(\mathbb{C})$$

which is Hopf fibration.

Let $T_P(M)$ be the tangent space of M at P. Hence $T_P(M)$ can be regarded as $\mathbb{C}^n$ on which we obtain the hypersurface $S^{2n-1} = S_P(1)$. We consider the differentiable S^1 action on S^{2n-1} from which we obtain the complex projective space $P^{n-1}(C)$, which is mapped under the exponential mapping onto $C(P)$. Therefore $C(P)$ is diffeomorphic to $P^{n-1}(\mathbb{C})$.

From the above and the given conditions of pinching we construct a diffeomorphism of M onto the complex projective space $P^n(\mathbb{C})$.

9. EXISTENCE OF AN ALMOST COMPLEX STRUCTURE ON A SPECIAL MANIFOLD

Let M be a compact orientable four-dimensional manifold. The following theorem gives a condition for the existence of an almost complex structure on M [12].

Theorem 9.1. *We consider a compact orientable four-dimensional manifold* M. *This admits an almost complex structure if there exists a closed 2-form* γ *on* M *such that*

$$\int_M \gamma^2 = 2X(M) + 3 \text{ sign } (M) \tag{9.1}$$

Now we assume that the manifold M can carry a riemannian metric which is positively δ-pinched with $\delta > 4/19$. Then we have [24]

Theorem 9.2. *Let* M *be a compact four-dimensional riemannian manifold which is positively* δ*-pinched* $\delta > 19$. *Then for every element* $\alpha \in H^2(M, \mathbb{R})$ *different from zero we have* $\int_M \alpha^2 \neq 0$.

Combining both theorems, we obtain

Theorem 9.3. *We consider a compact orientable four-dimensional riemannian manifold* δ*-pinched with* $\delta > 4/19$. *We assume that* $2X(M) + 3 \text{ sign } (M) = k \neq 0$. *If* $H^2(M, \mathbb{R}) \neq \{0\}$, *then* M *can carry an almost complex structure.*

Proof. We choose a harmonic 2-form $\alpha \neq 0$ such that

$$\int_M \alpha^2 = \lambda, \quad k\lambda > 0$$

Now, if we take $\gamma = (\sqrt{k\lambda}/\lambda)/\alpha$, we have

$$\int_M \gamma^2 = \int_M \frac{k}{\lambda}\alpha^2 = k = 2X(M) + 3 \text{ sign } (M)$$

Hence M admits an almost complex structure, q.e.d.

A consequence of the above are the two following corollaries.

Corollary 9.4. *Let* M *be a compact orientable four-dimensional manifold which is a boundary of another manifold. We assume that* $H^2(M, \mathbb{R}) \neq \{0\}$ *and* M *admits a riemannian metric whose sectional curvature is* δ*-pinched with* $\delta > 4/19$, *then there exists an almost complex structure on* M.

Proof. Since M is the boundary of another manifold,we have

$$3 \text{ sign } (M) = \int_M P_1 = 0$$

where P_1 is the highest Pontrjagin class of M. We also know that for such a manifold $X(M) = k > 0$ is valid [8]. Let α be a harmonic 2-form on M different from zero. Therefore we obtain

$$\int_M \alpha^2 \Lambda \alpha^2 = \int_M \alpha^2 = \lambda > 0$$

If we take $\gamma = (\sqrt{2k}/\sqrt{\lambda})\,\alpha$, the condition of Theorem 9.1 is satisfied. Hence M admits an almost complex structure.

Corollary 9.5. *Let* M *be a compact orientable four-dimensional positively* δ*-pinched riemannian manifold with* $\delta > 4/19$. *If* $\dim H^2(M, \mathbb{R}) > 1$, *then the riemannian metric* g *on* M *is not Kähler.*

Proof. The manifold M always admits an almost complex structure, because if $2X(M) + 3 \text{ sign } (M)$ we choose $\gamma = 0$ or if $2X(M) + 3 \text{ sign } (M) \neq 0$, then if follows from Theorem 9.3. If we assume that the almost complex structure is integrable and the metric g is hermitian, then it is not Kähler, and this follows from Theorem 5.7.

REFERENCES

[1] BERGER, M., Pincement riemannien et pincement holomorphique, Ann. Sc. Norm. Super. Pisa, Sci. Fis. Mat **14** (1960) 151–159.

[2] BERGER, M., Sur les variétés d'Einstein compactes, C.R. IIIe Réunion Math. Expression Latine, Namur (1965) 35–55.

[3] BERGER, M., Sur certaines variétés Kähleriennes à géodésiques toutes fermées, J. Diff. Geom. **9** (1974) 519–

[4] BISHOP, R., GOLDBERG, S., On the topology of positively curved manifolds, Tohoku Math. J. **15** (1963) 359–364.

[5] BISHOP, R., GOLDBERG, S., Some applications of the general Gauss-Bonnet theorem, Trans. Am. Math. Soc. **112** (1964) 508–535.

[6] BISHOP, R., GOLDBERG, S., On the 2nd cohomology group of a Kähler manifold with positive curvature, Proc. Am. Math. Soc. **16** (1965) 119–122.

[7] BISHOP, R., GOLDBERG, S., On the topology of positively curved Känler manifolds **2**, Tohoku Math. J. **17** (1965) 310–318.

[8] CHERN, S., On the curvature and characteristic classes of a Riemannian manifold, Abh. Math. Sem. Univ. Hamburg **20** (1955) 117–126.

[9] DOCARMO, M., The cohomology ring of certain Kählerian manifolds, Ann. Math. **81** (1965) 1–14.

[10] FRANKEL, T., Manifolds with positive curvature, Pac. J. Math. **11** (1961) 165–174.

[11] GOLDBERG, S., Curvature and Homology, Academic Press, New York (1962).

[12] HIRZEBRUCH, F., HOPF, H., Felder und Flächenelement in 4-dimensionalen Mannigfältigkeiten, Math. Ann. **136** (1958) 156–172.

[13] HIRZEBRUCH, F., Topological Methods in Algebraic Geometry, Springer-Verlag, New York (1966).

[14] KLINGENBERG, W., Manifolds with restricted conjugate locus, Ann. Math. **78** (1963) 527–547.

[15] KOBAYASHI, S., On compact Kähler manifolds with positive Ricci tensor, Ann. Math. **74** (1961) 570–574.

[16] KOBAYASHI, S., Topology of positively pinched Kähler manifolds, Tohoku Math. J. **15** (1963) 121–139.

[17] KOBAYASHI, S., NOMIZU, K., Foundations of Differential Geometry **2**, Interscience New York (1969).

[18] KOBAYASHI, S., OCHIAI, T., Three-dimensional Kähler manifolds with positive holomorphic bisectional curvature, Jap. J. Math. **24** (1972) 465–480.

[19] LICHNEROWITZ, A., Géométrie des groupes de transformations, Dunod, Paris (1958).

[20] LICHNEROWITZ, A., Variétes Kähleriennes à première classe de Chern, J. Diff. Geom. **1** (1967) 195–224.

[21] MYERS, S., Riemannian manifolds in the large, Duke Math. J. **1** (1935) 39–49.

[22] NIGAKAWA, H., SHIOHAMA, K., Geodesic and curvature structure characterizing projective spaces, Diff. Geom. in honour of K. Yano, Tokyo (1972).

[23] SHIOHAMA, K., Riemannian manifolds diffeomorphic to complex projective spaces, Math. Ann. **205** (1973) 55–88.

[24] TSAGAS, G., On the cohomology ring of a pinched Riemannian manifold, Math. Ann. **185** (1970) 55–88.

[25] TSAGAS, G., "Riemannian pinched manifolds", Global Analysis and its Applications (Proc. Int. Course Trieste, 1972) **3**, IAEA, Vienna (1974) 217.

[26] TSUKAMOTO, Y., On the Kählerian manifolds with positive holomorphic sectional curvature, Jap. Acad. **33** (1957) 333–335.

[27] WEINSTEIN, A., On the volume of manifolds all of whose geodesics are closed, J. Differ. Geom. **9** (1974) 513–517.

[28] YANO, K., BOCHNER, S., Curvature and Betti Numbers, Ann. Math. Studies No. 32, Princeton Univ. Press (1953).

ALMOST COMPLEX AND COMPLEX STRUCTURES ON s-MANIFOLDS

G. TSAGAS*
Department of Mathematics,
University of Patras,
Patras, Greece

Abstract

ALMOST COMPLEX AND COMPLEX STRUCTURES ON s-MANIFOLDS.

Let M be a riemannian s-manifold. This paper studies the existence of an almost complex and a complex structure on the manifold M which is compatible with the riemannian s-structure. Contents: s-structures; affine s-structures; riemannian s-structures; integrable almost complex structures on an RR s-manifold; Kähler and nearly Kähler RR s-manifolds.

1. s-STRUCTURES

Let M be a connected differentiable manifold of dimension n. An s-structure on the manifold M is a family $\{s_x : x \in M\}$ of transformations on M such that to each point $x \in M$ corresponds a transformation s_x of this family having x as an isolated fixed point. This can also be expressed as s_x having x as a fixed point and that the differential $(ds_x)_x$, which is a linear transformation on $T_x(M)$, does not have eigenvalue 1.

Theorem 1.1. *Let* M *be a connected differentiable n-dimensional manifold. Then* M *always has an s-structure.*

Proof. Let x be a point of the manifold. Then we can choose a chart (U,φ) on M such that U is an open neighbourhood of x and $\varphi(x) = 0 \in \mathbb{R}^n$, where $0 = (0, ..., 0)$ is the origin of $\mathbb{R}^n$. We can construct a map f of $\mathbb{R}^n$ into $\mathbb{R}^n$ with the two following properties: (i) f has 0 as an isolated fixed point; and (ii) outside the open subset V of $\varphi(U)$ is the identity map on $\mathbb{R}^n$. Therefore the mapping

$$\varphi^{-1} \circ f : \varphi^{-1}(V) \to \varphi^{-1}(V)$$

has x as an isolated fixed point and outside $\varphi^{-1}(V)$ is the identity map on the neighbourhood U. Therefore we can extend $\varphi^{-1} \circ f$ on the whole manifold, which gives a diffeomorphism s_x on M having x as an isolated fixed point.

The following proposition gives a method of construction of the mapping f.

Proposition 1.2. *There exists a mapping* Ψ *of* $\mathbb{R}$ *onto* $\mathbb{R}$ *which has the point* $P(\beta\sqrt{2}/2)$, $\beta > 0$, *as an isolated fixed point and outside an interval containing* P *is the identity map on* $\mathbb{R}$.

Proof. We consider two positive numbers $0 < \alpha < \beta$ and construct the following function:

$$\lambda : \mathbb{R} \to \mathbb{R}, \lambda : x \to \lambda(x) : \begin{cases} \exp\left(\dfrac{1}{x-\beta} - \dfrac{1}{x-\alpha}\right) & \text{if } \alpha < x < \beta \\ 0 & \text{otherwise} \end{cases}$$

* Present address: Department of Mathematics, University of Thessaloniki, Thessaloniki, Greece.

which is differentiable, and the same holds for the function Λ defined by

$$\Lambda : \mathbb{R} \to \mathbb{R},\ \Lambda : x \to \Lambda(x) = \frac{\int_x^\beta \lambda(t)\,dt}{\int_\alpha^\beta \lambda(t)\,dt}$$

which has value 1 for $x \leqslant \alpha$ and 0 for $x \geqslant \beta$. The graph c of the function Λ is given by Fig. 1.

We consider the reflection of that part of the curve c up to the point β with respect to the straight line 1 and so obtain another curve c_1, shown in Fig. 2. We can also construct a function $\Lambda_2 : \mathbb{R} \to \mathbb{R}$ whose graph (see Fig. 3) is given by the curve c_2, which is c^∞. Finally we consider the function $\Psi : \mathbb{R} \to \mathbb{R}$ whose graph c_3 is defined as shown in Fig. 4. This proves the proposition, q.e.

Let M be a connected differentiable manifold on which we consider an s-structure $\{s_x : x \in M\}$ This s-structure determines a tensor field S of type (1,1) defined by the relation $S_x = (ds_x)_x$ $\forall x \in M$ which is called a symmetry tensor field. If S is differentiable $\{s_x : x \in M\}$ is called differentiable. We assume that the s-structure $\{s_x : x \in M\}$ has the property that s_x^k = identity, where k is a positive integer and for every $x \in M$ $\{s_x : x \in M\}$ is called an s-structure of order k. If the s-structure $\{s_x : x \in M\}$ on M is differentiable and simultaneously we have $(ds_x)(SX) = S(ds_x)X$ $\forall x \in M$ and for every vector field X on M, $\{s_x : x \in M\}$ is called a regular s-structure.

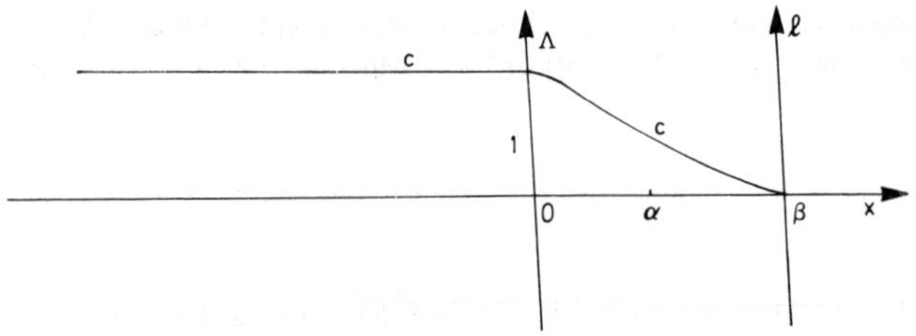

FIG.1. Curve c of the function Λ.

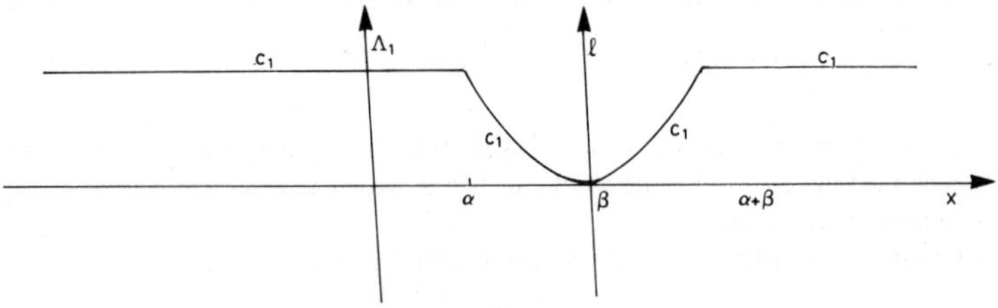

FIG.2. Curve c_1 of the function Λ.

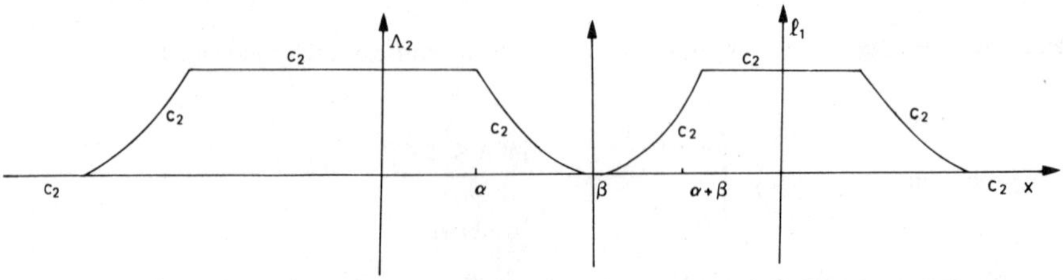

FIG.3. Function $\Lambda_2 : \mathbb{R} \to \mathbb{R}$, whose graph is given by the curve c_2.

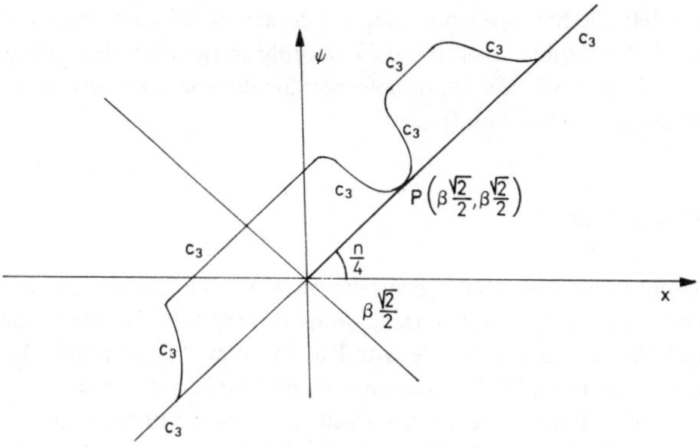

FIG.4. Function $\Psi : \mathbb{R} \to \mathbb{R}$*, whose graph is* c_3*.*

Let M be a connected differentiable manifold. On this manifold we consider a special structure which must be one of the following: an almost complex structure; a complex structure; an affine connection; or a riemannian metric. What are the conditions under which the given structure on M is compatible with an s-structure on the manifold M? In other words, is there an s-structure on the manifold which preserves the given structure on M?

Let J be an almost complex structure on a connected manifold M.

A diffeomorphism f of M onto itself which preserves the almost complex structure, i.e.

$$f : M \to M,\ \ f : P \to f(P),\ \ (f_{*P}) \circ J_P = J_{f(P)} \circ (f_*)_P \ \ \forall P \in M$$

is called an almost complex diffeomorphism. If on the manifold M there exists an s-structure $\{s_x : x \in M\}$ such that each symmetry s_x is an almost complex diffeomorphism, then $\{s_x : x \in M\}$ is called an almost complex s-structure. If the s-structure on M is differentiable or regular and is compatible with the almost complex structure it is called a differentiable or regular almost complex s-structure on M.

Example 1.3. *Let* S^6 *be the six-dimensional sphere provided with the standard almost complex structure. Then there exists an almost complex s-structure on* S^6.

Proof. The standard almost complex structure on S^6 can be constructed by means of the Cayley numbers. Let P be any point of S^6; then the rotation of S^6 round the point P is an angle $2\pi/k$, where k, a positive integer, gives a diffeomorphism s_P, which has P as an isolated fixed point and s_P^k = identity. It can be easily seen that if J is the almost complex structure on S^6, then we have $J_P \circ (s_P)_* = (s_P)_* \circ J_P$. Therefore we obtain on S^6 a regular almost complex s-structure of order k, q.e.d.

Let M be a complex manifold. We assume that for every point $P \in M$ there exists a holomorphic diffeomorphism s_P such that s_P has the point P as an isolated fixed point. The family $\{s_P : P \in M\}$ is called a holomorphic s-structure on M. If this s-structure on M is differentiable or regular, it is called a differentiable or regular holomorphic s-structure.

Example 1.4. *Let* D *be any bounded homogeneous domain in* $\mathbb{C}^3$. *Then* D *admits a regular holomorphic s-structure of order 2.*

Proof. It is known that any homogeneous bounded domain in $\mathbb{C}^3$ is symmetric [1], i.e. at each point $P \in D$ there exists a holomorphic involutive diffeomorphism s_P having P an isolated fixed point. Hence we obtain the family $\{s_P : P \in D\}$ of holomorphic diffeomorphisms on D which gives a regular holomorphic s-structure of order 2 on D.

2. AFFINE s-STRUCTURES

Let M be a connected differentiable manifold on which we consider an affine connection ∇. We assume that there is a family of affine transformations $\{s_P : P \in M\}$ on M such that for every $P \in M$ we have the affine transformation s_P with P as an isolated fixed point. The family $\{s_P : P \in M\}$ is called an affine s-structure on M. We also have the notions of a differentiable affine s-structure and regular affine s-structure. The manifold (M, ∇) with an affine s-structure $\{s_P : P \in M\}$ is called an affine s-manifold and is denoted by (M, ∇, s). If $\{s_P : P \in M\}$ is regular, then (M, ∇, s) is called an affine regular s-manifold or, briefly, AR s-manifold.

Example 2.1. *We consider a subset* H *of* G = SO(3) *defined as follows:*

$$H = \left\{ \alpha = \begin{pmatrix} 1 & b & c \\ c & a & -b \\ -b & -c & a \end{pmatrix} \in SO(3) \right\}$$

Then the manifold $M = SO(5)/H \times SO(2)$ *with the canonical connection is an AR s-manifold of order 3.*

Proof. It can be easily seen that H is a closed subgroup of SO(3). $H \times SO(2)$ can be embedded in SO(5) as follows:

$$(A,B) \rightarrow \begin{pmatrix} A & 0 \\ 0 & B \end{pmatrix}, \quad A \in H, \ B \in SO(2)$$

Now we define the map $s : SO(5) \rightarrow GL(5,\mathbb{R})$ as follows:

$$s : M \rightarrow s(M) = TMT^{-1}$$

where T is defined by

$$T = \begin{pmatrix} \begin{matrix} 0 & 1 & 0 \\ 0 & 0 & -1 \\ 1 & 0 & 0 \end{matrix} & 0 \\ 0 & I_2 \end{pmatrix}$$

The fixed point set of s is $H \times SO(2)$ and we have s^3 = identity, and s is an affine transformation with respect to the canonical connection on the homogeneous space $M = SO(5)/H \times SO(2)$.

Theorem 2.2. *Let* (M, ∇, s) *be an affine s-manifold whose s-structure is differentiable. Then the group of affine transformations* A(M) *acts transitively on* M *and hence* $M = A(M)/H$ *where* H *is the isotropy group of* A(M) *at one point of* M.

Proof. The differentiability of the symmetry tensor field S implies that the mapping $s : M \to A(M)$, $s : P \to sp$ is differentiable. Therefore (from [5]) the theorem follows.

3. RIEMANNIAN s-STRUCTURES

Let (M,d) be a connected riemannian manifold whose riemannian metric is d. We assume that on M there exists an s-structure $\{s_x : x \in M\}$ such that s_x is an isometry $\forall x \in M$. The s-structure $\{s_x : x \in M\}$ is called riemannian and M with $\{s_x : x \in M\}$ is called a riemannian s-manifold and is denoted by (M,d,s). If the riemannian s-structure $\{s_x : x \in M\}$ on (M,d,s) is regular, then (M,d,s) is called a riemannian regular s-manifold or, briefly, RR s-manifold.

If each s_x of the riemannian s-structure $\{s_x : x \in M\}$ on (M,d,s) has finite order, i.e. s_x^k = identity, $\forall x \in M$, the riemannian s-manifold is called a k-symmetric space. If k = 2, we have the usual riemannian symmetric spaces whose symmetry tensor field is −I, where I is the Kronecker tensor field.

For the riemannian s-manifold we have [5]

Theorem 3.1. *Let* (M,d,s) *be a riemannian s-manifold. The group of isometries* I(M) *acts transitively on* M *and hence* M *is a homogeneous space* M = I(M)/H, *where* H *is the isotropy group of* I(M) *at one point of* M.

Proof. We prove that for each $P \in M$ the I(M)-orbit of P contains a neighbourhood at the point P. This proves the theorem.

For such manifolds we also have

Theorem 3.2. *Let* (M,d,s) *be a riemannian s-manifold. There always exists another s-structure on* M *such that* (M,d,s) *becomes a riemannian k-symmetric space.*

The study of riemannian s-manifolds is therefore reduced to the study of the same manifolds of finite order.

We assume that (M,d,s) is an RR s-manifold of finite order k. Hence the symmetry tensor field satisfies the equation $S^k = I$, which implies that the eigenvalues of S are the kth roots of the unit. From the continuity of S we obtain that each of these eigenvalues must be constant over M. Since M is real, the eigenvalues of S appear as pairs of conjugates except for the eigenvalue −1, if it exists. Therefore for every point $P \in M$ the tangent space $T_P(M)$ splits as follows:

$$T_P(M) = T_P^{-1}(M) \oplus T_P^1(M) \oplus \ldots \oplus T_P^r(M) \qquad (3.1)$$

where $T_P^{-1}(M)$ is the eigenspace corresponding to the eigenvalue −1 and $T_P^i(M)$, $1 \leqslant i \leqslant r$, are the eigenspaces corresponding to the eigenvalues $\cos\varphi_i + \sqrt{-1}\,\sin\varphi_i$. Hence we obtain mutually orthogonal differentiable distributions K_{-1}, K_i, $1 \leqslant i \leqslant r$, on M. From the decomposition (3.1) we have a decomposition of the tensor field S as follows:

$$S = S_{-1} \oplus S_1 \oplus \ldots \oplus S_r \qquad (3.2)$$

where each factor acts on the corresponding space in (3.1).

On each subspace $T_P^i(M)$, $1 \leqslant i \leqslant r$, of $T_P(M)$ we put

$$J_i = \frac{S_i - I\cos\varphi_i}{\sin\varphi_i} \qquad (3.3)$$

which is well defined for each i since $\sin\varphi_i \neq 0$. Thus we take a tensor field J of type (1,1) on M defined by

$$J = J_{-1} \oplus J_1 \oplus \ldots \oplus J_r \tag{3.4}$$

where J_{-1} is the zero tensor on $T_p^{-1}(M)$. Obviously J satisfies the equation $J^3 + J = 0$ and has rank equal to $\dim K_1 + \ldots + \dim K_r$.

If we assume that S does not have eigenvalue −1, then $K_{-1} = 0$ and J defines an almost complex structure on M which in addition is orthogonal with respect to the riemannian metric d and hence d is hermitian with respect to the J.

From this we obtain

Theorem 3.3. *Let* (M,d,s) *be an RR s-manifold of order* k, *whose symmetry tensor field* S *does not have eigenvalue* −1. *Then* M *is an almost hermitian manifold.*

A consequence of this theorem is

Corollary 3.4. *Let* (M,d,s) *be an RR s-manifold of odd order. Then* M *is an almost hermitian manifold.*

Proof. Since k is odd, it implies that the symmetry tensor field S does not have eigenvalue −1 and therefore M is an almost hermitian manifold.

4. INTEGRABLE ALMOST COMPLEX STRUCTURE ON AN RR s-MANIFOLD

Let (M,d,s) be an RR s-manifold of order k. We assume that S does not have eigenvalue −1 and hence M is an almost complex manifold.

Theorem 4.1. *We consider an RR s-manifold* (M,d,s) *whose symmetry tensor field* S *does not have eigenvalue* −1. *Then the almost complex structure* J *on* M = G/H *is G-invariant.*

Proof. The RR s-manifold (M,d,s) is a homogeneous space M = G/H and therefore we obtain g = h + m, where g and h are the Lie algebras of G and H, respectively, and m can be identified with the tangent space of M at its origin 0 under the restriction of the mapping

$$\pi_* : g = h + m \to T_0(M)$$

in the subspace m and π is the projection map of G into M = G/H. From J we obtain a complex structure J_0 on m. The almost complex structure J is G-invariant, if J_0 commutes with the linear isotropy representation λ of H. If $\alpha \in H$, then $\lambda(\alpha) = \alpha_*$ where α_* denotes the differential of α at 0. But we have $J_0 = (S_0 - \cos\varphi I)/\sin\varphi$ and since we have $S_0\alpha_* = \alpha_* S_0$ we obtain $\alpha_* J_0 = J_0 \alpha_*$ $\forall \alpha \in H$, q.e.d.

The linear endomorphism J_0 on $T_0(M)$ can be extended to another linear endomorphism J_0 on g by setting $J_0 X = 0$ for $\forall X \in h$, which satisfies the relations:

(i) $J_0 X = 0$, $\forall X \in h$
(ii) $J_0^2 X = -X$, mod(h) for $X \in g$
(iii) $J_0(\mathrm{ad}(\alpha)X) = \mathrm{ad}(\alpha) J_0 X$, mod(h) for $\alpha \in H$ and $X \in g$
(iv) $J_0[X,Y] = [Y, J_0 X]$, mod(h) for $X \in g$ and $Y \in h$

where ad(α) denotes the adjoint action of α on g which is related to λ(α) by the formula:

$$\lambda(\alpha)X = (\mathrm{ad}(\alpha)X)m \quad \text{for } \alpha \in H \text{ and } X \in m$$

Theorem 4.2. *We consider an RR s-manifold* (M = G/H, d,s) *whose symmetry tensor field* S *does not have eigenvalue* −1. *Then* M *is a hermitian manifold if and only if* S *satisfies the relation*

$$[SX,SY] - [X,Y] - S[X,SY] - S[SX,Y] + 2\cos\varphi S[X,Y] \in h \tag{4.1}$$

for all X,Y ∈ g, *where* g *and* h *are the Lie algebras of* G *and* H, *respectively, and* φ *is one of the angles which determine the eigenvalues of* S.

Proof. The manifold M = G/H has an almost complex structure J which is invariant by G. This determines a complex structure J_0 on m; J_0 can be extended to a linear endomorphism $\tilde{J}_0$ on g with the above properties. The G-invariant, almost complex, structure J on M = G/H is integrable if and only if J_0 satisfies ([4], p. 217)

$$[\tilde{J}_0 X, \tilde{J}_0 Y] - [X,Y] - \tilde{J}_0[X, \tilde{J}_0 Y] - \tilde{J}_0[\tilde{J}_0 X, Y] \in h \tag{4.2}$$

for all X,Y ∈ g. For the linear endomorphism J_0 we have

$$\tilde{J}_0 : g \to g, \quad \tilde{J}_{0/m} = J_0 = \frac{S_0 - \cos\varphi I}{\sin\varphi} : m \to m, \quad \tilde{J}_{0/h} : h \to 0$$

Hence when we apply $\tilde{J}_0$ on g the essential part of it is J_0. In this context, (4.2) takes the form

$$\frac{1}{\sin^2\varphi}[(S-\cos\varphi)X, (S-\cos\varphi I)Y] - [X,Y] - \frac{1}{\sin^2\varphi}(S-\cos\varphi I)\,[X,(S-\cos\varphi I)Y]$$

$$-\frac{1}{\sin^2\varphi}(S-\cos\varphi I)\,[(S-\cos\varphi I)X,Y] \in h$$

and after some estimates it implies (4.1), q.e.d.

Let M = G/H be an RR s-manifold whose symmetry tensor field S gives an almost complex structure J. The torsion field N of J, which is of type (1,2), is given by

$$N(X,Y) = 2\{[JX,JY] - [X,Y] - J[X,JY] - J[JX,Y]\} \qquad X,Y \in D^1(M) \tag{4.3}$$

and it is skew-symmetric with respect to the contravariant type.

Let U be an open neighbourhood of the origin 0 of M on which we consider a local co-ordinate system $(x^1, \ldots, x^{2n})$. By setting $X = \partial/\partial x^i$ and $Y = \partial/\partial x^k$ in Eq. (4.3) we obtain the components N^i_{jk} of N with respect to the local co-ordinate system $(x^1, \ldots, x^{2n})$. These are given by

$$N^i_{jk} = 2\sum_{h=1}^{2n} (J^h_j \partial_h I^i_k - J^h_k \partial_h J^i_j - J^i_h \partial_j J^h_k + J^i_h \partial_k J^h_j) \tag{4.4}$$

Theorem 4.3. *Let* M *be an RR s-manifold whose symmetry tensor field* S *defines an almost complex structure* J *on* M. *This is integrable if and only if* S *satisfies the following system of partial differential equations:*

$$\sum_{h=1}^{2n} (S^h_j \partial_h S^i_k - S^h_k \partial_h S^i_j - S^i_h \partial_j S^h_k + S^i_k \partial_h S^h_j) = 0 \tag{4.5}$$

with respect to a local co-ordinate system $(x^1, ..., x^{2n})$, *where* ∂_h *denotes the partial differentiation* $\partial/\partial x^h$.

Proof. The almost complex structure J is integrable if and only if its torsion is zero. In the local co-ordinate system, $(x^1, ..., x^{2n})$ on M, this can be expressed by the equations:

$$N^i_{jk} = 2 \sum_{h=1}^{2n} (J^h_j \partial_h J^i_k - J^h_k \partial_h J^i_j - I^i_h \partial_j J^h_k + J^i_h \partial_k J^h_j) = 0 \tag{4.6}$$

If we substitute in (4.6) $J^\lambda_\mu = (S^\lambda_\mu - I^\lambda_\mu \cos\varphi)/\sin\varphi$ and take into consideration that

$$I^\lambda_\mu = \delta^\lambda_\mu = \begin{cases} 1 & \lambda = \mu \\ 0 & \lambda \neq \mu \end{cases}$$

then we have (4.5).

5. KÄHLER AND NEARLY KÄHLER RR s-MANIFOLDS

We shall give the conditions for an RR s-manifold to be Kähler or nearly Kähler with respect to the given metric and almost complex structure which is induced by the symmetry tensor field S.

Proposition 5.1. *Let* M *be an RR s-manifold. If the symmetry tensor field* S *is parallel, then* M *is locally symmetric.*

Proof. Let $T_P(M)$ be the tangent space of M at the point P. It is known that the curvature tensor R at the point P can be considered as a real-valued multilinear mapping defined by

$$R_P : T^*_P(M) \times T_P(M) \times T_P(M) \times T_P(M) \to \mathbb{R}$$

$$R_P : (\omega,X,Y,Z) \to R_P(\omega,X,Y,Z), \quad \omega \in T^*_P(M), \quad X,Y,Z \in T_P(M)$$

The isometry s_P preserves R_P. Therefore we have

$$R_P(\omega,X,Y,Z) = R_P(S^*_P(\omega), S_P(X), S_P(Y), S_P(Z)) \tag{5.1}$$

where S^*_P denotes the transpose of S_P. The covariant derivative ∇R of R is a tensor field of type (1

Hence we obtain

$$(\nabla R)_P(\omega,X,Y,Z,W) = (\nabla R)_P(S_P^*(\omega), S_P(X), S_P(Y), S_P(Z), S_P(W)) \tag{5.2}$$

We differentiate (5.1) covariantly in the direction of $S_P(W)$, considering that it is true in a neighbourhood of P; then we have

$$(\nabla R)_P(\omega,X,Z,S_P(W)) = (\nabla R)_P(S_P^*(\omega), S_P(X), S_P(Y), S_P(Z), S_P(W)) \tag{5.3}$$

From (5.2) and (5.3) we obtain

$$(\nabla R)_P(\omega,X,Y,Z, (S_P-I)W) = 0$$

which holds for any $\omega \in T_P^*(M)$ and for all $X,Y,Z,W \in T_P(M)$. Thus we have $(\nabla R)_P = 0$ which implies $\nabla R = 0$. Hence the manifold M is a locally symmetric space.

Theorem 5.2. *We consider an RR s-manifold* (M,d,s) *which is Kähler with respect to the complex structure defined by the symmetry tensor field* S. *Then* M *is a locally symmetric space.*

Proof. Let J be the almost complex structure on M defined by S. These two tensor fields satisfy the equation:

$$S = J \cos\varphi + I \sin\varphi \tag{5.4}$$

Since J with the riemannian metric d gives a Kähler structure on M, we conclude that ([3], p. 287) J = 0, which implies

$$\nabla S = \cos\varphi \ \nabla \cdot J + \sin\varphi \ \nabla \cdot I = 0$$

and from Proposition 5.1 the theorem follows, q.e.d.

Theorem 5.3. *Let* (M,d,s) *be an RR s-manifold whose symmetry tensor field* S *defines an almost complex structure* J. *The manifold* M *is nearly Kähler if and only if* $\nabla_X(S)X = 0$ *for every vector field* X *on* M.

Proof. We assume that M is nearly Kähler, which means $\nabla_X(J)X = 0 \ \ \forall X \in D^1(M)$ [2]. Since $J = (S-I\cos\varphi)/\sin\varphi$, the relation $\nabla_X(J)X = 0$ takes the form

$$\nabla_X \frac{(S-I\cos\varphi)}{\sin\varphi} X = 0, \quad \nabla_X(S)X = 0$$

Conversely, if $\nabla_X(S)X = 0$, this implies $\nabla_X(J)X = 0$, $\forall X \in D^1(M)$, q.e.d.

REFERENCES

[1] CARTAN, E., Sur les domaines bornés de l'espace de n variables complexes, Abh. Math. Sem. Hamburg **11** (1935) 116–162.

[2] GRAY, A., Nearly Kähler manifolds, J. Differ. Geom. **4** (1970) 283–310.

[3] HELGASON, S., Differential Geometry and Symmetric Spaces, Academic Press, New York (1962).
[4] KOBAYASHI, S., NOMIZU, K., Foundations of Differential Geometry 2, Interscience, New York (1969).
[5] LEDGER, A., OBATA, M., Affine and Riemannian s-manifolds, J. Differ. Geom. 2 (1968) 451–459.
[6] TSAGAS, G., LEDGER, A., Riemannian s-manifolds, to appear in J. Differ. Geom.

NEARLY KÄHLER MANIFOLDS

G. TSAGAS*
Department of Mathematics,
University of Patras,
Patras, Greece

Abstract

NEARLY KÄHLER MANIFOLDS.

A nearly Kähler manifold is a special almost hermitian manifold. The geometry and topology of a nearly Kähler manifold are studied. Contents: introduction; nearly Kähler manifolds which are not Kähler; sectional curvatures of a nearly Kähler manifold; homotopy groups of a nearly Kähler manifold; cohomology structure of a nearly Kähler manifold; Chern classes of a nearly Kähler manifold; submanifolds of a nearly Kähler manifold; nearly Kähler structure in a local co-ordinate system.

1. INTRODUCTION

We consider an almost hermitian manifold M with metric g, Riemannian connection ∇, and almost complex structure J. The manifold M is called nearly Kähler if the condition is satisfied that $\nabla_X(J)X = 0$ for every vector field X on M. (These manifolds were introduced and studied by Gray [5]).

Let M be a Kähler manifold. Then we have $\nabla_X(J)Y = 0$ for any two vector fields X and Y on M. Therefore any Kähler manifold is nearly Kähler and the converse is not true. The geometry and topology of a nearly Kähler manifold are studied in this paper. Some new results, not included in Ref. [5], are given.

2. NEARLY KÄHLER MANIFOLDS WHICH ARE NOT KÄHLER

Let M be a nearly Kähler manifold of dimension 2 or 4. Then we have

Theorem 2.1. *We consider a nearly Kähler manifold of dimension 2 or 4. Then* M *is Kähler.*

Proof. Let U be an open subset of M. If dim M = 2, we can choose X,JX such that they form an orthonormal frame field on $D^1(U)$. Since M is nearly Kähler we have $\nabla_X(J)X = 0$. It will be proved in Eq.(8.13) that we have

$$\nabla_X(J) = [\nabla_X, J] = \nabla_X J - J\nabla_X \tag{2.1}$$

from which we obtain

$$\nabla_X(J)X = \nabla_X(JX) - J\nabla_X X = 0 \quad \text{or} \quad \nabla_X(JX) = J\nabla_X X \tag{2.2}$$

From (2.1) we have

$$\nabla_X(J)(JX) = \nabla_X J(JX) - J\nabla_X(JX)$$

---

* Present address: Department of Mathematics, University of Thessaloniki, Thessaloniki, Greece

which by means of (2.2) takes the form

$$\nabla_X(J)(JX) = \nabla_X(-X) - J^2(\nabla_X X) = 0$$

Hence we obtain that the kernel of $\nabla_X(J)$ is dimension 2, which is the dimension of $D^1(U)$ over $D^0(U)$. Thus we have $\nabla_X(J)(Y) = 0$ for every vector field $Y \in D^1(U)$.

If dim M = 4, we choose the vector fields X, Y, J(X), J(Y) such that they form an orthonormal frame field on $D^1(U)$. By the same method we prove that $\nabla_X(J)Y$ is orthogonal to the vector fields X, Y, J(X) and J(Y) and [4] therefore $\nabla_X(J)Y = 0$, q.e.d.

From this we conclude that for the study of nearly Kähler manifolds we must assume dim M $\geqslant$ 6.

Example 2.2. *Let* $S^6 = SO(7)/SO(6)$ *be the six-dimensional sphere with the canonical almost complex structure and the canonical metric. Then* S^6 *is a nearly Kähler manifold.*

Proof. The almost complex structure on S^6 can be obtained by using Cayley numbers. For more details see the paper by Robertson in Volume I of these Proceedings [10]. The canonical metric g_0 on S^6 is the induced metric from the metric

$$ds^2 = \sum_{i=1}^{7} dx_i^2$$

on $\mathbb{R}^7$, since S^6 is a submanifold of $\mathbb{R}^7$ defined by

$$S^6 = \left\{(x_1, \ldots, x_7) \in \mathbb{R}^7 : \sum_{i=1}^{7} x_i^2 = 1\right\}$$

It can be easily seen that the riemannian connection ∇, defined by g_0, satisfies $\nabla_X(J)X = 0$ for every vector field X on S^6, q.e.d.

On the riemannian manifold (S^6, g_0) there are some other almost complex structures which do not make (S^6, g_0) a nearly Kähler manifold [8].

Example 2.3. *Let* M = G/H *be a homogeneous space, where* G *is a compact semisimple Lie group and* H *is the fixed point set of an automorphism of* G *of order 3. Then* M *can carry a nearly Kähler structure.*

Proof. Let g,h be the Lie algebras of G and H, respectively. Then we have the decomposition g = h + m, where the vector space m can be identified with the tangent space $T_0(M)$ of M at its origin 0. The automorphism on G induces an automorphism ϑ of order 3 on the Lie algebra g such that h is the fixed point set of ϑ. This automorphism ϑ induces a complex structure on m which determines uniquely an almost complex structure J on M. Let ds^2 be a metric on M which is the projection of a bi-invariant metric on G. Then (M, ds^2) becomes a nearly Kähler manifold [13].

3. SECTIONAL CURVATURES OF A NEARLY KÄHLER MANIFOLD

Let M be a nearly Kähler manifold whose riemannian curvature is denoted by R. If X,Y are two vector fields on M, then R(X,Y) can be considered as a linear mapping on the Lie algebra $D^1(M)$ of all vector fields on M given by

$$R(X,Y) : D^1(M) \to D^1(M),\ \ R(X,Y) : Z \to R(X,Y)Z = \nabla_X \nabla_Y Z - \nabla_Y \nabla_X Z - \nabla_{[X,Y]} Z$$

where R(X,Y) is called the curvature operator determined by X and Y.

In our case the curvature tensor field R satisfies some relations [6].

Proposition 3.1. *Let* M *be a nearly Kähler manifold. Then for its curvature operator of* M *we have*

$$R(X,Y,Z,W) - R(X,Y,JZ,JW) = \langle \nabla_X(J)Y, \nabla_Z(J)W \rangle \qquad (3.1)$$

$$\begin{aligned} R(X,Y,Z,W) &= R(JX,JY,JZ,JW) \\ &= R(JX,JY,Z,W) + R(JX,Y,JZ,W) + R(JX,Y,Z,JW) \end{aligned} \qquad (3.2)$$

where $X,Y,Z,W \in D^1(M)$, $R(X,Y,Z,W) = \langle R(X,Y)Z,W \rangle$ *and* $\langle\ \rangle$ *denotes the inner product on* $D^1(M)$.

Proof. These equalities can be proved if we use the properties of the curvature operator and the conditions

$$J^2 = -I,\ \ \nabla_X(J)X = 0,\ \ X \in D^1(M), \qquad \text{q.e.d.}$$

Let $T_P(M)$ be the tangent space of an almost hermitian manifold M at its point P. If λ is a plane in $T_P(M)$ which is invariant by J_P, the sectional curvature $\sigma(\lambda)$ is called holomorphic and is denoted by $h(\lambda)$. If u is a unit vector in λ, then $u, J_P(u)$ form an orthonormal base of λ and the holomorphic sectional curvature $h(\lambda)$ is given by

$$h(\lambda) = \langle R(u,J_P(u))u, J_P(u) \rangle = R(u,J_P(u),u,J_P(u)) \qquad (3.3)$$

and since it depends only on u, it is for this reason denoted by h(u). If h(u) is constant for every $u \in T_P(M)$ and for every $P \in M$, then M is called space of constant holomorphic sectional curvature.

Example 3.2. *Let* S^6 *be the six-dimensional sphere provided by the canonical almost complex structure and the canonical metric* g_0. *Then* (S^6, g_0) *is a space of constant holomorphic sectional curvature.*

Proof. That S^6 has constant sectional curvature implies it has constant holomorphic sectional curvature.

We consider two unit vectors $u,v \in T_P(M)$. The holomorphic bisectional curvature of u and v is defined by

$$b(u,v) = \langle R(u,J_P(u))v, J_P(v) \rangle \qquad (3.4)$$

If $u = v$, then $b(u,v) = h(v)$. If b(u,v) is constant for every pair of unit vectors $u,v \in T_P(M)$, then M is called space of constant holomorphic bisectional curvature.

Proposition 3.3. *Let* M *be a nearly Kähler manifold. Then we have*

$$b(u,v) = \sigma(u,v) + \sigma(u,J_P(v)) - 2\|\nabla_u J_P(v)\|^2 \tag{3.5}$$

for every pair of orthogonal unit vectors u *and* v *of* $T_P(M)$.

Proof. The relation (3.5) is obtained by using the formula (3.1) and the first Bianchi identity, q.e.d.

We consider two vectors $u,v \in T_P(M)$, where M is an almost hermitian manifold. If u,v satisfy the relations $\langle u,v\rangle = \langle u,J_P(v)\rangle = 0$, the sectional curvature $\sigma(u,v)$ is called antiholomorphic.

Let M be an almost hermitian manifold. This is said to be of constant type at $P \in M$ if for all vectors $v,u,w \in T_P(M)$ we have $\|\nabla_u J_P(v)\| = \|\nabla_u J_P(w)\|$ whenever $\langle u,v\rangle = \langle J_P(u),v\rangle = \langle u,w\rangle = \langle J_P(u),w\rangle = 0$ and $\|v\| = \|w\|$. If this is true for every $P \in M$, we say that M is pointwise constant type.

We assume that M is pointwise constant type and for $X,Y \in D^1(M)$, with $\langle X,Y\rangle = \langle JX,Y\rangle = 0$, and the function $\|\nabla_X(J)Y\|^2$ is constant whenever $\|X\| = \|Y\| = 1$, then M is called global constant type.

The concepts of pointwise constant type and global constant type play an important role for nearly Kähler manifolds.

Proposition 3.4. *We consider a nearly Kähler manifold* M. *Then* M *is pointwise constant type* a *if and only if there exists a function* $a \in D^0(M)$ *such that*

$$\|\nabla_X(J)Y\|^2 = a\{|X\wedge Y|^2 - \langle X,JY\rangle^2\} \tag{3.6}$$

where $|X\wedge Y|^2 = \|X\|^2\,\|Y\|^2 - \langle X,Y\rangle^2$ and $X,Y \in D^1(M)$. *Furthermore,* M *has global constant type* a *if and only if (3.6) holds with a constant function* a.

Proof. This is an immediate consequence of the above definitions of pointwise constant type and global constant type of a manifold and the relation $\nabla_X(J)X = 0$, $\forall X \in D^1(M)$.

We also have

Proposition 3.5. *Let* M *be a nearly Kähler manifold of constant holomorphic sectional curvature* c *and pointwise constant type* a. *Then we have:*

(i) *The manifold* M *is an Einsteinian with* $4\overline{R}(u,u) = (n+3)c + 3(n-1)a$, *where* $\overline{R}$ *is the Ricci curvature tensor and* u *a unit vector belonging to* $T_P(M)$, $\dim M = 2n$.

(ii) *The manifold* M *has at each point constant antiholomorphic sectional curvature and is equal to* $(c+3a)/4$.

Proof. Since M is nearly Kähler, we have ([5], p.288)

$$\sigma(u,v) = \frac{c}{4}\left\{1 + 3\,\langle J_P(u),v\rangle^2\right\} + \frac{3}{4}\,\|\nabla_u J_P(v)\|^2, \text{ if } \langle u,v\rangle = 0 \tag{3.7}$$

$$b(u,v) = \frac{c}{2}\left\{1 + \langle u,v\rangle^2 + \langle J_P(u),v\rangle^2\right\} - \frac{1}{2}\,\|\nabla_u J_P(v)\|^2 \tag{3.8}$$

where u and v are unit vectors. The above relations imply the proposition, q.e.d.

From these propositions we have

Corollary 3.6. *Let* M *be a nearly Kähler manifold of global constant type* a *and constant holomorphic sectional curvature* c. *Then* M *is an Einstein manifold of constant antiholomorphic sectional curvature.*

4. HOMOTOPY GROUPS OF A NEARLY KÄHLER MANIFOLD

In this section we study the homotopy structure of a nearly Kähler manifold as well as the conditions which imply that the manifold is compact.

Theorem 4.1. *Let* M *be a compact nearly Kähler manifold, whose holomorphic sectional curvature is positive, then* $\pi_1(M) = \{0\}$.

Proof. We assume the contrary ([5], p.295), that $\pi_1(M)$ is not trivial. Then there exists a non-trivial homotopy class of loops which contains a non-trivial minimal geodesic γ. We can assume that γ has unit speed and is defined on $[0,b]$. We denote by γ' the velocity vector of γ. Since M is nearly Kähler, $J\gamma'$ is parallel on γ. The deformation of γ given by $J\gamma'$ has a second variation:

$$I(J\gamma', J\gamma') = -\int_0^b \sigma(\gamma', J\gamma')(t)\,dt < 0$$

Therefore γ cannot be a minimal geodesic. Hence $\pi_1(M) = \{0\}$, i.e. M is simply connected, q.e.d.

We also have ([5], p. 296)

Theorem 4.2. *Let* M *be a complete nearly Kähler manifold whose holomorphic sectional curvature is bounded below* $h(u) > \delta$ *for any unit vector* $u \in T_P(M)$ *and for every point* $P \in M$. *Then* M *is compact and its diameter is not greater than* $\pi/\sqrt{\delta}$.

Proof. We consider two points $P_1, P_2 \in M$. Since M is complete there exists a geodesic γ on $[0,b]$ such that $\gamma(0) = P_1$ and $\gamma(b) = P_2$. Since M is nearly Kähler we obtain that $J\gamma'$ is parallel on γ. Let $X(t)$ be a vector field on γ defined by $X(t) = \sin(\pi t/\sqrt{b})\, J\gamma'(t)$. The deformation of γ given by X has second variation:

$$L(X,X) = \int_0^b \left\{ \|X'\|^2 - \langle R(X,\gamma')X, \gamma'\rangle \right\}(t)\,dt$$

$$< \int_0^b \left\{ \frac{\pi^2}{b^2} \cos^2 \frac{\pi t}{b} - \delta \sin^2 \frac{\pi t}{b} \right\}$$

$$\leqslant b^2(\pi^2/b^2 - \delta)$$

Now, if we assume that $b > \pi/\sqrt{\delta}$, then $L(X,X) < 0$, and therefore γ does not have a conjugate point. Since any two points are connected by a unique geodesic the theorem follows, q.e.d.

The following proposition is known ([11], p.62):

Proposition 4.3. *Let* M *be a connected, complete and differentiable riemannian manifold whose diameter satisfies* $d(M) > \pi/2\sqrt{\delta}$ *for any* $0 < \delta \leqslant 1$. *Then* M *is simply connected.*

From this we have

Theorem 4.4. *Let* M *be a connected and complete nearly Kähler manifold whose sectional curvature* $\sigma(u)$ *satisfies* $\sigma(u) > \delta > 0$ *for every unit vector* $u \in T_P(M)$ *and* $P \in M$. *If* $\delta < 4$, *then* $\pi_1(M)$ *is not trivial.*

Proof. From Theorem (4.2) we conclude that the manifold whose diameter $d(M) < \pi/2\sqrt{k}$ is compact and, since $0 < \delta < 4$, this implies $0 < k < 1$. Using Proposition (4.3), we have that M is not simply connected and therefore $\pi_1(M)$ is not trivial.

Example 4.5. *We consider the manifold* $M = P^7(\mathbb{R}) \times P^7(\mathbb{R})$, *where* $P^7(\mathbb{R})$ *is the real projective space of dimension 7. There is a nearly Kähler structure on* M *with non-negative sectional curvature.*

Proof. It is known that $P^7(\mathbb{R}) = S^7/Z_2$ has a metric g with constant sectional curvature. Therefore the manifolds $M = P^7(\mathbb{R}) \times P^7(\mathbb{R})$ with the metric $g \times g$ has non-negative sectional curvature which can carry an almost complex structure J [13]. The almost complex manifold (M,J) with the metric $g \times g$ becomes nearly Kähler.

Therefore there exist compact non-simply connected near Kähler manifolds with non-negative sectional curvature which are not Kähler.

5. COHOMOLOGY STRUCTURE OF A NEARLY KÄHLER MANIFOLD

Let (M,J) be an almost complex manifold. By complexification of the Lie algebra $D^1(M)$ of the vector fields on M we obtain $D^{1\mathbb{C}}(M) = D^1(M) \otimes \mathbb{C}$. We decompose $D^{1\mathbb{C}}(M)$ as follows:

$$D^{1\mathbb{C}}(M) = D^{1\mathbb{C}}_{+1}(M) + D^{1\mathbb{C}}_{-1}(M), \text{ where } D^{1\mathbb{C}}_{\pm 1} = \{X \in D^{1\mathbb{C}}(M) : JX = \pm iX\}$$

Let w be a differential form (possibly complex) on an almost complex manifold M. Then w is called bi-degree (p,q) if and only if it is of degree $p+q$ and $w(X_1, \ldots, X_{p+q}) = 0$, whenever more than p of the X; are in $D^{1,\mathbb{C}}_{-1}$ or more than q of the X; are in $D^{1,\mathbb{C}}_{+1}(M)$. We denote by $\Lambda^{p,q}(M)$ the set of complex differential forms of bi-degree (p,q) on M. Then we have

$$d : \Lambda^{p,q}(M) \to (\Lambda^{p,q}(M)) = \Lambda^{p-1,q+2}(M) + \Lambda^{p,q+1}(M) + \Lambda^{p+1,q}(M) + \Lambda^{p+2,q-1}(M)$$

Let $H^{p+q}(M,\mathbb{R})$ be the vector space of harmonic $(p+q)$ forms on M. We put

$$H^{p,q}(M,\mathbb{C}) = (H^{p+q}(M,\mathbb{R}) \times \mathbb{C}) \cap \Lambda^{p,q}(M,\mathbb{C})$$

These vector spaces have been studied in the case for which M is a Kähler manifold [9, 14]. Now we study the vector spaces for nearly Kähler manifolds.

Theorem 5.1. *We consider a compact non-Kähler near Kähler manifold* M *such that its sectional curvature is positive and its holomorphic bisectional curvature* b *is non-negative. Then* $H^{1,1}(M,\mathbb{C}) = 0$.

Proof. If a is any p-form on the manifold M, we have the relation ([8], p.3):

$$\tfrac{1}{2}\,\Delta(|a|^2) = \langle a, \Delta a\rangle - \frac{1}{p!}\,|\nabla a|^2 - \frac{1}{(p-1)!}\,Q_P(a) \tag{5.1}$$

where

$$|\nabla a|^2 = \nabla_\ell a_{j_1 \dots j_p}\, \nabla^\ell a^{j_1 \dots j_p} \tag{5.2}$$

$$Q_p(a) = -(p-1) R_{k\ell,mn}\, a^{k\ell j_3 \dots j_p}\, a^{mn}_{\ j_3 \dots j_p} + 2 R_{k\ell}\, a^{kj_2 \dots j_p}\, a^{\ell}_{\ j_2 \dots j_p} \tag{5.3}$$

It is known that if a is harmonic and $Q_p(a) > 0$, then we have a = 0. We assume that a is the harmonic form of bi-degree (1,1), then a(X,Y) = a(JX,JY) for all $X,Y \in D^1(M)$. Without loss of generality we may assume that a is real. From Ref. [1] we obtain that there exists a local orthonormal frame field $\{X_1, \dots, X_n, JX_1, \dots, JX_n\}$ such that $a(X_i, JX_j) = 0$.

To estimate $Q_2(a)$ we use the index convention that $1 \leqslant i,j,k,\ell \leqslant n$ and $1 \leqslant \alpha,\beta,\gamma,\delta \leqslant 2n$. We also set $JX_i = X_{i^*}$ so that $n + 1 \leqslant i^*, j^*, k^*, \ell^* \leqslant 2n$. Now we define

$$a_{\alpha\beta} = a(X_\alpha, X_\beta)$$

$$\psi_{\alpha\beta} = \nabla_{X_\alpha}(J)(X_\beta)$$

$$R_{\alpha\beta\gamma\delta} = \langle R(X_\alpha, X_\beta)\, X_\gamma, X_\delta \rangle$$

$$R_{\alpha\beta} = \bar{R}(X_\alpha, X_\beta)$$

Let P be a point of M which is taken as the origin of a normal co-ordinate system; then $Q_2(a)$ takes the form

$$[Q_2(a)]_P = 2\Big(\sum_{\alpha,\beta,\gamma} R_{\alpha\beta}\, a_{\alpha\gamma}\, a_{\beta\gamma} - \frac{1}{2} \sum_{\alpha,\beta,\gamma,\delta} R_{\alpha\beta\gamma\delta}\, a_{\alpha\beta}\, a_{\gamma\delta} \Big)$$

On the assumption of the theorem we obtain $[Q_2(a)]_P > 0$ and therefore a = 0 which implies $H^{1,1}(M,\mathbb{C}) = 0$.

Theorem 5.2. *Let* M *be a compact nearly Kähler manifold with non-negative holomorphic bisectional curvature. If the sectional curvature* σ *of* M *satisfies the inequality*

$$\sigma(u,v) + \sigma(u, J_P(v)) > 0$$

for linear independent vectors $u, v, J_P(u), J_P(v) \in T_P(M)$ *and for every* $P \in M$, *then* $\dim H^{1,1}(M,\mathbb{C}) = 1$ *if* M *is Kähler and* $\dim H^{1,1}(M,\mathbb{C}) = 0$ *if* M *is not Kähler.*

Proof. If M is not Kähler, we use the same technique as in Theorem 5.2, i.e. we obtain an element $a \in H^{1,1}(M,\mathbb{C})$ and prove $Q_2(a) > 0$ which implies a = 0.

If M is Kähler the proof is the same as in Ref. [1].

Theorem 5.3. *Let* M *be a compact nearly Kähler manifold of pointwise constant type whose Ricci tensor* $\overline{R}$ *satisfies*

$$\overline{R}(u,v) > \tfrac{1}{2}(p-1)\|\nabla_u(J)v\|^2$$

for $u,v \in T_P(M)$ *with* $\|u\| = \|v\| = 1$ *and* $\langle u,v\rangle = \langle J_P(u),v\rangle = 0$ *for all* $P \in M$. *Then* $H^{p,0}(M,\mathbb{C}) = H^{0,p}(M,\mathbb{C}) = 0$, *for* $p > 0$.

Proof. We obtain $a \in H^{p,0}(M,\mathbb{C})$ or $a \in H^{0,p}(M,\mathbb{C})$ and we form $Q_p(a)$ and, under the assumption on the manifold M, we obtain $Q_p(a) > 0$, which implies $a = 0$ and therefore $H^{p,0}(M,\mathbb{C}) = H^{0,p}(M,\mathbb{C}) = 0$ for $p > 0$.

Theorem 5.4. *Let* M *be a compact nearly Kähler manifold of point constant type* a *which is holomorphic pinching* δ *such that*

$$\delta > \frac{(n-1)(2a+1)}{6(n-1)a+3n+1} \quad \text{if } n \leqslant 5 \qquad , \qquad \delta > \frac{(n-1)a+n-3}{(n-1)(3a+2)} \quad \text{if } n > 5$$

where dim M = 2n. *Then* $H^{p,0}(M,\mathbb{C}) = H^{0,p}(M,\mathbb{C}) = 0$ *for* $p > 0$.

Proof. We use the same technique as in Theorem (5.4).

Theorem 5.5. *We consider a compact nearly Kähler manifold of pointwise constant whose sectional curvature* $\sigma(\lambda)$ *satisfies* $\sigma(\lambda) > \alpha$. *Then* $\dim H^2(M,\mathbb{R}) = 1$ *if* M *is Kähler and* $H^2(M,\mathbb{R}) = 0$ *otherwise.*

Proof. If M is Kähler the proof is the same as in Ref. [1]. We assume that M is not Kähler and prove that if $a \in H^2(M,\mathbb{R})$ then $Q_2(a) > 0$ and hence $H^2(M,\mathbb{R}) = 0$.

Corollary 5.6. *Let* $S^2 \times \ldots \times S^2$ *be the topological product of* S^2 k *times* $k \geqslant 2$. *Then the manifold* $S^2 \times \ldots \times S^2$ *cannot carry a nearly Kähler metric such that it becomes pointwise constant type* a *whose sectional curvature satisfies* $\sigma(\lambda) > a$.

Proof. In this case we have $\dim H^2(S^2 \times \ldots \times S^2,\mathbb{R}) = k \geqslant 2$ and therefore Theorem 5.5 implies the Corollary.

Theorem 5.7. *Let* M *be a compact nearly Kähler manifold of pointwise constant type* a *which is holomorphic pinching* $\delta > \frac{1}{2}(a+1)$, *then* $\dim H^2(M,\mathbb{R}) = 1$ *if* M *is Kähler and* $H^2(M,\mathbb{R}) = 0$ *otherwise.*

Proof. This is a modification of the proof of Theorem 5.5.

6. CHERN CLASSES OF A NEARLY KÄHLER MANIFOLD

Let M be a compact almost hermitian manifold whose riemannian connection, defined by the hermitian metric, is denoted by ∇. We define a new connection D on M by

$$D_X Y = \tfrac{1}{2}(\nabla_X Y - J\nabla_X JY), \quad X, Y \in D^1(M) \tag{6.1}$$

It can be easily seen that we have $D_X(J)Y = 0$. Therefore D is a hermitian connection in the sense of Ref. [7] (p. 178) on the tangent bundle $T^{\mathbb{C}}(M)$, where $T^{\mathbb{C}}(M)$ is viewed as a complex vector bundle on M.

Let S be a tensor field of type (1,3) defined by

$$\langle S(X,Y)Z,W\rangle = \tfrac{1}{2}\langle R(X,Y)Z,W\rangle + \tfrac{1}{2}\langle R(X,Y)JZ,JW\rangle$$
$$+ \tfrac{1}{4}\langle \nabla_X(J)Z, \nabla_Y(J)W\rangle - \tfrac{1}{4}\langle \nabla_X(J)W, \nabla_Y(J)Z\rangle \tag{6.2}$$

where $X,Y,Z,W \in D^1(W)$.

It can be proved that S is the curvature operator of D. Therefore we have

$$S(X,Y) = D_{[X,Y]} - [D_X, D_Y] \tag{6.3}$$

for $X, Y \in D^1(M)$. If $\{X_1, \ldots, X_n, JX_1, \ldots, JX_n\}$ is a local frame field on M, then the components Ω_{ij} of the curvature 2-form Ω of D with respect to the local frame field are

$$\Omega_{ij}(X,Y) = \langle S(X,Y)X_i, X_j\rangle - \sqrt{-1}\,\langle S(X,Y)X_i, JX_j\rangle \tag{6.4}$$

We define the first polynomial functions $f_0, f_1, \ldots, f_n$ on the Lie algebra $g\ell(n,\mathbb{C})$ by

$$\det\left(\lambda I_\lambda - \frac{1}{2\pi\sqrt{-1}}\, a\right) = \sum_{k=0}^{n} f_k\, \lambda^{n-k}, \text{ for } a \in g\ell(n,\mathbb{C}) \tag{6.5}$$

which are invariant by every $ad(\tau)$, $\forall \tau \in GL(n,\mathbb{C})$.

We consider the projection $p : T^{\mathbb{C}}(M) \to M$. Then there is a unique 2k-form γ_k on M such that

$$P^*(\gamma_k) = f_k(\Omega) \tag{6.6}$$

The cohomology class determined by γ_k is independent of the connection, which means that γ_k does not depend on Ω. The following theorem is known ([7], p. 307):

Theorem 6.1. *The* k^{th} *Chern class* $c_k(T^{\mathbb{C}}(M))$ *of the complex vector bundle* $T^{\mathbb{C}}(M)$ *over the compact almost hermitian manifold* M *is represented by a closed 2k-form defined above.*

Let M be a compact almost hermitian manifold. Then we have ([5], p. 304)

Theorem 6.2. *We consider a compact almost hermitian manifold* M. *Then* $\det(\delta_{ij} - \Omega_{ij}(2\pi\sqrt{-1}))$ *is globally defined, and via de Rham's theorem it represents the total Chern class of* M, *where* Ω_{ij} *are defined by (6.4).*

From the above theorems and the properties of the curvature operator of a nearly Kähler manifold we obtain

Corollary 6.3. *Let* M *be a compact nearly Kähler manifold. The total Chern class of M is represented by* $\det(\delta_{ij} - \Omega_{ij}(2\pi\sqrt{-1}))$, *where* Ω_{ij} *are defined by (6.4), but in this case we have*

$$\langle S(X,Y)Z,W\rangle = \langle R(X,Y)Z,W\rangle - \tfrac{1}{2}\langle\nabla_X(J)Y,\ \nabla_Z(J)W\rangle + \tfrac{1}{4}\langle\nabla_X(J)Z,\ \nabla_Y(J)W\rangle - \tfrac{1}{4}\langle\nabla_X(J)W,\ \nabla_Y(J)Z\rangle$$

for $X,Y,Z,W \in D^{1\mathbb{C}}(M)$

Corollary 6.4. *We consider a compact nearly Kähler manifold* M; *then the first Chern class* γ_1 *of* M *is given by*

$$\gamma_1(X,Y) = \frac{1}{2\pi}\sum_{i=1}^{n}\{\langle R(X,Y)X_i, JX_i\rangle - \tfrac{1}{2}\langle\nabla_X(J)(X_i),\ J\nabla_Y(J)(X_i)\rangle\} \tag{6.7}$$

for $X,Y \in D^1(M)$ *where* $\{X_1,\ldots,X_n, JX_1,\ldots,JX_n\}$ *is a local frame field on* M. *Hence for* $X \in D^1(M)$, *(6.7) takes the form*

$$2\pi\gamma_1(X,JX) = \overline{R}(X,Y) + \tfrac{3}{2}\sum_{i=1}^{n}\|\nabla_X(J)(X_i)\|^2$$

7. SUBMANIFOLDS OF A NEARLY KÄHLER MANIFOLD

Let M be a riemannian manifold. It is important to study the submanifolds of this manifold. From these submanifolds and their properties we can obtain basic information for M.

If M is a nearly Kähler manifold then some of the properties of its submanifolds can be expressed by the following theorems.

Theorem 7.1. *Let* M *be a compact connected nearly Kähler manifold whose sectional curvature satisfies*

$$\sigma(u,v) + \sigma(J_P(u),v) > \|\nabla_u(J)v\|^2 \tag{7.1}$$

for all $u,v \in T_P(M)$ *with* $\|u\| = \|v\| = 1$ *and* $\langle u,v\rangle = \langle J_P(u),v\rangle = 0$ *and for all* $P \in M$. *If* M_1, M_2 *are compact almost hermitian submanifolds of* M *such that* $\dim M_1 + \dim M_2 \geqslant \dim M$, *then* $M_1 \cap M_2 \neq \emptyset$.

Proof. We assume that $M_1 \cap M_2 = \emptyset$. Let α be a unit speed shortest geodesic from M_1 to M_2. We suppose that α is defined on $[0,b]$ such that $\alpha(0) \in M_1$ and $\alpha(b) \in M_2$. We use the method of the second variation of the length integral and obtain a contradiction. Therefore we have $M_1 \cap M_2 \neq \emptyset$.

Let M be an almost hermitian manifold. We consider an almost hermitian submanifold N of $M \times M$. We say that N has a fixed point if we have $N \cap D(M \times M) \neq \emptyset$, where $D(M \times M)$ is the diagonal of $M \times M$.

Theorem 7.2. *Let* M *be a compact connected nearly Kähler manifold whose sectional curvature satisfies*

$$\sigma(u,v) + \sigma(J_P(u),v) > \|\nabla_u J_P(v)\|^2 \tag{7.2}$$

for all $u,v \in T_P(M)$ *with* $\|u\| = \|v\| = 1$, $\langle u,v\rangle = \langle J_P(u),v\rangle = 0$ *and for all* $P \in M$. *Then every almost hermitian manifold of* $M \times M$ *has a fixed point.*

Proof. First we prove that the sectional curvature of the manifold $M \times M$ satisfies the inequalities (7.2). This fact and Theorem 7.1 prove the theorem.

It is possible for a nearly Kähler manifold to have Kähler submanifolds. This can be expressed by

Theorem 7.3. *Let* M *be a non-Kähler, nearly Kähler manifold of pointwise constant type. We assume that* M *has a Kähler submanifold* N; *then* $\dim N \leqslant \dim M - 4$.

Proof. If we assume that $\dim M - \dim N = 2$, we obtain a contradiction. This implies the theorem.

From the above theorem we conclude that the six-dimensional sphere S^6 with the standard nearly Kähler structure has no four-dimensional Kähler submanifold.

By using nearly Kähler manifolds we can construct foliations in some manifolds.

Theorem 7.4. *Let* M *be a nearly Kähler manifold. We construct for every* $P \in M$ *the following set:*

$$S_P = \{u \in T_P(M) : \nabla_u(J)(v) = 0, \ \forall v \in T_P(M)\}$$

If $\dim (S_P) = \text{const}$ *in an open subset of* M, *the distribution* $P \to S_P$ *is integrable and the leaves are Kähler submanifolds of* M.

Proof. Let X,Y be vector fields on M such that $X_P, Y_P \in S_P$, $\forall P \in M$. If $Z,W \in D^1(M)$, we have

$$\langle \nabla_{[X,Y]} JZ,W\rangle = \langle R(X,Y)JZ,W\rangle + \langle \big[[\nabla_X,\nabla_Y],J\big] Z,W\rangle$$

$$= \langle R(X,Y)JZ,W\rangle + \langle R(X,Y)Z,JW\rangle = \langle \nabla_X(J)Y, \nabla_{JZ}JW\rangle = 0 \tag{7.3}$$

From (7.3) we conclude that [X,Y] lies in the distribution $P \to S_P$ and is therefore integrable on open sets of M on which $\dim S_P = \text{const}$. Let N be a leaf of the foliation $P \to S_P$ through the point P. It is known that N is a riemannian submanifold of M. It can be easily verified that N is an almost hermitian submanifold of M. We denote by ∇_1 and T_1 the connection and the configuration tensor field of N. Therefore for every $P \in N$ and for every $u,v \in T_P(N) = S_P$ we have

$$\nabla_u(J)v = \nabla_{1u}(J)v + T_{1u}Jv - JT_1 v = 0$$

from which we conclude that $\nabla_{1u}(J)v = 0$, which implies that N is Kähler.

The above theorem gives a technique for foliating a manifold. Let M be a differentiable manifold and we assume that M admits a nearly Kähler structure. We construct the distribution $P \to S_P$. If this has the property $\dim S_P = \text{const.}$ on open subsets of M, then it defines a foliation on the manifold whose leaves are Kähler manifolds.

8. NEARLY KÄHLER STRUCTURE IN A LOCAL CO-ORDINATE SYSTEM

Let U be an open subset of an almost hermitian manifold. Let $\{X_1,\ldots,X_n, JX_1,\ldots,JX_n\}$ be a local orthonormal frame field on U. This means $\{X_1,\ldots,X_n, JX_1,\ldots,JX_n\}$ is an orthonormal basis of $D^1(U)$, where the inner product $\langle\ \rangle$ on $D^1(U)$ is defined by the relation

$$\langle X,Y\rangle = \sum_{i=1}^{2n} \sum_{j=1}^{2n} g_{ij}\, X^i Y^j \qquad (8.1)$$

where $\{X^i\}$, $\{Y^j\}$ are the co-ordinates of X and Y respectively, with respect to the local orthonormal frame field $\{E_1,\ldots,E_n, E_{n+1},\ldots,E_{2n}\}$, where $E_i = X_i$, $i = 1,\ldots,n$, $E_{n+j} = JX_j$, $j = 1,\ldots,n$. It can be easily seen that the vector fields

$$Z_1 = \frac{X_1 - iJX_1}{2}, \ldots, Z_n = \frac{X_n - iJX_n}{2}, \quad Z_{\bar{1}} = \frac{X_1 + iJX_1}{2}, \ldots, Z_{\bar{n}} = \frac{X_n + iJX_n}{2} \qquad (8.2)$$

form a local orthonormal frame field on $D^{1\mathbb{C}}(U) = D^1(U) \otimes \mathbb{C}$. The tensor fields $\{Z_1,\ldots,Z_n\}$ are of the type (1,0), i.e.

$$JZ_1 = iZ_1, \ldots, JZ_n = iZ_n \qquad (8.3)$$

and the tensor fields $Z_{\bar{1}} \ldots Z_{\bar{n}}$ are of the type (0,1), i.e.

$$JZ_{\bar{1}} = iZ_{\bar{1}}, \ldots, JZ_{\bar{n}} = -iZ_{\bar{n}} \qquad (8.4)$$

The hermitian metric on M gives a connection ∇ which is characterized on U by the Christoffel symbols $\Gamma^i_{\ell j}$, $i,j,\ell = 1,\ldots,2n$ which are given by the relations:

$$\nabla_{Z_\alpha} Z_\beta = \sum_{\gamma=1}^{n} \Gamma^{\gamma}_{\alpha\beta} Z_\gamma + \sum_{\gamma=1}^{n} \Gamma^{\bar{\gamma}}_{\alpha\beta} Z_{\bar{\gamma}} \qquad (8.5)$$

$$\nabla_{Z_\alpha} Z_{\bar{\beta}} = \sum_{\gamma=1}^{n} \Gamma^{\gamma}_{\alpha\bar{\beta}} Z_\gamma + \sum_{\gamma=1}^{n} \Gamma^{\bar{\gamma}}_{\alpha\bar{\beta}} Z_{\bar{\gamma}} \qquad (8.6)$$

$$\nabla_{Z_{\bar{\alpha}}} Z_\beta = \sum_{\gamma=1}^{n} \Gamma^{\gamma}_{\bar{\alpha}\beta} Z_\gamma + \sum_{\gamma=1}^{n} \Gamma^{\bar{\gamma}}_{\bar{\alpha}\beta} Z_{\bar{\gamma}} \qquad (8.7)$$

$$\nabla_{Z_{\bar{\alpha}}} Z_{\bar{\beta}} = \sum_{\gamma=1}^{n} \Gamma^{\gamma}_{\bar{\alpha}\bar{\beta}} Z_\gamma + \sum_{\gamma=1}^{n} \Gamma^{\bar{\gamma}}_{\bar{\alpha}\bar{\beta}} Z_{\bar{\gamma}} \qquad (8.8)$$

where $1 \leqslant \alpha,\beta,\gamma \leqslant n$.

Theorem 8.1. *Let* M *be an almost hermitian manifold. This is nearly Kähler if and only if the following relations are satisfied:*

$$\Gamma^{\bar{\gamma}}_{\alpha\alpha} = \Gamma^{\gamma}_{\bar{\alpha}\bar{\alpha}} = 0 \qquad (8.9)$$

Proof. We assume that M is a nearly Kähler manifold and therefore we have

$$\nabla_X(J)X = 0, \forall X \in D^1(U) \tag{8.10}$$

We consider the set $D_1(U)$ of linear mappings from $D^1(U)$ into itself, i.e.

$$D_1(U) = \{A/A : D^1(U) \to D^1(U), \text{ where A is } D^0(U)\text{-linear}\} \tag{8.11}$$

where $D^0(U)$ is the algebra of all differentiable functions on U. This is a $D^0(U)$-module on which we define a Lie bracket as follows:

$$[AB-BA] = AB - BA, \qquad A,B \in D_1(U) \tag{8.12}$$

From this we conclude that $\nabla_X \in D_1(U), \forall X \in D^1(U)$; also, $J \in D^1(U)$. It can be easily verified that we have

$$\nabla_X(J) = [\nabla_X, J] = \nabla_X J - J\nabla_X \tag{8.13}$$

where $\nabla_X(J)$ means the covariant derivative with respect to X of the tensor field J. From (8.10) and (8.13) we obtain

$$\nabla_X(J)X = (\nabla_X J - J\nabla_X)X = 0 \text{ or } \nabla_X J(X) = J\nabla_X X \tag{8.14}$$

which are also valid for the vector fields $Z \in D^1(U) \otimes \mathbb{C}$. Hence we have

$$J(\nabla_{Z_\alpha} Z_\alpha) = \nabla_{Z_\alpha} JZ_\alpha, \; J(\nabla_{Z_{\bar\alpha}} Z_{\bar\alpha}) = \nabla_{Z_{\bar\alpha}} JZ_{\bar\alpha} \tag{8.15}$$

which can be written

$$J(\nabla_{Z_\alpha} Z_\alpha) = i\nabla_{Z_\alpha} Z_\alpha, \; J(\nabla_{Z_{\bar\alpha}} Z_{\bar\alpha}) = -i\nabla_{Z_{\bar\alpha}} Z_{\bar\alpha} \tag{8.16}$$

i.e. the vector fields $\nabla_{Z_\alpha} Z_\alpha$ and $\nabla_{Z_{\bar\alpha}} Z_{\bar\alpha}$ are of the type (1,0) and (0,1) respectively. From (8.5), (8.8) and (8.16) we obtain

$$\Gamma^{\bar\gamma}_{\alpha\alpha} = \Gamma^{\gamma}_{\bar\alpha\bar\alpha} = 0$$

Conversely we assume that Christoffel symbols of an almost hermitian manifold satisfy the relations (8.9). Therefore from (8.5) and (8.8) we conclude that

$$\nabla_{Z_\alpha} Z_\alpha = \sum_{\gamma=1}^{n} \Gamma^{\gamma}_{\alpha\alpha} Z_\gamma, \; \nabla_{Z_{\bar\alpha}} Z_{\bar\alpha} = \sum_{\gamma=1}^{n} \Gamma^{\bar\gamma}_{\bar\alpha\bar\alpha} Z_{\bar\gamma}$$

which imply

$$J(\nabla_{Z_\alpha} Z_\alpha) = \sum_{\gamma=1}^{n} \Gamma^{\gamma}_{\alpha\alpha} J(Z_\gamma) = i \sum_{\gamma=1}^{n} \Gamma^{\gamma}_{\alpha\alpha} Z_\gamma = i\nabla_{Z_\alpha} Z_\alpha = \nabla_{Z_\alpha} J(Z_\alpha) \tag{8.17}$$

$$J(\nabla_{Z_{\bar{\alpha}}} Z_{\bar{\alpha}}) = \sum_{\gamma=1}^{n} \Gamma^{\bar{\gamma}}_{\bar{\alpha}\bar{\alpha}} J(Z_{\bar{\gamma}}) = -i \sum_{\gamma=1}^{n} \Gamma^{\bar{\gamma}}_{\bar{\alpha}\bar{\alpha}} Z_{\bar{\gamma}} = i\nabla_{Z_{\bar{\alpha}}} Z_{\bar{\alpha}} = \nabla_{Z_{\bar{\alpha}}} J(Z_{\alpha}) \tag{8.18}$$

From (8.17) and (8.18) by means of (8.14) we obtain

$$\nabla_{Z_\alpha}(J)Z_\alpha = 0, \quad \nabla_{Z_{\bar{\alpha}}}(J)Z_{\bar{\alpha}} = 0 \tag{8.19}$$

from which we have

$$\nabla_X(J)X = 0, \quad X \in D^1(U)$$

and therefore the manifold is nearly Kähler.

Proposition 8.2. *Let* M *be a nearly Kähler manifold of dimension* 2n. *If* $(Z_1, ..., Z_n, Z_{\bar{1}}, ..., Z_{\bar{n}})$ *is a local orthonormal frame field on* M *such that* Z_α, $\alpha = 1, ..., n$ *are vector fields of type* (1,0) *and* $Z_{\bar{\beta}}$, $\beta = 1, ..., n$ *are vector fields of type* (0,1), *we have*

$$R_{\bar{\alpha}\bar{\beta}\bar{\gamma}\delta} = R_{\alpha\beta\gamma\bar{\delta}} = R_{\alpha\beta\gamma\delta} = R_{\bar{\alpha}\bar{\beta}\bar{\gamma}\bar{\delta}} = 0 \tag{8.20}$$

$$R^{\bar{\epsilon}}_{\beta\gamma\bar{\delta}} = R^{\epsilon}_{\bar{\beta}\bar{\gamma}\delta} = R^{\epsilon}_{\beta\gamma\delta} = R^{\bar{\epsilon}}_{\beta\gamma\delta} = R^{\epsilon}_{\bar{\beta}\bar{\gamma}\bar{\delta}} = R^{\bar{\epsilon}}_{\bar{\beta}\bar{\gamma}\bar{\delta}} = 0 \tag{8.21}$$

$$R_{\beta\gamma} = R_{\bar{\beta}\bar{\gamma}} = 0 \tag{8.22}$$

where $R_{\beta\gamma}$, $R_{\bar{\beta}\bar{\gamma}}$ *are the components of the Ricci tensor field and all these are taken with respect to the local orthonormal frame field* $(Z_1, ..., Z_n, Z_{\bar{1}}, ..., Z_{\bar{n}})$.

Proof. From the relation (3.2) if we put $X = Z_\alpha$, $Y = Z_\beta$, $Z = Z_\gamma$ and $W = Z_{\bar{\delta}}$, we get

$$R(Z_\alpha, Z_\beta, Z_\gamma, Z_{\bar{\delta}}) = R(JZ_\alpha, JZ_\beta, JZ_\gamma, JZ_{\bar{\delta}}) = R(iZ_\alpha, iZ_\beta, iZ_\gamma, -iZ_{\bar{\delta}})$$

$$= -(i)^4 R(Z_\alpha, Z_\beta, Z_\gamma, Z_{\bar{\delta}})$$

or $\quad 2R(Z_\alpha, Z_\beta, Z_\gamma, Z_{\bar{\delta}}) = 2R_{\alpha\beta\gamma\bar{\delta}} = 0$

Similarly we obtain the other relations of (8.20).

It is known that

$$R^{\bar{\epsilon}}_{\alpha\beta\bar{\delta}} = \sum_{\alpha=1}^{n} g^{\bar{\epsilon}\alpha} R_{\alpha\beta\gamma\bar{\delta}}$$

which by the second term of (8.20) implies $R^{\bar{\epsilon}}_{\alpha\beta\gamma\bar{\delta}} = 0$. Similarly we have the other relations of (8.21

We also know that

$$R_{\alpha\beta} = \sum_{\gamma=1}^{n} (R^{\gamma}_{\alpha\gamma\beta} + R^{\bar{\gamma}}_{\alpha\bar{\gamma}\beta}), \qquad R_{\bar{\alpha}\bar{\beta}} = \sum_{\gamma=1}^{n} (R^{\gamma}_{\bar{\alpha}\gamma\bar{\beta}} + R^{\bar{\gamma}}_{\bar{\alpha}\bar{\gamma}\bar{\beta}})$$

from which by means of (8.21) we obtain (8.22).

REFERENCES

[1] BISHOP, R., GOLDBERG, S., On the second cohomology group of a Kähler manifold of positive curvature, Proc. Am. Math. Soc. **16** (1965) 112–122.
[2] GOLDBERG, S., KOBAYASHI, S., Holomorphic bisectional curvature, J. Differ. Geom. **1** (1967) 225–233.
[3] GRAY, A., Vector cross products on manifolds, Trans. Am. Math. Soc. **141** (1969) 465–504.
[4] GRAY, A., Almost complex submanifolds of the six sphere, Proc. Am. Math. Soc. **20** (1969) 277–279.
[5] GRAY, A., Nearly Kähler manifolds, J. Differ. Geom. **4** (1970) 283–310.
[6] GRAY, A., Riemannian manifolds with geodesic symmetry of order 3, J. Differ. Geom. **7** (1972) 343–370.
[7] KOBAYASHI, S., NOMIZU, K., Foundations of Differential Geometry **2**, Wiley, New York (1969).
[8] LICHNEROWICZ, A., Géométrie des groupes de transformations, Dunod, Paris (1958).
[9] LICHNEROWICZ, A., Variétés et première classe de Chern, J. Differ. Geom. **1** (1967) 195–224.
[10] ROBERTSON, S., "Elementary geometry of complex manifolds", these Proceedings.
[11] SHIOHAMA, K., The diameter of δ-pinched manifolds, J. Differ. Geom. **5** (1971) 61–74.
[12] WOLF, J., GRAY, A., Homogeneous spaces defined by Lie group automorphisms I, J. Differ. Geom. **2** (1968) 77–114.
[13] WOLF, J., GRAY, A., Homogeneous spaces defined by Lie group automorphisms II, J. Differ. Geom. **2** (1968) 115–159.
[14] YANO, K., BOCHNER, S., Curvature and Betti numbers, Ann. Math. Studies No. 32, Princeton Univ. Press (1952).

IAEA-SMR-18/61

BOUNDED HOMOGENEOUS DOMAINS WHICH ARE NOT SYMMETRIC

G. TSAGAS*
Department of Mathematics,
University of Patras,
Patras, Greece

Abstract

BOUNDED HOMOGENEOUS DOMAINS WHICH ARE NOT SYMMETRIC.

Let $\mathbb{C}^n$ be a complex euclidean space. A bounded open connected subset D of $\mathbb{C}^n$ is called a bounded domain. Bounded homogeneous domains in $\mathbb{C}^n$ are studied. Contents: bounded homogeneous domains; j-Lie algebras; Siegel domains; s-structure on a bounded domain.

1. BOUNDED HOMOGENEOUS DOMAINS

Let D be a bounded domain in $\mathbb{C}^n$. We denote by S(D) the set of holomorphic functions on D. Therefore we have

$$S(D) = \{f/f{:}D \to D, f \text{ holomorphic}\}$$

This is a vector space on which we define an inner product as follows:

$$\langle\ \rangle : S(D) \times S(D) \to \mathbb{C}, \quad \langle\ \rangle : (f_1, f_2) \to \langle f_1, f_2\rangle = \int_D f_1(Z) f_2(Z) d\mu(Z)$$

where $Z = (Z_1, ..., Z_n)$, $\|f_1\| = \langle f_1, f_1\rangle^{1/2}$ and $\mu(Z)$ is the Lebesgue measure in $\mathbb{R}^{2n}$. The vector space S(D) with the inner product $\langle\ \rangle$ becomes a Hilbert space.

Theorem 1.1. *Let $\varphi_0, \varphi_1, ...$ be any orthonormal basis for the Hilbert space* S(D), *where* D *is a bounded domain in* $\mathbb{C}^n$. *Then the series*

$$\sum_{n=0}^{\infty} \varphi_n(Z)\overline{\varphi_n(J)}$$

converges uniformly on each compact subset B of D × D. The sum $K(Z,\overline{J})$ is independent of the choice of the orthonormal basis ([4] p.295).

From this we conclude that given a bounded domain D in $\mathbb{C}^n$ we can define a complex function K on D × D as follows:

$$K{:}D \times D \to \mathbb{C}, \qquad K{:}(Z,J) \to K(Z,J) = \sum_{n=0}^{\infty} \varphi_n(Z)\overline{\varphi}_n(J)$$

---

* Present address: Department of Mathematics, University of Thessaloniki, Thessaloniki, Greece.

where $\varphi_0, \varphi_1, \ldots$ is any orthonormal basis of S(D); K is called the Bergman kernel function for D. On D we consider the following tensor field:

$$h = \sum_{i=1}^{n} \sum_{j=1}^{n} \frac{\log K(Z,\bar{Z})}{\partial Z_i \partial \bar{Z}_j} dZ_i \otimes d\bar{Z}_j \tag{1.1}$$

where $\partial/\partial Z_1, \ldots, \partial/\partial Z_n$ are complex vector fields of type (1,0) and $\partial/\partial \bar{Z}_1, \ldots, \partial/\partial \bar{Z}_n$ are complex vector fields of type (0,1) on D and $(dZ_1, \ldots, dZ_n)$, $(d\bar{Z}_1, \ldots, d\bar{Z}_n)$ are the dual bases of $(\partial/\partial Z_1, \ldots, \partial/\partial Z_1)$ and $(\partial/\partial \bar{Z}_1, \ldots, \partial/\partial \bar{Z}_n)$, respectively.

Let g be the real part of the restriction of h on $D^1(D) \times D^1(D)$, where $D^1(D)$ is the Lie algebra of all real vector fields on D. The metric g is called the Bergman metric on D.

Theorem 1.2. *Let* D *be a bounded domain in* $\mathbb{C}^n$. *If* g *is the real part of* h *defined by Eq.(1.1), then* (D,g) *is a Kähler manifold* ([4], p.296).

Let D be a bounded domain in $\mathbb{C}^n$. If f is a holomorphic diffeomorphism of D onto itself, f is an isometry for the Kähler manifold (D,g). We consider the set H(D) of holomorphic diffeomorphisms of D onto itself. This group is a subgroup of I(D), where I(D) is the group of isometries on D provided with the Bergman metric. We take on I(D) the compact open topology. It can be easily seen that H(D) is a closed subgroup of I(D).

If H(D) is transitive on D, then the bounded domain D is called homogeneous. Therefore, if D is a bounded homogeneous domain in $\mathbb{C}^n$, we have D = H(D)/K, where K is an isotropy subgroup of H(D) at one point of D.

2. j-LIE ALGEBRAS

To study the bounded homogeneous domain in $\mathbb{C}^n$ we introduce special Lie algebras. Let t be a Lie algebra over $\mathbb{R}$ having a distinguished subalgebra t_0. We assume that t has an endomorphism j with the following properties:

(i) $j(t_0) = 0$ (ii) $j^2(X) + X \in t_0 \quad \forall X \in t$

The triplet (t,t_0,j) is said to be j-Lie algebra if the following conditions are satisfied:

(a) $[X,Y] + j([j(X),Y]) + j([X,j(Y)]) - [j(X), j(Y)] \in t_0 \quad \forall X,Y \in t$

(b) There exists a linear form w(X) on t such that

$w([j(X), j(Y)]) = w([X,Y]),\ w([j(X),X]) > 0$ for $X,Y \in t$, but $X \notin t_0$

(c) If k is a compact subalgebra of t and $j(k) \subseteq k + t_0$ then $k \subset t_0$

The j-Lie algebras are related to bounded homogeneous domains. These relations can be stated as follows ([10], pp. 47–48).

Theorem 2.1. *We consider a bounded homogeneous domain* D = G/K *in* $\mathbb{C}^n$, *where* G *is a Lie group of holomorphic transformations on* D, *and* K *is the isotropy subgroup of* G *at one point* *of* D. *Let* $\mathfrak{t},\mathfrak{t}_0$ *be the Lie algebras of* G *and* K *respectively. If* j *is the linear endomorphism on* $\mathfrak{t}$ *induced by the complex structure on* D, *then the triplet* $(\mathfrak{t},\mathfrak{t}_0,j)$ *is a* j*-Lie algebra.*

In general there are many j-Lie algebras corresponding to the same bounded homogeneous domain D, because there is more than one Lie subgroup of H(D) acting transitively on D.

Theorem 2.2. *Let* $(\mathfrak{t},\mathfrak{t}_0,j)$ *be a* j*-Lie algebra. Then there is always a bounded homogeneous domain* $D = G/H$ *whose* j*-Lie algebra is isomorphic to* $(\mathfrak{t},\mathfrak{t}_0,j)$.

3. SIEGEL DOMAINS

Let T be an n-dimensional vector space over $\mathbb{R}$. A domain V in T is called a convex cone if the following three conditions are satisfied:

(i) For any $x \in V$ and for any $\lambda \in \mathbb{R}$; $\lambda x \in V$;
(ii) If $x,y \in V$, then $x + y \in V$.
(iii) V contains no entire straight lines.

Let W be a complex vector space of complex dimension m. A mapping F of $W \times W$ into $T^{\mathbb{C}} \cong \mathbb{C}^n$ is called a V-hermitian form if it satisfies the following four conditions:

(i) $F(u,v)$ is $\mathbb{C}$-linear in u;
(ii) $\overline{F(u,v)} = F(v,u)$;
(iii) $F(u,u) \in \overline{V}$, where $\overline{V}$ is the closure of V in $T \cong \mathbb{R}^n$;
(iv) $F(u,u) = 0 \rightarrow u = 0$.

Let D(V,F) be a subset of the complex vector space $T^{\mathbb{C}} \times W$ defined by

$$D(V,F) = \{(z,u) \in T^{\mathbb{C}} \times W : z = x + iy \in T^{\mathbb{C}},\ y - F(u,u) \in V\}$$

D(V,F) is a domain in $T^{\mathbb{C}} \times W$ which is called a Siegel domain of type II. If $W = \{0\}$, the domain D(V,F) is reduced to the tube domain $\{z : x + iy \in T^{\mathbb{C}} : x,y \in T,\ y \in V\}$ and denoted by D(V). D(V) is called a Siegel domain of type I. Therefore a Siegel domain of type I is regarded as a special case of Siegel domains of type II.

Example 3.1. Let $T = H(n,\mathbb{R})$ be the set of all real symmetric matrices $n \times n$. We consider the subset $H^+(n,\mathbb{R})$ of T defined by

$$H^+(n,\mathbb{R}) = \{\alpha \in H^+(n,\mathbb{R}) : \mathrm{Det}(\alpha) > 0\} \tag{3.1}$$

Then $D(H^+(n,\mathbb{R})) = \{\alpha_1 + i\alpha_2 : \alpha_1, \alpha_2 \in H(n,\mathbb{R}),\ \det\alpha_1 > 0\}$ is a Siegel domain of type II.

Proof. It can be easily proved that $H^+(n,\mathbb{R})$ is a convex cone in $H(n,\mathbb{R})$. After that we conclude that $D(H^+(n,\mathbb{R}))$is a Siegel domain of type I and hence type II. This is the Siegel upper half-plane of deg. n.

Proposition 3.2. *Let* D(V,F) *be a Siegel domain of type II in* $T^{\mathbb{C}} \times W$. *This is holomorphically equivalent to a bounded domain in* $T^{\mathbb{C}} \times W$ ([5], p.2).

Let D(V,F) be a Siegel domain of type II in $T^{\mathbb{C}} \times W$. We put

$$G = \{f \in A(T^{\mathbb{C}} \times W) : f(D(V,F)) = D(V,F)\}$$

where $A(T^{\mathbb{C}} \times W)$ is the Lie group of affine transformations on the vector space $T^{\mathbb{C}} \times W$. G is a closed subgroup of $A(T^{\mathbb{C}} \times W)$ and is called the affine automorphism group of D(V,F).

Let D(V,F) be a Siegel domain of type II in $T^{\mathbb{C}} \times W$. If its affine automorphism group G acts transitively, D(V,F) is called an affine homogeneous Siegel domain of type II.

Theorem 3.3. *Let* D *be a bounded homogeneous domain in* $\mathbb{C}^n$. *Then there exists an affine homogeneous Siegel domain* D(V,F) *of type II holomorphically equivalent to* D ([5], p.12).

Example 3.4. Let T = H(2, ℝ) be the vector space over ℝ of all real symmetric matrices 2 × 2. We consider the following Siegel domain $D(H^+(2,\mathbb{R}),F)$ of type II in $T^{\mathbb{C}} \times \mathbb{C}$, where

$$F : \mathbb{C} \times \mathbb{C} \to H(2,\mathbb{R}),\ F : (u,v) \to F(u,v) = \begin{pmatrix} u\bar{v} & 0 \\ 0 & 0 \end{pmatrix}$$

Then $D(H^+(2,\mathbb{R}),F)$ is an affine homogeneous Siegel domain of type II.

Proof. It can be easily proved that the affine automorphism group G of $D(H^+(2,\mathbb{R}),F)$ acts transitively on it. Let D_1 be the bounded homogeneous domain in $\mathbb{C}^4$ which is holomorphically equivalent to $D(H^+(2,\mathbb{R}),F)$.

Example 3.5. We consider the following Siegel domain $D(H^+(2,\mathbb{R}),F_1)$ of type II in $H(2,\mathbb{R})^{\mathbb{C}} \times \mathbb{C}^2$, where F_1 is defined as follows:

$$F_1 : \mathbb{C}^2 \times \mathbb{C}^2 \to H(2,\mathbb{R})$$

$$F_1 = \left(u = \begin{pmatrix} u_1 \\ u_2 \end{pmatrix}, v = \begin{pmatrix} v_1 \\ v_2 \end{pmatrix}\right) \to F_1(u,v) = \tfrac{1}{2}(u^t\bar{v} + \bar{v}^t u)$$

$$= \begin{pmatrix} u_1\bar{v}_1 & \dfrac{u_1\bar{v}_2 + u_2\bar{v}_1}{2} \\ \dfrac{u_1\bar{v}_2 + u_2\bar{v}_1}{2} & u_2\bar{v}_2 \end{pmatrix}$$

Then $D(H^+(2,\mathbb{R}),F_1)$ is an affine homogeneous Siegel domain of type II.

Proof. It is the same as in example (3.4). Let D_2 be the bounded homogeneous domain in $\mathbb{C}^5$ which is holomorphically equivalent to $D(H^+(2,\mathbb{R}),F_1)$.

D_1 and D_2 were first examples of bounded homogeneous domains in $\mathbb{C}^4$ and $\mathbb{C}^5$, respectively, which were given by Pyatetzkij-Shapiro [9], and they are not symmetric.

4. s-STRUCTURE ON A BOUNDED DOMAIN

Let D be a bounded domain in $\mathbb{C}^n$. Let $\{s_z : z \in D\}$ be a family of holomorphic diffeomorphisms on D such that for every $z \in D$ there exists one member of the family $\{s_z : z \in D\}$

which has z as an isolated fixed point. The family $\{s : z \in D\}$ is called a holomorphic s-structure on D, which is called a bounded s-domain.

Theorem 4.1. *Let* D *be a bounded domain. If there exists a holomorphic s-structure* $\{s_z : z \in D\}$ *on* D, *then* D *is a bounded homogeneous domain.*

Proof. Since each s_z is an isometry for (D,g), we obtain that the holomorphic s-structure is riemannian. Therefore the theorem follows from Ref.[7].

Let $\{s_z : z \in D\}$ be a holomorphic s-structure on a bounded domain D in $\mathbb{C}^n$. This defines a tensor field S of type (1.1) defined by $S_z = (s_{z*})_z$ $\forall z \in D$. If S is differentiable, then $\{s_z : z \in D\}$ is called differentiable. If S is differentiable and satisfies $Ss_{z*}X = s_{z*}SX$ for every vector field X on D and $\forall z \in D$, then the $\{s_z : z \in D\}$ is called regular. A bounded domain D with a regular holomorphic s-structure $\{s_z : z \in D\}$ is called a regularly bounded s-domain or, briefly, RB s-domain. If there exists a positive integer k such that $s_z^k = \mathrm{id}, \forall z \in D$, then $\{s_z : z \in D\}$ is called a holomorphic s-structure of order k. A bounded domain D in $\mathbb{C}^n$ with holomorphic s-structure of order k is called a k-symmetric domain. If k = 2, we obtain the usual symmetric domains. In this case S = –I, where I is the Kronecker tensor field and therefore symmetric domains in $\mathbb{C}^n$ are RB s-domains. A bounded s-domain D is denoted by (D,s).

Theorem 4.2. *Let* (D,S) *be a bounded s-domain in* $\mathbb{C}^n$ *with holomorphic s-structure* $\{s_z : z \in D\}$. *Then there is another holomorphic s'-structure* $\{s'_z : z \in D\}$ *of finite order on* D *and hence* {D,s'} *becomes a* k-*symmetric domain.*

Proof. We can prove the theorem by the same technique as in Ref.[11]. From Theorem 4.2 we conclude that the study of bounded s-domains is reduced to the study of k-symmetric domains.

For the symmetric domains in $\mathbb{C}^n$ (in this case we have k = 2) there are the following theorems.

Theorem 4.3. *Let* D = G/H *be a bounded homogeneous domain in* $\mathbb{C}^n$, *where* G *is a Lie group of holomorphic diffeomorphisms and acting transitively on* D. *If* G *is semisimple,* D *is a symmetric domain* [1,6].

Theorem 4.4. *We consider a bounded homogeneous domain* D = G/H *in* $\mathbb{C}^n$. *If* G *is reductive,* D *is a symmetric domain* [8].

Theorem 4.5. *Let* D = G/H *be a bounded homogeneous domain in* $\mathbb{C}^n$. *If* G *is unimodular,* D *is a symmetric domain* [3].

There are bounded homogeneous domains in $\mathbb{C}^n$, $n \geqslant 4$, which are not symmetric: Examples 3.4 and 3.5. These can be classified up to higher order than 2, which corresponds to the symmetric domains in $\mathbb{C}^n$. This classification will appear elsewhere.

REFERENCES

[1] BOREL, A., A Kählerian coset space of semisimple Lie groups, Proc. Natl Acad. Sci. USA **12** (1954) 1147–1151.

[2] CARTAN, E., Sur les domaines bornés homogènes de l'espace de n variables complexes, Abh. Math. Sem. Hamburg Univ. **11** (1935) 116–162.

[3] HANO, J., On Kählerian homogeneous spaces of unimodular Lie groups, Am. J. Math. **79** (1957) 885–900.

[4] HERGASON, S., Differential Geometry and Symmetric Spaces, Academic Press, New York (1962).
[5] KANEYUKI, S., Homogeneous Bounded Domains and Siegel Domains, Springer-Verlag, New York (1971).
[6] KOSZUL, J., Sur la forme hermitienne canonique des espaces homogènes complexes, Can. J. Math. **7** (1955) 562–576.
[7] LEDGER, A., OBATA, M., Affine and Riemannian s-manifolds, J. Differ. Geom. **2** (1968) 451–459.
[8] MOTSUSHIMA, Y., Sur les espaces homogènes Kählériens d'un groupe de Lie réductif, Nagoya Math. J. **11** (1957) 56–60.
[9] PYATETSKIJ-SHAPIRO, J., On a problem proposed by E. Cartan, Dokl. Akad. Nauk SSSR **124** (1959) 272–
[10] PYATETSKIJ-SHAPIRO, J., Automorphic function and the geometry of classical domains, Gordon & Breach, New York (1969).
[11] TSAGAS, G., LEDGER, A., Riemannian s-manifolds, to appear in J. Differ. Geom.

HOLOMORPHIC FUNCTIONS OF SEVERAL COMPLEX VARIABLES WITH NON-NEGATIVE IMAGINARY PART AND SOME APPLICATIONS

V.S. VLADIMIROV
Steklov Institute of Mathematics,
Moscow, USSR

Abstract

HOLOMORPHIC FUNCTIONS OF SEVERAL COMPLEX VARIABLES WITH NON-NEGATIVE IMAGINARY PART AND SOME APPLICATIONS.

Integral representations for holomorphic functions with non-negative imaginary part in the tube domain over a proper cone are derived in terms of the Cauchy kernel and in terms of its inverse Laplace transform. The results are applied to convolution equations which are passive with respect to a proper convex solid cone.
1. Estimates for holomorphic functions with non-negative imaginary part. 2. Holomorphic functions with non-negative imaginary part in the upper half-plane. 3. Non-negative pluriharmonic functions in $T^{\mathbb{R}^n_+}$. 4. Holomorphic functions with non-negative imaginary part in the tube domain T^C. 5. Linear passive systems.

We use the theory of the Laplace transform of tempered distributions presented by the author at the Summer Course on Global Analysis and its Applications, Trieste, 1972 [1]. For distribution theory see Schwartz [13].

1. ESTIMATES FOR HOLOMORPHIC FUNCTIONS WITH NON-NEGATIVE IMAGINARY PART

By $x = (x_1, ..., x_n)$, y, ξ, ... we denote points of the n-dimensional real Euclidean space $\mathbb{R}^n$. $z = (z_1, ..., z_n) = x + iy$, ζ, ... designate points of the n-dimensional complex space $\mathbb{C}^n$; and

$$(z, \xi) = z_1\xi_1 + ... + z_n\xi_n, \; z \in \mathbb{C}^n, \; \xi \in \mathbb{R}^n$$

is the scalar product. Let $\alpha = (\alpha_1, ..., \alpha_n)$ be a multi-index. We denote

$$D_j = \frac{\partial}{\partial x_j}, \quad D = \left(\frac{\partial}{\partial x_1}, ..., \frac{\partial}{\partial x_n}\right), \quad D^\alpha = \frac{\partial^{|\alpha|}}{\partial x_1^{\alpha_1} ... \partial x_n^{\alpha_n}}, \quad |\alpha| = \alpha_1 + ... + \alpha_n$$

Let C be a cone in $\mathbb{R}^n$ with vertex in 0. The cone

$$C^* = [\xi : (y,\xi) \geqslant 0, \quad \forall y \in C]$$

is called a **conjugate** to the cone C.

Obviously, C^* is a closed convex cone with the vertex in 0; $(\text{ch}C)^* = C^*$, $C^{**} = \overline{\text{ch}C}$. Here chC is the convex hull of C.

The cone C is called **proper** if there exists a plane of support to $\overline{\text{ch}C}$ having 0 as the unique common point with $\overline{\text{ch}C}$. The cone C' is called **compact** in the cone C if $\overline{C}' \subset C \cup \{0\}$; we then write $C' \Subset C$.

Examples of proper cones

(1) The origin of co-ordinates: $\{0\}$, $\{0\}^* = \mathbb{R}^n$.
(2) The positive octant: $\mathbb{R}^n_+ = [y : y_1 > 0, ..., y_n > 0]$, $\mathbb{R}^{n*}_+ = \overline{\mathbb{R}^n_+}$.
(3) The future light cone in $\mathbb{R}^{n+1}$:

$$V^+ = [y = (y_0, \mathbf{y}) : y_0 > 0, y^2 > 0], \qquad V^{+*} = \overline{V^+}$$

Here $y^2 = y_0^2 - |\mathbf{y}|^2$ is the Lorentz square and $\mathbf{y} = (y_1, ..., y_n)$.
(4) The cone of positive $n \times n$ matrices:

$$P_n = [A : A > 0], \quad P_n^* = [B : B \geqslant 0] = \overline{P_n}$$

Lemma 1.1. *The following statements are equivalent:*

(i) *The cone* Γ *is proper.*
(ii) *The cone* $\overline{\mathrm{ch}\Gamma}$ *does not contain a whole line.*
(iii) *The cone* $C = \mathrm{int}\Gamma^*$ *is not empty.*
(iv) *For any cone* $C' \Subset C$ *there exists a number* $\sigma > 0$ such that the inequality

$$(y,\xi) \geqslant \sigma|y|\,|\xi|, \quad y \in C', \quad \xi \in \overline{\mathrm{ch}\Gamma}$$

holds.

(v) *For any vector* $e \in C$ *the set*

$$[\xi : 0 \leqslant (e, \xi) \leqslant 1, \quad \xi \in \overline{\mathrm{ch}\Gamma}]$$

is bounded.

Let Γ be a closed convex proper cone in $\mathbb{R}^n$. By Lemma 1.1, $C = \mathrm{int}\ \Gamma^* \neq \emptyset$.

We denote by $\mathscr{S}'(\Gamma)$ the space of all tempered distributions $\mathscr{S}'$ with support contained in the cone Γ. The topology of $\mathscr{S}'(\Gamma)$ is induced by the topology of $\mathscr{S}'$. The set $\mathscr{S}'(\Gamma)$ is a convolution algebra (associative and commutative) which contains an identity element. The algebra $\mathscr{S}'(\Gamma)$ is isomorphic to the algebra $H(C)$ which consists of all functions $f(z)$ holomorphi in the tube domain $T^C = \mathbb{R}^n + iC$ over the cone C and satisfying the following growth conditio for any cone $C' \Subset C$ there exists a number $M(C')$ such that the inequality

$$|f(z)| \leqslant M(C') \frac{1 + |z|^\alpha}{|y|^\beta}, \; z \in T^{C'}$$

holds for some $\alpha \geqslant 0$ and $\beta \geqslant 0$ (depending only on f). This isomorphism is effected by the Laplace transform $\mathscr{L}$ (see [1]),

$$f(z) = \mathscr{L}[g] = F[g(\xi)e^{-(y,\xi)}]$$

Let C be a connected open cone in $\mathbb{R}^n$ and let $f(z)$ be a holomorphic function and $\mathrm{Im}\, f(z) \geqslant 0$ in the tube T^C. Without loss of generality we may assume that the cone C is convex and $\mathrm{Im}\, f(z)$ is positive in T^C. In fact, $f(z)$ is holomorphic in the envelope of holomorph

T^{chC} (Bochner's theorem) and f(z) takes the same values in T^{chC} as in T^C; then we also have Im f(z) $\geqslant 0$ in T^{chC}. Moreover, if there exists a point $z_0 \in T^C$ such that Im $f(z_0) = 0$, then, by the maximum principle for harmonic functions, we have Im f(z) = 0 in T^C, and then f(z) = real const.

Theorem I. *If a function* f(z) *is holomorphic and* Im f(z) $\geqslant 0$ *in* T^C, *then for any cone* $C' \Subset C$ *there exists* M(C') *such that the inequality*

$$|f(z)| \leqslant M(C') \frac{1 + |z|^2}{|y|}, \; z \in T^{C'} \tag{1.1}$$

holds.

Corollary 1. *Under the conditions of Theorem I,* f(z) *belongs to* H(C); *if furthermore* f(z) $\not\equiv 0$ *then* $1/f \in H(C)$.

Corollary 2. *If* $g \in \mathscr{S}'(C^*)$ *and* Im $\mathscr{L}$ [g](z) > 0 *in* T^C, *then the convolution equation*

$$g*u = f, \; f \in \mathscr{S}'(C^*)$$

has a (unique) solution in the algebra $\mathscr{S}'(C^*)$.

Corollary 3. *Under conditions of Theorem I there exists a boundary value*

$$f^+(x) = \lim f(x + iy), \; y \to 0, \; y \in C$$

in the topology of the space $\mathscr{S}'$.

Remark. The existence of boundary values for holomorphic functions has been proved by many authors: Fatou [2] ($\mathscr{L}^\infty$); Riesz [3] ($\mathscr{L}^p$); Köthe [4] ($\mathscr{D}'$); Sato [5] (hyperfunctions); Vladimirov [6] (see also [1]); Tillmann [7] ($\mathscr{S}'$); Tillmann [8]; Luszczki and Zielezny [9] ($\mathscr{D}'_{\mathscr{L}^p}$); Komatsu [10] (ultradistributions); Martineau [11].

The estimate (1.1) was first proved by Vladimirov [15]. For proof of Theorem I we use the following three lemmas.

Lemma 1.2. *If a function* f(z) *is holomorphic and* Im f(z) $\geqslant 0$ *in the unit polycircle* $U^n = [z : |z_1| < 1, \ldots, |z_n| < 1]$, *the following estimates hold:*

$$\text{Im } f(0) \frac{1 - \max|z_j|}{1 + \max|z_j|} \leqslant |f(z) - \text{Re } f(0)| \leqslant \text{Im } f(0) \frac{1 + \max|z_j|}{1 - \max|z_j|} \tag{1.2}$$

Corollary

$$|f(z)| \leqslant \frac{2|f(0)|}{1 - \max|z_j|}, \; z \in U^n$$

For proof we fix $z \in U^n$ and denote $\rho = \max_j |z_j|$; then $0 \leqslant \rho < 1$. Let $\rho > 0$ (for $\rho = 0$ the estimate (1.2) is trivial). The function $\varphi(\lambda) = f(\lambda z/\rho)$ is holomorphic and Im $\varphi(\lambda) \geqslant 0$ in the circle $|\lambda| < 1$.

The function

$$\psi(\lambda) = \frac{\varphi(\lambda) - \varphi(0)}{\varphi(\lambda) - \bar{\varphi}(0)}$$

is holomorphic and $\psi(0) = 0$, $|\psi(\lambda)| < 1$ in the circle $|\lambda| < 1$. By Schwartz's lemma $|\psi(\lambda)| \leqslant |\lambda|$; then we have

$$\operatorname{Im} \varphi(0) \frac{1 - |\lambda|}{1 + |\lambda|} \leqslant |\varphi(\lambda) - \operatorname{Re} \varphi(0)| = |i \operatorname{Im} \varphi(0)| \left| \frac{1 + \psi(\lambda)}{1 - \psi(\lambda)} \right| \leqslant \operatorname{Im} \varphi(0) \frac{1 + |\lambda|}{1 - |\lambda|}$$

Putting $\lambda = \rho < 1$ we get Lemma 1.2.

Lemma 1.3. *If* f(z) *is holomorphic and* Im f(z) $\geqslant 0$ *in* $T^{\mathbb{R}^n_+}$, *the following estimate holds:*

$$|f(z)| \leqslant \sqrt{2} |f(\mathbf{i})| \max_j \frac{1 + |z_j|^2}{y_j}, \quad z \in T^{\mathbb{R}^n_+}$$

Here $\mathbf{i} = (i, \ldots, i)$.

Proof. The mapping

$$w_j = \frac{z_j - i}{z_j + i}, \quad z_j = i \frac{1 + w_j}{1 - w_j}, \quad j = 1, \ldots, n$$

transforms $T^{\mathbb{R}^n_+}$ biholomorphically onto U^n. The function

$$\varphi(w) = f\left(i \frac{1 + w_1}{1 - w_1}, \ldots, i \frac{1 + w_n}{1 - w_n} \right)$$

is holomorphic and Im $\varphi(w) \geqslant 0$ in U^n. By the corollary to Lemma 1.2 we have the estimate:

$$|f(z)| \leqslant \frac{2|f(\mathbf{i})|}{1 - \max_j \left| \frac{z_j - i}{z_j + i} \right|}, \quad z \in T^{\mathbb{R}^n_+}$$

The inequality

$$\left| \frac{z - i}{z + i} \right| < 1 - \frac{\sqrt{2}\, y}{1 + |z|^2}, \quad y > 0$$

is true because for $\alpha = (1 + x^2/y) + y \geqslant 2$ we have

$$2\alpha^2 - (\alpha + 2)(\sqrt{2}\alpha - 1) > 0$$

Lemma 1.3 follows from the estimates obtained.

Lemma 1.4. *If* f(z) *is holomorphic and* Im f(z) $\geqslant 0$ *in* T^C *where* $C = [y : (y, e_j) > 0, j = 1, \ldots,$ $|e_j| = 1$, *is the* n-*faced cone, the following estimate holds:*

$$|f(z)| \leqslant \sqrt{2} |f(T^{-1}_{\mathbf{i}})| \frac{1 + |z|^2}{\Delta(y)}, \quad z \in T^C$$

Here T *is the linear mapping:*

$$y \to Ty = [(y, e_1), \ldots, (y, e_n)]$$

and $\Delta(y)$ *is the (Euclidean) distance from the point* $y \in C$ *to the boundary* ∂C *of* C.

Proof. The mapping $w = Tz$, $z = T^{-1}w$ transforms T^C biholomorphically onto $T^{\mathbb{R}^n_+}$. The function $f(T^{-1}w)$ is holomorphic and $\operatorname{Im} f(T^{-1}w) \geqslant 0$ in $T^{\mathbb{R}^n_+}$. By Lemma 1.3,

$$|f(T^{-1}w)| \leqslant \sqrt{2}|f(T^{-1}_{\ \mathbf{i}})| \max_j \frac{1 + |w_j|^2}{\operatorname{Im} w_j}, \quad w \in T^{\mathbb{R}^n_+}$$

$$|f(z)| \leqslant \sqrt{2}|f(T^{-1}\mathbf{i})| \max_j \frac{1 + |(z,e_j)|^2}{(y,e_j)}, \quad z \in T^C \tag{1.3}$$

Taking into account

$$|(z,e_j)| \leqslant |z|, \qquad \Delta(y) = \min_j (y,e_j)$$

we get Lemma 1.4 from the estimate (1.3).

Proof of Theorem I. Let $C' \Subset C$. We cover the cone $\overline{C}'$ by a finite number of n-faced cones $C_k \Subset C$, $k = 1, \ldots, N$.

We choose cones $C'_k \Subset C_k$, $1 \leqslant k \leqslant N$, such that cones $\{C'_k\}$ also cover the cone C'. By Lemma 1.4 we have the estimates:

$$|f(z)| \leqslant \sqrt{2}|f(T_k^{-1}\,\mathbf{i})| \frac{1 + |z|^2}{\Delta_k(y)}, \quad z \in T^{C_k}, k = 1, \ldots, N \tag{1.4}$$

Here $\Delta_k(y)$ is the distance from $y \in C_k$ to ∂C_k. By Lemma 1.1 we have $\Delta_k(y) \geqslant \sigma_k |y|$, $y \in C'_k \Subset C_k$, for some $\sigma_k > 0$. Hence, owing to (1.4), we have the estimates:

$$|f(z)| \leqslant \sqrt{2}|f(T_k^{-1}\mathbf{i})| \frac{1 + |z|^2}{\sigma_k |y|}, \quad z \in T^{C'_k}, \quad k = 1, \ldots, N$$

Theorem I follows if we put

$$M(C') = \max_{1 \leqslant k \leqslant N} \frac{\sqrt{2}}{\sigma_k} |f(T_k^{-1}\,\mathbf{i})|$$

Remark. For future tube $\tau^+ = \mathbb{R}^4 + iV^+$ the corresponding estimates are (see Vladimirov [16])

$$\operatorname{Im} f(\mathbf{i}) \frac{2y^2}{|(z + \mathbf{i})^2|^2} \leqslant |f(z) - \operatorname{Re} f(\mathbf{i})| \leqslant \operatorname{Im} f(\mathbf{i}) \frac{|(z + \mathbf{i})^2|^2}{2y^2}, z \in \tau^+ \tag{1.5}$$

here $\mathbf{i} = (i, 0)$, $z^2 = z_0^2 - z_1^2 - z_2^2 - z_3^2$. For the "generalized unit circle" $\tau_0 = [w : ww^* < I]$, which is biholomorphically equivalent to the future tube τ^+, the estimates are

$$\frac{\operatorname{Im} f(0)}{8} \det (I - ww^*) \leqslant |f(w) - \operatorname{Re} f(0)| \leqslant \frac{8 \operatorname{Im} f(0)}{\det (I - ww^*)}, w \in \tau_0 \tag{1.6}$$

Here w are complex 2 X 2 matrices. The estimates (1.6) can be refined as follows:

$$\text{Im } f(0) \min_i \frac{1-\lambda_i}{1+\lambda_i} \leqslant |f(w) - \text{Re } f(0)| \leqslant \text{Im } f(0) \max_i \frac{1+\lambda_i}{1-\lambda_i}$$

where λ_1 and λ_2 are the eigenvalues of the matrix $\sqrt{ww^*}$. A similar refinement can be made for the estimate (1.5).

2. HOLOMORPHIC FUNCTIONS WITH NON-NEGATIVE IMAGINARY PART IN THE UPPER HALF-PLANE

Let f(z) be a holomorphic function and Im f(z) ⩾ 0 in the upper half-plane y > 0. Then by Theorem I the estimate

$$|f(z)| \leqslant M \frac{1+|z|^2}{y}, \quad y > 0 \tag{2.1}$$

holds. Let δ and R be positive numbers, |z| < R, y > 0. By the residue theorem we have

$$\frac{f(z+i\delta)}{1+z^2} = \frac{1}{2\pi i}\left(\int_{-R}^{R} + \int_{C_R}\right) \frac{f(z'+i\delta)dz'}{(i+z'^2)(z'-z)} + \frac{f(i+i\delta)}{2i(z-i)}, \quad y>0,\ |z|<R \tag{2.2}$$

Here the contour C_R is shown in Fig.1. Similarly for the function $\bar{f}(\bar{z}+i\delta)$, which is holomorphic in the lower half-plane y < 0, we have

$$0 = \frac{1}{2\pi i}\left(\int_{R}^{-R} + \int_{-C_R}\right) \frac{\bar{f}(\bar{z}'+i\delta)\,dz'}{(1+z'^2)(z'-z)} - \frac{\bar{f}(i+i\delta)}{2i(z+i)}, \quad y>0,\ |z|<R \tag{2.3}$$

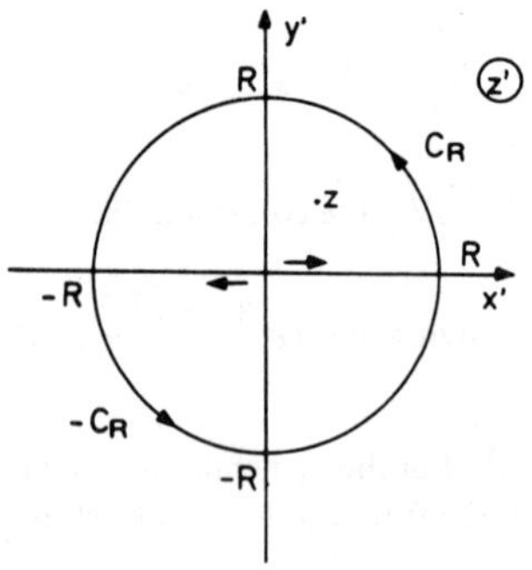

FIG.1. The contour C_R of integration.

Taking into account the estimate (2.1), we evaluate the integrals over the contours C_R and $-C_R$ in Eqs (2.2) as $R > 1$:

$$\left|\int_{C_R} \frac{f(z' + i\delta)\, dz'}{(1 + z'^2)(z' - z)}\right| = \left|\int_0^\pi \frac{f(Re^{i\varphi} + i\delta)\, iRe^{i\varphi} d\varphi}{(1 + R^2 e^{2i\varphi})(Re^{i\varphi} - z)}\right|$$

$$\leqslant M \int_0^\pi \frac{(1 + |Re^{i\varphi} + i\delta|^2)\, R d\varphi}{(R \sin\varphi + \delta)|1 + R^2 e^{2i\varphi}|\, |Re^{i\varphi} - z|} \leqslant \frac{MR[1 + (R + \delta)^2]}{(R^2 - 1)(R - |z|)} \int_0^\pi \frac{d\varphi}{R\sin\varphi + \delta}$$

The integral over the contour $-C_R$ has a similar estimate. Hence, as $R \to +\infty$ in Eqs (2.2) and (2.3) we get

$$f(z + i\delta) = \frac{1 + z^2}{2\pi i} \int_{-\infty}^{\infty} \frac{f(x' + i\delta)\, dx'}{(1 + x'^2)(x' - z)} + \frac{f(i + i\delta)}{2i}(z + i)$$

$$0 = -\frac{1 + z^2}{2\pi i} \int_{-\infty}^{\infty} \frac{\bar{f}(x' + i\delta)\, dx'}{(1 + x'^2)(x' - z)} - \frac{\bar{f}(i + i\delta)}{2i}(z - i)$$

Adding these equations, we get the integral representation for the function $f(z + i\delta)$:

$$f(z + i\delta) = \frac{1 + z^2}{\pi} \int_{-\infty}^{\infty} \frac{v(x',\delta)\, dx'}{(1 + x'^2)(x' - z)} + zv(0, 1 + \delta) + \operatorname{Re} f(i + i\delta), \quad y > 0 \tag{2.4}$$

where $v(x,y) = \operatorname{Im} f(z)$. We separate the imaginary part in Eq.(2.4). Then we get the integral representation for the function $v(x,y + \delta)$:

$$v(x,y + \delta) = \frac{y}{\pi} \int_{-\infty}^{\infty} v(x',\delta) \left[\frac{1}{(x - x')^2 + y^2} - \frac{1}{1 + x'^2}\right] dx' + yv(0,1 + \delta), \quad y > 0 \tag{2.5}$$

Since $v \geqslant 0$ we get from Eq.(2.5) the estimate

$$\frac{1}{\pi} \int_{-\infty}^{\infty} v(x',\delta) \left[\frac{1}{1 + x'^2} - \frac{1}{(x - x')^2 + y^2}\right] dx' \leqslant v(0, 1 + \delta), \; y > 0 \tag{2.6}$$

Finally, passing on to the limit in Eq.(2.6) as $y \to +\infty$, and using Beppo Levi's theorem, we get the estimate:

$$\frac{1}{\pi} \int_{-\infty}^{\infty} \frac{v(x',\delta)}{1+x'^2}\, dx' \leqslant v(0, 1+\delta), \quad \delta > 0 \tag{2.7}$$

Now we proceed as follows. The function

$$\sigma_\delta(x) = \int_{-\infty}^{x} \frac{v(x',\delta)}{1+x'^2}\, dx'$$

does not decrease and by the estimate (2.7) it is uniformly bounded for $0 < \delta < 1$. Therefore, by Helly's theorem, in the set of functions $\{\sigma_\delta(x), 0 < \delta < 1\}$ we can choose a sequence $\sigma_{\delta_k}(x)$, $k = 1, 2, \ldots$, which converges to a non-negative measure σ which, by (2.7), satisfies the inequality

$$\frac{1}{\pi} \int_{-\infty}^{\infty} \sigma(dx) \leqslant v(0,1) \tag{2.8}$$

We set

$$\mu = (1 + x^2)\sigma$$

The measure μ is non-negative and, by (2.8), satisfies the estimate

$$\frac{1}{\pi} \int_{-\infty}^{\infty} \frac{\mu(dx)}{1+x^2} \leqslant v(0, 1) \tag{2.9}$$

Further, by another theorem of Helly's for any continuous functions $\varphi(x)$, $\varphi(\infty) = 0$, we have the limit relation:

$$\int_{-\infty}^{\infty} \frac{v(x',\delta_k)}{1+x'^2} \varphi(x')dx' \to \int_{-\infty}^{\infty} \varphi(x')\,\sigma(dx') = \int_{-\infty}^{\infty} \frac{\varphi(x')}{1+x'^2}\,\mu(dx'), \; k \to \infty \tag{2.10}$$

The variable δ in (2.10) may approach $+0$ in any manner. This is shown using standard arguments and the estimate (2.7). Now we pass to $\delta \to +0$ in Eqs (2.4) and (2.5): using the limit relation (2.1 we get the well-known Herglotz-Nevanlinna representation (see e.g. Nevanlinna [12], Ch.VII).

Theorem II. *A function* f(z) *is holomorphic and has a non-negative imaginary part in the upper half-plane if and only if it is represented in the form*

$$f(z) = \frac{1+z^2}{\pi} \int_{-\infty}^{\infty} \frac{\mu(dx')}{(1+x'^2)(x'-z)} + az + b, \quad y > 0 \tag{2.11}$$

where a measure μ *is non-negative and satisfies the inequality*

$$\frac{1}{\pi} \int_{-\infty}^{\infty} \frac{\mu(dx')}{1+x'^2} \leqslant a \tag{2.12}$$

b *is a real number. In addition the representation (2.11) is unique,* a = Im f(i), b = Re f(i) *and* $\mu = \mathrm{Im}\, f^+$,

$$\int_{-\infty}^{\infty} \frac{\mathrm{Im}\, f(x+iy)}{1+x^2} \varphi(x)dx \to \int_{-\infty}^{\infty} \frac{\varphi(x)\,\mu(dx)}{1+x^2}, \varphi \in \mathscr{C}, \varphi(\infty) = 0 \tag{2.13}$$

Corollary. *The function* $v(x,y) \geqslant 0$ *is harmonic in the upper half-plane if and only if it is represented (uniquely) in the form*

$$v(x,y) = \frac{y}{\pi} \int_{-\infty}^{\infty} \frac{\mu(dx')}{(x-x')^2 + y^2} + a'y, \quad y > 0 \tag{2.14}$$

where a measure $\mu \geqslant 0$ *and a number* $a' \geqslant 0$; *in addition*

$$a' = v(0,1) - \frac{1}{\pi} \int_{-\infty}^{\infty} \frac{\mu(dx')}{1+x'^2} = \lim_{y \to +\infty} \frac{v(x,y)}{y} \tag{2.15}$$

and μ *is the boundary value of* v(x,y) *as* $y \to +0$ *in the sense of the limit relation (2.13).*

Let $f \in \mathscr{C}^2(\mathbb{R}^1)$. Then the equality

$$e^{-y|\xi|} D^2 f(\xi) = [D^2 + y^2 + 2yD\,\mathrm{sign}\xi - 2y\delta(\xi)](e^{-y|\xi|} f(\xi)) \tag{2.16}$$

holds. But the right-hand side of Eq.(2.16) makes sense in $\mathscr{D}'$ for $f \in \mathscr{C}(\mathbb{R}^1)$ as well, and we take it for the definition of a distribution in the left-hand side of Eq.(2.16). It is easy to verify: if $f \in \mathscr{C}(\mathbb{R}^1)$ and $f(\xi) = 0$, $\xi < 0$ then

$$e^{-y\xi} D^2 f(\xi) = e^{-y|\xi|} D^2 f(\xi) \tag{2.17}$$

Lemma 2.1. *Let* $f = F^{-1}[\sigma]$ *be a continuous positive definite function in* $\mathbb{R}^1$. *Then for every* $y > 0$ *the distribution* $e^{-y|\xi|}(1 - D^2)f(\xi)$ *is positive definite and the equality*

$$F[e^{-y|\xi|}(1 - D^2)f] = \frac{y}{\pi} \int_{-\infty}^{\infty} \frac{(1 + x'^2)\,\sigma(dx')}{(x - x')^2 + y^2} \tag{2.18}$$

holds.

Proof. By Bochner's theorem, $\sigma = F[f]$ is a non-negative and finite measure on $\mathbb{R}^1$ satisfying the equality

$$f(0) = \frac{1}{2\pi} \int_{-\infty}^{\infty} \sigma(dx) \tag{2.19}$$

From (2.16) it follows for all $y > 0$:

$$F[e^{-y|\xi|}(1 - D^2)f] = F[1 - D^2 - y^2 - 2yD\,\mathrm{sign}\,\xi + 2y\delta(\xi)](e^{-y|\xi|}f(\xi))$$

$$= (1 + x^2 - y^2)F[e^{-y|\xi|}f(\xi)] + 2ixyF[\mathrm{sign}\,\xi\, e^{-y|\xi|}f(\xi)] + 2yf(0) \tag{2.20}$$

Taking into account the equations:

$$F[e^{-y|\xi|}](x) = 2 \int_0^{\infty} e^{-y\xi} \cos x\xi\, d\xi = \frac{2y}{x^2 + y^2}$$

$$F[\mathrm{sign}\,\xi\; e^{-y|\xi|}](x) = 2i \int_0^{\infty} e^{-y\xi} \sin x\,\xi\, d\xi = \frac{2xi}{x^2 + y^2}$$

we get

$$F[f(\xi)e^{-y|\xi|}] = \frac{1}{2\pi} F[f] * F[e^{-y|\xi|}] = \frac{y}{\pi} \int_{-\infty}^{\infty} \frac{\sigma(dx')}{(x - x')^2 + y^2}$$

$$F[f(\xi)\,\mathrm{sign}\,\xi\, e^{-y|\xi|}] = \frac{1}{2\pi} F[f] * F[\mathrm{sign}\,\xi\, e^{-y|\xi|}] = \frac{i}{\pi} \int_{-\infty}^{\infty} \frac{(x - x')\sigma(dx')}{(x - x')^2 + y^2}$$

Substituting these formulas in Eq.(2.20) and taking into account Eq.(2.19), we get the formula (2.18). By the Bochner-Schwartz theorem the distribution $e^{-y|\xi|}(1 - D^2)f$ is positive definite for all $y > 0$ because the right-hand side of Eq.(2.18) is a non-negative tempered function in x. Lemma 2.1 is proved.

Lemma 2.2. *Let a function* $v(\xi)$ *be continuous bounded in* $\mathbb{R}^1$ *and* $v(\xi) = 0$, $\xi < 0$. *Then the solution of the equation* $D^2u = (1 - D^2)\,v$ *exists and it is unique in the set of continuous functions vanishing in* $\xi < 0$ *and satisfying the estimate*

$$|u(\xi)| \leqslant C(1 + \xi^2) \tag{2.21}$$

Proof. The solution of the equation $D^2 u = (1 - D^2)v$ is unique even in the algebra $\mathscr{D}'_+$ and is represented in the form

$$u = (\theta\xi) * (1 - D^2)v = \int_0^{\xi} v(\xi')(\xi - \xi')d\xi' - v(\xi)$$

It is a continuous function in $\mathbb{R}^1$ with the support in $[0, \infty)$ and satisfies the estimate (2.21). Lemma 2.2 is proved.

Lemma 2.3. *Let a function* $u(\xi)$ *be continuous tempered in* $\mathbb{R}^1$. *Then the solution of the equation* $(D^2 - 1)v = D^2u$ *exists and is unique in the set of continuous tempered functions.*

Proof. The solution v of the equation $(D^2 - 1)v = D^2u$ is unique in the set of tempered distributions as

$$F[D^2\delta - \delta] = -x^2 - 1 \neq 0, \quad x \in \mathbb{R}^1$$

The function v is represented in the form

$$v = \tfrac{1}{2}\, e^{-|\xi|} * D^2u = \tfrac{1}{2}\,(e^{-|\xi|})'' * u = \left(\delta - \tfrac{1}{2}\, e^{-|\xi|}\right) * u = u(\xi) - \tfrac{1}{2}\int_{-\infty}^{\infty} u(\xi')e^{-|\xi - \xi'|}d\xi'$$

It is a continuous tempered function. Lemma 2.3 is proved.

Let g be a distribution. We denote by g^* the Hermitian conjugate to $g : g^*(\xi) = \overline{g(-\xi)}$.

Theorem III. *A function* $f(z)$ *is holomorphic in the upper half-plane with a non-negative imaginary part if and only if it is the Laplace transform of a distribution* $g(\xi)$ *possessing the properties:*

(i) $-ig + ig^*$ *is the positive definite distribution in the Bochner-Schwartz sense*

(ii) $g(\xi) = 2i\,D^2u(\xi) + ia'D\delta(\xi)$ (2.22)

where $a' \geqslant 0$ *and* $u(\xi)$ *is a continuous function in* $\mathbb{R}^1$ *vanishing for* $\xi < 0$ *and satisfying the growth condition* (2.21). *In the representation* (2.22) *the number* a' *and the function* $u(\xi)$ *with the indicated properties are unique.*

In addition the following equalities are true:

$$a' = \lim_{t \to +\infty} \frac{\operatorname{Im} f(it)}{t} \tag{2.23}$$

$$\mu = -x^2F[u + u^*] = \operatorname{Im} f^+ \tag{2.24}$$

Proof. Necessity of the conditions. Let a function $f(z)$ be holomorphic and let $\operatorname{Im} f(z) \geqslant 0$ for $y > 0$. By Theorem II it is the Laplace transform, $f(z) = \mathscr{L}[g]$, $f^+ = F[g]$, of a distribution

$$g(\xi) = i(1 - D^2)(\theta\,\chi) + iaD\,\delta(\xi) + b\delta(\xi) \tag{2.25}$$

where b is a real number and

$$\chi(\xi) = 2F^{-1}[\sigma] \qquad \left(\sigma = \frac{\mu}{1 + x^2} \geqslant 0\right) \tag{2.26}$$

is a continuous positive definite function satisfying the condition

$$\frac{1}{\pi} \int_{-\infty}^{\infty} \sigma(dx) = \chi(0) \leqslant a \tag{2.27}$$

The function $\chi(\xi)$ is continuous and bounded in $\mathbb{R}^1$. By Lemma 2.2 there exists a (unique) continuous function u_1 vanishing for $\xi < 0$ and satisfying the estimate (2.21) such that

$$i(1 - D^2)\{\theta(\xi)[\chi(\xi) - \chi(0)e^{-|\xi|}]\} = 2D^2 u_1(\xi)$$

Therefore owing to (2.25) we have

$$g(\xi) = i(1 - D^2)(\theta\chi) + iaD\delta(\xi) + b\delta(\xi)$$

$$= i(1 - D^2)\{\theta(\xi)[\chi(\xi) - \chi(0)e^{-|\xi|}]\} + i\chi(0)(1 - D^2)[\theta(\xi)e^{-|\xi|}] + iaD\delta(\xi) + b\delta(\xi)$$

$$= 2iD^2u_1(\xi) + [b + i\chi(0)]\delta(\xi) + i[a - \chi(0)]D\delta(\xi) = 2iD^2u(\xi) + ia'D\delta(\xi)$$

The representation (2.22) is proved now with

$$u(\xi) = u_1(\xi) + [b + i\chi(0)]\xi\theta(\xi), \qquad a' = a - \chi(0)$$

The function $u(\xi)$ possesses the required properties; the number $a' \geqslant 0$ by virtue of (2.27). Further, the following chain of equations takes place:

$$\frac{-ig + ig^*}{2} = \frac{1}{2i}[F^{-1}[f^+] - F^{-1}[f^+]^*] = F^{-1}\left[\frac{f^+ - \bar{f}^+}{2i}\right]$$

$$= F^{-1}[\operatorname{Im} f^+] = F^{-1}[\mu] = D^2(u + u^*)$$

which gives the condition (i) of Theorem III: $-ig + ig^* \gg 0$ (by the Bochner-Schwartz theorem) and the equality (2.24): $\mu = -x^2F[u + u^*]$.

Finally, it follows from (2.22) that

$$f(z) = 2iz^2 \int_0^{\infty} e^{iz\xi}u(\xi)d\xi + a'z, \quad y > 0 \tag{2.28}$$

Therefore the limit relation (2.23) is true:

$$\lim_{t\to+\infty}\frac{\operatorname{Im} f(it)}{t} = -2\lim_{t\to+\infty}\left[t\int_0^\infty e^{-t\xi}\operatorname{Re} u(\xi)d\xi\right] + a'$$

$$= a' - 2\lim_{t\to+\infty}\int_0^\infty e^{-\alpha}\operatorname{Re} u\left(\frac{\alpha}{t}\right)d\alpha = a'$$

The limit of the last integral is equal to 0 as, by virtue of the estimate (2.21) and by Lebesgue's theorem, the passage to the limit under the integral sign is possible and the integrand tends to 0 as $t \to +\infty$ by virtue of the continuity of $u(\xi)$ and $u(0) = 0$.

Sufficiency of the conditions. Let a function $f(z)$ be the Laplace transform of a distribution $g(\xi)$ satisfying the conditions (i) and (ii) of Theorem III. Then $f(z)$ is holomorphic in the upper half-plane and is represented in the form (2.28). We prove that $\operatorname{Im} f(z) \geqslant 0$ for $y > 0$. We have

$$\operatorname{Im} f(z) = \frac{f(z) - \bar{f}(z)}{2i} = F\left[\frac{g(\xi)e^{-y\xi} - g^*(\xi)e^{y\xi}}{2i}\right]$$

$$= F[e^{-y\xi}D^2u(\xi) + e^{y\xi}D^2\bar{u}(-\xi)] + \frac{a'}{2}F[e^{-y\xi}D\delta(\xi) - e^{y\xi}D\delta(\xi)] \qquad (2.29)$$

By virtue of Eq.(2.17) we have for $y > 0$

$$e^{-y\xi}D^2u(\xi) + e^{y\xi}D^2\bar{u}(-\xi) = e^{-y|\xi|}D^2[u(\xi) + u^*(\xi)] \qquad (2.30)$$

By Lemma 2.3 there exists a (unique) continuous tempered function $v(\xi)$ such that

$$(1 - D^2)v = D^2(u + u^*) \qquad (2.31)$$

Hence owing to the condition (i) we have

$$(1 - D^2)v = -ig + ig^* \gg 0$$

so, by the Bochner-Schwartz theorem,

$$F[v] = \frac{1}{1 + x^2}F[-ig + ig^*] \geqslant 0, \quad v \gg 0$$

From this, using (2.30), (2.31) and Lemma 2.1, we conclude that

$$F[e^{-y\xi}D^2u(\xi) + e^{y\xi}D^2\bar{u}(-\xi)] = F[e^{-y|\xi|}(1 - D^2)v] \geqslant 0, \quad y > 0 \qquad (2.32)$$

Finally, using the equalities

$$e^{\pm y\xi}D\delta(\xi) = D\delta(\xi) \mp y\delta(\xi)$$

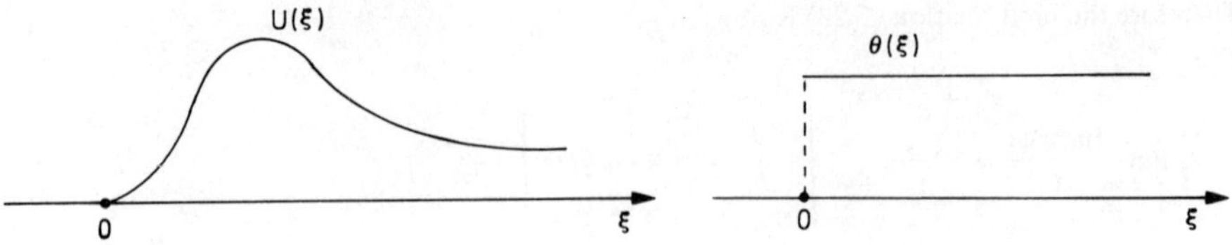

FIG.2. The main singularities in the spectral function g(ξ) appear from the ∞-point.

we get

$$\frac{a'}{2}F[e^{-y\xi}D\delta(\xi) - e^{y\xi}D\delta(\xi)] = a'yF[\delta] = a'y \geqslant 0, \quad y > 0$$

From this and from (2.32) and (2.29) it follows that Im $f(z) \geqslant 0$, $y > 0$. Theorem III is proved.

Remark 1. Theorem III was first proved by König and Zemanian [14].

Remark 2. The main singularities in the spectral function $g(\xi)$ appear from the ∞-point because $\delta' = \theta''$ (see Fig.2).

3. NON-NEGATIVE PLURIHARMONIC FUNCTIONS IN $T^{\mathbb{R}^n_+}$

Our purpose is to extend the results of § 2 for the upper half-plane (one complex variable) for any tube domain T^C over an arbitrary proper convex cone C. First we shall study non-negative pluriharmonic functions in the tube domain over the cone $\mathbb{R}^n_+ = [y : y_1 > 0, \ldots, y_n > 0]$.

A real function v(x,y) of 2n variables (x,y) is called pluriharmonic in a domain G if it is a real part of a holomorphic function in G. It is known that the real distribution v(x,y) from $\mathscr{D}'(G)$ is pluriharmonic in G if and only if it satisfies in G the system of equations:

$$\frac{\partial^2 v}{\partial z_j \partial \bar{z}_k} = 0, \quad 1 \leqslant j, k \leqslant n, \; z_j = x_j + iy_j$$

Here

$$\frac{\partial}{\partial z} = \frac{1}{2}\left(\frac{\partial}{\partial x} - i\frac{\partial}{\partial y}\right), \quad \frac{\partial}{\partial \bar{z}} = \frac{1}{2}\left(\frac{\partial}{\partial x} + i\frac{\partial}{\partial y}\right)$$

First we state the following lemmas.

Lemma 3.1. *Let a function* v(x,y) *be non-negative and pluriharmonic in* $T^{\mathbb{R}^n_+}$. *Then the following estimate holds:*

$$\frac{1}{\pi^n}\int \frac{v(x,y)dx}{(1+x_1^2)\ldots(1+x_n^2)} \leqslant v(0, y + \mathbf{1}), \quad y \in \mathbb{R}^n_+ \tag{3.1}$$

here $\mathbf{1} = (1, \ldots, 1)$.

Proof. We shall prove the estimate (3.1) by induction on n. For n = 1 it is true (see corollary of Theorem II). Supposing that it is true for n − 1, for every $x_n \in \mathbb{R}^1$ and $y \in \mathbb{R}^n_+$ we obtain the inequality

$$\frac{1}{\pi^{n-1}} \int \frac{v(x_1, \ldots, x_n, y_1, \ldots, y_n)}{(1+x_1^2)\ldots(1+x_{n-1}^2)} dx_1 \ldots dx_{n-1} \leqslant v(0, \ldots, 0, x_n, 1+y_1, \ldots, 1+y_{n-1}, y_n)$$

Dividing this inequality by $\pi(1 + x_n^2)$ and integrating it over x_n, we get, by Fubini's theorem, the inequality

$$\frac{1}{\pi^n} \int \frac{v(x,y)dx}{(1+x_1^2)\ldots(1+x_n^2)} \leqslant \frac{1}{\pi} \int_{-\infty}^{\infty} \frac{v(0, \ldots, 0, x_n, 1+y_1, \ldots, 1+y_{n-1}, y_n)}{1+x_n^2} dx_n$$

For the integral on the righ-hand side of this inequality we apply estimate (3.1) for n = 1 as the function $v(0, \ldots, 0, x_n, 1+y_1, \ldots, 1+y_{n-1}, y_n)$ is non-negative and harmonic in (x_n, y_n) for $y_n > 0$. As a result we obtain the estimate (3.1). Lemma 3.1 is proved.

Lemma 3.2. *Let the function* v(x,y) *satisfy the conditions of Lemma 3.1. Then there exists a non-negative measure* μ *in* $\mathbb{R}^n$ *which satisfies the inequality*

$$\frac{1}{\pi^n} \int \frac{\mu(dx)}{(1+x_1^2)\ldots(1+x_n^2)} \leqslant v(0, \mathbf{1}) \tag{3.2}$$

and the limit relation

$$\int \frac{v(x,y)\varphi(x)dx}{(1+x_1^2)\ldots(1+x_n^2)} \to \int \frac{\varphi(x)\mu(dx)}{(1+x_1^2)\ldots(1+x_n^2)}, \quad y \to 0, \quad y \in \mathbb{R}^n_+ \tag{3.3}$$

for any function $\varphi \in \mathscr{C}$, $\varphi(\infty) = 0$.

The proof is similar to the case n = 1 (see §2).

Lemma 3.3. *Let a function* $v(\xi)$ *be continuous bounded in* $\overline{\mathbb{R}}^2_+ \times \mathbb{R}^{n-2}$, $n \geqslant 2$, *and satisfy the homogeneous equation:*

$$(1 - D_1^2) \ldots (1 - D_n^2) v(\xi) = 0, \qquad \xi \in \mathbb{R}^2_+ \times \mathbb{R}^{n-2} \tag{3.4}$$

Then it is represented in the form

$$v(\xi) = e^{-\xi_1} v(0, \xi_2, \tilde{\xi}) + e^{-\xi_2} v(\xi_1, 0, \tilde{\xi}) - e^{-\xi_1 - \xi_2} v(0, 0, \tilde{\xi}) \tag{3.5}$$

where $\tilde{\xi} = (\xi_3, \ldots, \xi_n)$.

A proof is reduced to the classical case when $\chi \in \mathscr{C}^\infty \cap \mathscr{L}^\infty$ satisfy the equation:

$$(1 - D_1^2)(1 - D_2^2)\chi(\xi_1, \xi_2) = 0, \quad \xi_1 > 0, \xi_2 > 0$$

Lemma 3.4. *Let a function* v *be continuous bounded in* $\mathbb{R}^n$ *and* supp v $\subset \overline{\mathbb{R}}^n_+$. *Then the solution of the equation*

$$D_1^2 \dots D_n^2 u(\xi) = (1 - D_1^2) \dots (1 - D_n^2) v(\xi) \tag{3.6}$$

exists and is unique in the set of continuous functions with support in $\overline{\mathbb{R}}^n_+$ *and satisfying the estimat*

$$|u(\xi)| \leqslant C(1 + \xi_1^2) \dots (1 + \xi_n^2) \tag{3.7}$$

The proof is similar to that for case n = 1(see Lemma 2.2).

Lemma 3.5. *Let a function* $u(\xi)$ *be continuous tempered in* $\mathbb{R}^n$. *Then the solution of the equation*

$$(1 - D_1^2) \dots (1 - D_n^2) v(\xi) = D_1^2 \dots D_n^2 u(\xi) \tag{3.8}$$

exists and it is unique in the set of continuous tempered functions.

The proof is similar to that for the case n = 1 (see Lemma 2.3).
Let $f \in \mathscr{C}^2(\mathbb{R}^n)$. Then the equality

$$e^{-(y,\xi^+)} D_1^2 \dots D_n^2 f(\xi) = T_1 \dots T_n [e^{-(y,\xi^+)} f(\xi)] \tag{3.9}$$

holds; here $\xi^+ = (|\xi_1|, \dots, |\xi_n|)$ and

$$T_j = D_j^2 + y_j^2 + 2y_j D_j \operatorname{sign} \xi_j - 2y_j \delta(\xi_j), \quad j = 1, \dots, n$$

But we take the right-hand side of Eq.(3.9) for the definition of a distribution in the left-hand side of Eq.(3.9) if $f \in \mathscr{C}(\mathbb{R}^n)$. It is easy to verify, as in §2: if $f \in \mathscr{C}(\mathbb{R}^n)$ and supp $f \subset \overline{\mathbb{R}}^n_+$ then

$$e^{-(y,\xi)} D_1^2 \dots D_n^2 f(\xi) = e^{-(y,\xi^+)} D_1^2 \dots D_n^2 f(\xi) \tag{3.10}$$

Lemma 3.6. *Let* $f = F^{-1}[\sigma]$ *be a continuous positive definite function in* $\mathbb{R}^n$. *Then for every* $y \in \mathbb{R}^n_+$ *the distribution*

$$e^{-(y,\xi^+)} (1 - D_1^2) \dots (1 - D_n^2) f(\xi)$$

is positive definite and the following equality holds:

$$F[e^{-(y,\xi^+)}(1 - D_1^2) \dots (1 - D_n^2) f] = \frac{y_1 \dots y_n}{\pi^n} \int \frac{(1 + x_1'^2) \dots (1 + x_n'^2)\sigma(dx')}{[(x_1 - x_1')^2 + y_1^2] \dots [(x_n - x_n')^2 + y_n^2]}$$

The proof is similar to that of Lemma 2.1.

Let a function v(x,y) be pluriharmonic and non-negative in $T^{\mathbb{R}^n_+}$; let the non-negative measure μ be its boundary value as $y \to 0$, $y \in \mathbb{R}^n_+$ (see Lemma 3.2). We construct $2^n - 2$ measure $\mu_{j_1 \dots j_k}$, $1 \leqslant k \leqslant n-1$, $1 \leqslant j_1 < \dots < j_k \leqslant n$, depending on k variables $(x_{j_1}, \dots, x_{j_k})$, by the formula: for any $\varphi \in \mathscr{C}$, $\varphi(\infty) = 0$

$$\int \frac{\varphi(x_{j_1}, \dots, x_{j_k}) \mu_{j_1 \dots j_k}(d(x_{j_1}, \dots, x_{j_k}))}{(1 + x_{j_1}^2) \dots (1 + x_{j_k}^2)} = \int \frac{\varphi(x_{j_1}, \dots, x_{j_k}) \mu(dx)}{(1 + x_1^2) \dots (1 + x_n^2)} \tag{3.11}$$

From this definition and from Lemma 3.2 the following properties follow:

(1) $\mu_{j_1 \dots j_k} \geqslant 0, \quad \dfrac{\mu_{j_1 \dots j_k}}{(1+x_{j_1}^2) \dots (1+x_{j_k}^2)} = \sigma_{j_1 \dots j_k} \geqslant 0$ (3.12)

(2) $\mathscr{C} \ni \chi_{j_1, \dots j_k}(\xi_{j_1}, \dots, \xi_{j_k}) = \dfrac{1}{(2\pi)^{n-k}} F^{-1}[\sigma_{j_1 \dots j_k}] \gg 0$ (3.13)

(3) $\chi_{j_1 \dots j_k}(\xi_{j_1}, \dots, \xi_{j_k}) = \chi(\xi)|_{\xi_{j_{k+1}}} = \dots = \xi_{j_n} = 0$ (3.14)

(4) $F^{-1}[\mu_{j_1 \dots j_k}](\xi_{j_1}, \dots, \xi_{j_k}) = 0$ if $(\xi_{j_1}, \dots, \xi_{k_j}) \bar{\epsilon} - \bar{\mathbb{R}}_+^k \cup \bar{\mathbb{R}}_+^k$ (3.15)

here $\chi = \chi_{1 \dots n}, \sigma = \sigma_{1 \dots n}, \mu = \mu_{1 \dots n}$

(5) $(1 - D_{j_1}^2) \dots (1 - D_{j_k}^2)\chi_{j_1 \dots j_k}(\xi_{j_1}, \dots, \xi_{j_k}) = 0$ if $(\xi_{j_1}, \dots, \xi_{j_k}) \bar{\epsilon} - \bar{\mathbb{R}}_+^k \cup \bar{\mathbb{R}}_+^k$ (3.16)

Equations (3.16) follow from Eqs (3.12), (3.13) and (3.15).

(6) $$\chi(\xi) = \sum_{2 \leqslant k \leqslant n} \sum_{1 \leqslant j_1 < \dots < j_k \leqslant n} \exp(-|\xi_{j_{k+1}}| - \dots - |\xi_{j_n}|)\phi_{j_1 \dots j_k}(\xi_{j_1}, \dots, \xi_{j_k})$$

$$+ \exp(-|\xi_2| - \dots - |\xi_n|)\chi(\xi_1, 0, \dots, 0) + \dots + \exp(-|\xi_1| - \dots - |\xi_{n-1}|)\chi(0, \dots, 0, \xi_n)$$

$$- (n-1)\exp(-|\xi_1| - \dots - |\xi_n|)\chi(0) \tag{3.17}$$

where $\phi_{j_1 \dots j_k}$ are continuous bounded functions in $\mathbb{R}^k$ with a support in $-\bar{\mathbb{R}}_+^k \cup \bar{\mathbb{R}}_+^k$.

We prove the representation (3.17) by induction on n. It is trivial for n = 1. Let n be ⩾2. The function $\chi(\xi) = \chi_{1 \dots n}(\xi)$ as well as the functions $\chi_{j_1 \dots j_k}$ are continuous and bounded in $\mathbb{R}^k$ and they satisfy Eqs (3.16) outside of $-\bar{\mathbb{R}}_+^k \cup \bar{\mathbb{R}}_+^k$ (see Eqs (3.13) and (3.15)). Therefore for n = 2 the representation (3.17) is true by Lemma 3.3 with

$$\phi_{12}(\xi) = \chi(\xi) - e^{-|\xi_1|}\chi(0, \xi_2) - e^{-|\xi_2|}\chi(\xi_1, 0) + e^{-|\xi_1| - |\xi_2|}\chi(0) \tag{3.18}$$

Let the representation (3.17) be true for all k < n, so the functions $\chi_{j_1 \dots j_k}$ are represented in $\mathbb{R}^k$ by the formulas (3.17). We prove the representation (3.17) for χ in the quadrant-shaped domain $\xi_1 < 0, \xi_2 > 0, \tilde{\xi} \in \mathbb{R}^{n-2}$. By Lemma 3.3, the function χ is represented in this domain in the form

$$\chi(\xi) = e^{-|\xi_1|}\chi(0, \xi_2, \tilde{\xi}) + e^{-|\xi_2|}\chi(\xi_1, 0, \tilde{\xi}) - e^{-|\xi_1| - |\xi_2|}\chi(0, 0, \tilde{\xi}) \tag{3.19}$$

According to the inductive assumption for functions $\chi(0, \xi_2, \tilde{\xi}) = \chi_{2 \dots n}, \chi(\xi_1, 0, \tilde{\xi}) = \chi_{13 \dots n}$ and $\chi(0, 0, \tilde{\xi}) = \chi_{3 \dots n}$ (see Eqs (3.14)), the corresponding representations (3.17) are true. Substituting them in (3.19), we obtain the representation (3.17) in the domain $\xi_1 < 0$, $\xi_2 > 0$. Similarly the remaining domains outside $-\mathbb{R}^n_+ \cup \mathbb{R}^n_+$ can be considered. Hence the representations (3.17) are true outside the octants $\mathbb{R}^n_+$ and $-\mathbb{R}^n_+$. Introducing the function

$$\phi_{1\ldots n}(\xi) = \chi(\xi) - \sum_{2\leqslant k\leqslant n-1} \; \sum_{1\leqslant j_1<\ldots<j_k\leqslant n} \exp(-|\xi_{j_{k+1}}| - \ldots - |\xi_{j_n}|)\phi_{j_1\ldots j_k}(\xi_{j_1}, \ldots, \xi_{j_k})$$

$$- \exp(-|\xi_2| - \ldots - |\xi_n|)\chi(\xi_1, 0, \ldots, 0) - \ldots - \exp(-|\xi_1| - \ldots - |\xi_{n-1}|)\chi(0, \ldots, 0, \xi_n)$$

$$+ (n-1)\exp(-|\xi_1| - \ldots - |\xi_n|)\chi(0)$$

which is continuous bounded in $\mathbb{R}^n$ with a support in $-\overline{\mathbb{R}}^n_+ \cup \overline{\mathbb{R}}^n_+$, we establish the representation (3.17) in the whole space $\mathbb{R}^n$.

Theorem IV. *If a non-negative measure μ is the boundary value of a non-negative pluriharmonic in the $T^{\mathbb{R}^n_+}$ function $v(x, y)$ as $y \to 0$, $y \in \mathbb{R}^n_+$ then its Fourier transform $F^{-1}[\mu]$ can be represented in the form*

$$F^{-1}[\mu] = D_1^2 \ldots D_n^2 u(\xi) \tag{3.20}$$

where u is a continuous tempered Hermitian function in $\mathbb{R}^n$, vanishing outside the set $-\overline{\mathbb{R}}^n_+ \cup \overline{\mathbb{R}}^n_+$.

Proof. From Eqs (3.12) and (3.13) it follows that

$$F^{-1}[\mu] = (1-D_1^2) \ldots (1-D_n^2)\chi(\xi) \tag{3.21}$$

Let n be $\geqslant 2$. Noticing that

$$(1-D^2)e^{-|\xi|} = 2\delta(\xi)$$

and using the representation (3.17), we get from Eq.(3.21)

$$F^{-1}[\mu] = \sum_{2\leqslant k\leqslant n} 2^{n-k} \sum_{1\leqslant j_1<\ldots<j_k\leqslant n} \delta(\xi_{j_{k+1}}) \times \ldots \times \delta(\xi_{j_n}) \times (1-D_{j_1}^2) \ldots (1-D_{j_k}^2)$$

$$\times \phi_{j_1\ldots j_k}(\xi_{j_1}, \ldots, \xi_{j_k}) + 2^{n-1}\delta(\xi_2) \times \ldots \times \delta(\xi_n) \times (1-D_1^2)\chi(\xi_1, 0, \ldots, 0)$$

$$\ldots + 2^{n-1}\delta(\xi_1) \times \ldots \times \delta(\xi_{n-1}) \times (1-D_n^2)\chi(0, \ldots, 0, \xi_n) - 2^n(n-1)\chi(0)\delta(\xi) \tag{3.22}$$

where $\phi_{j_1\ldots j_k}$ are continuous bounded functions in $\mathbb{R}^k$ with support in $-\overline{\mathbb{R}}^k_+ \cup \overline{\mathbb{R}}^k_+$. Each term in the sum in the right-hand side of Eq.(3.22) can be represented in the form

$$2^{n-k}D_{j_{k+1}}^2 \ldots D_{j_n}^2[\theta(\xi_{j_{k+1}})\xi_{j_{k+1}} \ldots \theta(\xi_{j_n})\xi_{j_n}] \times (1-D_{j_1}^2) \ldots (1-D_{j_k}^2)$$

$$\times [\theta(\xi_{j_1}) \ldots \theta(\xi_{j_k})\phi_{j_1\ldots j_k}(\xi_{j_1}, \ldots, \xi_{j_k})] + (-2)^{n-k}D_{j_{k+1}}^2 \ldots D_{j_n}^2[\theta(-\xi_{j_{k+1}})\xi_{j_{k+1}}$$

$$\ldots \theta(-\xi_{j_n})\xi_{j_n}] \times (1-D_{j_1}^2) \ldots (1-D_{j_k}^2)[\theta(-\xi_{j_1}) \ldots \theta(-\xi_{j_k})\phi_{j_1\ldots j_k}(\xi_{j_1}, \ldots, \xi_{j_k})]$$

and hence by Lemma 3.4 it can be represented in the form of the right-hand side of Eq.(3.20). Each of the last $n-1$ terms in the right-hand side of Eq.(3.22) can be represented in a form similar to the following:

$$2^{n-1}\delta(\xi_2)\times\ldots\times\delta(\xi_n)\times(1-D_1^2)\chi(\xi_1,0,\ldots,0)-2^n\chi(0)\,\delta(\xi)$$

$$=2^{n-1}\delta(\xi_2)\times\ldots\times\delta(\xi_n)\times(1-D_1^2)\,[\chi(\xi_1,0,\ldots,0)-e^{-|\xi_1|}\chi(0)]$$

and hence it can be represented in the form of the right-hand side of Eq.(3.20). The latter argument is also suitable for case $n = 1$ (and see the proof of Theorem III).

We can suppose that in the representation (3.20) the function $u(\xi)$ is Hermitian; otherwise, we can change it by the function $\frac{1}{2}(u+u^*)$ owing to the equations:

$$F^{-1}[\mu]=D_1^2\ldots D_n^2u(\xi)=F^{-1}[\mu]^*=D_1^2\ldots D_n^2\,u^*(\xi)$$

Theorem IV is proved.

4. HOLOMORPHIC FUNCTIONS WITH NON-NEGATIVE IMAGINARY PART IN THE TUBE DOMAIN T^C

Theorem V. *A function* $f(z)$ *is holomorphic and has a non-negative imaginary part in the tube* $T^{\mathbb{R}_+^n}$ *if and only if it is the Laplace transform of a distribution* $g(\xi)$ *with the following properties:*

$$\begin{aligned}&(i)\quad -ig+ig^*\geqslant 0\\ &(ii)\quad g(\xi)=2iD_1^2\ldots D_n^2u(\xi)+i(a,D)\,\delta(\xi)\end{aligned}\tag{4.1}$$

where $a\in\overline{\mathbb{R}}_+^n$ *and* $u(\xi)$ *is a tempered continuous function in* $\mathbb{R}^n$ *with a support in* $\overline{\mathbb{R}}_+^n$. *In the representation (4.1) the vector* a *and the function* $u(\xi)$ *with the indicated properties are unique. In addition, the following equalities are true:*

$$a_j=\lim_{t_j\to+\infty}\frac{\operatorname{Im}f(it)}{t_j}=\lim_{t_j\to+\infty}\frac{f(it)}{t_j},\qquad j=1,\ldots,n,\quad t\in\mathbb{R}_+^n\tag{4.2}$$

$$\operatorname{Im}f(z)=\frac{y_1\ldots y_n}{\pi^n}\int\frac{\mu(dx')}{[(x_1-x_1')^2+y_1^2]\ldots[(x_n-x_n')^2+y_n^2]}+(a,y),\qquad z\in T^{\mathbb{R}_+^n}\tag{4.3}$$

$$\mu=(-1)^n x_1^2\ldots x_n^2F[u+u^*]=\operatorname{Im}f^+\tag{4.4}$$

Proof: Necessity of the conditions. Let the function $f(z)$ be holomorphic and let $\operatorname{Im}f(z)\geqslant 0$ in $T^{\mathbb{R}_+^n}$. By Theorem I, $f(z)$ is the Laplace transform of a tempered distribution g from $\mathscr{S}'(\overline{\mathbb{R}}_+^n)$: $f(z)=\mathscr{L}[g]$, $f^+=F[g]$. By Lemma 3.2,

$$\operatorname{Im}f^+=\mu\geqslant 0,\qquad \frac{g-g^*}{2i}=F^{-1}[\mu]\tag{4.5}$$

and hence, by the Bochner-Schwartz theorem, condition (i) is fulfilled (see proof of Theorem III). To prove condition (ii) we use Theorem IV which states that

$$F^{-1}[\mu] = D_1^2 \dots D_n^2 u_1(\xi) \tag{4.6}$$

where u_1 is a continuous tempered Hermitian function with a support in $-\overline{\mathbb{R}}^n_+ \cup \overline{\mathbb{R}}^n_+$. Substituting the expression (4.6) in the formula (4.5) we obtain for the tempered distribution $g \in \mathscr{S}'(\overline{\mathbb{R}}^n_+)$ the equation:

$$\frac{1}{2i}[g(\xi) - g^*(\xi)] = D_1^2 \dots D_n^2 u_1(\xi) \tag{4.7}$$

We denote by $\theta_n(\xi) = \theta(\xi_1) \dots \theta(\xi_n)$ the characteristic function of the cone $\overline{\mathbb{R}}^n_+$. The distribution

$$g_0(\xi) = 2i D_1^2 \dots D_n^2[\theta_n(\xi) u_1(\xi)] \tag{4.8}$$

satisfies Eq.(4.7) in $\mathbb{R}^n$. A general solution of the homogeneous equation corresponding to Eq.(4.7), $g - g^* = 0$, in the set $\mathscr{S}'(\overline{\mathbb{R}}^n_+)$, has a support in the point 0 and hence by Schwartz's theorem is represented in the form

$$a_0 \delta(\xi) + \sum_{1 \leqslant |\alpha| \leqslant N} i^{|\alpha|} a_\alpha D^\alpha \delta(\xi)$$

where a_α are arbitrary real constants. From this and from (4.8) it follows that the distribution g can be represented in the form

$$g(\xi) = 2i D_1^2 \dots D_n^2 \left\{ \theta_n(\xi) \left[u_1(\xi) + \frac{a_0}{2i} \xi_1 \dots \xi_n \right] \right\} + \sum_{1 \leqslant |\alpha| \leqslant N} i^{|\alpha|} a_\alpha D^\alpha \delta(\xi) \tag{4.9}$$

We denote

$$u(\xi) = \theta_n(\xi) \left[u_1(\xi) + \frac{a_0}{2i} \xi_1 \dots \xi_n \right]$$

The function $u(\xi)$ satisfies all conditions listed in Theorem V. Equation (4.9) takes the form

$$g(\xi) = 2i D_1^2 \dots D_n^2 u(\xi) + \sum_{1 \leqslant |\alpha| \leqslant N} i^{|\alpha|} a_\alpha D^\alpha \delta(\xi) \tag{4.10}$$

Hence for every $z \in T^{\mathbb{R}^n_+}$ we have

$$f(z) = \mathscr{L}[g] = 2i(-1)^n z_1^2 \dots z_n^2 \int_{\mathbb{R}^n_+} u(\xi) e^{i(z,\xi)} d\xi + \sum_{1 \leqslant |\alpha| \leqslant N} a_\alpha z^\alpha \tag{4.11}$$

Putting $z = it$, $t \in \mathbb{R}^n_+$ into (4.11), we get

$$f(it) = 2it_1^2 \ldots t_n^2 \int_{\mathbb{R}^n_+} u(\xi)e^{-(t,\xi)}\,d\xi + \sum_{1 \leqslant |\alpha| \leqslant N} i^{|\alpha|} a_\alpha t^\alpha \tag{4.12}$$

But for each $j = 1, \ldots, n$ the following limit relations hold:

$$\lim_{t_j \to +\infty} \frac{t_1^2 \ldots t_n^2}{t_j} \int_{\mathbb{R}^n_+} u(\xi)\, e^{-(t,\xi)}\,d\xi = 0, \qquad t \in \mathbb{R}^n_+ \tag{4.13}$$

(cf. the proof of Theorem III).

Now taking into account the estimate (1.1) (see Theorem I), we obtain from (4.12) the estimate:

$$|2it_1^2 \ldots t_n^2 \int_{\mathbb{R}^n_+} u(\xi)e^{-(t,\xi)}\,d\xi + i(a,t) + \sum_{2 \leqslant |\alpha| \leqslant N} i^{|\alpha|} a_\alpha t^\alpha| \leqslant M(C')\frac{1+|t|^2}{|t|}, \qquad t \in C' \Subset \mathbb{R}^n_+$$

from which, and from (4.13), it follows that $a_\alpha = 0$, $|\alpha| \geqslant 2$ and the equalities (4.2) are true, so $a_j \geqslant 0$, i.e. $a \in \overline{\mathbb{R}^n_+}$. By Eq.(4.10) the representation (4.1) is proved. From (4.1) and from (4.6) the formulas (4.5) follow.

The uniqueness of the representation (4.1) follows from (4.3) and from Lemma 3.4.

Sufficiency of the conditions is proved in the same way as in Theorem III. For this Lemmas 3.5 and 3.6 are used. Theorem V is proved.

Remark. Theorem V was first proved by Vladimirov [15].

We write out the analogy of Herglotz-Nevanlinna's representation (see § 2) for the case $n=2$: *a function* $f(z)$ *is holomorphic and* $\operatorname{Im} f(z) \geqslant 0$ *in* $T^{\mathbb{R}^2_+}$ *if and only if it is represented in the form*

$$f(z_1, z_2) = -\frac{i}{2\pi^2}(1+z_1^2)(1+z_2^2)\int \frac{\sigma_{12}(dx')}{(x_1'-z_1)(x_2'-z_2)} - \frac{i}{2\pi}(1+z_1^2)(i+z_2)$$

$$\times \int \frac{\sigma_1(dx_1')}{x_1'-z_1} - \frac{i}{2\pi}(i+z_1)(1+z_2^2)\int \frac{\sigma_2(dx_2')}{x_2'-z_2} - i\left[\frac{1}{2}(i+z_1)(i+z_2)+1\right] a + b \tag{4.14}$$

where measures σ_{12}, σ_1 *and* σ_2 *are non-negative and finite on* $\mathbb{R}^2$ *and* $\mathbb{R}^1$ *respectively, a number* a *is non-negative and a number* b *is real, satisfying the equation:*

$$4F^{-1}[\sigma_{12}](\xi_1, \xi_2) - 2F^{-1}[\sigma_1](\xi_1)e^{-|\xi_2|} - 2F^{-1}[\sigma_2](\xi_2)e^{-|\xi_1|} + ae^{-|\xi_1|-|\xi_2|} = 0 \tag{4.15}$$

for $\xi_1\xi_2 < 0$ *and the inequalities*

$$\frac{1}{\pi}\int \sigma_1(dx_1) \leqslant a, \qquad \frac{1}{\pi}\int \sigma_2(dx_2) \leqslant a \tag{4.16}$$

The representation (4.14) is unique and

$$a = \mathrm{Im}\, f(\mathbf{i}), \quad b = \mathrm{Re}\, f(\mathbf{i}), \quad (1+x_1^2)(1+x_2^2)\sigma_{12} = \mathrm{Im}\, f^+(x_1, x_2)$$

$$(1+x_1^2)\sigma_1 = \mathrm{Im}\, f^+(x_1, i), \quad (1+x_2^2)\sigma_2 = \mathrm{Im}\, f^+(i, x_2)$$

We notice that, unlike the case $n = 1$ where inequality-type conditions are present for the case $n = 2$, parallel with similar conditions, the equality (4.15) is present. For $n \gtrsim 2$ the number of such equations is equal to $2^n - n - 1$.

From Theorem V follows immediately

Theorem VI. *A function* $f(z)$ *is holomorphic and* $\mathrm{Im}\, f(z) \geqslant 0$ *in the tube* T^C *over a (convex) proper cone* C *if and only if it is the Laplace transform of a distribution* $g(\xi)$ *with the following properties:*

(i) $-ig + ig^* \geqslant 0$

(ii) *for any* n*-faced cone* $C' = [y : (e_1, y) > 0, \ldots, (e_n, y) > 0]$ *contained in the cone* C, *it is (uniquely) representable in the form*

$$g(\xi) = 2i(e_1, D)^2 \ldots (e_n, D)^2\, u_{C'}(\xi) + i(a_{C'}, D)\,\delta(\xi) \tag{4.17}$$

where $a_{C'} \in C'^*$ *and* $u_{C'}(\xi)$ *is a continuous tempered function in* $\mathbb{R}^n$ *with support in* C'^*.

For the future tube τ^+ (see § 1) we have

Theorem VII (see Vladimirov [16]). *The following assertions are equivalent:*

(i) The function $f(z)$ *is holomorphic and* $\mathrm{Im}\, f(z) \geqslant 0$ *in* τ^+;

(ii) The function $f(z)$ *is representable in the form*

$$f(z) = \frac{i}{\pi^3}[(z+\mathbf{i})^2]^2 \int \frac{\mu(dx')}{[(z-x')^2(x'+\mathbf{i})^2]^2} - i\left(\frac{2}{\pi}\right)^3 \int \frac{\mu(dx')}{|(x'+\mathbf{i})^2|^4} + (a, z) + b \tag{4.18}$$

$$z \in \tau^+$$

where μ *is a non-negative measure,* $\mu = \mathrm{Im}\, f^+(x)$, a *is a vector from* $\overline{V}^+$, *and* b *is a real number.*

(iii) The function $f(z)$ *is the Laplace transform of a distribution* g *representable in the form*

$$g(\xi) = 2i[(D+\mathbf{1})^2]^2\{\theta(\xi)[(D-1)^2]^2\chi(\xi)\} - [128i\chi(0) + b]\,\delta(\xi) + i(a, D)\,\delta(\xi) \tag{4.19}$$

where $\chi(\xi)$ *is a continuous positive definite function satisfying the condition*

$$[(D+\mathbf{1})^2(D-\mathbf{1})^2]^2\chi(\xi) = [(D+\mathbf{1})^2]^2\{\theta(\xi)[(D-\mathbf{1})^2]^2\chi(\xi)\}$$

$$+ [(D-\mathbf{1})^2]^2\{\theta(-\xi)[(D+\mathbf{1})^2]^2\chi(\xi)\} - 128\pi\chi(0)\,\delta(\xi) \tag{4.20}$$

Here, $\mathbf{1} = (1, \mathbf{0})$, $a \in \overline{V}^+$, b *is real, and* θ *is the characteristic function of the cone* $\overline{V}^+$.

Here the following equations are valid:

$$\mu = \mathrm{Im}\, f^+, \quad b = \mathrm{Re}\, f(\mathbf{i})$$

(4.21)

$$\mathrm{Im}\, f(z) = \left(\frac{2}{\pi}\right)^3 \int \frac{(y^2)^2 \mu(dx')}{|(x - x' + iy)^2|^4} + (a, y), \quad z \in \tau^+;$$

(a,y) *is the best linear minorant in the cone* V^+ *of the concave function*

$$h(y) = \lim_{t \to +\infty} \frac{\operatorname{Im} f(ity)}{t}, \quad y \in V^+ \tag{4.22}$$

Example. The function $\sqrt{z^2}$ is holomorphic and $\operatorname{Im}\sqrt{z^2} > 0$ in τ^+. For it $h(y) = \sqrt{y^2}$ and $(a,y) = 0$, $y \in V^+$.

Remark. A description of holomorphic functions with a non-negative imaginary part in the polycircle has been given by Koranyi and Pukansky [18] (see also [17]) and in "the generalized unit circle" by Vladimirov [16]. In the last case all such functions are described by the following integral representation:

$$f(w) = i \int_{U(2)} \left[\frac{2}{\det^2(I - WX^*)} - 1\right] \sigma(dX) + \operatorname{Re} f(0) \tag{4.23}$$

where σ is a non-negative measure on the group U(2) (unitary 2 × 2 matrices) orthogonal on U(2) to the spherical functions $\Delta^{jm}_{q_1 q_2}(X)$ with the neutral indices $2j = 2, 3, \ldots, m = -2j + 1, \ldots, -1$, $-j \leq q_1, q_2 \leq j$. These results can be extended for bounded strongly starlike circular domains; in particular for the classical symmetric domains (see Aisenberg and Dautov [35]).

5. LINEAR PASSIVE SYSTEMS

We shall apply previous results to study systems of convolution equations. Let $Z(x) = (Z_{kj}(x))$ be a N × N matrix with real components $Z_{kj}(x)$ from the space of distributions $\mathscr{D}'(\mathbb{R}^n)$. Consider a linear system of the convolution equations

$$Z * u = f \tag{5.1}$$

where $f(x) = (f_1(x), \ldots, f_N(x))$ is a given N-vector and $u(x)$ is an unknown N-vector. We assume that Eq.(5.1) satisfies the so-called **passivity condition with respect to the** (closed convex solid) **cone** Γ: for any N-vector-function $\varphi(x)$ from $\mathscr{D}^{\times N}$, the inequality

$$\operatorname{Re} \int_{-\Gamma} \langle Z * \varphi, \varphi \rangle \, dx \geq 0 \tag{5.2}$$

holds; here $\langle\, , \rangle$ is the Euclidean scalar product in $\mathbb{C}^N$. As the matrix Z is assumed to be real, the passivity condition (5.2) is equivalent to the condition

$$\int_{-\Gamma} \langle Z * \varphi, \varphi \rangle \, dx \geq 0, \quad \varphi \in \mathscr{D}_r^{\times N} \tag{5.2'}$$

where $\mathscr{D}_r$ consists of real test functions from $\mathscr{D}$.

The inequality (5.2) is of the energetic type; it reflects the ability of a physical system to absorb energy rather than to generate it. In addition, it incorporates the causality with respect to the cone Γ.

The convolution operator $Z*$ satisfying the condition (5.2) is called a **passive operator with respect to the cone** Γ.

The corresponding matrix function $\tilde{Z}(\zeta)$, which is the Laplace transform of the matrix $Z(x)$, is called an **impedance** of the physical system under consideration.

Linear passive systems often occur in mathematical physics: e.g. electrical networks, linear thermodynamic systems, scattering of electromagnetic waves and elementary particles, and so on (see Refs [14, 19–31]). The results for one-dimensional ($n = 1$) passive systems are summarized in the two monographs (1965–66) by Zemanian [22] and Beltrami and Wohlers [25]. Many-dimensional ($n \geqslant 2$) linear passive systems were first investigated by Vladimirov [27, 28].

The following are some consequences of the passivity condition:

(a) Strong form

The passivity condition (5.2) is fulfilled in the strong form:

$$\mathrm{Re} \int_{-\Gamma + x_0} \langle Z * \varphi, \varphi \rangle dx \geqslant 0, \quad \varphi \in \mathscr{D}^{\times N}, \ x_0 \in \mathbb{R}^n \tag{5.3}$$

For proof of (5.3) it is sufficient to apply the inequality (5.2) to the vector function $\varphi_{x_0}(x) = \varphi(x + x_0)$ from $\mathscr{D}^{\times N}$.

(b) Dissipativity

$$\mathrm{Re} \int \langle Z * \varphi, \varphi \rangle dx \geqslant 0, \quad \varphi \in \mathscr{D}^{\times N} \tag{5.4}$$

In fact, putting $x_0 = \lambda e$, $e \in \mathrm{int}\,\Gamma$, into (5.3), and passing on to the limit as $\lambda \to +\infty$, we get (5.4).

(c) Causality with respect to the cone Γ

$$\mathrm{supp}\, Z(x) \subset \Gamma \tag{5.5}$$

It follows from the inequality that if φ and ψ belong to $\mathscr{D}_{\Gamma}^{\times N}$,

$$\left[\int_{-\Gamma} \langle Z * \varphi, \psi \rangle dx + \int_{-\Gamma} \langle Z * \psi, \varphi \rangle dx\right]^2 \leqslant 4 \int_{-\Gamma} \langle Z * \varphi, \varphi \rangle dx \int_{-\Gamma} \langle Z * \psi, \psi \rangle dx$$

The last inequality follows from (5.2′).

(d) Positive definiteness

$$\langle Za + Z^* a, a \rangle \gg 0, \quad a \in \mathbb{C}^n \tag{5.6}$$

or, equivalently,

$$\mathrm{Re}(\langle Za, a\rangle, \varphi * \varphi^*) \geqslant 0, \quad a \in \mathbb{C}^N, \ \varphi \in \mathscr{D} \tag{5.6'}$$

This follows from (5.2) for $\varphi = a\varphi_0(-x)$ where $a \in \mathbb{C}^N$ and $\varphi_0 \in \mathscr{D}$. Here $Z^*(x)$ is the Hermitian conjugate matrix to the matrix $Z(x): Z^*(x) = \overline{Z}^{T(-x)}$.

In the following we assume that the cone Γ is proper.

(e) Growth condition

$$Z_{kj} \in \mathscr{S}' \tag{5.7}$$

It follows from (c) and (d), by the Bochner-Schwartz theorem.

(f) The passivity condition (5.2) is satisfied for all $\varphi \in \mathscr{S}^{\times N}$.
It follows from (e).

(g) The existence of the impedance

The matrix function $\widetilde{Z}(\zeta) = \mathscr{L}[Z]$, $\zeta = p + iq$, is holomorphic in the tube $T^C = \mathbb{R}^n + iC$ where $C = \mathrm{int}\,\Gamma^*$. It follows from (c) and (e).

(h) Reality of the impedance

$$\widetilde{Z}(\zeta) = \overline{\widetilde{Z}}(-\overline{\zeta}), \quad \zeta \in T^C \tag{5.8}$$

or, equivalently, the matrix $\widetilde{Z}(iq)$ is real.
It follows from the reality of the matrix $Z(x)$.

(i) Positivity of the impedance

$$\mathrm{Re}\,\widetilde{Z}(\zeta) \geqslant 0, \quad \zeta \in T^C \tag{5.9}$$

It follows from (f) if we put

$$\varphi(x) = a\eta(-x)e^{-i(\zeta,x)}, \quad a \in \mathbb{C}^N, \quad \zeta \in T^C$$

where a function $\eta \in \mathscr{C}^\infty$, $\eta(x) = 1$, in the ϵ-neighbourhood of Γ, that $\eta(x) = 0$ outside the 2ϵ-neighbourhood of Γ, $|D^\alpha \eta(x)| \leqslant C_\alpha$.

From properties (g), (h) and (i), it follows that *the impedance* $\widetilde{Z}(\zeta)$ *belongs to the set of positive real matrix functions in* T^C.

A matrix function $A(\zeta)$ which is holomorphic in the tube T^C is called **positive real** in T^C if it satisfies the conditions $\mathrm{Re}\,A(\zeta) \geqslant 0$, $\zeta \in T^C$; $A(iq)$ is real for all $q \in C$.

From Theorem VI follows

Theorem VIII. *A matrix function* $A(\zeta)$ *is positive real in a tube* T^C *over a proper (convex) cone* C *if and only if it is the Laplace transform of a matrix* $Z(x)$ *with the following properties:*

$$\text{(i)} \ \langle Za + Z^*a, a\rangle \gg 0, \quad a \in \mathbb{C}^N \tag{5.10}$$

(ii) *For any* n-*faced cone* $C' = [q:(e_1,q) > 0, \ldots, (e_n,q) > 0]$ *contained in the cone* C, *it is (uniquely) representable in the form*

$$Z(x) = (e_1,D)^2 \ldots (e_n,D)^2 Z_{C'}(x) + \sum_{1 \leqslant j \leqslant n} Z_{C'}^{(j)} D_j \delta(x) \tag{5.11}$$

where the matrix function $Z_{C'}(x)$ *is real continuous tempered in* $\mathbb{R}^n$ *with a support in the cone* C'^*; *matrices* $Z_{C'}^{(j)}$, $j = 1, \ldots, n$, *are real symmetric and such that*

$$\sum_{1 \leqslant j \leqslant n} q_j Z_{C'}^{(j)} \geqslant 0, \quad q \in \bar{C}' \tag{5.12}$$

In addition, the following inequality holds:

$$\mathrm{Re} \int \langle Z * \varphi, \varphi \rangle dx \geqslant 0, \qquad \varphi \in \mathscr{S}^{\times N} \tag{5.13}$$

Remark. For n = 1 this theorem was proved by König and Zemanian [14], and for $n \geqslant 2$ by Vladimirov [15].

Now we shall prove the basic theorem of the linear passive systems theory.

Theorem IX. *A matrix* Z(x) *defines a passive operator with respect to a proper cone* Γ *if and only if its impedance* $\tilde{Z}(\zeta)$ *is a positive-real matrix function in the tube* T^C *where* $C = \mathrm{int}\, \Gamma^*$.

Corollary 1. *If a system is passive with respect to a proper cone* Γ *it is passive also with respect to any proper cone which is contained in* Γ.

Corollary 2. *A matrix* Z(x) *defines a passive operator with respect to a proper cone* Γ *if and only if it satisfies conditions (i) and (ii) of Theorem VIII.*

Remark. For n = 1, Theorem IX was proved by Zemanian [24], and for $n \geqslant 2$ by Vladimirov [27]

Proof. Necessity for the conditions has been just proved. We now prove sufficiency of the conditions. Let a matrix function $\tilde{Z}(\zeta)$ be positive real in T^C. Then by Theorem VIII it is the Laplace transform of a matrix Z(x) satisfying the conditions of the lemma cited below for $\Gamma_0 = \mathbb{R}^n$. By this lemma the matrix Z(x) defines a passive operator with respect to a half-space $\Gamma_1 = [x:(e_1,x) \geqslant 0]$ where e_1 is some (unit) vector from $\bar{C}$. Applying again the lemma for the cone Γ_1, and for some vector $e_2 \in \bar{C}$, $|e_2| = 1$, we get the passivity of Z(x) with respect to the cone $\Gamma_2 = [x:(e_1, x) \geqslant 0, (e_2,x) \geqslant 0]$, and so on. Repeating this process m times, we conclude that the matrix Z(x) defines a passive operator with respect to the cone:

$$\Gamma_m = [x:(e_1,x) \geqslant 0, \ldots, (e_m, x) \geqslant 0$$

i.e. the following inequality holds:

$$\int_{-\Gamma_m} \langle Z * \varphi, \varphi \rangle dx \geqslant 0, \quad \varphi \in \mathscr{D}_r^{\times N} \tag{5.14}$$

But the convex cone $C^* = [x:(x,q) \geqslant 0, q \in \bar{C}]$ can be approximated from the above by n-faced cones Γ_m as $m \to \infty$. Therefore, passing on to the limit as $\Gamma_m \to C^*$ in the passivity condition (5.14), we get the passivity condition (5.2′) for the cone $C^* = (\text{int } \Gamma^*)^* = \Gamma$, q.e.d.

It remains to prove the following

Lemma. *Let a* $N \times N$ *matrix* $Z(x)$ *define a passive operator with respect to a cone* $\Gamma_0 \supset C^*$ *with a piecewise boundary and, further, let the matrix* $Z(x)$ *satisfy condition (ii) of Theorem VIII. Then* $Z(x)$ *defines a passive operator with respect to all cones* $\Gamma_e = [x:(e,x) \geqslant 0, x \in \Gamma_0]$ *where* e *is any (unit) vector from the cone* $\bar{C}$.

We omit the proof of the lemma: it takes some hard work. For details see Vladimirov [27].

A matrix $A(x)$, $A_{kj} \in \mathscr{D}'$, is called a **fundamental solution** of a passive operator $Z*$ if it satisfies the matrix convolution equation:

$$Z * A = I\delta(x) \tag{5.15}$$

The matrix function $\tilde{A}(\zeta)$, which is the Laplace transform of the matrix $A(x)$, is called the **admittance** of the physical system. A passive operator $Z*$ with respect to a cone Γ is called **non-degenerate** if the cone Γ is proper and $\det \tilde{Z}(\zeta) \neq 0$, $\zeta \in T^C$ where $C = \text{int } \Gamma^*$.

Theorem X. *Every non-degenerate passive operator with respect to a cone* Γ *has a unique fundamental solution which defines a non-degenerate passive operator with respect to the same cone* Γ.

Proof. If $Z*$ is a non-degenerate passive operator with respect to a cone Γ, then by Theorem IX the matrix function $\tilde{Z}(\zeta)$ is positive real and $\det \tilde{Z}(\zeta) \neq 0$ in T^C where $C = \text{int } \Gamma^*$. We shall prove that there exists a solution of Eq.(5.15) which is unique in the set of matrices $A(x)$ which define non-degenerate and passive operators with respect to the cone Γ. Passing to the Laplace transform in Eq.(5.15), we get the following (equivalent) matrix equation:

$$\tilde{Z}(\zeta)\tilde{A}(\zeta) = I, \quad \zeta \in T^C \tag{5.16}$$

Equation (5.16) has a unique solution $\tilde{A}(\zeta) = \tilde{Z}^{-1}(\zeta)$ for all $\zeta \in T^C$ which is holomorphic and $\det \tilde{A}(\zeta) \neq 0$ in T^C. Moreover, from the reality of $\tilde{Z}(iq)$ it follows that $\tilde{A}(iq)$ is real for all $q \in C$ and, finally, from the condition $\text{Re } \tilde{Z}(\zeta) \geqslant 0$, $\zeta \in T^C$ we conclude

$$\text{Re } \tilde{A}(\zeta) = \tilde{A}^T(\zeta) [\text{Re } \tilde{Z}(\zeta)] \tilde{A}(\zeta) \geqslant 0, \quad \zeta \in T^C$$

Hence the matrix function $\tilde{A}(\zeta)$ is positive real in T^C. By Theorem IX the matrix $A(x)$ defines a (non-degenerate) passive operator with respect to the cone Γ. The matrix $A(x)$ is unique, q.e.d.

Remark. Passive systems behave like hyperbolic systems (see Hörmander [32] and Friedrichs [33]).

Example. A symmetric (in the sense of Friedrichs [33]) linear differential operator with constant coefficients

$$\sum_{1 \leqslant j \leqslant n} Z_j \frac{\partial}{\partial x_j} = \sum_{1 \leqslant j \leqslant n} Z_j \frac{\partial}{\partial x_j} \delta(x) * \tag{5.17}$$

defines a non-degenerate passive operator with respect to the cone

$$\Gamma = [x : x_1 = \langle Z_1 a,a\rangle, ..., x_n = \langle Z_n a,a\rangle, \quad a \in \mathbb{C}^N]$$

In (5.17), Z_j, j = 1, ..., n, are real symmetric N × N matrices and there exists a unit vector ℓ such that

$$\sum_{1\leqslant j\leqslant n} \ell_j Z_j > 0$$

In particular, the Dirac operator (see Bogolubov, Logunov and Todorov [34])

$$i \sum_{0\leqslant\mu\leqslant 3} \gamma^\mu D_\mu - m \tag{5.18}$$

after multiplying by the matrix $-i\gamma^0$,

$$\sum_{0\leqslant\mu\leqslant 3} \gamma^0 \gamma^\mu D_\mu + im\gamma^0$$

becomes a passive non-degenerate operator with respect to the future light cone $\overline{V}^+$.

In (5.18) γ^μ are the 4 × 4 Dirac matrices.

REFERENCES

[1] VLADIMIROV, V.S., "The Laplace transform of tempered distributions", Global Analysis and its Application 3 (Proc. Int. Course,Trieste, 1972), IAEA, Vienna (1974) 243–270.

[2] FATOU, P., Séries trigonométriques et séries de Taylor, Acta Math. **30** (1906) 335–400.

[3] RIESZ, F., Über die Randwerte einer analytischen Funktion, Math. Z. **18** (1922) 87–95.

[4] KÖTHE, G., Die Randverteilungen analytischer Funktionen, Math. Z. **57** (1952) 13–33.

[5] SATO, M., (a) On a generalization of the concept of functions, Proc. Jap. Acad. **34** (1958) 126–130; 604–60 (b) Theory of hyperfunctions, J. Fac. Sci., Univ. Tokyo, Section I., **8** (1959/60) 139–193; 387–436.

[6] VLADIMIROV, V.S., O postroenii obolochek golomorfnosti dlya oblastej spetsial'nogo vida, DAN SSSR **134** (1960) 251–254; O postroenii obolochek golomorfnosti dlya oblastej spetsial'nogo vida i ikh primeneniya, Trudy Matem. instituta AN SSSR **60** (1961) 101–144.

[7] TILLMANN, H.G., Darstellung der Schwartzschen Distributionen durch analytische Funktionen, Math. Z. **77** (1961) 106–124.

[8] TILLMANN, H.G., Distributionen als Randverteilungen analytischer Funktionen **2**, Math. Z. **76** (1961) 5–21

[9] LUSZCZKI, Z., ZIELEZNY, Z., Distributionen der Räume $\mathscr{D}'_{\mathscr{L}^p}$ als Randverteilungen analytischer Funktione Colloq. Math. **8** (1961) 125–131.

[10] KOMATSU, H., "Ultradistributions and hyperfunctions", Hyperfunctions and Pseudo-differential Equations, Lecture Notes in Math. No. 287, Springer (1973) 164–179.

[11] MARTINEAU, A., "Distributions et valeurs au bord des fonctions holomorphes", Théorie des distributions, Gulbenkian Inst. Science, Lisbon (1964) 193–326.

[12] NEVANLINNA, R., Eindeutige analytische Funktionen, Springer, Berlin (1936).

[13] SCHWARTZ, L., Théorie des distributions **1–2**, Paris (1950–51).

[14] KÖNIG, H., ZEMANIAN, A.H., Necessary and sufficient conditions for matrix distributions to have a positive-real Laplace transform, SIAM J. Appl. Math. **13** (1965) 1036–1040.

[15] VLADIMIROV, V.S., Golomorfnye funktsii s neotritsatel'noj mnimoj chast'yu v trubchatoj oblasti nad konusom, Matem. Sb. **79** 121 (1969) 128–152.

[16] VLADIMIROV, V.S., Golomorfnye funktsii s polozhitel'noj mnimoj chast'yu v trube budushchego, Matem. Sb. **93** 135 (1974), 3–17; **94** 136 (1974) 499–515; **98** 140 (1975) 292–297.

[17] VLADIMIROV, V.S., DROZHZHINOV, Yu.N., Golomorfnye funktsii v polikruge s neotritsatel'noj mnimoj chast'yu, Matem. Sametki **15** (1974) 55–61.

[18] KORANYI, A., PUKANSKY, J., Holomorphic functions with positive real part in polycylinder, Trans. Am. Math. Soc. **108** (1963) 449–456.

[19] KÖNIG, H., MEIXNER, T., Lineare Systeme und lineare Transformationen, Math. Nachr. **19** (1958) 265–322.

[20] YOULA, D., CASTRIOTA, L., CARLIN, H., Bounded real scattering matrices and the foundation of linear passive network theory, IRE Trans. Circuit Theory, CT-6 (1959) 102–124.

[21] WU, T., Some properties of impedance as a causal operator, J. Math. Phys. **3** (1962) 262–271.

[22] ZEMANIAN, A., Distribution theory and transform analysis, McGraw-Hill, New York (1965).

[23] ZEMANIAN, A., The Hilbert port, SIAM J. Appl. Math. **18** (1970) 98–138.

[24] ZEMANIAN, A., An N-port realizability theory based on the theory of distributions, IEEE Trans. Circuit Theory, CT-10 (1963) 265–274.

[25] BELTRAMI, E.J., WOHLERS, M.R., Distributions and the Boundary Values of Analytic Functions, Academic Press, New York and London (1966).

[26] GÜTTINGER, W., Generalized functions in elementary particle physics and passive system theory: recent trends and problems, SIAM J. Appl. Math. **15** (1967) 964–1000.

[27] VLADIMIROV, V.S., Linejnye passidnye sistemy, Teoretich. i Matem. Fisika **1** (1969) 67–94.

[28] VLADIMIROV, V.S., Mnogomernye linejnye passidnye sistemy, v Sb. "Mekhanika sploshnoj sredy i rodstvennye problemy analisa" (1972) 121–134.

[29] LAX, P., PHILLIPS, R., Scattering theory, Academic Press, New York and London (1967).

[30] RAÑADA, A., Causality and the S-matrix, J. Math. Phys. **8** (1967) 2321–2326.

[31] HACKENBROCH, W., Integraldarstellungen einer Klasse dissipativer linearer Operatoren, Math. Z. **109** (1969) 273–287.

[32] HÖRMANDER, L., Linear Partial Differential Operators, Springer (1963).

[33] FRIEDRICHS, K., Symmetric hyperbolic linear differential equations, Commun. Pure Appl. Math. **7** (1954) 345–392.

[34] BOGOLUBOV, N.N., LOGUNOV, A.A., TODOROV, I.T., Osnovy Aksiomate – Maticheskogo Podkhoda v Kvantovoj Teorii Polya, Isd-vo "Nauka", 1970.

[35] AJSENBERG, L.A., DAUTON, Sk. A., Golomorfnye funktsii mnogikh kompleksnykh peremennykh s neotritsatel'noj dejstvitel'noj chast'yu. Sledy golomorfnykh i plyurigarmonicheskikh funktsij na granitse Shilova, Matem. Sb. **99** (1976) 343–355.

HARMONIC MAPS AND COMPLEX ANALYSIS

J.C. WOOD
Mathematics Department,
Brighton Polytechnic,
Brighton, Sussex,
United Kingdom

Abstract

HARMONIC MAPS AND COMPLEX ANALYSIS.

The properties of harmonic maps between complex manifolds are studied. In particular, it is shown that there is no harmonic map from the torus to the sphere of degree 1.

INTRODUCTION

A harmonic map is a map between Riemannian manifolds which extremizes a certain simple functional called the energy integral. As for harmonic functions, these mappings have nice properties when the manifolds are complex. It is the purpose of this paper to describe some such results. The paper consists of four sections:

1. Harmonic maps between real manifolds. We give the definition of a harmonic map, some properties and some examples.

2. Harmonic maps between complex manifolds. If the domain manifold is two-dimensional, we require only a complex structure to define harmonicity. If both manifolds are Kähler, holomorphic maps are harmonic. Some results due to Lichnerowicz are given.

3. Quadratic differentials and harmonic maps. To a smooth map from a Riemann surface a quadratic differential is associated which is holomorphic if the map is harmonic. We use this in particular to show that all harmonic maps from the Riemann sphere are conformal.

4. Non-existence of certain harmonic maps into the 2-sphere. We study the zeros of the partial derivatives of a harmonic map between Riemann surfaces and give a new result which has as Corollary (4.4): there is no harmonic map of degree 1 from the torus to the sphere.

The new results were proved after collaboration between the author and Professor J. Eells and discussions with other participants at the Summer School at Trieste, 1975.

1. HARMONIC MAPS BETWEEN REAL MANIFOLDS

(A) Let M,N be smooth ($=C^\infty$) connected manifolds of dimension m,n equipped with smooth Riemannian metrics g,h and the canonical induced (Levi-Cività) connections. Let $(x^1, \ldots, x^m)$, $(u^1, \ldots, u^n)$ denote smooth local co-ordinates on M,N; in these co-ordinates we have $g = g_{ij}\,dx^i dx^j$, $h = h_{\alpha\beta}\,du^\alpha du^\beta$. Let Γ^k_{ij}, $L^\gamma_{\alpha\beta}$ denote the Christoffel symbols of M,N. For a smooth map $f: M \to N$ set

$$\tau(f)^\gamma(P) = \Delta f^\gamma + g^{ij} L^\gamma_{\alpha\beta} \frac{\partial f^\alpha}{\partial x^i} \frac{\partial f^\beta}{\partial x^j}$$

where all quantities are evaluated at P or f(P), and Δ denotes the Laplacian on M.

This expression is independent of choice of local co-ordinates on M and, for any change of local co-ordinates on N, transforms as a vector in $TN_{f(P)}$. It thus defines a **vector field along** f, $\tau(f)$, i.e. a smooth map $\tau(f): M \to TN$ such that $\tau(f)(P) \in TN_{f(P)}$. $\tau(f)$ is called the **tension field of the mapping** f.

Definition 1.1. $f: M \to N$ *is called harmonic if* $\tau(f) \equiv 0$.

Note that $\tau(f)$ is given by

$$\tau(f)^\gamma = g^{ij} \left\{ \frac{\partial^2 f^\gamma}{\partial x^i \partial x^j} - \Gamma^k_{ij} \frac{\partial f^\gamma}{\partial x^k} + L^\gamma_{\alpha\beta} \frac{\partial f^\alpha}{\partial x^i} \frac{\partial f^\beta}{\partial x^j} \right\}$$

In particular, if $(x^1, \ldots, x^m)$, $(u^1, \ldots, u^n)$ are **normal co-ordinates** about P, f(P), respectively, then

$$\Gamma^k_{ij}(P) = 0, \quad \forall i, j, k, \; L^\gamma_{\alpha\beta}(f(P)) = 0, \quad \forall \alpha, \beta, \gamma$$

and so

$$\tau(f)^\gamma(P) = \frac{\partial^2 f^\gamma}{\partial x^{\ell 2}}(P) + \ldots + \frac{\partial^2 f^\gamma}{\partial x^{n^2}}(P)$$

(B) $\tau(f)$ can be defined invariantly as follows (see Eliasson [2, 3] and Eells-Sampson [1] for details and proofs). Pull back the bundle $TN \to N$ via f to give a bundle $E \to M$. The connections on M, N can be used to define covariant differentiations:

$$C^\infty(E) \xrightarrow{\tilde{\nabla}} C^\infty(TM^* \otimes E) \xrightarrow{\tilde{\nabla}} C^\infty(TM^* \otimes TM^* \otimes E) \xrightarrow{\tilde{\nabla}} \ldots$$

and

$$C^\infty(E) \xrightarrow{\tilde{d}} C^\infty(TM^* \otimes E) \xrightarrow{\tilde{d}} C^\infty(\Lambda^2 TM^* \otimes E) \to \ldots, \qquad (\text{Note } \tilde{d}^2 \neq 0)$$

Note that elements of $C^\infty(E)$ are simply vector fields along f. Elements of $C^\infty(TM^* \otimes \ldots \otimes TM^* \otimes$ (r factors) are called **r-tensors on M with values in** E, elements of $C^\infty(\Lambda^r TM^* \otimes E)$ are called **r-form on M with values in** E. **The bundles** $TM^* \otimes \ldots \otimes TM^* \otimes E$, $\Lambda^r TM^* \otimes E$ $(r \geqslant 0)$ inherit natural inner products $\langle \, , \rangle$ from those on TM and E; these give inner products $\langle \, , \rangle$ on the spaces of r-tensor or r-forms by integration over M, viz.

$$\langle \phi, \psi \rangle = \int_M \langle \phi(-), \psi(-) \rangle v(g)$$

where ϕ, ψ are r-tensors or forms, v(g) is the volume form on M, and $-$ denotes points of M.

We define $\widetilde{\delta} : C^\infty(\Lambda^{r+1} TM^* \otimes E) \to C^\infty(\Lambda^r TM^* \otimes E)$ as the formal adjoint of $\widetilde{d}$, i.e. we require

$$\langle \widetilde{\delta}\phi, \psi\rangle = \langle \phi, \widetilde{d}\psi\rangle, \quad \forall \phi \in C^\infty(\Lambda^{r+1} TM^* \otimes E), \quad \psi \in C^\infty(\Lambda^r \; TM^* \otimes E)$$

Noting $df \in C^\infty(TM^* \otimes E)$, we define the **tension field** or **Laplacian** of f by

$$\tau(f) = -\widetilde{\delta}\, df \in C^\infty(E)$$

If $Tr: C^\infty(TM^* \otimes TM^* \otimes E) \to C^\infty(E)$ is defined by contraction, $-\widetilde{\delta} = Tr\, \widetilde{\nabla}$; thus $\tau(f) = Tr\; \widetilde{\nabla} df$

Notes

(1) The Laplacian $\widetilde{\Delta}$ of an r-form with values in E can be defined by $\widetilde{\Delta} = -(\widetilde{\delta}\,\widetilde{d} + \widetilde{d}\,\widetilde{\delta})$ and such a form is called **harmonic** if it has zero Laplacian; then $f: M \to N$ is harmonic if and only if df is harmonic as a 1-form with values in E (c.f. the paper by Field, these Proceedings).

(2) $\widetilde{\nabla} df$ is called the (second) fundamental form of f.

A mapping f is called **totally geodesic** iff its second fundamental form is identically zero. Such a map sends geodesics to geodesics linearly. Since $\tau(f) = Tr\, \widetilde{\nabla}\, df$, harmonic maps can be interpreted as maps which take an orthogonal set of geodesics onto a set of curves which are on average geodesics (see Wood [15]).

(C) We shall now see that harmonic maps extremize a generalization of the Dirichlet integral, called the energy integral of f, E(f). This is defined for any smooth map $f: M \to N$, M compact, by

$$E(f) = \tfrac{1}{2} \int_M \|df\|^2 v(g)$$

Here $\| \; \|$ denotes the norm on $TM^* \otimes E$ induced by the norms on TM, TN; in local co-ordinates,

$$\|df\|^2 = g^{ij} h_{\alpha\beta} \frac{\partial f^\alpha}{\partial x^i} \frac{\partial f^\beta}{\partial x^j}$$

Note that if $\{e_1, \ldots, e_m\}$ is an orthogonal basis for TM_P,

$$\|df\|^2(P) = \sum_{i=1}^{m} \frac{\|df(e_i)\|^2_{TN}}{\|e_i\|^2_{TM}}$$

i.e. $\|df\|^2$ measures the sum of the squares of stretches of lengths along a complete set of mutually perpendicular directions. E gives a **real-valued functional** on a suitable manifold of maps $M \to N$.

Proposition 1.2. *If* M *is compact,* N *is complete, a smooth map* $f: M \to N$ *is harmonic if and only if it gives a critical point of the energy* E.

Proof. It can be shown [1] (see also Refs [13,2]) that for any smooth one-parameter family of mappings $f_t: M \to N$ with $f_0 = f$,

$$\frac{d}{dt} E(f_t)\Big|_{t=0} = -\int_M \langle w, \tau(f)\rangle_E v(g)$$

The proposition follows.

Note that this further shows that, for any smooth map $f: M \to N$, $\tau(f)$ "points" in the direction in which the energy decreases most rapidly.

We now ask whether, given an arbitrary map $f: M \to N$, it is possible to "deform" it so that it becomes harmonic.

(D) **Existence theorem 1.3 (Eells-Sampson [1]).** *Let M be a compact connected C^∞ Riemannian manifold. Let N be a compact connected C^∞ Riemannian manifold with non-positive sectional curvatures. Then in every homotopy class of maps $f: M \to N$ there is a harmonic map. Further, this map gives an absolute minimum of the energy integral amongst all smooth maps in the given homotopy class.*

Uniqueness theorem 1.4 (Hartman [5]). *If, further, N has strictly negative sectional curvatures, then any harmonic map $f: M \to N$ is the only harmonic map in its homotopy class unless: (1) f is constant; or (2) f maps into a geodesic arc γ, in which case all harmonic maps homotopic to f are obtained by a "rotation" of γ, i.e. by moving each point f(P) a fixed oriented distance along γ*

(E) Examples

(1) If $N = \underline{R}$, then $\tau(f) = \Delta f$, the energy integral is simply the Dirichlet integral of f, and a harmonic map is just a harmonic function on M.

(2) If $M = \underline{R}$, $\tau(f) = (D/ds)(df/ds)$, where D denotes covariant differentiation on N, s denote arc length along $\underline{R}$, and thus a smooth map $\underline{R} \to N$ is harmonic if and only if it defines a geodesic.

(3) There are many other examples including: minimal immersions; homomorphisms between Lie groups carrying bi-invariant metrics [1]; harmonic polynomial mappings $S^{m-1} \to S^{n-}$ [13, 17]; the Gauss map of a minimal immersion in Euclidean space [11]; and, to be discussed in § 2, holomorphic maps between Kähler manifolds. Note the result:

Theorem 1.5. *Let Γ be a lattice on $\underline{R}^m$ of maximal rank so that $\underline{R}^m/\Gamma$ is an m-dimensional real torus, and let Γ' be a lattice on $\underline{R}^n$ (not necessarily of maximal rank). Give the spaces $\underline{R}^m/\Gamma$, $\underline{R}^n/\Gamma'$ the metrics induced from the standard metrics on $\underline{R}^m$, $\underline{R}^n$. Then any harmonic map $f: \underline{R}^m/\Gamma \to \underline{R}^n/\Gamma'$ is of the form: constant + Lie group homomorphism. Conversely, any such map is harmonic.*

Proof. In standard co-ordinates $(x^1, \ldots, x^m)$ for $\underline{R}^m$, $(u^1, \ldots, u^n)$ for $\underline{R}^n$, the harmonic equations are simply

$$\sum_{i=1}^{m} \frac{\partial^2 f^\gamma}{\partial x^{i^2}} = 0$$

It follows that the partial derivatives $\partial f^\gamma/\partial x^i$ are harmonic functions on $\underline{R}^m/\Gamma$; since this manifold is **compact**, by the maximum principle for harmonic functions the partial derivatives must be constant. Therefore

$$f^\gamma = \text{const} + \sum_{i=1}^{m} \text{const } x^i$$

showing f is of the form: f = const + Lie group homomorphism.

For the converse, note that any Lie group homomorphism is of the form

$$f^\gamma = \sum_{i=1}^{m} \text{const } x^i$$

The converse now follows.

2. HARMONIC MAPS BETWEEN COMPLEX MANIFOLDS

(A) Special properties when domain is two-dimensional

Let M, N be smooth connected Riemannian manifolds as in § 1, but now suppose that M is two-dimensional.

Proposition 2.1 (Invariance of harmonicity under conformal change of metric). *Let the metric* g *on* M *be replaced by a conformally equivalent metric* $g' = \lambda g$ *where* $\lambda : M \to \underline{R}$ *is smooth and positive. Then for any smooth map* $f : M \to N$: *(1) the energy integral* E(f) *is unchanged; (2) the tension field* $\tau(f) : M \to TN$ *is multiplied by the scalar* $\lambda^{-1} : M \to \underline{R}$.

Proof

(1) The integrand $\|df\|^2$ of E(f) is multiplied by λ^{-2}, whereas, since M is two-dimensional, the volume element v(g) is multiplied by λ^2.

(2) In isothermal co-ordinates (x^1, x^2) on M, with $g_{11} = g_{22} = \rho^2$, $g_{12} = 0$,

$$\tau(f)^\gamma = \rho^{-2}\left\{\frac{\partial^2 f^\gamma}{\partial x^{12}} + \frac{\partial^2 f^\gamma}{\partial x^{22}} + \delta^{ij} L^\gamma_{\alpha\beta} \frac{\partial f^\alpha}{\partial x^i}\frac{\partial f^\beta}{\partial x^j}\right\}$$

(where δ^{ij} is the Kronecker delta symbol). The proposition follows.

Corollary 2.2. *The concept of harmonicity requires only a metric defined up to conformal equivalence on* M. *Thus we may take* M *to be a* **Riemann surface** *and no metric on* M *need be specified.*

Notes 2.3

(1) If z is a complex co-ordinate on M,

$$\tau(f) = 4\rho^{-2}\left\{\frac{\partial^2 f^\gamma}{\partial \bar{z}\partial z} + L^\gamma_{\alpha\beta}\frac{\partial f^\alpha}{\partial \bar{z}}\frac{\partial f^\beta}{\partial z}\right\}$$

(2) It can further be shown that a harmonic map $f : M \to N$ from a Riemann surface composed with a holomorphic or antiholomorphic map $k : \widetilde{M} \to M$, where $\widetilde{M}$ is another Riemann surface, is harmonic [15].

(B) Special properties when domain and codomain are two-dimensional

Suppose now that M and N are Riemann surfaces, i.e. connected complex manifolds of complex dimension 1. Given a hermitian metric h on N we may discuss mappings $f: M \to N$ harmonic with respect to h. By Corollary (2.2), no metric on M is required. Note the improved

Existence theorem 2.4 (Lemaire [9]). *Let* M, N *be compact Riemann surfaces,* N *equipped with a herm metric* h. *Then if genus* (N) > 0, *every homotopy class of mappings contains a harmonic map which gives an absolute minimum for the energy integral.*

Notes 2.5

(1) Such mappings may have general folds [15, 16].

(2) We shall see in §4 that this existence theorem is false for genus (N) = 0.

Now let M, N be equipped with complex co-ordinates z,w and write $h = \sigma^2 dw d\overline{w}$. Then the harmonic equations can be written:

$$\frac{\partial^2 w}{\partial z \partial \overline{z}} + 2\frac{\sigma_w}{\sigma}\frac{\partial w}{\partial \overline{z}}\frac{\partial w}{\partial z} = 0$$

Proposition 2.6. *Holomorphic or antiholomorphic mappings between Riemann surfaces are harmonic with respect to any hermitian metric on* N.

Proof

$f: M \to N$ is holomorphic or antiholomorphic $\Leftrightarrow \partial w/\partial \overline{z} = 0$ or $\partial w/\partial z = 0$, respectively, and thus the harmonic equations are satisfied.

This is true in higher dimensions, as we now describe.

(C) Harmonic maps between almost hermitian manifolds

Let M, N be smooth Riemannian manifolds of dimensions 2m, 2n with almost complex structures (see the paper by Robertson, these Proceedings) J, J′ such that the metrics g, h on M, N are hermitian, i.e.

$$\langle X, Y \rangle = \langle JX, JY \rangle \ \forall X, Y \in TM_p \ \forall p \in M$$

and similarly for N, where $\langle \, , \rangle$ denotes the inner product on TM defined by the metric on M. M and N are then called **almost-hermitian manifolds.**

The complexified tangent and cotangent bundles of M and N, viz.

$$TM^c = TM \otimes_{\underline{R}} \underline{C}, \quad TM^*_c = TM^* \otimes_{\underline{R}} \underline{C}, \quad TN^c = TN \otimes_{\underline{R}} \underline{C}, \quad TN^*_c = TN^* \otimes_{\underline{R}} \underline{C}$$

split up as direct sums (see Ref. [8]):

$$TM^c = TM^{1,0} \oplus TM^{0,1}, \qquad TM^*_c = TM^*_{1,0} \oplus TM^*_{0,1} \text{ (and similarly for N)}$$

Let $\{\theta^i, \ i = 1, \ldots, m\}$ be a local basis for $TM^*_{1,0}$; the complex conjugates $\{\theta^{\bar{i}} (= \overline{\theta^i})\}$ form a local basis for $TM^*_{0,1}$. Take similar bases $\{\phi^\alpha\}$, $\{\phi^{\bar{\alpha}}\}$ for $TN^*_{1,0}$, $TN^*_{0,1}$ and take dual bases for $TM^{1,0}$, $TM^{0,1}$, $TN^{1,0}$, $TN^{0,1}$. The metrics on M, N have the form

$$g = g_{i\bar{j}}\theta^i\theta^{\bar{j}}, \qquad h = h_{\alpha\bar{\beta}}\phi^\alpha\phi^{\bar{\beta}}$$

Now let $f: M \to N$ be a smooth map. With respect to the above bases,

$$\tau(f)^\gamma = -2g^{i\bar{j}}(\partial_i f_{\bar{j}}^\gamma - \Gamma_{\bar{j}i}^A f_A^\gamma + L_{KL}^\gamma f_{\bar{j}}^K f_i^L)$$

Here indices $i, j, \ldots$ range over $1, \ldots, m$; $\alpha, \beta, \ldots$ range over $1, \ldots, n$; $K, L, \ldots$ range over $1, \ldots, m, \bar{1}, \ldots, \bar{m}$; $A, B, \ldots$ range over $1, \ldots, n, \bar{1}, \ldots, \bar{n}$; ∂_i denotes derivation in direction dual to θ^i.

Note: for the invariant form of this formula, see Lichnerowicz [10].

To ensure that a holomorphic or antiholomorphic map between hermitian manifolds is harmonic, further conditions need to be imposed on the manifolds:

Definitions 2.7. *Let* M *be an almost hermitian manifold with metric* $g = g_{i\bar{j}}\theta^i\theta^{\bar{j}}$ *where* $\theta^1, \ldots, \theta^m, \theta^{\bar{1}}, \ldots, \theta^{\bar{m}}$ *is a local basis for* TM_c^*. *The* **fundamental 2-form** *of* M *is the complex-valued 2-form:* $\Theta = ig_{i\bar{j}}\theta^i \wedge \theta^{\bar{j}}$.

M *is said to be* **almost Kählerian** *if* Θ *is closed, i.e.* $d\Theta = 0$;

M *is said to be* **almost-hermitian special** *if* $d(\Theta^{m-1}) = 0$, *or equivalently* $\delta\Theta = 0$ *where* δ *is the adjoint of* d;

M *is said to be* **almost-hermitian special of pure type** *if the (1,2) part of* $d\Theta$ *is zero.*

Note: M Kählerian ⇒ M almost-hermitian special of pure type ⇒ M almost-hermitian special.

Lemma 2.8. *If* M *is almost hermitian special of pure type, the impure Christoffel symbols* $\Gamma_{\bar{j}i}^A$ *vanish.*

Proposition 2.9 (Lichnerowicz [10]). *If* M *and* N *are almost hermitian special of pure type, then any holomorphic or antiholomorphic mapping* $f: M \to N$ *is harmonic.*

Proof. Either $f_{\bar{i}}^\alpha \equiv 0, \forall i, \alpha$ or $f_i^\alpha \equiv 0, \forall i, \alpha$; in either case we see from the harmonic equations above that $\tau(f) \equiv 0$.

(D) Decomposition of the energy integral

Let M and N be almost hermitian manifolds, M compact, and let $f: M \to N$ be a smooth map. The derivative $df: TM \to TN$ can be extended to a complex linear map $df^c: TM^c \to TN^c$ which decomposes into partial derivatives:

$$\partial f_{1,0}: TM^{1,0} \subsetneq TM^c \xrightarrow{df^c} TN \xrightarrow[\text{projection}]{\text{natural}} TN^{1,0}$$

$$\partial f_{0,1}: TM^{1,0} \subsetneq TM^c \xrightarrow{df^c} TN \xrightarrow[\text{projection}]{\text{natural}} TN^{0,1}$$

This gives a decomposition of the energy integral:

$$E(f) = E_{1,0}(f) + E_{0,1}(f)$$

where

$$E_{1,0}(f) = \int_M g^{i\bar{j}} h_{\alpha\bar{\beta}} f_i^\alpha f_{\bar{j}}^{\bar{\beta}} v(g) = \int_M g^{i\bar{j}} h_{\alpha\bar{\beta}} f_i^\alpha \overline{f_j^\beta} v(g)$$

$$E_{0,1}(f) = \int_M g^{i\bar{j}} h_{\alpha\bar{\beta}} f_{\bar{j}}^{\alpha} f_{i}^{\bar{\beta}} v(g) = \int_M g^{i\bar{j}} h_{\alpha\bar{\beta}} \overline{f_j^{\bar{\alpha}}} f_i^{\bar{\beta}} v(g)$$

Note that if the inner product on $C^\infty(TM_c^* \otimes_{\underline{R}} E)$ (see § 1B) is extended to a hermitian inner product on $C^\infty(TM_c^* \otimes_{\underline{C}} E^c)$, $E_{1,0}(f)$ is the norm of $\partial f_{1,0}$ and $E_{0,1}(f)$ is the norm of $\partial f_{0,1}$.

Lemma 2.10. $E_{1,0}(f) = 0 \Leftrightarrow$ f *antiholomorphic;* $E_{0,1}(f) = 0 \Leftrightarrow$ f *holomorphic.*

Now consider the difference: $K(f) = E_{1,0}(f) - E_{0,1}(f)$.

Proposition 2.11 (Lichnerowicz [10]). *If* M *is almost-hermitian special and* N *is almost Kählerian,* K(f) *is dependent only on the homotopy class of* f.

Proof. Let Θ and Φ be the fundamental 2-forms of M and N. Θ and $f^*\Phi$ have natural inner product:

$$\langle \Theta, f^*\Phi \rangle = \int_M \{ g^{i\bar{j}} h_{\alpha\bar{\beta}} f_i^{\alpha} f_{\bar{j}}^{\bar{\beta}} - g^{i\bar{j}} h_{\alpha\bar{\beta}} f_{\bar{j}}^{\alpha} f_i^{\bar{\beta}} \} v(g)$$

We observe that this is equal to K(f). Now let $f_0 : M \to N$, $f_1 : M \to N$ be homotopic smooth maps. Then there exists a smooth homotopy $M \times [0,1] \to N$, $(p, t) \mapsto f_t(p)$. Using the fact that Φ is close we can find a 3-form Ψ on M such that

$$\frac{d}{dt}(f_t^* \Phi) = d\Psi$$

Then,

$$\frac{d}{dt} K(f_t) = \frac{d}{dt} \langle \Theta, f_t^* \Phi \rangle = \langle \Theta, d\Psi \rangle = \langle \partial\Theta, \Psi \rangle = 0 \text{ since M is almost-hermitian special}$$

The result follows.

Corollary 2.12 (Lichnerowicz [10]). *If* M *is almost hermitian special and* N *is almost Kählerian, a holomorphic or antiholomorphic map* $M \to N$ *gives an absolute minimum of the energy integral for mappings within the same homotopy class.*

Proof. Let $\mu : M \to N$ be holomorphic and let f be any other smooth mapping in the same homotop class,

$$E(\mu) = E_{1,0}(\mu) = K(\mu) = K(f) = E_{1,0}(f) - E_{0,1}(f) \leqslant E_{1,0}(f) + E_{0,1}(f) = E(f)$$

For an antiholomorphic map, the proof is similar.

Corollary 2.13 (Lichnerowicz [10]). *Let* M *be almost hermitian special and let* N *be almost Kählerian. A holomorphic mapping* $M \to N$ *cannot be homotopic to an antiholomorphic mapping* $M \to N$ *unless they are both constant.*

Proof. Let μ be holomorphic and μ' be antiholomorphic. If they are homotopic,

$$E(\mu) = E_{1,0}(\mu) = K(\mu) = K(\mu') = -E_{0,1}(\mu') = -E(\mu')$$

Since the energy integral is non-negative, it follows that

$$E(\mu) = E(\mu') = 0$$

and therefore μ and μ' are both constant.

3. QUADRATIC DIFFERENTIALS AND HARMONIC MAPS

(A) Definition 3.1. *Let* M *be a Riemann surface. A* **quadratic differential** *on* M *is a (symmetric) covariant tensor of type (2,0), i.e. a tensor which in a complex co-ordinate* z *has the form* $\eta = a(z)dz^2$ *where* $dz^2 = dz \otimes dz$. *If* z *denotes another complex co-ordinate with respect to which* η *has the form* $\eta = a'(z')dz'^2$, *we have the* **transformation law:**

$$a'(z') = a(z(z'))\left(\frac{dz}{dz'}\right)^2$$

A quadratic differential $\eta = a(z)dz^2$ *is said to be* **holomorphic** *if each local representative* a(z) *is holomorphic. Let* η *be a holomorphic quadratic differential which is not identically zero. Let* $P \in M$, *if* z *is a complex co-ordinate centred on* P, *then in a neighbourhood of* P,

$$\eta = \{a_m z^m + \ldots\}\, dz^2, \qquad a_m \in \underline{C}\backslash\{0\}, \qquad m \in \{0,1,\ldots\}$$

The integer m *is independent of the choice of local complex co-ordinate* z *and is called the* **order** *of* η *at the point* P. *If* $m > 0$, $\eta(P) = 0$ *and* η *is said to have a* **zero of order** m *at* P. Note: a holomorphic quadratic differential has **isolated** zeros unless it is identically zero. We shall use two facts about holomorphic quadratic differentials.

Proposition 3.2. *Any non-identically zero quadratic differential on* M *has 4 (genus* M*)-4 zeros counting according to order.*

Proof. Either by the Riemann-Roch theorem or by the methods of §4.

Corollary 3.3. *If genus* M = 0, *there are no non-identically zero holomorphic quadratic differentials on* M.

(B) The quadratic differential associated with a map into Euclidean space

Let M be a Riemann surface and let E^n denote n-dimensional real Euclidean space equipped with the standard inner product $\langle\ \rangle_{E^n}$ and norm $\|\ \|_{E^n}$. It is useful to consider the **complexification** $E^n \otimes_{\underline{R}} \underline{C}$ of E^n and to extend the inner product to a complex bilinear symmetric inner product on $E^n \otimes_{\underline{R}} \underline{C}$.

Let $f: M \to E^n$ be a smooth ($=C^\infty$) map with components $f^1, \ldots, f^n : M \to \underline{R}$.

Let $z = x + iy$ denote a local complex co-ordinate on M. Set

$$a(z) = \left(\frac{\partial f^1}{\partial z}\right)^2 + \ldots + \left(\frac{\partial f^n}{\partial z}\right)^2$$

where $\frac{\partial}{\partial z} = \frac{1}{2}\left(\frac{\partial}{\partial x} - i\frac{\partial}{\partial y}\right)$; $a(z)dz^2$ is independent of choice of local complex co-ordinate on M and thus defines a quadratic differential η_f on M. Note that

$$a(z) = \left\langle \frac{\partial f}{\partial z}, \frac{\partial f}{\partial z} \right\rangle$$

$$= \frac{1}{4}\left\langle \frac{\partial f}{\partial x} - i\frac{\partial f}{\partial y}, \frac{\partial f}{\partial x} - i\frac{\partial f}{\partial y} \right\rangle_{E^n \otimes \underline{C}}$$

$$= \frac{1}{4}\left\{ \left\| \frac{\partial f}{\partial x} \right\|_{E^n}^2 - \left\| \frac{\partial f}{\partial y} \right\|_{E^n}^2 - i\left\langle \frac{\partial f}{\partial x}, \frac{\partial f}{\partial y} \right\rangle_{E^n} \right\}$$

Definition 3.4. f *is said to be* **weakly conformal** *at a point* P ∈ M *iff*

$$\left\| \frac{\partial f}{\partial x}(P) \right\|_E = \left\| \frac{\partial f}{\partial y}(P) \right\|_E \text{ and } \left\langle \frac{\partial f}{\partial x}(P), \frac{\partial f}{\partial y}(P) \right\rangle_E = 0$$

f *is said to be* **weakly conformal on** M *if it is weakly conformal at all points* P ∈ M.

Note 3.5. A weakly conformal map from a Riemann surface is not necessarily harmonic unless the codomain is two-dimensional.

Proposition 3.6

$\eta_f(P) = 0 \Leftrightarrow f: M \to E^n$ *is weakly conformal at* P;

$\eta_f \equiv 0 \Leftrightarrow f: M \to E^n$ *is weakly conformal on* M.

We now wish to find out when η_f is a **holomorphic** quadratic differential.

$$\text{Now } \frac{\partial}{\partial \bar{z}} a(z) = \frac{\partial}{\partial \bar{z}} \left\{ \left(\frac{\partial f^1}{\partial z}\right)^2 + \ldots + \left(\frac{\partial f^n}{\partial z}\right)^2 \right\}$$

$$= 2\left\{ \frac{\partial^2 f^1}{\partial \bar{z} \partial z} \frac{\partial f^1}{\partial z} + \ldots + \frac{\partial^2 f^n}{\partial \bar{z} \partial z} \frac{\partial f^n}{\partial z} \right\}$$

$$= 2\left\langle \frac{\partial^2 f}{\partial \bar{z} \partial z}, \frac{\partial f}{\partial z} \right\rangle_{E^n \otimes \underline{C}}$$

or in (x, y)'s,

$$\frac{\partial}{\partial \bar{z}} a(z) = \frac{1}{4}\left\langle \frac{\partial^2 f}{\partial x^2} + \frac{\partial^2 f}{\partial y^2}, \frac{\partial f}{\partial x} \right\rangle_{E^n} - \frac{i}{4}\left\langle \frac{\partial^2 f}{\partial x^2} + \frac{\partial^2 f}{\partial y^2}, \frac{\partial f}{\partial y} \right\rangle_{E^n}$$

from this we see

Proposition 3.7. *If* f *satisfies*

$$\frac{\partial^2 f}{\partial x^2} + \frac{\partial^2 f}{\partial y^2} = 0$$

i.e. if f *is* **harmonic,** *then the quadratic differential*

$$\eta_f = \left\langle \frac{\partial f}{\partial z}, \frac{\partial f}{\partial z} \right\rangle dz^2$$

is holomorphic.

Note. Although the quadratic differential η_f can be defined more generally for maps from a complex manifold of any dimension, it does not have the above nice properties. However, we can replace $\underline{R}^n$ by any n-dimensional Riemannian manifold, as we now show.

(C) The quadratic differential associated with a map into a Riemannian manifold

Let M be a Riemann surface. Let N be a smooth connected Riemannian manifold of dimension n. The metric is given by a symmetric covariant 2-tensor h on N; in local co-ordinates $(u^1, \ldots, u^n)$ on N, we write $h = h_{\alpha\beta} du^\alpha du^\beta$. The metric defines an inner product $\langle\ \rangle_{TN}$ which we extend to a complex-bilinear symmetric inner product $\langle\ \rangle_{TN^c}$ on the complexification $TN^c = TN \otimes \underline{C}$ of TN. The inner product $\langle\ \rangle_{TN}$ defines a norm $\|\ \|_{TN}$.

Let $f: M \to N$ be a smooth map. We define a quadratic differential $\eta_f = a(z) dz^2$ on M by

$$a(z) = \left\langle \frac{\partial f}{\partial z}, \frac{\partial f}{\partial z} \right\rangle_{TN^c} = h_{\alpha\beta} \frac{\partial f^\alpha}{\partial z} \frac{\partial f^\beta}{\partial z}$$

η_f can be alternatively defined as follows. Pull back the metric on N to a symmetric covariant 2-tensor f^*h on M. Set $\eta_f = (2,0)$ part of f^*h. As before,

$$a(z) = \frac{1}{4}\left\{ \left\| \frac{\partial f}{\partial x} \right\|^2_{TN} - \left\| \frac{\partial f}{\partial y} \right\|^2_{TN} - i \left\langle \frac{\partial f}{\partial x}, \frac{\partial f}{\partial y} \right\rangle_{TN} \right\}$$

Thus

Proposition 3.8

$\eta_f(P) = 0 \Leftrightarrow f: M \to N$ *is weakly conformal at* P;

$\eta_f \equiv 0 \Leftrightarrow f: M \to N$ *is weakly conformal on* M.

To calculate $(\partial/\partial\bar{z})\, a(z)$ nicely, we need some machinery which we now describe. Let $E = f^*TN \to M$ be the pull-back of the tangent bundle $TN \to N$ via the mapping f. $TN^c = TN \otimes \underline{C}$ pulls back to $E^c = E \otimes \underline{C}$. E and E^c inherit an inner product from TN^c, viz. $\langle v, w \rangle_{E^c} = \langle f_* v, f_* w \rangle_{TN^c}$. Recall the covariant differentiation

$$\tilde{\nabla}: C^\infty(E) \to C^\infty(TM^* \otimes_{\underline{R}} E)$$

Extend this to

$$\tilde{\nabla}: C^\infty(E^c) \to C^\infty(TM^*_c \otimes_{\underline{C}} E^c)$$

by requiring $\tilde{\nabla}$ to be complex-linear. For any $X \in C^\infty(TM^c)$ we may define a linear map:

$$\tilde{\nabla}_X : C^\infty(E^c) \to C^\infty(E^c)$$

If $(u^1, \ldots, u^n)$ are local co-ordinates for N, the pull-backs of the vectors $\partial/\partial u^1, \ldots, \partial/\partial u^n$ give a local basis for $C^\infty(E^c)$. For this basis

$$(\tilde{\nabla}_X w)^\gamma = \partial_X w^\gamma + (\partial_X f^\beta) L^\gamma_{\alpha\beta} w^\alpha, \quad \forall w \in C^\infty(E^c), \quad \forall X \in C^\infty(TM^c)$$

Now let $z = x + iy$ be a local complex co-ordinate on M. By $\tilde{D}/\partial z$ we shall mean $\tilde{\nabla}_{\partial/\partial z}$ etc.

Proposition 3.9. *Let* $f: M \to N$ *be a smooth map. The harmonic equations* $\tau(f) = 0$ *can be written:*

$$\frac{\tilde{D}}{\partial \bar{z}} \frac{\partial f}{\partial z} = 0 \quad \text{or equivalently} \quad \frac{\tilde{D}}{\partial z} \frac{\partial f}{\partial \bar{z}} = 0$$

$$\text{or equivalently} \quad \frac{\tilde{D}}{\partial x} \frac{\partial f}{\partial x} + \frac{\tilde{D}}{\partial y} \frac{\partial f}{\partial y} = 0$$

Proof. Use local co-ordinates and formula above for $\tilde{\nabla}_X$.

Lemma 3.10. E^c *is* **Riemannian-connected,** *i.e. if* $X \in TM^c$, $v, w \in C^\infty(E^c)$,

$$\partial_X \langle v, w \rangle_{E^c} = \langle \tilde{\nabla}_X v, w \rangle_{E^c} + \langle v, \tilde{\nabla}_X w \rangle_{E^c}$$

Proof. Either by local co-ordinates or by interpreting the connection and metric on E as the pull-back of the connection and metric on TN which is, of course, Riemannian connected (see Eliasson [2, 3] for further details).

We are now ready to calculate:

$$\frac{\partial}{\partial \bar{z}} a(z) = \frac{\partial}{\partial \bar{z}} \left\langle \frac{\partial f}{\partial z}, \frac{\partial f}{\partial z} \right\rangle_{TN^c}$$

$$= \frac{\partial}{\partial \bar{z}} \left\langle \frac{\partial f}{\partial z}, \frac{\partial f}{\partial z} \right\rangle_{E^c}$$

$$= \left\langle \frac{\tilde{D}}{\partial \bar{z}} \frac{\partial f}{\partial z}, \frac{\partial f}{\partial z} \right\rangle_{E^c} + \left\langle \frac{\partial f}{\partial z}, \frac{\tilde{D}}{\partial \bar{z}} \frac{\partial f}{\partial z} \right\rangle_{E^c}$$

$$= 2 \left\langle \frac{\tilde{D}}{\partial \bar{z}} \frac{\partial f}{\partial z}, \frac{\partial f}{\partial z} \right\rangle_{E^c}$$

$$= 2 \left\langle \frac{\tilde{D}}{\partial \bar{z}} \frac{\partial f}{\partial z}, \frac{\partial f}{\partial x} \right\rangle_{E} - i \left\langle \frac{\tilde{D}}{\partial \bar{z}} \frac{\partial f}{\partial z}, \frac{\partial f}{\partial y} \right\rangle_{E}$$

Proposition 3.11. *If* $f: M \to N$ *is harmonic, the quadratic differential*

$$\eta_f = \left\langle \frac{\partial f}{\partial z}, \frac{\partial f}{\partial z} \right\rangle_{TN^c} dz^2$$

is holomorphic.

Proof. Directly from the formula for $(\partial/\partial\bar{z})\,a(z)$ above.

For a converse, note from this formula that $(\partial/\partial\bar{z})\,a(z) = 0$ at $P \in M$ iff $\tau(f)(P) \in TN_{f(P)}$ is normal to $df(TM_P) \subset TN_{f(P)}$. Thus

Proposition 3.12. *If* N *is two-dimensional and the derivative* $df: TM \to TN$ *has rank 2 on* M *or on a dense subset of* M, η_f *holomorphic* $\Rightarrow$ f *harmonic.*

In particular,

Corollary 3.13. *If* N *is two-dimensional and* $f: M \to N$ *is a smooth bijection,* f *is harmonic iff*

$$\eta_f = \left\langle \frac{\partial f}{\partial z}, \frac{\partial f}{\partial z} \right\rangle_{TN^c} dz^2$$

is holomorphic.

Proof. By Sard-Brown's theorem and bijectivity the derivative of f will have rank 2 on a dense subset of M.

Note that if we are only interested in homeomorphisms, a harmonic map can be defined as a homeomorphism $f: M \to N$ such that η_f is holomorphic (see Refs [4, 12]).

(D) Consequences

We use quadratic differentials to classify harmonic maps from the Riemann sphere.

Theorem 3.14. *Let* $f: S \to N$ *be a harmonic map from the Riemann sphere into any Riemannian manifold. Then* f *is weakly conformal.*

Proof. η_f is a holomorphic quadratic differential on S, but any holomorphic quadratic differential on the Riemann sphere is identically zero. Therefore by Proposition 3.8, f is weakly conformal.

Corollary 3.15. *If* N *is a compact Riemann surface with any chosen metric, the harmonic maps* $f: S \to N$ *may be classified as follows:*

If genus (N) = 0, *only weakly conformal maps (since* N *is two-dimensional these are either holomorphic or antiholomorphic and therefore by Proposition 2.6 are harmonic).*

If genus (N) > 0, *only constant maps.*

The work on quadratic differentials also tells us about the zeros of the derivative of a harmonic map from a Riemann surface M to a Riemannian manifold N which is not conformal. Then η_f is holomophic but not identically zero; also $\eta_f(P) = 0 \Leftrightarrow$ f is conformal at P. In particular, $\eta_f(P) = 0$ when $df(P) = 0$. Say df **has a zero of order** $(k-1)$ at $P \in M$ if, with respect to any smooth local co-ordinates (x^1, x^2) on M, $(u^1, \ldots, u^n)$ on N, the derivatives

$$\frac{\partial^{\alpha_1 + \ldots + \alpha_n} f^\gamma}{\partial x^{\alpha_1} \ldots \partial x^{\alpha_n}}$$

of all orders $\alpha_1 + \cdots + \alpha_n \leqslant k-1$ vanish at P, $\forall \gamma$, but one or more derivatives of order k is non-zero at P.

Lemma 3.16. *If* df *has a zero of order* $(k-1)$ *at* P, *then* η_f *has a zero of order* $\geqslant 2(k-1)$ *at* P.

Proof. $\eta_f = a(z)\,dz^2$ where $a(z) = h_{\alpha\beta} \dfrac{\partial f^\alpha}{\partial z} \dfrac{\partial f^\beta}{\partial z}$. It is clear that the partial derivatives of a(z) of all orders $\leqslant 2(k-1)$ thus vanish.

Theorem 3.17. *Let* $f: M \to N$ *be a non-weakly conformal harmonic map from a Riemann surface to a Riemannian manifold. Then*

(1) f *is weakly conformal at isolated points: in particular,* df *has isolated zeros.*
(2) *If* M *is compact of genus* g: *(a)* f *is weakly conformal at (at most)* $4g - 4$ *points of* M;. *(b)* df *has at most* $2g - 2$ *zeros (counting according to order).*

Proof. By Definition 3.1 and Lemma 3.16.

4. NON-EXISTENCE OF CERTAIN HARMONIC MAPS INTO THE 2-SPHERE

(A) In this section we prove, amongst other results, a new result that there is no harmonic map of degree 1 from a compact surface of genus 1 (= a torus) to a compact surface of genus 0 (= a sphere) whatever (smooth) metrics these surfaces are given. Our method is as follows.

Let M, N be Riemann surfaces and let $f: M \to N$ be a smooth map which is harmonic with respect to some hermitian metric on N. Consider the derivative $df: TM \to TN$. As described before, this may be extended to a complex linear map $df^c: TM^c \to TN^c$ and we may consider:

$$\partial f_{1,0}: TM^{1,0} \xrightarrow{\subset} TM^c \xrightarrow{df^c} TN^c \xrightarrow[\text{projection}]{\text{natural}} TN^{1,0}$$

$$\partial f_{0,1}: TM^{1,0} \xrightarrow{\subset} TM^c \xrightarrow{df^c} TN^c \xrightarrow[\text{projection}]{\text{natural}} TN^{0,1}$$

Note $\partial f_{1,0} = 0$ or $\partial f_{0,1} = 0 \Leftrightarrow$ f is antiholomorphic or holomorphic respectively. These partial derivatives are sections of the complex line bundles over $M: TM^*_{1,0} \otimes_{\underline{C}} f^*TN^{1,0}$, $TM^*_{1,0} \otimes_{\underline{C}} f^*TN^{0,1}$ respectively.

Now the holomorphic quadratic differential η_f (§ 3) is essentially the "product" of these partial derivatives (see Lemma 4.19), and using this fact we show (Lemma 4.19) that $\partial f_{1,0}$ and $\partial f_{0,1}$ cannot have zeros of infinite order. We then define the index of an isolated zero of a section of a comple line bundle and show, using the harmonic equations, that $\partial f_{1,0}$ and $\partial f_{0,1}$ have isolated zeros of positive index only (unless identically zero) (see Proposition 4.21). Next, assuming M,N are compact, we show any section with isolated zeros of $TM^*_{1,0} \otimes_{\underline{C}} f^*TN^{1,0}$ (or ... $TN^{0,1}$) has $-e(M) + (\text{or}) - d_f e(N)$ zeros, respectively, where d_f is the degree of the map $f: M \to N$, and e( ) denotes "Euler characteristic of". For values of d_f for which one (or both) of these are negative, we have a contradiction and hence

Theorem 4.1. *Let* M, N *be compact Riemann surfaces of Euler characteristic* e(M), e(N). *Let* $f: M \to N$ *be a smooth map which is harmonic with respect to some smooth hermitian metric on* N. *Denote the degree of* f *by* d_f. *Then if*

$$|d_f| > \frac{-e(M)}{|e(N)|}$$

f *is holomorphic or antiholomorphic.*

Corollary 4.2. *Let* M *be a compact Riemann surface of genus* p *and let* N *be a compact Riemann surface of genus* 0. *Let* $f: M \to N$ *be a smooth map which is harmonic with respect to some smooth hermitian metric on* N. *Then if* $|d_f| \geqslant p$, f *is holomorphic or antiholomorphic.*

Notes 4.3. With M, N as in Corollary 4.2, holomorphic or antiholomorphic maps of all degrees d_f with $|d_f| > p$ exist. This can be shown by the Riemann-Roch theorem (see Ref. [15]).

Corollary 4.4. *There is no harmonic map of degree* ±1 *from a compact surface of genus* 1 (= *torus) to a compact surface of genus* 0 (= *sphere) whatever (smooth) metrics these surfaces are given.*

Proof. By Theorem 4.1, such a harmonic map must be holomorphic or antiholomorphic. But any holomorphic or antiholomorphic map of degree ± 1 must be a homeomorphism, which is clearly impossible.

For genus (N) ⩾ 2, Theorem 4.1 gives no new results but gives a new proof of an old result:

Theorem 4.5 (Kneser [7]). *If* M *and* N *are compact orientable surfaces of genus* ⩾ 2, *there are no homotopy classes of mappings* M → N *of degree* d *with*

$$|d| > \frac{e(M)}{e(N)}$$

Proof. By the existence theorem (1.3) or (2.4) any homotopy class of mappings is representable by a harmonic map. By Theorem 4.1 this must be holomorphic or antiholomorphic. But by the Hurwitz formula (see the paper by Drasin, these Proceedings) for a holomorphic map:

$$e(M) + r = d_f e(N)$$

where $r \geqslant 0$, $d_f \geqslant 0$, there are no holomorphic maps of degree $> e(M)/e(N)$ and therefore no holomorphic or antiholomorphic maps of $|\text{degree}| > e(M)/e(N)$.

We now fill in the details of the proof of Theorem 4.1.

(B) Zeros of a section of a bundle

Let E → M be a vector bundle with fibre $\underline{R}^q$ and with space M a connected oriented q-dimensional real manifold. We shall refer to the bundle simply by its total space E. We suppose E is **oriented**, i.e. each fibre of E is an oriented real vector space of dimension q, and there exists an open cover $\{U_i\}$ of M and trivializations:

$$E|_{U_i} \xrightarrow{\tau_i} U_i \times R^q$$

which are orientation-preserving on the fibres (R^q is given its natural orientation). We shall use only such trivializations.

We study the zeros of an arbitrary section s of E.

Definition 4.6. p ∈ M *is said to be a* **zero** *of* s *if* s(p) *is the zero vector of the fibre* E_p *of* E *over* p.

We shall denote the set of zero vectors of E by E_0.

Definition 4.7. p ∈ M *is said to be an* **isolated zero** *of* s *if there exists a neighbourhood* U *of* p *such that none of the points of* U \ p *is a zero.*

From now on we assume s has isolated zeros. Then for any p ∈ M we can choose a Jordan region U containing p such that:

(1) $s|_{\overline{U}\setminus p}$ has no zeros;
(2) $E|_{\overline{U}}$ is trivial.

We define the index of the section s at p as follows. Let

$$E|_{\overline{U}} \xrightarrow{\tau_{\overline{U}}} \overline{U} \times \underline{R}^q$$

be a trivialization. Then the section s has local representative

$$s_{\overline{U}} : \overline{U} \xrightarrow{s} E|_{\overline{U}} \xrightarrow{\tau_U} \overline{U} \times \underline{R}^q \xrightarrow[\text{projection}]{\text{natural}} \underline{R}^q$$

This restricts to $s_U : \partial U \to \underline{R}^q\backslash 1$. Since ∂U is homeomorphic to the (q-1)-sphere, if $h : S^{q-1} \to \partial U$ is an orientation-preserving homeomorphism, the composition $\tau_U \circ h$ defines an element $[s_U] \in \pi_{q-1}(\underline{R}^q\backslash 0)$. Now $\pi_{q-1}(\underline{R}^q\backslash 0)$ is infinite cyclic with a preferred generator given by the orientation on the fibre $\underline{R}^q$. We thus have a preferred isomorphism $\deg : \pi_{q-1}(\underline{R}^q \backslash 0) \to \underline{Z}$ sending the preferred generator to 1.

Definition 4.8. *Let* s *be a continuous section of an oriented* $\underline{R}^q$*-vector bundle over an oriented* q*-dimensional real manifold* M. *Suppose that the zeros of* s *are isolated. If* $p \in M$, *we define the* **index of** s **at** p *to be the integer* $\deg[s_U]$.

Notes 4.9

(1) Thus the index of s at p is simply the degree of the mapping $s_U : \partial U \to \underline{R}^q\backslash 0$. The definition is easily shown to be independent of the particular trivialization of E.

(2) If $p \in M$ is not a zero of s, the index of s at p equals 0. The converse is false.

Definition 4.10. *If* M *is a compact oriented* q*-dimensional real manifold and* $E \to M$ *is an oriented* $\underline{R}^q$*-vector bundle over* M, *then* **the index of a section** s **of** E **all of whose zeros are isolated** *is defined as*

$$\sum_{p \in M} \{\textit{index of } s \textit{ at } p\} = \textit{number of zeros of } s \textit{ counted according to index}$$

Now for any oriented R^q-vector bundle over a polyhedron M we may define the qth Stiefel-Whitney class $W^q(E) \in H^q(M,\underline{Z})$.[1] If now M is a compact oriented q-dimensional manifold, $H^q(M,\underline{Z})$ is infinite cyclic with a preferred generator given by the orientation class of M. We thus have a preferred isomorphism $\deg : H^q(M,\underline{Z}) \to \underline{Z}$ sending the orientation class to 1 (see Husemoller [6] for details of orientation classes).

Proposition 4.11. If M is a compact q-dimensional oriented real manifold and $E \to M$ is an oriented R^q-vector bundle, the index of any section all of whose zeros are isolated = $\deg(W^q(E))$, the degree of the qth Stiefel-Whitney class.

Proof

(1) Triangulate M such that E is trivial over each closed q-simplex. We give a definition of $W^q(E)$ using obstruction theory (c.f. Steenrod [14]). Let s be a non-zero section on the (q-1)-skeleton M_{q-1} of M, i.e. a section of the fibre bundle $E \backslash E_0$. We define the obstruction to extending this

[1] Our terminology is that of Steenrod [14]; the more modern name for $W^q(E)$ is "Euler class of E", "q^{th} Stiefel-Whitney class" being used for the mod 2 reduction of our $W^q(E)$.

to a non-zero section on the q-skeleton $M_q(= M)$ as follows. For each q-simplex σ, $s|_{\partial\sigma}$ has local representative:

$$\partial\sigma \xrightarrow{s} E\setminus E_0\big|_{\partial\sigma} \xrightarrow{\tau} \partial\sigma \times (\underline{R}^q\setminus 0) \xrightarrow[\text{projection}]{\text{natural}} \underline{R}^q\setminus 0$$

where τ is a trivialization of $E\setminus E_0|_{\partial\sigma}$ obtained by restricting a trivialization of $E|_{\overline{\sigma}}$. This defines an element of $\pi_{q-1}(\underline{R}^q\setminus 0)$ and thus an integer $c(s,\sigma)$ and hence a q-cochain $\overline{c}(s) \in C^q(M,\underline{Z})$ by the requirement $\langle\overline{c}(s),\sigma\rangle = c(s,\sigma)$ where $\langle\ \ \rangle$ is the natural pairing between q-chains and q-cochains. Standard obstruction theory [14] shows:

(2) Any non-zero section defined on a r-dimensional skeleton M_r $(0 \leqslant r \leqslant q-2)$ can always be extended to a non-zero section on M_{q-1} but a non-zero section on M_{q-1} can be extended to a non-zero section on M_q iff $\overline{c}(s) = 0$. Note $\overline{c}(s)$ is a cocycle, called the **primary obstruction cocycle.**

(3) Any two non-zero sections s,s′ on M_{q-1} define obstruction cocycles $\overline{c}(s), \overline{c}(s')$ which are cohomologous; thus we get a well defined cohomology class $W^q(E) \in H^q(M,\underline{Z})$ – this is none other than **the** q^{th} **Stiefel-Whitney class of** E (this can be shown to be independent of the triangulation used).

Note that $\deg\{W^q(E)\} = \sum c(s,\sigma)$ summing over all q-simplexes where s is any non-zero section of E defined on M_{q-1}.

(4) We now consider a section of E defined on M, and suppose that all the zeros of s are isolated. We may triangulate M such that:

(a) E is trivial over each closed q-simplex;
(b) s is non-zero on M_{q-1};
(c) no q-simplex contains more than one zero of s.

Then, if σ is a q-simplex, comparing appropriate definitions,

$$c(s,\sigma) = \begin{cases} 0, \text{ if } \sigma \text{ contains no zero of s} \\ \text{index of zero, if } \sigma \text{ contains a zero of s} \end{cases}$$

Hence $\sum c(s,\sigma)$ is precisely the sum of the indices of all the zeros of s and the proposition is proved.

(C) Special properties for complex line bundles

Let $E \to M$ be a complex line bundle (i.e. a vector bundle with fibres a complex vector space of dimension 1) over a compact surface M. For such bundles we may define the **first Chern class** $c^1(E) \in H^2(M,\underline{Z})$ and the **Euler class** $\in H^2(M,\underline{Z})$. We may also consider E to be an oriented real two-dimensional bundle and define the second Stiefel-Whitney class $W^2(E) \in H^2(M,\underline{Z})$.

Proposition 4.12

(a) $c^1(E) = W^2(E)$;
(b) $c^1(E) =$ **Euler class of** E.

Proof. (a) Steenrod [14]; (b) Husemoller [6]. Recall the isomorphism $\deg : H^2(M,\underline{Z}) \to \underline{Z}$; we shall call $\deg(c^1(E)) = \deg(W^2(E)) = \deg(\text{Euler class})$ simply the **degree of the bundle** E.

Proposition 4.13. *Degree of the tangent bundle of* M = *Euler characteristic of* M.

Proof. Husemoller [6] (a property of the Euler class).

Proposition 4.14. *If* F *is another complex line bundle over* M, $\deg(E \otimes_{\underline{C}} F) = \deg(E) + \deg(F)$.

Proof. Property of first Chern class of a line bundle (see Ref. [6]).

Proposition 4.15. *Degree of the trivial line bundle is* 0.

Proof. (Husemoller [6]).

Proposition 4.16. *Let* E^* *be the dual complex line bundle to* E, *then* $\deg(E^*) = -\deg(E)$.

Proof. $E \otimes_{\underline{C}} E^*$ is trivial.

Proposition 4.17. *Let* $f : M \to N$ *be a continuous map between compact oriented surfaces* M, N *of degree* d_f. *Then if* F *is any complex line bundle over* N, *and* f^*F *denotes its pull-back to* M, $\deg f^*F = d_f \deg F$.

Proof. By functorial property of characteristic classes [Husemoller].

Let $f : M \to N$ be a smooth map between Riemann surfaces of degree d_f. Recall $\partial f_{1,0}$ is a section of the complex line bundle $TM^*_{1,0} \otimes_{\underline{C}} f^*TN^{1,0}$. $\partial f_{0,1}$ is a section of the complex line bundle $TM^*_{1,0} \otimes_{\underline{C}} f^*TN^{0,1}$.

Proposition 4.18. *Any non-identically zero section of* $TM^*_{1,0} \otimes_{\underline{C}} f^*TN^{1,0}$ *has index* $-e(M) + d_f e(N)$, *assuming the section has isolated zeros. Any non-identically zero section of* $TM^*_{1,0} \otimes_{\underline{C}} f^*TN^{0,1}$ *has index* $-e(M) - d_f e(N)$, *assuming the section has isolated zeros.*

Proof. Apply previous propositions 4.13, 4.14, 4.16, 4.17, noting $TM^*_{1,0}$ is canonically isomorphic as a complex line bundle to TM^*, $TN^{1,0}$ is canonically isomorphic as a complex line bundle to TN.

(D) Application to harmonic mappings

Let $f : M \to N$ be a smooth map between Riemann surfaces which is harmonic with regard to some hermitian metric h on N. Suppose f is not holomorphic or antiholomorphic so that $\partial f_{1,0} \not\equiv 0$ and $\partial f_{0,1} \not\equiv 0$. We now make a local study of the zeros of $\partial f_{1,0}$ and $\partial f_{0,1}$. Let $p \in M$. Take local complex co-ordinates z, w for M, N centred on p, f(p) respectively. Write $h = \sigma^2(w) dw d\overline{w}$. Then $\partial f_{1,0}$, $\partial f_{0,1}$ are represented locally by $\partial w/\partial z$, $\partial \overline{w}/\partial z$. Now the Taylor series of $\partial w/\partial z$ either has the form:

$$\text{(A)} \quad \frac{\partial w}{\partial z} = Q_m(z, \overline{z}) + R(z, \overline{z})$$

where Q_m is a homogeneous polynomial of degree $m \geqslant 0$ and $R(z, \overline{z})$ is $o(|z|^m)$ as $z \to 0$, or

$$\text{(B)} \quad \frac{\partial w}{\partial z} = o(|z|^m) \text{ as } z \to 0, \text{ for all } m \geqslant 0$$

If (B) holds, we shall say that $\partial w/\partial z$ (or $\partial f_{1,0}$) has a **zero of infinite order at** p. A similar definition applies to $\partial \overline{w}/\partial z$ (or $\partial f_{0,1}$).

Lemma 4.19

$\partial w/\partial z$ *cannot have a zero of infinite order.*
$\partial \overline{w}/\partial z$ *cannot have a zero of infinite order.*

Proof. Recall the holomorphic quadratic differential of § 3:

$$\eta_f = a(z)dz^2$$

Note $a(z) = \sigma^2(w(z))\,(\partial w/\partial z)\,(\partial \overline{w}/\partial z)$.

If either $\partial w/\partial z$ or $\partial \overline{w}/\partial z$ has a zero of infinite order at a point $p \in M$, then a(z) will also have such a zero, i.e. in a complex co-ordinate centred on p, a(z) will be $o(|z|^m)$ for all $m \geqslant 0$. Since a(z) is holomorphic this implies $a(z) \equiv 0 \Rightarrow \eta_f \equiv 0 \Rightarrow f$ weakly conformal $\Rightarrow f$ is holomorphic or antiholomorphic in contradiction to hypotheses.

Lemma 4.20. *Let* $p \in M$. *In any complex co-ordinates* z,w *centred on* p,f(p), $\partial f_{1,0}$, $\partial f_{0,1}$ have the form:

$$\frac{\partial w}{\partial z} = Az^m + o(|z|^m) \quad \text{for some} \quad m \geqslant 0, \quad A \in \underline{C}\backslash 0$$

$$\frac{\partial \overline{w}}{\partial z} = Bz^n + o(|z|^n) \quad \text{for some} \quad n \geqslant 0, \quad B \in \underline{C}\backslash 0$$

Proof. By Lemma 4.19, $\partial w/\partial z = Q_m(z,\overline{z}) + o(|z|^m)$ for some $m \geqslant 0$ where Q_m is a homogeneous polynomial of degree m. Substituting into the harmonic equations:

$$\frac{\partial}{\partial \overline{z}}\left(\frac{\partial w}{\partial z}\right)_{+2}\frac{\sigma_w}{\sigma}\frac{\partial w}{\partial z}\frac{\partial w}{\partial \overline{z}} = 0$$

we have $$\frac{\partial}{\partial \overline{z}}\left\{Q_m(z,\overline{z}) + o(|z|^m)\right\} + 2\frac{\sigma_w}{\sigma}\left\{Q_m(z,\overline{z}) + o(|z|^m)\right\}\frac{\partial w}{\partial \overline{z}} = 0$$

Now the term $(\partial/\partial\overline{z})Q_m(z,\overline{z})$ is either identically zero or a homogeneous polynomial of degree m–1. All other terms are $o(|z|^{m-1})$. It follows that $(\partial/\partial\overline{z})Q_m(z,\overline{z}) \equiv 0$. Therefore $Q_m(z,\overline{z})$ is a holomorphic homogeneous polynomial of degree m and therefore has the form Az^m. We deal with $\partial\overline{w}/\partial z$ similarly.

Proposition 4.21. *The zeros of* $\partial f_{1,0}$, $\partial f_{0,1}$ *are isolated and are of strictly positive index.*

Proof. Let $p \in M$ be a zero of $\partial f_{1,0}$. In complex co-ordinates centred on p (by Lemma 4.20) $\partial f_{1,0}$ has the form $\partial w/\partial z = Az^m + o(|z|^m)$ where $m > 0$, $A \in C\backslash 0$. It easily follows that $\partial f_{1,0}$ has a zero of index $m > 0$. We deal with $\partial f_{0,1}$ similarly.

Proof of Theorem 4.1. If f is not holomorphic or antiholomorphic, $\partial f_{1,0}$ and $\partial f_{0,1}$ are not identically zero. By Proposition 4.18, $\partial f_{1,0}$ has zeros of total index $-e(M) + d_f e(N)$. By Proposition 4.18, $\partial f_{0,1}$ has zeros of total index $-e(M) - d_f e(N)$. If $|d_f| > (-e(M))/(|e(N)|)$, one of these indices is negative, contradicting Proposition 4.21. Theorem 4.1 is thus proven.

REFERENCES

[1] EELLS, J., SAMPSON, J.H., Harmonic mappings of Riemannian manifolds, Am. J. Math. **86** (1964) 109-160.

[2] ELIASSON, H.I., Geometry of manifolds of maps, J. Diff. Geom. **1** (1967) 169-194.

[3] ELIASSON, H.I., "Introduction to global calculus of variations", Global Analysis and its Applications (Proc. Int. Course Trieste, 1972) **2**, IAEA, Vienna (1974) 113–135.

[4] GERSTENHABER, M., RAUCH, H.E., On extremal quasi-conformal mappings I, Proc. Natl Acad. Sci. **40** (1954) 808-812.

[5] HARTMAN, P., On homotopic harmonic maps, Can. J. Math. **19** (1967) 673-687.

[6] HUSEMOLLER, D., Fibre Bundles, McGraw-Hill, New York (1966).

[7] KNESER, H., Die kleinste Bedeckungszahl innerhalb einer Klasse von Flächenabbildungen, Math. Ann. **103** (1930) 347-358.

[8] KOBAYASHI, S., NOMIZU, K., Foundations of Differential Geometry **2**, Interscience, New York (1969).

[9] LEMAIRE, L., Applications harmoniques de surfaces, C.R. Acad. Sci. Paris **280** Ser. A (1975) 897-899.

[10] LICHNEROWICZ, A., Applications harmoniques et variétés Kähleriennes, Symposia Matematica III (1970) 341-402.

[11] RUH, E.A., VILMS, J., The tension field of the Gauss map, Trans. Am. Math. Soc. **149** (1970) 569-573.

[12] SHIBATA, K., On the existence of a harmonic mapping, Osaka Math. J. **15** (1963) 173-211.

[13] SMITH, R.T., Harmonic mappings of spheres, PhD Thesis, Univ. of Warwick (1972).

[14] STEENROD, N., Topology of Fibre Bundles, Princeton Univ. Press (1951).

[15] WOOD, J.C., Harmonic mappings between surfaces, PhD Thesis, Univ. of Warwick (1974).

[16] WOOD, J.C., Singularities of harmonic maps and applications of the Gauss-Bonnet formula (to appear in Am. J. Math.).

[17] WOOD, R., A note on harmonic polynomial maps (to appear).

SECRETARIAT OF THE COURSE

DIRECTORS

A. Andreotti — Department of Mathematics,
School of Science,
Oregon State University,
Corwallis, Oregon 97331,
United States of America
and
Istituto Matematico,
Università di Pisa,
Via Derna 1,
Pisa,
Italy

J. Eells — Mathematics Institute,
University of Warwick,
Coventry CV4 7AL,
Warwickshire,
United Kingdom

F. Gherardelli — Istituto Matematico "U. Dini",
Università di Firenze,
Viale Morgagni 67/A,
Firenze,
Italy

EDITOR

Miriam Lewis — Division of Publications, IAEA,
Vienna, Austria

LIST OF LECTURERS

An asterisk indicates that a lecturer's contribution is not published in these Proceedings

G.R. Allan
Dept of Pure Mathematics,
University of Leeds,
Leeds, Yorkshire LS2 9JT, United Kingdom

J.M. Anderson*
Dept of Mathematics,
University of Illinois,
Urbana, Illinois 61801,
United States of America

S.D. Bajpai*
College of Science and Technology,
Port Harcourt, Nigeria

M. Cornalba
Dept of Mathematics,
University of California,
Berkeley, California 94720,
United States of America

Present address:
Istituto Matematico,
Università di Pavia,
I-27100 Pavia, Italy

P. de la Harpe
Institut de mathématiques,
Université de Lausanne,
Dorigny, 1015 Lausanne, Switzerland

M.M. Djrbashian
Institute of Mathematics,
Academy of Sciences of the Armenian SSR,
Yerevan, USSR

D. Drasin
Dept of Mathematics,
Purdue University,
West Lafayette, Indiana 47907,
United States of America

M. Essén
Dept of Mathematics,
Royal Institute of Technology,
S-100 44 Stockholm 70, Sweden

M. Field
Mathematics Institute,
University of Warwick,
Coventry, Warwickshire CV4 7AL,
United Kingdom
Present address:
Dept of Pure Mathematics,
University of Sydney,
Sydney, NSW 2006, Australia

G. Fournier
Mathematics Institute,
University of Warwick,
Coventry, Warwickshire CV4 7AL,
United Kingdom

W. Fuchs
Dept of Mathematics,
Cornell University,
Ithaca, N.Y. 14850,
United States of America

F.W. Gehring
Dept of Mathematics,
University of Michigan,
Ann Arbor, Michigan 48104,
United States of America

R. Gérard
Centre d'équations différentielles,
Institut de recherche mathématique avancée,
Département de mathématique,
Université de Strasbourg,
7 rue René Descartes,
F-67084 Strasbourg, France

A.A. Goncar*
Mathematics Dept,
Academy of Sciences of the USSR,
Leninsky Prospekt 14,
Moscow B-71, USSR

J.J. Kohn*
Mathematics Dept,
Princeton University,
Princeton, N.J. 08540,
United States of America

H.H. Martens
Norges Tekniske Høgskole,
Trondheim, Norway

S.N. Merguelyan*
Mathematics Dept,
Academy of Sciences of the USSR,
Leninsky Prospekt 14,
Moscow B-71, USSR

J.-C. Mitteau
Ecole nationale supérieure aéronautique,
B.P. 5032, Toulouse 31, France

B. Moishezon*
Dept of Mathematics,
University of Tel Aviv,
Ramat Aviv, Tel Aviv, Israel

M.S. Narasimhan
School of Mathematics,
Tata Institute of Fundamental Research,
Homi Bhabha Road,
Bombay 5, India

R. Narasimhan*
Dept of Mathematics,
University of Chicago,
5734 University Avenue,
Chicago, Illinois 60637,
United States of America

N. O'Brian
Institute for Advanced Study,
Princeton, N.J. 08540,
United States of America

B.E. Petersen
Dept of Mathematics,
Orgeon State University,
Corvallis, Oregon 97331,
United States of America

A. Pfluger*
Mathematical Seminar, Eidgenössische Technische Hochschule,
CH-8006 Zürich, Switzerland

H. Pittie
Dept of Mathematics,
University of Georgia,
Athens, Georgia 30602,
United States of America

C. Pommerenke
Fachbereich Mathematik,
Technische Universität Berlin,
1 Berlin 12,
Federal Republic of Germany

S. Robertson
Dept of Mathematics,
University of Southampton,
Southampton, Hampshire SO9 5NH,
United Kingdom

J. Tarski
Fakultät für Physik,
Universität Bielefeld,
Universitätsstrasse,
48 Bielefeld 1,
Federal Republic of Germany

G.S. Vladimirov
Steklov Institute of Mathematics,
Moscow, USSR

H. Widom
Division of Natural Sciences,
University of California,
Santa Cruz, California 95060,
United States of America

J.C. Wood
Dept of Mathematics,
Brighton Polytechnic,
Moulsecombe, Brighton, Sussex,
United Kingdom

A.B. Zizcenko*
Mathematics Dept,
Academy of Sciences of the USSR,
Leninsky Prospekt 14, B-71 Moscow, USSR

LIST OF PARTICIPANTS

R. Abiodun	University of Ife, Ile-Ife, Nigeria	Nigeria
J. Ahsan	Dept of Mathematics, University of Islamabad, Islamabad, Pakistan	Pakistan
S.R. Al-Ani	Dept of Mathematics, College of Science, Adhamiya, Baghdad, Iraq	Iraq
K. Alladi	Vivekananda College, Sullivan Garden Road, Mylapore, Madras, India	India
M. Allen	University of Warwick, Coventry, Warwickshire CV4 7AL, United Kingdom	United Kingdom
M.A. Amer	Dept of Mathematics, University of Cairo, Giza, Cairo, Egypt	Egypt
S. Athel	College of Engineering, University of Riyadh, PO Box 800, Riyadh, Saudi Arabia	Saudi Arabia
B. Ba	Université de Niamey, B.P. 237, Niamey, Niger	Niger
V.A. Babalola	Dept of Mathematics, University of Ibadan, Ibadan, Nigeria	Nigeria
A.G. Babiker	Dept of Mathematics, Faculty of Science, University of Khartoum, PO Box 321, Khartoum, Sudan	Sudan
F. Baldassarri	Seminario Matematico, Università di Padova, Via Paolotti 2, I-35100 Padova, Italy	Italy
A. Battinelli	Laboratorio per Ricerche di Dinamica dei Sistemi e di Elettronica Biomedica, Consiglio Nazionale delle Ricerche, Galleria Trieste 6, I-35100 Padova, Italy	Italy

A. Bayoumi	Matematiska Institution, Uppsala University, Sysslomansgatan 8, S-752 23 Uppsala, Sweden	Sweden/Egypt
Pak-Soong Chee	Dept of Mathematics, University of Malaya, Kuala Lumpur, Malaysia	Malaysia
I.J.P.J. Cnop	Departement Wiskunde, Fakulteit der Wetenschappen, Vrije Universiteit Brussel, Adolphe Buyllaan 105, B-1050 Brussels, Belgium	Belgium
F. Cnop-Grandsard	Departement Wiskunde, Fakulteit der Wetenschappen, Vrije Universiteit Brussel, Adolphe Buyllaan 105, B-1050 Brussels, Belgium	Belgium
A.A. Daffá	University of Petroleum and Minerals, House No. 205, South Compound, Dhahran, Saudi Arabia	Saudi Arabia
P. Dodds	Dept of Mathematics, Flinders University of South Australia, Bedford Park, S.A., Australia	Australia
T.K.-Y. Dodds	Dept of Mathematics, Flinders University of South Australia, Bedford Park, S.A., Australia	Australia
A. Dubson	Institut des hautes études scientifiques, Bures-sur-Yvette, France	France/Argentina
R. Dutt	Dept of Physics, Visva-Bharati, Santiniketan, West Bengal, India	India
M.M. Elhosh	Dept of Mathematics, University of Tripoli, Tripoli, Libya	Libya
A.A. Fadlalla	Dept of Mathematics, Faculty of Science, Cairo University, Giza, Cairo, Egypt	Egypt
O. Fajuyigbe	Dept of Mathematics, University of Benin, Benin City, Nigeria	Nigeria
F. Favilli	Istituto Matematico, Università di Pisa, Via Derna 1, I-56100 Pisa, Italy	Italy

C.J. Ferraris	Departamento de Matemática, Universidad Simón Bolivar, Baruta, Sartenejas, Edo. Miranda, Apartado Postal 5354, Caracas, Venezuela	Venezuela/Argentina
F. Gaeta	Dept of Mathematics, State University of New York, Buffalo, N.Y., United States of America	United States of America/ Spain
P.M. Gauthier	Département de mathématique, Université de Montréal, CP 6128, Montreal 101, Quebec, Canada	Canada
K. Geetha	Ramanujan Institute for Advanced Study in Mathematics, University of Madras, Madras 600005, India Present address: Dept of Mathematics, Pennsylvania State University, 215 McAllister Bldg., University Park, Pennsylvania 16802, United States of America	United States of America/ India
M.A. Gwaiz	College of Engineering, University of Riyadh, Riyadh, Saudi Arabia	Saudi Arabia
A. Hefez	Instituto de Matemática Pura e Aplicada, Rua Luis de Camoes 68, 20 000 Rio de Janeiro, Brazil	Brazil/Italy
J. Hillairet	UER Sciences exactes et naturelles, 40 avenue du Recteur Pineau, F-86000 Poitiers, France	France
M. Hongoh	Centre de recherches mathématiques, Université de Montréal, CP 6128, Montreal, Quebec, Canada	Canada/Japan
A. Huckleberry	University of Notre Dame, Notre Dame, Indiana 46556, United States of America	United States of America
C.M. Hussain	Dept of Mathematics, Islamabad University, Islamabad, Pakistan	Pakistan
S. Ianus	Facultatea de Matematica, Str. Academie 14, Bucharest, Romania	Romania

E.M. Ibrahim	Dept of Mathematics, Faculty of Engineering, Abbassia, Cairo, Egypt	Egypt
S.O. Ilori	Dept of Mathematics, University of Ibadan, Ibadan, Nigeria	Nigeria
S. Invernizzi	Istituto di Matematica, Università di Trieste, Piazzale Europa 1, Trieste, Italy	Italy
M.A.M. Ismail	Dept of Mathematics, Faculty of Science, University of Khartoum, PO Box 321, Khartoum, Sudan	Sudan
S.O. Iyahen	University of Benin, Benin City, Nigeria	Nigeria
R.N. Jain	Dept of Mathematics and Statistics, Holkar Science College, University of Indore, Indore (MP), India	India
I. Khan	Dept of Physics, University of Khartoum, Khartoum, Sudan	Sudan/Pakistan
R. Kortram	Dept of Mathematics, University of Nijmegen, Toernooiveld, Nijmegen, The Netherlands	The Netherlands
M. Lakshmanan	Dept of Theoretical Physics, AC College Buildings, University of Madras, Guindy, Madras 600025, India	India
J. Ławrynowicz	Institute of Mathematics, Polish Academy of Sciences, Łódż Branch, ul. Kilińskiegó 86, Pl-90-012-Łódż, Poland	Poland
J. Lesmes	Instituto de Matemática Pura e Aplicada, Rua Luis de Camoes 68, 20 000 Rio de Janeiro, Brazil	Brazil/Colombia
L.S.O. Liverpool	Dept of Mathematics, Fourah Bay College, Freetown, Sierra Leone	Sierra Leone
L. Luquet	Fundación Bariloche, Casilla de Correo 138, San Carlos de Bariloche, Rio Negro, Argentina	Argentina

C.H. Lutterodt	Dept of Mathematics, University of Cape Coast, Cape Coast, Ghana	Ghana
P.R. Manandhar	Dept of Mathematics, Tribhuvan University, Kirtipur Campus, Kirtipur, Kathmandu, Nepal	Nepal
P. Mathieu	Institut de mathématique pure, Université catholique de Louvain, Chemin du Cyclotron 2, B-1348 Louvain-la-Neuve, Belgium	Belgium
G. Michelacci	Facoltà di Ingegneria, Università di Trieste, Trieste, Italy	Italy
F. Mulla	Mathematics Dept, University of Kuwait, Kuwait	Kuwait/Iraq
M. Nacinovich	Istituto di Matematica, Università di Pisa, I-56100 Pisa, Italy	Italy
A.G. Naoum	Mathematics Dept, College of Science, University of Baghdad, Adhamiya, Baghdad, Iraq	Iraq
R. Narasimhan	Dept of Mathematics, Madras Institute of Technology, Madras 600 044, India	India
A.S. Nouh	College of Engineering, Riyadh University, Riyadh, Saudi Arabia	Saudi Arabia
M.A. Obeid	College of Engineering, PO Box 800, Riyadh, Saudi Arabia	Saudi Arabia
M.A. Onawale	Nigerian Defence Academy, PMB 2109, Kaduna, Nigeria	Nigeria
K.S. Padmanabhan	Ramanujan Institute for Advanced Study in Mathematics, University of Madras, Madras 600005, India	India
L. Papaloucas	Mathematics Institute, University of Athens, Athens, Greece	Greece
R. Parvatham	Ramanujan Institute for Advanced Study in Mathematics, University of Madras, Madras 600005, India	India

G.A. Perez	Departamento de Física, Universidad Nacional Autónoma de Honduras, Ciudad Universitaria, Tegucigalpa, Honduras	Honduras
P. Pflug	Institut für Mathematik, Universität Kaiserslautern, Pfaffenbergstrasse, 6750 Kaiserslautern, Federal Republic of Germany	Federal Republic of Germany
A. Qadir	Mathematics Dept, Islamabad University, Islamabad, Pakistan	Pakistan
A. Ramanathan	School of Mathematics, Tata Institute of Fundamental Research, Homi Bhabha Road, Bombay 400005, India	India
E. Ramirez de Arellano	Centro de Investigación del IPN, Departamento de Matemáticas, Apartado 14740, Mexico 14, DF, Mexico	Mexico
M.A. Rashid	Dept of Mathematics, University of Islamabad, PO Box 1090, Islamabad, Pakistan	Pakistan
F. Recillas-Juarez	Instituto de Matemáticas, Ciudad Universitaria, Torre de Ciencias, Mexico 20, DF, Mexico	Mexico
S. Recillas-Pishmish	Instituto de Matemáticas, Torre de Ciencias, Ciudad Universitaria, Mexico 20, DF, Mexico	Mexico
A.L. Rice	School of Mathematical Science, Flinders University of South Australia, Bedford Park, SA., Australia	Australia
J.W. Rice	School of Mathematical Science, Flinders University of South Australia, Bedford Park, SA., Australia	Australia
L.J. Riihentaus	Dept of Mathematics and Physics, University of Joensuu, SF-80100 Joensuu 10, Finland	Finland
M.A. de Souza Rocha	Instituto de Matemática Pura e Aplicada, Rua Luis de Camoes 68, 20000 Rio de Janeiro, Brazil	Brazil

J. Sakong	Dept of Mathematics, Korea University, Anam-Dong, Sungbook-Ku, Seoul, Korea	Korea
M.R.A. Sardar	Dept of Mathematics, University of Dacca, Dacca-2, Bangladesh	Bangladesh
N. Schäfer	Institut für Theoretische Physik der Technischen Universität Clausthal, Leibnizstrasse, D-3392 Clausthal-Zellerfeld, Federal Republic of Germany	Federal Republic of Germany
G. Seriani	Università di Trieste, Trieste, Italy	Italy
D. Sundararaman	School of Mathematics, Tata Institute of Fundamental Research, Bombay, India	India
I. Szczyrba	Dept of Mathematical Methods in Physics, University of Warsaw, Hoża 74, Warsaw, Poland	Poland/USSR
G. Tanyi	Dept of Mathematics, University of Yaounde, BP 812, United Republic of Cameroon	United Republic of Cameroon
N. Teleman	Istituto Matematico "G. Castelnuovo" Università di Roma, Rome, Italy	Italy/Romania
M. Teleman-Pasqua	Istituto Matematico "G. Castelnuovo", Università di Roma, Rome, Italy	Italy
K. Tennakone	Dept of Physics, Vidyodaya University of Sri Lanka, Nugegoda, Sri Lanka	Sri Lanka
K. Tillekeratne	Dept of Mathematics, University of Sri Lanka, Peradeniya Campus, Sri Lanka	Sri Lanka
G. Tsagas	Dept of Mathematics, University of Thessaloniki, Thessaloniki, Greece	Greece
P. Urbanski	Dept of Mathematical Methods in Physics, University of Warsaw, Hoża 74, Warsaw, Poland	Poland

L. Verhoustraete	Institut de physique théorique, Université catholique de Louvain, Chemin du Cyclotron 2, B-1348 Louvain-la-Neuve, Belgium	Belgium
B. Wajnryb	Dept of Mathematics, Hebrew University, Jerusalem, Israel	Israel
G.G. Weill	Polytechnic Institute of New York, 333 Jay Street, Brooklyn, N.Y. 11201, United States of America	United States of America/ France
M.Y.A. Youssef	Mathematics Dept, Sana'a University, Sana'a, Yemen	Yemen/Egypt

The following conversion table is provided for the convenience of readers and to encourage the use of SI units.

FACTORS FOR CONVERTING UNITS TO SI SYSTEM EQUIVALENTS *

SI base units are the metre (m), kilogram (kg), second (s), ampere (A), kelvin (K), candela (cd) and mole (mol).
[For further information, see International Standards ISO 1000 (1973), and ISO 31/0 (1974) and its several parts]

Multiply		*by*	*to obtain*
Mass			
pound mass (avoirdupois)	1 lbm	= 4.536×10^{-1}	kg
ounce mass (avoirdupois)	1 ozm	= 2.835×10^{1}	g
ton (long) (= 2240 lbm)	1 ton	= 1.016×10^{3}	kg
ton (short) (= 2000 lbm)	1 short ton	= 9.072×10^{2}	kg
tonne (= metric ton)	1 t	= 1.00×10^{3}	kg
Length			
statute mile	1 mile	= 1.609×10^{0}	km
yard	1 yd	= 9.144×10^{-1}	m
foot	1 ft	= 3.048×10^{-1}	m
inch	1 in	= 2.54×10^{-2}	m
mil (= 10^{-3} in)	1 mil	= 2.54×10^{-2}	mm
Area			
hectare	1 ha	= 1.00×10^{4}	m^2
(statute mile)^2	1 mile^2	= 2.590×10^{0}	km^2
acre	1 acre	= 4.047×10^{3}	m^2
yard^2	1 yd^2	= 8.361×10^{-1}	m^2
foot^2	1 ft^2	= 9.290×10^{-2}	m^2
inch^2	1 in^2	= 6.452×10^{2}	mm^2
Volume			
yard^3	1 yd^3	= 7.646×10^{-1}	m^3
foot^3	1 ft^3	= 2.832×10^{-2}	m^3
inch^3	1 in^3	= 1.639×10^{4}	mm^3
gallon (Brit. or Imp.)	1 gal (Brit)	= 4.546×10^{-3}	m^3
gallon (US liquid)	1 gal (US)	= 3.785×10^{-3}	m^3
litre	1 l	= 1.00×10^{-3}	m^3
Force			
dyne	1 dyn	= 1.00×10^{-5}	N
kilogram force	1 kgf	= 9.807×10^{0}	N
poundal	1 pdl	= 1.383×10^{-1}	N
pound force (avoirdupois)	1 lbf	= 4.448×10^{0}	N
ounce force (avoirdupois)	1 ozf	= 2.780×10^{-1}	N
Power			
British thermal unit/second	1 Btu/s	= 1.054×10^{3}	W
calorie/second	1 cal/s	= 4.184×10^{0}	W
foot-pound force/second	1 ft·lbf/s	= 1.356×10^{0}	W
horsepower (electric)	1 hp	= 7.46×10^{2}	W
horsepower (metric) (= ps)	1 ps	= 7.355×10^{2}	W
horsepower (550 ft·lbf/s)	1 hp	= 7.457×10^{2}	W

* Factors are given exactly or to a maximum of 4 significant figures

Multiply		*by*	*to obtain*
Density			
pound mass/inch^3	1 lbm/in^3	= 2.768 × 10^4	kg/m^3
pound mass/foot^3	1 lbm/ft^3	= 1.602 × 10^1	kg/m^3
Energy			
British thermal unit	1 Btu	= 1.054 × 10^3	J
calorie	1 cal	= 4.184 × 10^0	J
electron-volt	1 eV	≃ 1.602 × 10^{-19}	J
erg	1 erg	= 1.00 × 10^{-7}	J
foot-pound force	1 ft·lbf	= 1.356 × 10^0	J
kilowatt-hour	1 kW·h	= 3.60 × 10^6	J
Pressure			
newtons/metre^2	1 N/m^2	= 1.00	Pa
atmosphere[a]	1 atm	= 1.013 × 10^5	Pa
bar	1 bar	= 1.00 × 10^5	Pa
centimetres of mercury (0°C)	1 cmHg	= 1.333 × 10^3	Pa
dyne/centimetre^2	1 dyn/cm^2	= 1.00 × 10^{-1}	Pa
feet of water (4°C)	1 ftH_2O	= 2.989 × 10^3	Pa
inches of mercury (0°C)	1 inHg	= 3.386 × 10^3	Pa
inches of water (4°C)	1 inH_2O	= 2.491 × 10^2	Pa
kilogram force/centimetre^2	1 kgf/cm^2	= 9.807 × 10^4	Pa
pound force/foot^2	1 lbf/ft^2	= 4.788 × 10^1	Pa
pound force/inch^2 (= psi)[b]	1 lbf/in^2	= 6.895 × 10^3	Pa
torr (0°C) (= mmHg)	1 torr	= 1.333 × 10^2	Pa
Velocity, acceleration			
inch/second	1 in/s	= 2.54 × 10^1	mm/s
foot/second (= fps)	1 ft/s	= 3.048 × 10^{-1}	m/s
foot/minute	1 ft/min	= 5.08 × 10^{-3}	m/s
mile/hour (= mph)	1 mile/h	= { 4.470 × 10^{-1}	m/s
		1.609 × 10^0	km/h
knot	1 knot	= 1.852 × 10^0	km/h
free fall, standard (= g)		= 9.807 × 10^0	m/s^2
foot/second^2	1 ft/s^2	= 3.048 × 10^{-1}	m/s^2
Temperature, thermal conductivity, energy/area·time			
Fahrenheit, degrees −32	°F − 32 }	$\frac{5}{9}$	{ °C
Rankine	°R }		K
1 Btu·in/ft^2·s·°F		= 5.189 × 10^2	W/m·K
1 Btu/ft·s·°F		= 6.226 × 10^1	W/m·K
1 cal/cm·s·°C		= 4.184 × 10^2	W/m·K
1 Btu/ft^2·s		= 1.135 × 10^4	W/m^2
1 cal/cm^2·min		= 6.973 × 10^2	W/m^2
Miscellaneous			
foot^3/second	1 ft^3/s	= 2.832 × 10^{-2}	m^3/s
foot^3/minute	1 ft^3/min	= 4.719 × 10^{-4}	m^3/s
rad	rad	= 1.00 × 10^{-2}	J/kg
roentgen	R	= 2.580 × 10^{-4}	C/kg
curie	Ci	= 3.70 × 10^{10}	disintegration/s

[a] atm abs: atmospheres absolute;
atm (g): atmospheres gauge.

[b] lbf/in^2 (g) (= psig): gauge pressure;
lbf/in^2 abs (= psia): absolute pressure.

HOW TO ORDER IAEA PUBLICATIONS

An exclusive sales agent for IAEA publications, to whom all orders and inquiries should be addressed, has been appointed in the following country:

UNITED STATES OF AMERICA	UNIPUB, P.O. Box 433, Murray Hill Station, New York, N.Y. 10016

In the following countries IAEA publications may be purchased from the sales agents or booksellers listed or through your major local booksellers. Payment can be made in local currency or with UNESCO coupons.

ARGENTINA	Comisión Nacional de Energía Atómica, Avenida del Libertador 8250, Buenos Aires
AUSTRALIA	Hunter Publications, 58 A Gipps Street, Collingwood, Victoria 3066
BELGIUM	Service du Courrier de l'UNESCO, 112, Rue du Trône, B-1050 Brussels
CANADA	Information Canada, 171 Slater Street, Ottawa, Ont. K1A 0S9
C.S.S.R.	S.N.T.L., Spálená 51, CS-110 00 Prague Alfa, Publishers, Hurbanovo námestie 6, CS-800 00 Bratislava
FRANCE	Office International de Documentation et Librairie, 48, rue Gay-Lussac, F-75005 Paris
HUNGARY	Kultura, Hungarian Trading Company for Books and Newspapers, P.O. Box 149, H-1011 Budapest 62
INDIA	Oxford Book and Stationery Comp., 17, Park Street, Calcutta 16; Oxford Book and Stationery Comp., Scindia House, New Delhi-110001
ISRAEL	Heiliger and Co., 3, Nathan Strauss Str., Jerusalem
ITALY	Libreria Scientifica, Dott. de Biasio Lucio "aeiou", Via Meravigli 16, I-20123 Milan
JAPAN	Maruzen Company, Ltd., P.O.Box 5050, 100-31 Tokyo International
NETHERLANDS	Marinus Nijhoff N.V., Lange Voorhout 9-11, P.O. Box 269, The Hague
PAKISTAN	Mirza Book Agency, 65, The Mall, P.O.Box 729, Lahore-3
POLAND	Ars Polona, Centrala Handlu Zagranicznego, Krakowskie Przedmiescie 7, Warsaw
ROMANIA	Cartimex, 3-5 13 Decembrie Street, P.O.Box 134-135, Bucarest
SOUTH AFRICA	Van Schaik's Bookstore, P.O.Box 724, Pretoria Universitas Books (Pty) Ltd., P.O.Box 1557, Pretoria
SPAIN	Diaz de Santos, Lagasca 95, Madrid-6 Calle Francisco Navacerrada, 8, Madrid-28
SWEDEN	C.E. Fritzes Kungl. Hovbokhandel, Fredsgatan 2, S-103 07 Stockholm
UNITED KINGDOM	Her Majesty's Stationery Office, P.O. Box 569, London SE1 9NH
U.S.S.R.	Mezhdunarodnaya Kniga, Smolenskaya-Sennaya 32-34, Moscow G-200
YUGOSLAVIA	Jugoslovenska Knjiga, Terazije 27, YU-11000 Belgrade

Orders from countries where sales agents have not yet been appointed and requests for information should be addressed directly to:

Division of Publications
International Atomic Energy Agency
Kärntner Ring 11, P.O.Box 590, A-1011 Vienna, Austria